TABLE OF ATOMIC MASS
(Based on Carbon-12, the Most Common Isotope of Carbon)

Element	Symbol	Atomic number	Atomic mass	Element	Symbol	Atomic number	Atomic mass
Actinium	Ac	89	(227)	Mercury	Hg	80	200.59
Aluminum	Al	13	26.9815	Molybdenum	Mo	42	95.94
Americium	Am	95	(243)	Neodymium	Nd	60	144.24
Antimony	Sb	51	121.75	Neon	Ne	10	20.183
Argon	Ar	18	39.948	Neptunium	Np	93	(237)
Arsenic	As	33	74.9216	Nickel	Ni	28	58.71
Astatine	At	85	(210)	Niobium	Nb	41	92.906
Barium	Ba	56	137.34	Nitrogen	N	7	14.0067
Berkelium	Bk	97	(247)	Nobelium	No	102	(253)
Beryllium	Be	4	9.0122	Osmium	Os	76	190.2
Bismuth	Bi	83	208.980	Oxygen	O	8	15.9994
Boron	B	5	10.811	Palladium	Pd	46	106.4
Bromine	Br	35	79.909	Phosphorus	P	15	30.9738
Cadmium	Cd	48	112.40	Platinum	Pt	78	195.09
Calcium	Ca	20	40.08	Plutonium	Pu	94	(242)
Californium	Cf	98	(249)	Polonium	Po	84	(210)
Carbon	C	6	12.01115	Potassium	K	19	39.102
Cerium	Ce	58	140.12	Praseodymium	Pr	59	140.907
Cesium	Cs	55	132.905	Promethium	Pm	61	(145)
Chlorine	Cl	17	35.453	Protactinium	Pa	91	231
Chromium	Cr	24	51.996	Radium	Ra	88	226
Cobalt	Co	27	58.9332	Radon	Rn	86	222
Copper	Cu	29	63.54	Rhenium	Re	75	186.2
Curium	Cm	96	(247)	Rhodium	Rh	45	102.905
Dysprosium	Dy	66	162.50	Rubidium	Rb	37	85.47
Einsteinium	Es	99	(254)	Ruthenium	Ru	44	101.07
Erbium	Er	68	167.26	Samarium	Sm	62	150.35
Europium	Eu	63	151.96	Scandium	Sc	21	44.956
Fermium	Fm	100	(253)	Selenium	Se	34	78.96
Fluorine	F	9	18.9984	Silicon	Si	14	28.086
Francium	Fr	87	(223)	Silver	Ag	47	107.870
Gadolinium	Gd	64	157.25	Sodium	Na	11	22.9898
Gallium	Ga	31	69.72	Strontium	Sr	38	87.62
Germanium	Ge	32	72.59	Sulfur	S	16	32.064
Gold	Au	79	196.967	Tantalum	Ta	73	180.948
Hafnium	Hf	72	178.49	Technetium	Tc	43	(99)
Helium	He	2	4.0026	Tellurium	Te	52	127.60
Holmium	Ho	67	164.930	Terbium	Tb	65	158.924
Hydrogen	H	1	1.00797	Thallium	Tl	81	204.37
Indium	In	49	114.82	Thorium	Th	90	232.038
Iodine	I	53	126.9044	Thulium	Tm	69	168.934
Iridium	Ir	77	192.2	Tin	Sn	50	118.69
Iron	Fe	26	55.847	Titanium	Ti	22	47.90
Krypton	Kr	36	83.80	Tungsten	W	74	183.85
Lanthanum	La	57	138.91	Uranium	U	92	238.03
Lawrencium	Lw	103	(257)	Vanadium	V	23	50.942
Lead	Pb	82	207.19	Xenon	Xe	54	131.30
Lithium	Li	3	6.939	Ytterbium	Yb	70	173.04
Lutetium	Lu	71	174.97	Yttrium	Y	39	88.905
Magnesium	Mg	12	24.312	Zinc	Zn	30	65.37
Manganese	Mn	25	54.9380	Zirconium	Zr	40	91.22
Mendelevium	Md	101	(256)				

Values in parentheses denote mass numbers of most stable known isotopes.

Basic Modern Chemistry/SECOND EDITION

Basic Modern Chemistry

/SECOND EDITION

Jean-Paul Gravel / DEUX-MONTAGNES REGIONAL HIGH SCHOOL

Gordon G. Hall / DAVID THOMPSON HIGH SCHOOL

Samuel Madras / SIR GEORGE WILLIAMS UNIVERSITY

McGraw-Hill Company of Canada Limited / TORONTO MONTREAL NEW YORK LONDON SYDNEY JOHANNESBURG MEXICO PANAMA

BASIC MODERN CHEMISTRY
/SECOND EDITION

92509

Library of Congress Catalog Card Number:
77-85197

1 2 3 4 5 6 7 8 9 10 BP-69 8 7 6 5 4 3 2 1 0 9

Printed and bound in Canada

Preface

The second edition has been largely re-written to reflect the changes in the teaching of chemistry which have occurred in the past five years.

The twin objectives of observing through experiment and explaining through models are the important themes to which students have responded enthusiastically. The challenge facing the teacher is to work toward these objectives by integrating experiment and theory into a clear and logical presentation at the student level. Wherever possible, the experimental work should be done by the students themselves and the theory or explanation should be proposed by them. But it is common knowledge that the topics expected in a good introductory course derive in large measure from sophisticated experimentation and theory. Nevertheless even in this area, facts should come before theory.

The early part of this edition develops some necessary terms and experimental observations. To cope with these, a theory about atoms is presented in the chapters on atomic structure and the periodic table written at an elementary level. A fuller treatment of atomic structure must await a further round of experimentation and collection of data both by the student and research workers.

In presenting atomic structure and bonding, now regarded as essential in a modern text, an author is faced with a real dilemma. On the one hand, these are powerful tools for understanding chemistry. On the other, they are abstract and difficult, especially to the beginning student. For this reason these topics have to be presented with great concern for the intellectual level of the student. In this work, these ideas are presented in a "stage by stage" style, with the aid of many graphics. There are two chapters on atomic structure (5 and 15) and two on the periodic table (6 and 16) with this purpose in mind.

The descriptive chemistry of the elements and their compounds is treated from the viewpoint of periodicity and bonding. Again graphics are used to illustrate molecular structures and chemical equations.

Each chapter is provided with an adequate number of graded questions and problems to help the student.

The authors are grateful to the many teachers using the first edition who have offered their helpful comments. In particular, the authors would like to acknowledge the work of Mr. Martin Hardiman of Lower Canada College, Mr. Maurice Dupré of St. Joseph's Teachers' College, both of Montreal, Quebec, and Dr. Brian Newbold of the University of Moncton, Moncton, New Brunswick, for their reading of the manuscript, followed by their submission of many useful suggestions. One of the authors, Dr. Madras, would like to extend his thanks to the members of his class in "Chemistry 401, Chemical Pedagogy" who have used parts of the manuscript as "working papers" in discussion on the pedagogy of such topics as atomic structure and the mole. The artwork was done by Mr. Leslie Takash, Miss Pat Dewes, and Mr. Brian Day under the supervision of Dr. Madras.

J.P.G.

G.H.

S.M.

Contents

1 Chemistry and Science

1:1 Definition of Chemistry

Chemistry deals with matter and its changes. Chemists are particularly interested in these changes where one or more substances are transformed into others quite different from the original. They try to understand the chemical changes in a very profound sense. They picture the submicroscopic particles involved such as atoms, molecules, and electrons. They try to determine how these interact and what energies are released or required. This is all done to have greater control over chemical change whether it occurs in an industrial process, a research experiment, or in a living organism. There is always the hope of finding new and better materials for the service of man.

1:2 The Work of Chemists

The chemist is interested in the properties and composition of all forms of matter that surround him. Air, water, food, cloth, steel, cement, glass, and gasoline, as well as any other material you could name, are all examples of matter.

The chemist's work is to be seen all around us – on the farm, in the home, and in industry. Chemical products and methods are used by the farmer to produce better crops and livestock and by the food-processing industries to prepare foods and protect them from spoilage. Vitamins produced in laboratories are added to foods for enrichment. Our homes are decorated with paints and enamels, textiles, plastics, and glass. The convenience of the automobile is possible largely because of the chemical reactions that help produce gasoline and oils, steel, rubber, and even the pavement of our streets and highways. Rocket fuels and the materials that go into nuclear reactors are some of the most recent achievements of the chemist.

Most of these products are made in factories, where chemical changes and reactions are supervised by industrial chemists. Raw materials from mines, forests, oil wells, and oceans are turned into products for our use by means of chemical processes. For example, the pulp and paper industry uses chemical reactions to convert the wood of the tree into paper and cellulose products.

We should not forget, however, that Nature is still the greatest chemist, and some of the most remarkable chemical changes are found in living organisms. Hundreds of chemical reactions go on harmoniously to provide the normal functioning of the individual animal or plant.

1:3 Man's Curiosity

Men have always been curious about Nature, and many theories, and even legends and myths, have resulted from this curiosity. The ancient Greeks had some interesting ideas about matter, but these were based on speculation and were not checked by experiment. Most believed that there were only four elements: air, earth, fire, and water. However, some believed that matter was made of small, invisible particles which they called atoms. "There is nothing but atoms and void," said Democritus.

Today we believe once again that matter consists of elements or combinations of elements, and that the elements are composed of atoms. Our belief, however, is based upon experimental proof, direct or indirect, whereas the beliefs of the ancient Greeks were based upon speculation.

Courtesy The Fisher Collection
of Alchemical and Historical Pictures

Fig. 1.1   *The alchemist*
*The alchemist was a pioneer of science whose
contributions to scientific knowledge laid the
foundations of modern chemistry, metallurgy,
pharmacology, and medicine.*

Courtesy Fisher Scientific Company

Fig. 1.2   *The Modern Alchemist*
A modern scientist works in a modern laboratory.

During the Middle Ages, the alchemists searched for the "Philosopher's Stone", a subtle substance which would change base metals, like lead, into precious metals, such as silver and gold. They failed in their quest but did succeed in discovering many other substances. They also developed methods and processes that were later to prove useful in chemistry. It is interesting to compare their attitudes with those of modern scientists. The alchemists often hid their knowledge in secrecy; the modern chemist, on the other hand, is anxious to publish what he finds and explain what he knows.

Chemistry is one of the physical sciences. It is intimately related to physics and mathematics. The modern ideas of the structure of atoms can be expressed by using the concepts of physics and the language of mathematics.

Biology and medicine are closely allied to chemistry. Many major advances in these fields have been and are being made through the application of chemical knowledge. Animals and plants are composed of different kinds of matter that are constantly undergoing many, perhaps hundreds, of different chemical changes.

1:4   The Scientific Method

The Renaissance saw a revival of learning, but even more important than the revival was a renewed emphasis on investigation and experiment as methods of learning. Francis Bacon proposed that, in order to learn, one should consult Nature rather than the ancient authorities. He emphasized that it was necessary to collect facts before proposing theories or explanations. This method of learning became known as the *scientific method*.

One of the pioneers of chemistry was Robert Boyle. He devoted himself to experimental work and did much to further the development of the scientific method. He discarded the view that air, earth, fire, and water were elements and suggested instead that only those substances that could not be decomposed into simpler substances by chemical methods should be called elements.

The first step in applying the scientific method is to recognize the problem at hand. For example, an automobile tire is observed to be harder on a hot day than on a cold day, even though the amount of air in it has not been changed. Upon checking, it is found that the air pressure in the tire is higher on the hot day. Is there a relationship between the temperature and the pressure of the air in the tire? To answer this question, one should gather as much information as possible by experiment. If an apparatus were set up in which the pressure of air is measured at different temperatures, a relationship between temperature and pressure might then be found.

If, in repeating an experiment, a definite regularity is found in the results, it may be stated in the form of a scientific law. A *scientific law* is a statement of a regularity of behavior in Nature that has been tested and proved.

A *theory* is an attempt to explain the observed facts. Preferably, a theory should be the simplest explanation of the facts for which it is proposed; it should also explain as many facts as possible.

Often a theory may have to be changed to explain newly discovered facts. In this way theories of science gradually change from time to time. The basic observed facts remain the same, while our ideas change with increasing knowledge.

QUESTIONS

1. Define *chemistry*.

2. List ten important chemical industries.

3. What is the difference between an applied and a research chemist?

4. Write a paragraph on the influence of chemistry on your daily life.

5. Outline the procedure of the scientific method as a means of solving problems.

6. Imagine some social problem, and then show how it might be solved by application of the scientific method.

7. Why should the knowledge of the ancient peoples not be termed a science?

8. How did the Greeks of old explain the differences in the properties and behavior of matter?

9. What was the "Philosopher's Stone"?

10. Describe some of the values of the alchemists' work, and explain why their contribution to general knowledge was so limited.

11. Describe the contributions to learning made by Francis Bacon and Robert Boyle.

12. What is a *scientific law*?

13. Outline the steps necessary for the establishment of a scientific law.

14. (a) What is a *scientific theory*?
    (b) List the essential characteristics of a theory.

2 Matter and Energy

Of what is the earth composed? What makes up the soils, the air, the water, the plants, the animals, and anything else?

The physical world may be described in terms of matter and energy. Matter exists and undergoes changes, while energy is either the cause or the result of such changes.

2:1 Properties of Matter

Matter is best described and recognized by its *properties*. These are identifying features such as density, color, state, boiling point, melting point, and similar characteristics.

Properties of substances may be chemical and physical. A *chemical property* of a substance is its behavior during chemical change. For example, carbon burns in oxygen to yield the gas carbon dioxide. Sodium reacts vigorously with water to form sodium hydroxide and hydrogen. Platinum does not react with water. Each example is only one of many chemical properties of the substance named.

A *physical property* of a substance is a characteristic that can be determined without causing a change in the composition of the substance. The melting point and crystalline form are physical properties of a solid. The boiling point and freezing point are physical properties of a liquid.

2:2 The Measurement of Properties: The Metric System

To describe properties quantitatively, they must be measured, and such measurement requires standard units with which the properties can be compared. All measurements are, in reality, only comparisons. The length of a pencil can be measured only by reference to a scale on which units of length are printed. A brief discussion on measurements is given in Appendix 1.

In science, the most widely used units are those of the metric system. Length is often measured in meters and centimeters, mass in kilograms and grams, volume in liters and cubic meters. The metric system consistently uses multiples and submultiples of ten; for example,

$$1 \text{ meter} = 10 \text{ decimeters}$$
$$= 100 \text{ centimeters}$$
$$= 1000 \text{ millimeters.}$$

Metric system prefixes are presented in Table 2.1 and in Appendix 3.

TABLE 2.1		
Prefixes Used in the Metric System		
micro	$= \dfrac{1}{1,000,000}$	deca $= 10$
milli	$= \dfrac{1}{1,000}$	hecto $= 100$
centi	$= \dfrac{1}{100}$	kilo $= 1,000$
deci	$= \dfrac{1}{10}$	mega $= 1,000,000$

In the chemical laboratory, the quantities used are expressed most conveniently in terms of centimeters and grams as the units of length and mass. In other studies, the meter and the kilogram may prove more convenient.

Courtesy National Research Council, Ottawa

Fig. 2.1 An ultraprecise balance for accurately intercomparing mass

Mass

The term *mass* is used to express the amount of matter in a body and is related to its inertia.

A convenient unit of mass for chemical work is the gram (g), an arbitrarily chosen amount of matter. The mass of very large amounts of matter is often expressed in kilograms. One kilogram (1 kg) is equal to 1000 g. The mass of a very small quantity of matter may be expressed in milligrams. One milligram (1 mg) is equal to 0.001 g; 1 g of matter contains 1000 mg.

A dime has a mass of about 2.5 g; a teaspoonful of water has a mass of about 5 g; a pound is equal to 453.6 g. One kilogram is equal to 2.205 lb.

Remember: 1 kilogram = 1000 grams
1 gram   = 1000 milligrams
1 kilogram = 2.205 pounds
1 pound   = 453.6 grams

Weight

The *weight* of a given amount of matter, as measured on or near the earth, is the force exerted on the mass by the gravitational attraction of the earth. Since weight is a force exerted on a mass, weight and mass are not identical.

A given object would have a much smaller weight on the moon than on the earth because the gravitational attraction of the moon is much less than that of the earth. The mass of an object is the same on the earth as on the moon because the amount of matter is constant. In interstellar space an object may have no weight at all but its mass is the same as on earth.

Volume

The *volume* of a substance is the amount of space it occupies. The volume of a regular object or vessel may be calculated from its dimensions.

The unit of length in the metric system is the meter (m). Since the meter is a rather large unit, the centimeter (cm) is commonly used. The centimeter is equal to 0.01 meter. The millimeter (mm) is equal to 0.001 meter. There are 10 mm in a centimeter, 100 cm in a meter, and 1000 mm in a meter. There are 2.54 cm in 1 inch. Extremely small dimensions such as diameters of atoms, are expressed using the Angstrom unit (Å). One Angstrom unit is equal to 1×10^{-8} cm.

The cubic centimeter (cm^3) is used commonly to indicate the volume of regularly shaped objects or vessels. Since it is difficult to determine the volume of an irregularly-shaped object from its dimensions, another means for the expression of volume is available, namely the liter.

The chemist often uses the liter (*l*) as the unit of volume. The liter was designed as the volume of 1 kg of water. One liter is equal to 1000 cm^3, and 1 cm^3 is equal to 1 milliliter (m*l*). The milliliter is exactly 0.001 *l*.

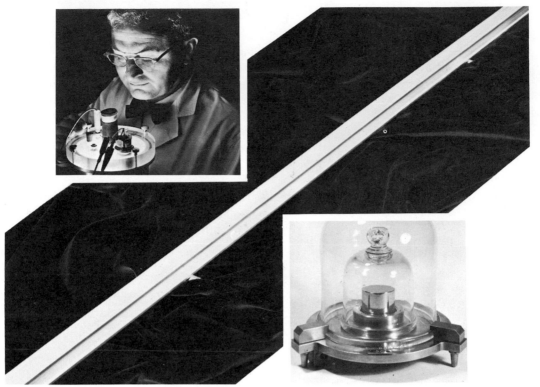

Top and center, courtesy National Bureau Standards, U.S.A., bottom, courtesy National Research Council, Ottawa

Fig. 2.2   *In the upper left picture, a scientist adjusts a krypton-86 lamp. The wave length of the orange-red light emitted by the lamp has recently been adopted as the International Standard of Length. The middle picture shows the "old" meter standard. A copy of the standard kilogram is represented in the lower picture.*

Remember: 1 kilometer = 1000 meters
1 meter   = 100 centimeters
1 meter   = 1000 millimeters
1 meter   = 39.37 inches
1 kilometer = 0.6214 miles
1 inch   = 2.54 centimeters
1 liter   = 1000 milliliters
1 milliliter = 1 cm³

Density

Density is the mass per unit volume, and refers to the compactness of a sample of matter.

The density of solids and liquids is usually indicated in grams per cubic centimeter or milliliter. Since ordinary gases are much less dense than solids and liquids, densities of gases are usually reported in grams per liter (Table 2.2). Density expressed in grams per milliliter is identical to that in terms of grams per cubic centimeter.

Sometimes, it is stated that lead (density = 11.34 g/cm³) is heavier than aluminum (density = 2.70 g/cm³). The statement would be more exact if the word "heavier" were replaced by the words "more dense". For example, 10 cm³ of aluminum is heavier than 2 cm³ of lead.

TABLE 2.2			
Densities of a Few Substances			
Solids (g/cm³)			
Aluminum	2.70	Platinum	21.73
Calcium	1.55	Potassium	0.87
Copper	8.30	Silver	10.42
Cork	0.24	Sodium	0.97
Diamond	3.50	Sulfur	2.00
Gold	19.30	Tin	7.24
Ice	0.90	Tungsten	18.60
Iron	7.85	Uranium	18.70
Lead	11.34	Wood (oak)	0.75
Magnesium	1.74	Zinc	7.04
Liquids (g/ml)			
Kerosene	0.88	Sulfuric acid (concentrated)	1.84
Mercury	13.60	Water (4°C)	1.00
Methanol	0.81	Water (sea)	1.03
Gases (g/l at 0°C and 760 mm pressure)			
Air	1.29	Oxygen	1.43
Hydrogen	0.089		

The density of a substance at constant pressure varies with the temperature. A piece of iron expands when heated and contracts when cooled. Expansion causes a decrease in density, whereas contraction results in an increase in density.

The density of a substance is found by dividing its mass by its volume. The formula for this operation is:

$$\text{Density} = \frac{\text{mass}}{\text{volume}} \quad \text{or} \quad D = \frac{m}{v}$$

2:3 Physical and Chemical Changes

One of the striking properties of matter is its ability to undergo changes. In some changes the material alters its size, shape, or state, but not its composition. This occurs when a sheet of paper is cut, a rock is chipped, or a metal is drawn out as a wire. Such changes are *physical changes*.

In other cases the composition of the matter is altered, as when paper burns or metal corrodes. The products of these changes have different chemical compositions and properties from those of the original materials. Such changes are *chemical changes*.

In this century, it has been discovered that matter can undergo a third kind of change. This type is more profound than either a physical or chemical change, since it involves the nuclei of the atoms in the matter. Examples of such changes would be the explosion of a nuclear bomb or the processes by which the sun emits its light and heat. Such changes are *nuclear changes*.

Example

A substance has a mass of 10.0 grams and a volume of 2.0 milliliters. What is its density?

Solution

The density is found by substituting the data given in the formula:

$$\text{Density} = \frac{m}{v} = \frac{10.0 \text{ g}}{2.0 \text{ ml}} = 5.0 \text{ g/ml}$$

2:4 Forms of Energy and Chemical Changes

Energy is the ability to do work. From physics we learn that every moving body has *kinetic energy*. *Potential energy* is the energy a body has because of its position, its condition, or its chemical nature. For example, the water behind a dam has potential energy. When the water falls, this energy is changed to kinetic energy.

All changes are either caused by energy or else they liberate energy. Physical changes usually involve the smallest amounts of energy, while nuclear changes involve by far the greatest. Chemical changes sometimes produce very large amounts of energy. Such chemical energy may appear as *heat energy* in the burning of fuels, as *electrical energy* in the dry cell of a flashlight, as *mechanical energy* in an explosion, or as *light energy* in a photoflash bulb. Chemical substances which are able to release energy when they react contain stored-up or *chemical energy*.

Sometimes energy is absorbed by substances to bring about chemical change as, for instance, when heat and light are required for the transformation of carbon dioxide and water into sugars and starches found in plants.

2:5 Heat and Temperature

Heat or thermal energy is related to molecular motion and is one of the most important physical concepts. Wherever there is molecular motion there is heat.

The *temperature* of a body indicates whether or not the body is hotter or colder than something else. The temperature also shows whether heat will flow from the material to its surroundings or in the reverse direction.

Temperature is related to heat, a form of energy. If two objects at different temperatures are placed in contact, heat flows from the hotter to the cooler until their temperatures are the same.

The most common scale of temperature used internationally by scientists is the *Celsius* (often called the centigrade scale, suggested by Celsius in 1742). On this scale there are 100 Celsius degrees or graduations of temperature between two fixed points. These are 0°C, at which water freezes, and 100°C, at which water boils at standard atmospheric pressure (Table 2.3).

The *Fahrenheit scale* of temperature was introduced by Fahrenheit in 1724. On this scale there are 180 degrees between the same "fixed" points as those used on the Celsius scale. Thus each Celsius degree is equal to 9/5 Fahrenheit degrees, and each Fahrenheit degree is 5/9 of a Celsius degree.

Conversion from one scale to the other is possible by using the equations:

$$°F = (9/5 \ °C) + 32$$
$$°C = 5/9 \ (°F - 32)$$

A most important scale is the *Kelvin scale* in which zero degrees of temperature represents the absence of heat, or at least minimum energy. The Kelvin scale is often called the absolute scale because 0°K is believed to be the lowest possible limit of temperature in the universe (Fig. 2.3).

Fig. 2.3   *Kelvin, Celsius, and Fahrenheit scales*

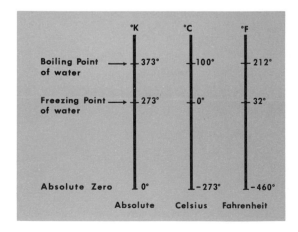

A degree of Kelvin temperature is equal to a degree of Celsius temperature, and 0°K corresponds to −273°C (more accurately, −273.16°C). The temperature 0°C is the same as 273°K. To convert any Celsius reading to the corresponding Kelvin reading, 273 is added to the Celsius reading, while 273 is subtracted from a Kelvin reading to obtain a Celsius reading:

$$°K = °C + 273$$
$$°C = °K - 273$$

TABLE 2.3

Comparisons of the "Fixed" Points

	°C	°K	°F
Boiling point of water	100	373	212
Freezing point of water	0	273	32
Differences	100	100	180

The Calorie

The unit of heat in the metric system is the calorie. The *calorie* is defined as the amount of heat that can increase the temperature of 1 g of water from 14.5°C to 15.5°C. Although this is the exact definition of the calorie, we may assume for most practical purposes that 1 calorie can raise the temperature of 1 g of water one Celsius degree measured anywhere between 0°C and 100°C. The kilocalorie (kcal or Cal) is used to identify large amounts of heat. One kilocalorie is equal to 1000 calories.

2:6 The Conservation Laws

Matter is continuously changing. However, it has been found that in all physical and chemical changes there is no change in the mass of the materials being transformed. The French chemist, Lavoisier, tried to learn about chemical changes by weighing the quantities of the substances used in chemical reactions. He was one of the first chemists to observe the surprising fact that even though substances are transformed into completely different ones in a chemical change, there is no destruction or creation of matter. The mass remains exactly the same. To all appearances, when a candle burns it is destroyed; but appearances are often misleading. When the reactants and products of a chemical reaction are weighed accurately, even if a substance is changed to a gas, there is no change of mass. Lavoisier expressed his finding as the *Law of Conservation of Mass: In a chemical change the sums of the masses of the original reactants and of the final products are the same.* Mass is neither created nor destroyed in a chemical change.

Energy can similarly be changed from one form to another, but it is not created or destroyed during transformations. This statement is the *Law of Conservation of Energy.* In nuclear changes a small amount of mass does disappear; but the mass is converted into energy, and the amount of energy released is equivalent to the mass destroyed. The above laws are combined in the general statement that the mass-energy of a system cannot change.

Matter can manifest itself in two distinct forms; it may appear either as a material substance occupying space and having mass, or it may appear as energy. The relationship between mass and energy is given by the formula:

$$E = mc^2$$

where E is the energy, m is the mass, and c is the speed of light.

2:7 The States of Matter and Changes of State

Matter may exist in three states: solid, liquid, or gas. A solid has definite volume and shape; a liquid has definite volume but no definite shape, because it takes on the shape of its container; and a gas has neither shape nor volume, because it expands indefinitely, if free to do so, until it fills its container.

The state in which a substance happens to exist depends on the temperature and the pressure. If the temperature and/or the pressure are changed, a substance may pass from one state to another. Such physical changes are called *changes of state*. These usually occur sharply when certain temperatures and pressures are reached. When they take place, heat is either absorbed or emitted.

Vaporization takes place when a liquid absorbs heat and turns into a gaseous form. When a gaseous substance changes to a liquid through loss of heat, the process is termed *condensation*. *Fusion* occurs when a solid absorbs heat and turns into a liquid. When a liquid loses heat and is transformed into a solid, *freezing* or solidification takes place. Several substances, such as "dry ice", may change directly from the solid state to that of a gas without liquefaction. This process is called *sublimation*. The reverse process, that is, the condensation of a gas to a solid is also possible. An example of such sublimation is the formation of frost. The various changes of state that matter can undergo are represented in Fig. 2.4.

Fig. 2.4   *Changes of state*

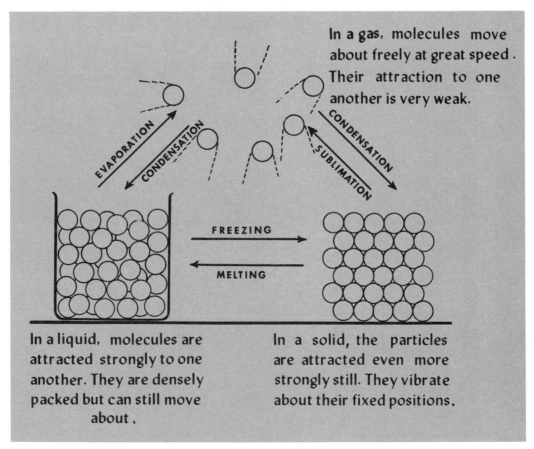

In a gas, molecules move about freely at great speed. Their attraction to one another is very weak.

EVAPORATION

CONDENSATION

CONDENSATION

SUBLIMATION

FREEZING

MELTING

In a liquid, molecules are attracted strongly to one another. They are densely packed but can still move about.

In a solid, the particles are attracted even more strongly still. They vibrate about their fixed positions.

QUESTIONS

1. Define the term *property*.

2. Decide whether the properties of the substances given below are physical or chemical properties:
   (a) hydrogen is a colorless gas;
   (b) oxygen supports combustion;
   (c) diamond is the hardest natural substance known;
   (d) methyl alcohol boils at 78°C;
   (e) potassium is a soft metal;
   (f) phosphorus ignites when exposed to air.

3. Give one major advantage that the Metric System has over the British System of measurement.

4. Define the terms:
   (a) *kilogram;*
   (b) *microsecond;*
   (c) *megaton;*
   (d) *millimeter;*
   (e) *deciliter.*

5. Explain why, although the mass of an object is constant, its weight may not be.

6. What advantage is there in basing the unit of length on the wavelength of light coming from a particular element?

7. (a) Change 1.2 liters to milliliters.
   (b) What is the mass in milligrams and in kilograms of 1.2 liters of water at 4°C?
   (c) Convert 1080 millimeters to (i) centimeters; (ii) decimeters; (iii) meters.

8. Define the term *density*.

9. (a) Find the density of a material if 30.0 m*l* of it has a mass of 75.0 grams.
   (b) Find the volume occupied by 10.0 g of kerosene.

10. Distinguish between the terms *physical change*, *chemical change*, and *nuclear change*.

11. Classify the following as physical or chemical changes:
    (a) the rusting of an iron nail;
    (b) the toasting of bread;
    (c) the evaporation of water from a lake;
    (d) the formation of clouds;
    (e) the tarnishing of silver;
    (f) the flashing of a bulb in a camera;
    (g) the liquefaction of air;
    (h) the burning of a candle;
    (i) the melting of ice;
    (j) the blowing of a horn.

12. (a) What is *energy?*
    (b) What is the difference between potential and kinetic energy?
    (c) List three different forms of energy and tell how one form might be changed into others.

13. Which one of the following choices represents the type(s) of energy possessed by a light bulb *falling* down a well?
    (A) kinetic energy only   (C) potential energy and kinetic energy
    (B) potential energy only   (D) electrical energy

14. Change the following to °C: (a) 70°F; (b) 98.6°F; (c) −20°F; (d) −40°F; (e) 190°F.

15. Change the following to °F: (a) 100°C; (b) 200°C; (c) −186°C; (d) 3500°C; (e) −40°C.

16. Change the following to °K: (a) −273°C; (b) −40°C; (c) 0°C; (d) 50°C; (e) 273°C.

17. Change the following to °C: (a) 500°K; (b) 100°K; (c) 272°K; (d) 50°K; (e) 300°K.

18. (a) What is a *calorie?*   (b) What is a *kilocalorie?*

19. State the Law of Conservation of Mass and the Law of Conservation of Energy.

20. Discuss the meaning of the statement that the mass-energy sum of a system does not change.

21. Give the distinguishing characteristics of the three states of matter.

22. What factors determine the state of a particular substance?

23. Indicate the change of state involved when: (a) dew forms on blades of grass; (b) water is boiling; (c) moth balls (naphthalene) placed in woolen garments "disappear"; (d) a tumbler full of ice is placed on a table; (e) the temperature drops below 0°C near a small pond.

3 The Composition of Matter

3:1 Elements

All the materials in the universe are composed of relatively few simple substances called the elements. An *element* is a substance that cannot be decomposed by chemical means into simpler substances.

Over one hundred elements are known today. Elements are not found in equal abundance in nature. Indeed some have been synthesized only recently in nuclear reactors, and they exist in very small amounts. Fig. 3.1 presents an estimate of the relative abundance of some elements found in the earth's crust. However, the importance of an element does not necessarily depend on its abundance. Carbon comprises less than 0.1 per cent of the total; yet without this element no life could have developed on the earth. Oxygen is an element that is both abundant and vitally important in many ways.

Fig. 3.1 *Approximate relative abundance of elements in the earth's crust*

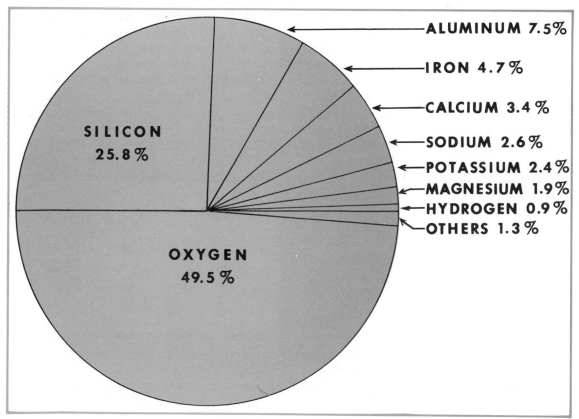

ALUMINUM 7.5%

IRON 4.7%

CALCIUM 3.4%

SODIUM 2.6%

POTASSIUM 2.4%

MAGNESIUM 1.9%

HYDROGEN 0.9%

OTHERS 1.3%

SILICON 25.8%

OXYGEN 49.5%

Elements are classified as metals or non-metals for convenience. Metals are recognized by their luster and high conductivity of heat and electricity. Some metals can be drawn into a wire; they are said to be ductile. Other metals can be hammered into various shapes; they are malleable. Some common metals are iron, copper, mercury, tin, lead, zinc, silver, and gold.

Examples of non-metals are carbon, sulfur, phosphorus, chlorine, and iodine. Their properties vary greatly. Carbon and silicon are solids and have a high melting point. Hydrogen and helium are gases which can be liquefied only at extremely low temperatures. As a general rule, non-metals are poor conductors of heat and electricity. They are neither ductile nor malleable.

3:2   Compounds

Elements combine with one another to form substances called *compounds*. These substances are homogeneous. Their properties and composition are the same throughout their entire mass. We are unable to distinguish particles of the constituent elements once they have combined to form a compound. Moreover, the properties of the compound are not like those of the free elements before combination. Water is a compound made of hydrogen and oxygen. Both of these elements in the free state are gases. Hydrogen is highly flammable, whereas oxygen supports combustion and life. The properties of water are entirely different from these. Sodium, a soft metallic element, corrodes very rapidly in air and reacts with water vigorously. Chlorine, a non-metal, is a greenish-yellow poisonous gas. A piece of sodium thrown into an atmosphere of chlorine burns violently as these elements combine to form a compound, sodium chloride, which proves to be common table salt. Sodium chloride is a compound made of the elements sodium and chlorine, and yet its properties are different from those of the free elements.

3:3   Molecules and Ions: The Physical Units of Matter

Let us perform the following experiment mentally. If we pour half the water from one vessel to another, each half will retain the composition and properties of the whole. If we were to continue subdividing the water in the same way, presumably a point would be reached at which there would be a particle of water so small that it would be impossible to subdivide it further by physical methods. The smallest particle of water able to exist physically and still retain its composition is called a *molecule*.

Molecules are extremely small and generally cannot be seen with the most powerful microscopes. Evidence for the existence of molecules had to be obtained indirectly, but more and more details about the structures of molecules are being amassed as chemistry progresses.

When salt is broken down into its finest particles, it is found that the smallest particles of which this compound is composed are electrically charged. These particles are called *ions*. In a salt crystal, there are sodium ions with a positive charge and chloride ions with a negative charge. The ions are arranged in the crystal so that each sodium ion is next to a chloride ion and vice versa (Fig. 3.2).

3:4   Atoms and their Symbols: The Chemical Units of Matter

Atoms are the smallest particles of matter able to undergo chemical change; consequently they are the basic chemical units of matter.

For the sake of convenience, brevity, and precision, the elements are represented by symbols which stand for the elements, the atoms of the elements and their atomic mass.*

*In this book, the term **atomic mass** is used in preference to the older term **atomic weight**.

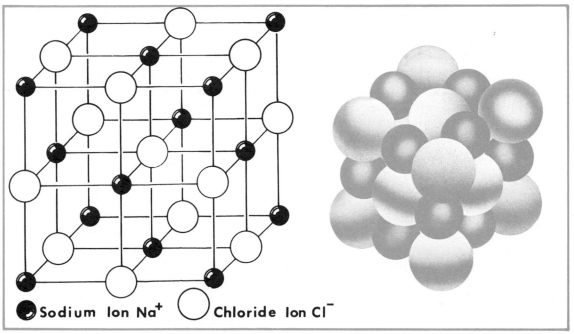

Sodium Ion Na⁺   **Chloride Ion Cl⁻**

Fig. 3.2   *The sodium chloride crystal*

TABLE 3.1

Symbols of Elements Derived From Latin or Other Sources

Element	Symbol	Source Name
Antimony	Sb	Stibium
Copper	Cu	Cuprum
Gold	Au	Aurum
Iron	Fe	Ferrum
Lead	Pb	Plumbum
Mercury	Hg	Hydrargyrum
Potassium	K	Kalium
Silver	Ag	Argentum
Sodium	Na	Natrium
Tin	Sn	Stannum
Tungsten	W	Wolfram

A *symbol* consists of a capital letter only, or a capital letter and a small letter. H is the symbol for hydrogen, O for oxygen, and S for sulfur. If there are several elements whose names begin with the same letter, two-letter symbols are used. Thus, since C stands for carbon, symbols of two letters are used for calcium (Ca), cadmium (Cd), cerium (Ce), cesium (Cs), cobalt (Co), and chromium (Cr). The second letter is always a small letter.

Some symbols are derived from the Latin names of the elements. The symbol for iron, Fe, is derived from ferrum; that of copper, Cu, from cuprum; of mercury, Hg, from hydrargyrum (Table 3.1). The symbols of all the elements will be found for ready reference in the table on the inside front cover of this book.

3:5   Formulas

A symbol stands for an atom of an element; a *formula* stands for a molecule of a substance. A formula for a molecule shows the symbols of its constituent elements together with their numbers placed below and to the right of each symbol. If only one atom of an element is to be found in the molecule, the number 1 is understood and is omitted. Thus, H_2O represents the molecule of water composed of two atoms of the element hydrogen and one atom of the element oxygen. O_2 is the formula for the molecule of oxygen which contains two atoms. Occasionally, formulas will be met which contain parentheses, e.g., $Cu(NO_3)_2$. In such cases, the number below and to the right of the parenthesis multiplies through the atoms enclosed in it. Such parentheses in formulas will be explained later.

As we have learned, crystals of salts are made up of ions and not of molecules. The formula NaCl for common salt indicates that there are equal numbers of sodium ions, Na^+, and chloride ions, Cl^-, in its crystal structure. Similarly $CaCl_2$, the formula for calcium chloride salt, indicates that there are twice as many chloride ions, Cl^-, as calcium ions, Ca^{2+}, in its crystals.

3:6   Mixtures

A *mixture* is formed by simply blending a number of ingredients. For example, when sugar is dissolved in water, the resulting mixture is homogeneous even under a microscope. Such homogeneous mixtures are called *solutions*.

Some mixtures differ from solutions in that there are always at least two distinctly recognizable parts or phases, whereas a solution consists of only one phase. Such mixtures are heterogeneous and can be called *mechanical mixtures*. A piece of granite is an example of a mechanical mixture. A close look reveals the presence of different crystalline materials: quartz, feldspar, and mica.

A mixture may be, therefore, either homogeneous or heterogeneous, but it is always made up of two or more substances. Furthermore, these substances may be mixed in any proportions if the mixture is heterogeneous. In the case of certain solutions, there is a limit to the solubility of one substance in another. Thus at 20°C no more than 36 grams of sodium chloride will dissolve in 100 g of water. However, more

dilute sodium chloride solutions of any desired composition may be prepared. The composition of a mixture is, therefore, variable. In this respect, if differs from a pure substance. Each of the components in a mixture keeps its original properties. The properties of a mixture are an "average" of those of the substances of which it is composed.

3:7   Chemical Equations

A *chemical equation* is an exact expression representing a chemical change. The reactants and the products are each represented by their chemical formulas. The reactants are written on the left-hand side, and the products on the right-hand side. An arrow separates the reactants from the products. For example:

$$2\,H_2 + O_2 \rightarrow 2\,H_2O$$

This equation tells us that two molecules of hydrogen combine with one molecule of oxygen to give two molecules of water.

It also tells us that each molecule of hydrogen contains two atoms, that each molecule of oxygen contains two atoms, and that each molecule of water contains two atoms of hydrogen and one atom of oxygen.

The numbers in front of the formulas are called *coefficients*. They show the number of molecules that react with each other and should not be confused with subscripts, which show the number of atoms of a particular kind in the molecule.

The expressions (g), (l), and (s) placed sometimes after the formulas of the reactants and products indicate the state, gaseous, liquid, or solid, of the substances involved. Another expression frequently used is (aq) for aqueous, showing that the substance is in the form of a water solution.

It is by means of coefficients that we "balance" the equation. The full meaning of chemical equations unfolds with your growing acquaintance with chemical reactions.

3:8   The Composition of Water

The composition of water may be determined either by decomposing water into its elements (analysis) or by forming water from its elements (synthesis).

(a)   Analysis of Water: Composition by Volume

Water may be decomposed into hydrogen and oxygen by passing a direct current of electricity through water containing a small amount of sulfuric acid. The acid is added to make the water a better conductor of electricity, and does not take part in the reaction. The result of this process called electrolysis is shown in the following equation:

$$\text{water} \rightarrow \text{hydrogen} + \text{oxygen}$$
$$2 H_2O \rightarrow 2 H_2 + O_2$$

The experiment is carried out in an apparatus consisting of two tubes fitted with platinum electrodes at one end and stop cocks at the other end. These permit the withdrawal of the gases for testing. The tubes are marked with a scale to permit measurement of the volumes of gases liberated. The apparatus is illustrated in Fig. 3.3.

Fig. 3.3   *The electrolysis of water*

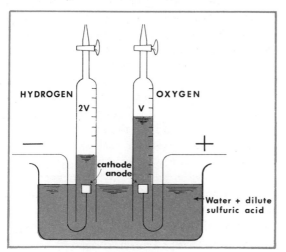

Five important points are illustrated by this simple experiment:

1. An electric current can cause a chemical reaction; in this case the decomposition of water.

2. The products of decomposition of water are oxygen and hydrogen.

3. The gas that collects at the positive electrode (anode) is recognized as oxygen by the fact that it causes a flame to burn more brightly or a glowing splint to burst into flame.

4. The gas that collects at the negative electrode (cathode) is recognized as hydrogen by the fact that it catches fire when ignited, and as it burns it produces water. This can be observed by inverting a cold, clean beaker over the hydrogen flame. A mist forms on the inside of the beaker.

5. The volume of the hydrogen evolved is twice as great as that of oxygen.

(b)   Synthesis of Water: Composition by Volume

Hydrogen gas and oxygen gas can be made to combine in a eudiometer, a heavy-walled glass tube fitted with two electrodes sealed through the glass near the closed end of the tube (Fig. 3.4).

Measured volumes of hydrogen and oxygen are mixed in the eudiometer. Then an electric spark is passed across the electrodes and the two gases combine forming water. The volumes of gases that combine can be compared.

In a typical experiment, the values of the volumes of gases measured were as follows:

1. Volume of hydrogen introduced   18 ml

2. Volume of oxygen introduced   17 ml

3. Volume of residual gas left in the tube 8 ml

The 8 ml of gas left in the eudiometer proved to be oxygen by the glowing splint test. There-

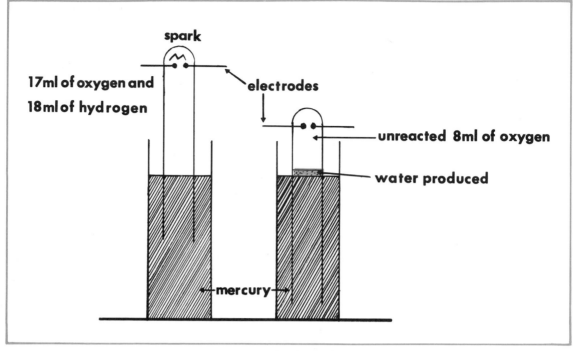

Fig. 3.4 *Synthesis of water (by volume)*

fore, 17 m*l* − 8 m*l* = 9 m*l* of oxygen combined with 18 m*l* of hydrogen. The ratio of the volume of hydrogen to the volume of oxygen that combined is 18:9 or 2:1. Regardless of the original volumes mixed, the result is always the same: 2 volumes of hydrogen combine with 1 volume of oxygen to form water.

(c) Synthesis of Water: Composition by Weight

When hydrogen is passed over hot copper (II) oxide, the hydrogen combines with the oxygen of the copper (II) oxide to form water, leaving behind the metallic copper. The copper (II) oxide is said to be reduced, while the hydrogen is oxidized in this reaction:

$$CuO + H_2 \rightarrow Cu + H_2O$$

The reaction between hydrogen and the oxygen of copper (II) oxide to form water provides an accurate method for finding the composition of water by weight. The apparatus used in the reaction is shown in Fig. 3.5.

Hydrogen, generated by the reaction of an acid and a metal is passed through the drying tube (A), containing anhydrous calcium chloride, to remove any moisture in the stream of hydrogen. Such moisture can cause an error since it is not the product of the reaction being studied. The glass tube (B) contains copper (II) oxide, and the drying tube (C) contains anhydrous calcium chloride to absorb the water formed by the hydrogen and the oxygen of the copper (II) oxide. Both tubes B and C are weighed before and after the reaction. The loss of weight by the copper (II) oxide indicates how much oxygen was removed by the hydrogen to form water, which may be weighed since it is collected in the drying tube C. Thus, it becomes evident how much oxygen is present in a weighed amount of water, and the composition of water can be calculated.

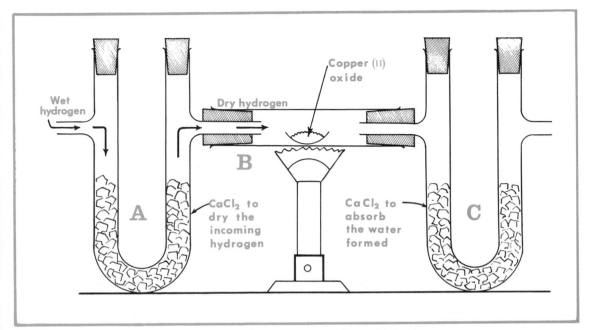

Fig. 3.5   *Synthesis of water (by weight)*

Example:

In an experiment on the determination of the composition of water, the following data were obtained:

Weight of the Tube (B) containing Copper (II) Oxide

Before: 60.46 g (1)
After: 60.30 g (2)

Weight of the Drying Tube (C)

Before: 75.40 g (3)
After: 75.58 g (4)

From these data, let us calculate: (i) the weight of oxygen used up, (ii) the weight of water formed, (iii) the weight of hydrogen used, (iv) the percentage by weight of oxygen and hydrogen in water, and (v) the ratio of the weight of oxygen to hydrogen.

Calculation:

(i) Weight of the oxygen (equals loss of weight of the copper (II) oxide, tube B)
$$(1) - (2) = 0.16 \text{ g } (5)$$

(ii) Weight of the water formed (equals gain in weight of the drying tube C):
$$(4) - (3) = 0.18 \text{ g } (6)$$

(iii) Weight of hydrogen in the water (equals weight of the water formed minus weight of oxygen in the water):
$$(6) - (5) = 0.02 \text{ g }$$

(iv) Percentage of oxygen: $\dfrac{0.16}{0.18} \times 100 = 88.8$

Percentage of hydrogen: $\dfrac{0.02}{0.18} \times 100 = 11.1$

(v) Ratio of the weight of oxygen to hydrogen $= 8:1$

3:9 Classification of Substances: a Summary

When a sample of matter has the same composition throughout it is said to be *homogeneous;* but when the sample has unlike parts it is said to be *heterogeneous.* The recognizable parts in a sample of matter are often referred to as *phases.* Thus, a homogeneous sample of matter has one phase while a heterogeneous sample contains two or more phases.

Homogeneous substances can be further classified into two groups: *pure substances* of constant composition, and *solutions* which are homogeneous mixtures varying in composition. Some pure substances, called *compounds,* can be decomposed into simpler substances by chemical means. Other pure substances, called *elements,* cannot be decomposed into anything simpler.

Mechanical mixtures have variable composition. They consist of two or more physically distinct phases. These heterogeneous forms of matter have the properties of the substances that make up the mixtures. The components of a mechanical mixture can be separated by physical means.

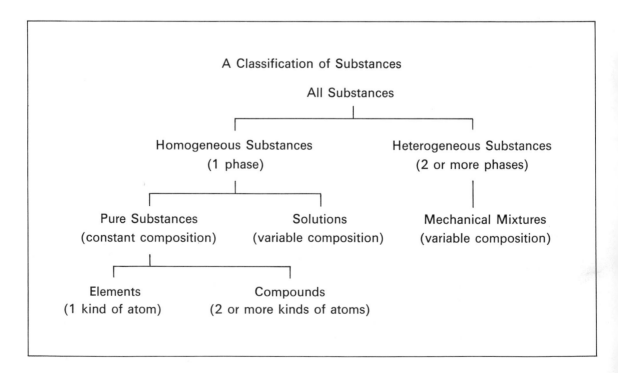

A Classification of Substances

QUESTIONS

1. Distinguish between elements and compounds.

2. Which three elements account for more than 80% of the earth's crust by weight?

3. List a few typical properties of (a) metals; (b) non-metals.

4. Explain what is meant by the term *molecule*.

5. Describe the smallest particles of which a crystal of salt is composed.

6. What is an *atom*?

7. (a) Define the term *chemical symbol*. (b) What do the following symbols represent?
   Na, Co, Ca, C, He, H.

8. What does a chemical formula represent?

9. List the information which each of the following formulas gives: (a) H_2O; (b) HCl;
   (c) CO_2; (d) CH_4; (e) $Ca(OH)_2$.

10. Give the meaning of each number and symbol in the equation: $H_2 + Cl_2 \rightarrow 2\,HCl$

11. Give two important differences between a compound and a mixture.

12. Classify the following as elements, compounds, mechanical mixtures, or solutions:
    (a) pure water; (b) oxygen gas; (c) granite; (d) brine; (e) sugar; (f) carbon dioxide;
    (g) dilute hydrochloric acid; (h) tomato juice; (i) nitrogen; (j) concrete; (k) mercury.

13. How could you separate the component parts of a mixture of sand and salt?

14. Air is said to be both a mixture and a solution. Explain.

15. Why is sulfuric acid used in the electrolysis of water?

16. How can we prove that the gases collected during the electrolysis of water are oxygen
    and hydrogen?

17. What is the ratio of the volumes of the two gases produced during the electrolysis of
    water?

18. What would happen if the direct current used during electrolysis were replaced by an
    alternating current?

19. If 10 ml of hydrogen and 10 ml of oxygen are placed in a eudiometer tube and sparked,
    name the gas remaining and find its volume.

20. Repeat question 19 assuming that:
    (a) 5 ml of hydrogen and 10 ml of oxygen are used.
    (b) 8 ml of hydrogen and 3 ml of oxygen are used.

21. In an experiment to find the percentage composition of water by weight (using the
    apparatus shown in Fig. 3.5), the following data were obtained:
    Weight of copper (II) oxide and tube before reduction: 682.63 g
    Weight of copper and tube after reduction: 622.63 g
    Weight of drying tube before experiment: 876.32 g
    Weight of drying tube after experiment: 943.89 g

    Calculate the percentage composition of water from this information.

4 Atoms and Molecules

4:1 The Law of Conservation of Mass

It has been pointed out earlier (sec. 2:6) that the products obtained from a chemical reaction have the same total mass as the original materials or reactants. This regularity of behavior found in nature is called the Law of Conservation of Mass.

4:2 The Law of Constant Composition

One of the main tasks of chemistry is to study the composition of compounds, and two general methods for doing this have been developed: analysis and synthesis. Illustrations of these methods were seen in determining the composition of water (Chapter 3).

The composition of about one million compounds has been determined with the aid of analysis and synthesis. In every compound tested, the percentage by weight of each element present was always found to be constant. This result is summed up in the *Law of Constant Composition* which states that *every pure chem-*

ical compound has a constant composition by weight. Some examples are given in Table 4.1

4:3 The Law of Multiple Proportions

It is not uncommon for the same elements to combine in more than one ratio to form different compounds. For example, 12 g of carbon combine with 16 g of oxygen to form carbon monoxide, and with 32 g of oxygen to form carbon dioxide. It can be seen that the masses of oxygen that combine with a fixed mass of carbon are in the ratio of 16:32 or 1:2.

In all cases there is a simple ratio among the several masses of an element that combine with a fixed mass of another. This fact is summed up in the *Law of Multiple Proportions: If two elements A and B combine to form more than one compound, then the different amounts of A that combine with a fixed amount of B are always in a simple ratio.*

The two compounds, water and hydrogen peroxide, offer another example of the law of multiple proportions. The relationships among the masses involved are shown in Table 4.2

TABLE 4.1

Percentage Composition of Some Compounds

Compound	Composition
Water, H_2O	88.8% oxygen, 11.2% hydrogen
Methane, CH_4	75.0% carbon, 25.0% hydrogen
Ethane, C_2H_6	80.0% carbon, 20.0% hydrogen
Methanol, CH_3OH	50.0% oxygen, 37.5% carbon, 12.5% hydrogen

TABLE 4.2

Illustration of the Law of Multiple Proportions

Compound	Parts by weight of oxygen and hydrogen	Ratio of the masses of oxygen that combine with 2.0 g of hydrogen
Water	16 g of 0 and 2.0 g of H	16 : 32 or 1 : 2
Hydrogen Peroxide	32 g of 0 and 2.0 g of H	

4:4 A Theory to Explain the Behavior of Matter and Chemical Change

Surely the laws of chemical combinations presented above must offer some important clue about the ultimate structure of matter and the way in which elements combine to form compounds. Do they answer such questions as, Why can compounds be broken down to elements but elements cannot be broken down into anything simpler? Why is matter not destroyed in chemical change? Why do the products weigh as much as the original reactants? Why do compounds have a definite composition?

About the year 1800, an English schoolteacher attempted to find the answer to these questions by imagining that matter is made up of atoms and that the behavior of atoms can explain chemical processes.

The main points of *Dalton's Atomic Theory* are the following:

1. The elements are made up of particles called atoms.

2. The atoms cannot be destroyed, or even divided, in a chemical change.

3. The atoms of a particular element have the same properties.

4. When atoms combine with other atoms, they do so in simple ratios, such as 1 : 1, or 2 : 1, or 3 : 2; never do fractions of an atom combine.

5. All chemical change is the result of the combination or the separation of atoms.

The first point of the theory is that there are atoms of elements but not of compounds. Dalton's view was that the atom is the smallest particle of an element, and that an atom is indivisible.

Perhaps the wisest point in the atomic theory is that all chemical change is the union or separation of atoms. When atoms combine they form molecules. If the atoms in the molecules are different, then such molecules account for the existence of compounds. It may happen also that atoms of the same element combine to form molecules. Oxygen is made up of molecules with two oxygen atoms each; hydrogen, nitrogen, and chlorine are similarly made of diatomic molecules. In these gases, each diatomic molecule is separated from other molecules by large distances. Molecules of the element sulfur have eight atoms each. The noble gases, helium, neon, argon, krypton, xenon, and radon consist of molecules which are single atoms.

Thus we can see how Dalton successfully defined elements, compounds, and chemical change in terms of atoms. Can the theory explain the observed laws of chemical combination? Let us see.

4:5   Explanation of the Law of Conservation of Mass

Why is there conservation of mass during a chemical reaction? According to the atomic theory, all chemical change is the combination of atoms with other atoms or the separation of atoms from other atoms. At no time is the mass of the atom itself altered, and there are as many atoms at the end of the reaction as there were at the beginning. They are simply combined differently. Therefore, there is conservation of mass in a chemical reaction.

Explaining the law of Conservation of Mass with the example of this Chemical Reaction:

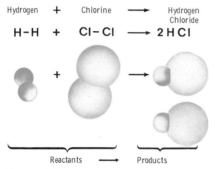

Hydrogen   +   Chlorine   ⟶   Hydrogen Chloride

H – H   +   Cl – Cl   ⟶   2 H Cl

Reactants   ⟶   Products

There are 2 atoms of hydrogen and 2 atoms of chlorine first among the reactants, and later among the products. They are respectively the same in number and mass, although differently combined. Hence, conservation of mass.

4:6   Explanation of the Law of Constant Composition

Why do compounds have a definite composition? According to the atomic theory, a compound forms when one (or two or three) atoms of an element A combine with one (or two or three) atoms of element B. But the atoms always combine in the same ratio in forming that compound. Because all the atoms of A are alike, and all the atoms of B are alike, all the molecules of the compound will be alike, each con-

taining the same ratio of atoms of A to atoms of B.

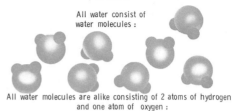

Explaining the law of Constant Composition with the example of water :

All water consist of water molecules :

All water molecules are alike consisting of 2 atoms of hydrogen and one atom of oxygen :

Therefore, all water has the same composition.
A similar explanation applies to all other chemical compounds

4:7   Explanation of the Law of Multiple Proportions

How does the atomic theory explain the law of multiple proportions? According to the atomic theory, when a particular element A combines with another element B, one atom of A combines with one atom of B to form a molecule AB. If conditions are altered, it may become possible for the atoms of A and B to combine in a different ratio. For example, two atoms of A might combine with one of B; now a new compound is formed whose molecule is AAB, or A_2B.

On comparing the composition of the two compounds formed out of the same elements A and B, we find that the different masses of A combined with the same mass of B are in the

Explaining the Law of Multiple Proportions with water and hydrogen peroxide as examples

The molecule of water has one atom of oxygen and two of hydrogen :

The molecule of hydrogen peroxide has two atoms of oxygen and two of hydrogen

The atoms of oxygen in the respective molecules are in the ratio of 1: 2 Hence, multiple proportions.

simple ratio of 1:2. This is precisely what had been found by experiment.

4:8 Dalton's Dilemma

Unfortunately, Dalton did not know the ratio in which atoms combine, and this was one of the chief weaknesses of the early atomic theory.

It can thus be seen that although Dalton was largely successful in explaining the laws of chemical combination by means of his atomic theory, at least three questions remained unanswered:

(a) If atoms are so small that they cannot be seen, how can we know anything about them? How do they compare to molecules?

(b) How many atoms are in a molecule?

(c) If the atoms of the different elements have different masses, what are these masses?

These are important and difficult questions, and because Dalton did not have the answer to them, the atomic theory met with some criticism and disbelief.

We know today that the atoms of the elements are built up of even more fundamental particles. These subatomic particles, the electron, the proton, and the neutron, are present in every kind of atom. The iron atom, for example, is the smallest particle of the element but it is composed of subatomic particles.

Dalton's view that all atoms are alike is now modified in the light of the discovery of isotopes (Chapter 5). This can hardly be considered a "mistake". It is rather a refinement of the atomic theory. We can say that the essential points of Dalton's atomic theory concerning chemical combination are still valid today.

4:9 Atomic Mass

We have discussed atoms and molecules descriptively. Could they be described quantitatively? Could we say something about their mass? Atoms and molecules are so small that weighing them individually on a balance is out of the question. However, this is hardly neces-

sary. If it is true that the atoms of each element have a certain mass, and that they combine with other atoms in a definite ratio, we could perform an experiment to find out what mass of two given elements combine with each other. If we knew also in what ratio the atoms combine, we could then find the relative mass of the atoms.

A chemical reaction that illustrates such relationships is the combination of carbon with oxygen to form carbon dioxide gas. We can weigh a definite mass of carbon and ignite it. We can determine the mass of carbon dioxide produced by capturing it in some limewater. Then, the mass of oxygen involved in the combination can be calculated by subtracting the mass of carbon used from the mass of carbon dioxide formed.

Such an experiment will permit us to know the respective mass of carbon and oxygen that combine in forming carbon dioxide. However, one other important item of information will be required before the relative mass of the atoms can be established. How many atoms of carbon and oxygen are there in a molecule of carbon dioxide? This is indeed a difficult question. Such was the problem that Dalton could not solve. For our present purpose we will use the now established fact that one atom of carbon combines with two atoms of oxygen to form a molecule of carbon dioxide:

$$C + O_2 \rightarrow CO_2$$

In doing this experiment, the following data are obtained:

Mass of carbon burned: 12 grams
Mass of carbon dioxide produced: 44 grams
∴ Mass of oxygen used (44 − 12): 32 grams

$$\text{Hence,} \frac{\text{mass of oxygen}}{\text{mass of carbon}} = \frac{32}{12}$$

The result obtained, 32:12, represents the ratio of the mass of oxygen to the mass of carbon that combine, forming carbon dioxide. Now, this carbon dioxide is made up of molecules which are all alike. Each molecule of carbon dioxide has 2 atoms of oxygen and 1 atom of carbon. Therefore, the mass of 2 oxygen atoms and the mass of 1 carbon atom are also in the ratio of 32:12. Hence, we may write:

$$\frac{\text{mass of 2 atoms of oxygen}}{\text{mass of 1 atom of carbon}} = \frac{32}{12}$$

or

$$\frac{\text{mass of 1 atom of oxygen}}{\text{mass of 1 atom of carbon}} = \frac{16}{12}$$

Thus we find that the masses of the atoms of oxygen and carbon are in the ratio of O:C = 16:12.

Although the experimental method of performing the above experiment might be somewhat difficult to carry out, the conclusion reached is fundamentally sound. We have found the relative mass of two atoms.

We could now devise other experiments to find the ratio of other pairs of atoms, until we have such information about as many elements as we please.

To convert our data from comparisons of the mass of atoms to a simpler independent expression of their mass, we need to select an appropriate standard element to whose atom all others may be compared, and an appropriate unit to express atomic mass.

The element chosen in 1961 is carbon, and the atom of its most abundant isotope is the standard to which the mass of all other atoms are compared. To this atom of carbon, a mass of 12 atomic mass units (amu) was assigned. Thus the amu can be defined as 1/12 the mass of the carbon-12 isotope.

Once the value of 12 amu is assigned to carbon, relative values can be assigned to the atoms of the other elements using such data as we found for oxygen. The mass of the oxygen atom is 16 amu; the mass of the hydrogen atom is 1 amu; etc. The mass of all the atoms of the elements are listed inside the front cover of the book.

A molecule consists of atoms. The mass of the molecule is the sum of the mass of its atoms. This sum is termed the *molecular mass* of the compound. The molecular mass of sulfur dioxide, SO_2, is equal to the sum of the mass of one sulfur atom and two oxygen atoms: $(1 \times 32) + (2 \times 16) = 64$ amu.

Both molecular and atomic masses are based on the same standard, carbon-12, and are both expressed in amu.

4:10   The Size of Atoms and Molecules

With the aid of modern experimental methods, the size of atoms and molecules have been

Fig. 4.1   *Chemical compounds are created artificially by combining known elements. In a pharmaceutical research laboratory, a scientist separates foreign substances to obtain a pure compound.*

Courtesy Chas. Pfizer and Company, Incorporated

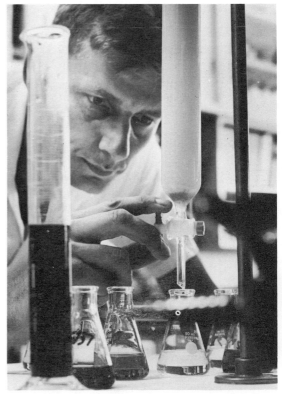

determined. Atoms are very small particles with diameters in the range of 2 to 5 Å. "Å" stands for the Angstrom unit and is equal to 10^{-8} cm, i.e., one hundred millionth of a centimeter. Thus if atoms whose diameter is 5 Å units could be placed side by side, it would require 20 million of them to make up 1 cm. Individual atoms or average-sized molecules are much too small to be seen by the most powerful of microscopes. By means of the electron microscope, however, in which a beam of electrons is used instead of visible light, photographs (more accurately, electron micrographs) of the giant protein molecules of disease-producing viruses have been made. Such giant molecules contain as many as 750,000 atoms.

QUESTIONS

1. Are there any exceptions to the law of conservation of mass? Give reasons for your answer.

2. (a) Define *analysis* and *synthesis*.
   (b) Give an example of each.

3. State the law of constant composition.

4. Iron sulfide, FeS, contains 36.5% sulfur. How much sulfur could be extracted from a ton of iron sulfide?

5. State the law of multiple proportions.

6. Two compounds of tin and oxygen have the following compositions:
   (A) tin 78.77%, oxygen 21.23%
   (B) tin 88.12%, oxygen 11.88%
   (a) Calculate the mass of oxygen combined with one gram of tin in each of the two compounds.
   (b) Do these two compounds illustrate the law of multiple proportions? Explain.

7. What was the purpose of Dalton's atomic theory?

8. State the main points of Dalton's atomic theory.

9. Why would the oxygen and mercury obtained from decomposing 10 g of mercury (II) oxide, HgO, together have a mass of 10 g?

10. Use Dalton's atomic theory to explain: (a) the law of conservation of mass; (b) the law of constant composition; (c) the law of multiple proportions.

11. List the questions that Dalton's atomic theory did not answer.

12. Suggest some advances that have been made in knowledge about atoms since Dalton's time.

13. Define the following terms: (a) *atomic mass*; (b) *molecular mass*; (c) *atomic mass unit*.

14. What is the present standard for atomic and molecular mass?

15. Find the molecular mass of the following substances:
   (a) hydrogen, H_2
   (b) sodium hydroxide, NaOH
   (c) water, H_2O
   (d) sucrose, $C_{12}H_{22}O_{11}$
   (e) hydrogen chloride, HCl
   (f) methane, CH_4
   (g) carbon dioxide, CO_2
   (h) sulfuric acid, H_2SO_4
   (i) nitrogen, N_2
   (j) ammonia, NH_3

5 Atoms and Electrons

5:1 Electrons, Protons, and Neutrons: The Electrical and Nuclear Units of Matter

Electricity is used for a variety of purposes. It supplies the energy for lighting, heating, refrigeration, communication, and for hundreds of other useful appliances.

The *electric current* is a flow of charged units called electrons. They are present in all atoms, and are chiefly responsible for the chemical behavior of atoms, molecules, and ions.

The *electron* carries a negative electric charge and is very light. The mass of the hydrogen atom, the lightest atom, is about 1840 times as great as that of the electron. Indeed, the mass of the electron is so small that it is not ordinarily considered in computing the mass of the atom.

Matter is generally electrically neutral, because the numbers of positive and negative charges in matter are equal. The particle with a positive charge is the *proton*. This positive particle has almost exactly the same mass as the hydrogen atom which consists of one proton and one electron, and the mass of the electron is negligible.

The *neutron* is another particle in the nucleus of atoms. The name neutron suggests that it is electrically neutral. It carries no negative nor positive charge. Its mass is almost the same as that of a proton or a hydrogen atom. Properties of the three important constituents of the atom are summarized in Table 5.1.

5:2 The Atomic Number

In any atom the total number of electrons is equal to that of the protons; so the atom as a

TABLE 5.1

Properties of the Fundamental Particles

Particle	Charge	Mass in Atomic Mass Units
Electron	−1	0.00055 or 1/1840 of the hydrogen atom
Proton	+1	1.0073
Neutron	0	1.0087

whole is electrically neutral. The number of protons or electrons in the atom is called the *atomic number*. Hydrogen has one electron and one proton, and therefore is said to have an atomic number of *one*. Helium has two electrons and two protons, and hence has an atomic number of *two*.

5:3 Electron Shells and Energy Levels

The knowledge of how the electrons, protons, and neutrons distribute themselves within the atom is of profound importance to chemistry and physics. Protons and neutrons are contained in the nucleus of the atom, while the electrons move about the nucleus at certain distances and in certain patterns. We speak of the whereabouts of electrons as *electron shells*, and these are lettered K, L, M, N, O . . .

To be at a certain distance from the nucleus and to move about the nucleus requires energy. The electron shells represent certain amounts of energy, and hence they are said to be at certain levels of energy. These *energy levels* are so important in describing electrons that they are numbered for reference. We speak of the first,

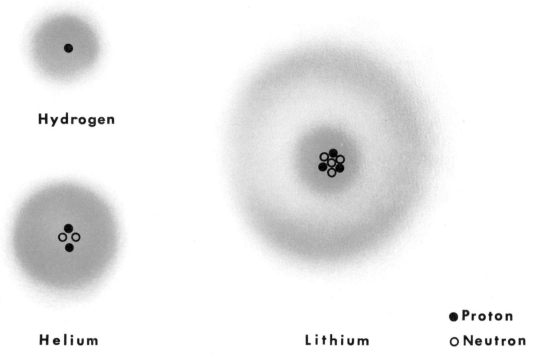

Hydrogen

Helium

Lithium

● **Proton**

○ **Neutron**

Fig. 5.1   *Representation of the first three atoms*

second, third . . . and higher energy levels. The electron shells lettered K, L, M, N, O . . . correspond to the energy levels numbered 1, 2, 3, 4, 5 . . . respectively.

The symbol for numbering the energy levels is n. Thus for the first energy level, n = 1, for the second, n = 2, and so forth. Thus to say that an electron is in the K shell of an atom is the same as saying that it is in the first energy level.

5:4   Imagining the Atom

The nucleus of an atom is extremely small compared to the size of the entire atom. The diameter of the nucleus is about 1/100,000 of the diameter of the whole atom. Yet, nearly all the mass of the atom is concentrated in this region because it contains all the protons and neutrons.

The rest of the volume of the atom is occupied by electrons.

By means of the atomic number we can start to build a picture of the atoms. The hydrogen atom, whose atomic number is 1, is the lightest and the simplest of all. It consists of a proton in the nucleus and an electron revolving about it. The atom of helium (atomic number 2) consists of two electrons revolving about a nucleus containing two protons and two neutrons. The first electron shell is now full.

The atom of lithium (atomic number 3) consists of three electrons. Two of these are in the first shell, and the third electron is in the second shell. The nucleus of lithium consists of three protons and four neutrons (Fig. 5.1).

Thus lithium's atom has the first electron of the second or L shell. This shell can hold a maximum of 8 electrons, and with neon, atom

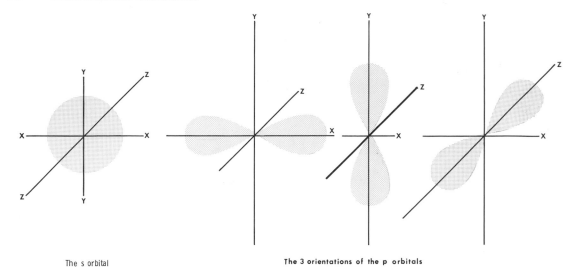

The s orbital   The 3 orientations of the p orbitals

Fig. 5.2   *The s and p orbitals*

number 10, this number is reached. Sodium is atom number 11. Its eleventh electron starts the third shell. The eighteenth electron of argon completes this shell.

5:5   The s and p Orbitals

The electrons found in a given shell do not all have the same amount of energy. The reason for this is that electrons move about the nucleus in different ways. Some electrons move about in such a way that they produce the effect of a spherical blur or cloud around the nucleus. Such electrons are called *s electrons* and are said to be in an *s orbital*. An *orbital* may be defined

TABLE 5.2				
The Electronic Shells for the First Twenty Elements				
The Electronic Shells	The Energy Levels Corresponding to the Shells	The Orbitals within the Electronic Shells	The Number of Electrons in the Orbitals	The Number of Electrons in the Shells
K	n = 1	1s	2	2
L	n = 2	2s 2p	2 6	8
M	n = 3	3s 3p	2 6	8
N	n = 4	4s	2	2

TABLE 5.3

Electrons in the Shells of the First Twenty Elements

Elements	Atomic Numbers	K or 1st 1s	L or 2nd 2s	L or 2nd 2p	M or 3rd 3s	M or 3rd 3p	N or 4th 4s
H	1	1					
He	2	2					
Li	3	2	1				
Be	4	2	2				
B	5	2	2	1			
C	6	2	2	2			
N	7	2	2	3			
O	8	2	2	4			
F	9	2	2	5			
Ne	10	2	2	6			
Na	11	2	2	6	1		
Mg	12	2	2	6	2		
Al	13	2	2	6	2	1	
Si	14	2	2	6	2	2	
P	15	2	2	6	2	3	
S	16	2	2	6	2	4	
Cl	17	2	2	6	2	5	
Ar	18	2	2	6	2	6	
K	19	2	2	6	2	6	1
Ca	20	2	2	6	2	6	2

as a region around the nucleus of an atom having at most two electrons which spin on their axes in opposite directions. There are two such electrons in the s orbital at any energy level. Other electrons move about three axes at right angles to each other (Fig. 5.2). Such are called *p electrons* and they are in *p orbitals*. There could be as many as six p electrons in orbitals beginning at the second shell.

Table 5.2 shows how the electron shells, energy levels, orbitals, and numbers of electrons are interrelated for the first twenty elements.

In the 3rd and 4th shells, there are other orbitals not shown here. They will be discussed later.

5:6 The First Twenty Elements

The electron make-up of the atoms in the first twenty elements is shown in Table 5.3.

The First Shell

Hydrogen has only one electron and it is located in the first electron shell. Helium has two electrons in the first shell; thereby they fill that shell completely. All atoms after helium will have two electrons in their first shell, plus other electrons in the higher shells.

The Second Shell

The lithium atom has three electrons in all, one of these in the second shell. This electron is in the orbital termed 2s. Beryllium has two electrons in 2s and thereby, they fill it to its maximum. All atoms above Be have a full 2s orbital. Boron has one electron in 2p and the five succeeding atoms have 2, 3, 4, 5, and 6 electrons in that sublevel. The term *sublevel* is used for one or more orbitals of the same kind. Thus in the second energy level, there are two sublevels, s and p (Chapter 15). With neon, Ne, it is filled to its maximum capacity of six electrons. All subsequent atoms also have a full 2p sublevel.

The Third Shell

Sodium starts the third electron shell with one electron in 3s and the magnesium orbital is filled with two electrons. Thereafter, all atoms have a full 3s orbital. Aluminum starts the 3p orbitals with its next electron, and the five elements which follow have 2, 3, 4, 5, and 6 electrons in those orbitals. Thus we reach argon, Ar, with six electrons in 3p. This sublevel is now full.

The Fourth Shell

The next element is potassium and its outermost electron starts the fourth shell by having one electron in the 4s orbital. Finally, with calcium, the twentieth element, the 4s orbital is filled with two electrons.

5:7   The Formation of Ions

In the lithium atom, the single electron in the outer shell may be transferred to another atom. This leaves the original atom with one more proton than it has electrons. Such a particle carries a positive charge and is an example of an ion. The following equation represents a neutral lithium atom becoming a lithium ion by losing an electron:

$$\text{lithium atom} \rightarrow \text{lithium ion} + \text{one electron}$$
$$\text{Li}^\circ \quad \rightarrow \quad \text{Li}^+ \quad + \quad 1\ e^-$$

By contrast, other atoms may easily add one or more electrons to their outer shells. The fluorine atom may easily gain one electron to become the negatively charged fluoride ion:

$$\text{fluorine atom} + \text{one electron} \rightarrow \text{fluoride ion}$$
$$\text{F}^\circ \quad + \quad 1\ e^- \quad \rightarrow \quad \text{F}^-$$

5:8   Isotopes

Atoms of the same element might have different numbers of neutrons despite the fact that they have the same number of electrons and protons. Such atoms have the same atomic number but different atomic mass, and they are called *isotopes*. Remember that the atomic mass is determined by the numbers of protons and neutrons and for this reason different numbers of neutrons would cause such atoms to have a different mass. Since the chemical properties of an element depend on the electrons in the shells, the isotopes of an element have the same chemical properties.

5:9   The Isotopes of Hydrogen

Ordinary hydrogen consists of two isotopes. The light isotope, of atomic mass 1, makes up 99.98% of ordinary hydrogen. The heavier isotope, called deuterium, of atomic mass 2, makes up 0.02%. The nucleus of the light isotope, called protium, consists of a single proton, whereas the nucleus of the heavy isotope consists of a proton and a neutron.

Still a third isotope of hydrogen is now known, namely tritium. It has two neutrons and

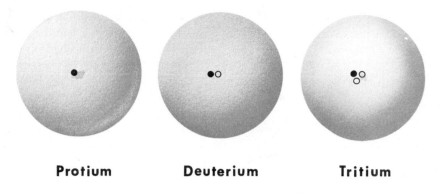

Protium   **Deuterium**   **Tritium**

● **Proton**
○ **Neutron**

Fig. 5.3   *The three isotopes of hydrogen*

one proton in its nucleus (Fig. 5.3). Tritium is exceedingly rare and occurs merely as traces in water. It can be prepared artificially for research.

It is now known that most elements are a mixture of two or more isotopes. The atomic mass of an element is the average mass of its isotopes, according to their abundance. The percentage of each isotope in a naturally occurring element is always the same.

5:10   Useful Representations of Atoms

In order to draw attention to important features in the structure of atoms, a number of special signs and symbols are used. A small ° placed at the upper right of the symbol stresses the fact that the atom is neutral. Thus, in section 5:7 neutral lithium and fluorine atoms were represented by Li° and F°.

Isotopes of an element are shown by having the atomic number below and the mass number* above the symbol. For example $^{35}_{17}Cl$ and $^{37}_{17}Cl$ represent the two common isotopes of chlorine. Often we represent them more simply as Cl-35 and Cl-37.

Diagrams similar to those shown in Fig. 5.4

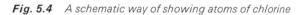

Fig. 5.4   *A schematic way of showing atoms of chlorine*

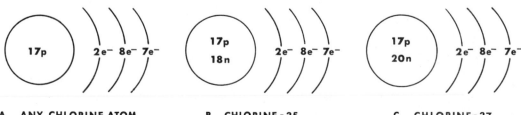

A. ANY CHLORINE ATOM   **B. CHLORINE-35**   **C. CHLORINE-37**

*Mass number is the sum of the protons and neutrons in the nucleus of an atom.

can be used to show the general location of protons, electrons, and neutrons within the atom.

TABLE 5.4			
Representations of the First Ten Elements			
Element	Symbol	Electron Distribution K L	Electron Dot Representation
Hydrogen	H	1	H·
Helium	He	2	He:
Lithium	Li	2, 1	Li·
Beryllium	Be	2, 2	Be:
Boron	B	2, 3	·B·
Carbon	C	2, 4	·C·
Nitrogen	N	2, 5	·N:
Oxygen	O	2, 6	:O:
Fluorine	F	2, 7	:F:
Neon	Ne	2, 8	:Ne:

The properties of an element depend on the number of electrons in the shells. More precisely, it is the number of electrons located in the outermost shell of the atom that usually determines its properties. Often we wish to use a simple way to show the outermost electrons. Dots around the symbol of the element are used for this purpose. The atoms of lithium, magnesium, carbon, chlorine, and neon are represented as follows:

$$Li \quad Mg \quad ·C· \quad :Cl: \quad :Ne:$$

Here, the symbol of each element represents the nucleus and the filled inner electronic shells. The outer electrons are represented by dots. Table 5.4 illustrates further the various representations of atoms referred to above.

Illustrating the Positions of Numbers used with Atomic Symbols

For atom A :

atomic mass   charge

A

atomic number   number of atoms

For example, 2 atoms of oxygen, each of mass 16, charge zero, and atomic number 8, would be shown as :

$${}_{8}^{16}O_{2}$$

The Carbon Atom and its Core

Symbol   C

Electron dot   ·C·

Protons, neutrons and electrons   (6p 6n)   2e 4e

The atomic core   (6p 6n)   2e

The atomic mass, number and charge

$${}_{6}^{12}C$$

QUESTIONS

1. What is an *electric current*?

2. Name the three most important "fundamental particles" found in the atoms. List their characteristics.

3. Why is an atom electrically neutral?

4. What is meant by the term *atomic number*?

5. What is meant by the term *energy level*?

6. What is meant by an *electron shell*?

7. What is the essential difference between an atom and an ion?

8. What is meant by the term *atomic mass*?

9. What is meant by the term *mass number?*

10. In what way do isotopes of a given element differ from one another?

11. Which of the following particles are electrically charged?
    (A) neutrons and protons   (C) electrons and neutrons
    (B) ions and protons   (D) isotopes and ions

12. How can the mass number of a given atom be calculated when the number of protons, the number of electrons, and the number of neutrons contained in the atom are known?

13. A given isotope of nitrogen contains 7 electrons, 7 protons, and 8 neutrons. (a) What is its mass number?   (b) What is its atomic number?

14. One isotope of magnesium has a mass number of 25. Which of the following represents this isotope correctly?

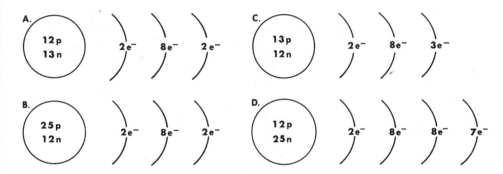

15. The nucleus of an atom contains 10 neutrons and 9 protons. The first two shells contain a total of 9 electrons. (a) What is the atomic number of this atom? (b) What is its mass number? (c) What is the name of the atom?

16. If a neutral atom has 11 protons and 12 neutrons, which of the following statements about the atom is *correct?*
    (A) It has a mass number of 11.
    (B) It has an atomic number of 23.
    (C) It has 11 electrons.
    (D) It has an atomic mass of 12.

17. Could neutral atoms of the same element have:
    (a) different mass numbers?
    (b) different numbers of electrons?
    (c) different numbers of protons?

18. A neutral atom has 2 electrons in the K shell, 8 electrons in the L shell, and 7 electrons in the M shell. From these data, supply the following information if possible:
    (a) the atomic number;
    (b) the mass number;
    (c) the number of protons in the nucleus;
    (d) the number of electrons in the outermost electron shell of the atom;
    (e) the number of neutrons in the nucleus;
    (f) the total number of s electrons in the atom.

19. Complete (in your notebook) the following table.

Isotopes	Atomic Numbers	Number of protons in the nucleus	Number of neutrons in the nucleus	Number of electrons in the shells		
				K	L	M
Helium-4	2					
Beryllium-9	4					
Carbon-14	6					
Oxygen-18	8					
Neon-22	10					
Potassium-39	19					
Argon-40	18					

20. Using the schematic models shown in Fig. 5.4, draw diagrams representing the following atoms: $^{12}_{6}C$, $^{23}_{12}Mg$, $^{23}_{11}Na$, $^{20}_{10}Ne$, and $^{32}_{16}S$.

21. Draw diagrams to represent the atoms of the first twenty elements listed in Table 5.3. Show the number of protons and electrons only and use the model shown in Fig. 5.4(a).

22. Draw diagrams to illustrate the lithium isotopes of mass number 6 and 7. Use the models shown in Fig. 5.4(b) and (c).

23. The electron distribution and the electron dot representations of the first ten elements are reproduced in Table 5.4. Prepare a similar table for the next ten elements (atomic number 11 to 20) using the information given in Table 5.3.

CHAPTER

6 The Periodic Table (I)

Over one hundred elements are known today. When we examine their properties, we find a bewildering array of reactions and compounds. However, it is possible to classify the elements according to resemblances and differences which they display.

6:1 Families of Elements

Many elements can be grouped into families on the basis of their strikingly similar chemical properties. Chlorine and bromine not only react with the same substances but the molecular formulas of the products formed are similar. With sodium they form the compounds NaCl and NaBr;* both form similar compounds with carbon, CCl_4 and CBr_4; both react with mercury to form not one but two different compounds: $HgCl_2$ and Hg_2Cl_2, $HgBr_2$ and Hg_2Br_2; and both react with hydrogen to form HCl and HBr.

This generalization is very valuable. Suppose that chlorine is known to react with metallic calcium to form the compound calcium chloride, $CaCl_2$. Then we may predict with reasonable assurance that bromine will also react with calcium, and that the formula of the compound will be $CaBr_2$, not $CaBr$, $CaBr_3$, or Ca_2Br, but specifically $CaBr_2$.

The existence of families of elements greatly simplifies the task of learning chemistry. If we know the reactions of just one member of a family, we can predict by analogy many of the reactions of the other members of the family.

6:2 Newlands' Octaves

What makes the similarity in chemical and physical properties among the elements of a family even more exciting is that the grouping occurs naturally.

Relationships between the atomic mass of the elements and their properties were first noted by Dobereiner as early as 1817. He suggested that certain elements could be placed in groups of three such as chlorine, bromine, and iodine. Not only did these elements resemble each other, but, in addition the atomic mass of the middle one was the average of the other two.

In 1865, Newlands, an English chemist, suggested that *if the elements are arranged in the order of increasing atomic mass a similar set of properties is displayed by every eighth element.* Omitting hydrogen, the lightest element, (remember that helium and neon were still unknown then), Newlands listed the elements in order of increasing atomic mass as shown in Table 6.1.

Starting from any given element in this arrangement, the eighth element is a kind of repetition of the first, just like the eighth note in an octave of music harmonizes with the first. For this

*The names of these compounds are:

NaCl   sodium chloride
NaBr   sodium bromide
CCl_4 carbon tetrachloride
CBr_4 carbon tetrabromide
$HgCl_2$ mercury (II) chloride
Hg_2Cl_2 mercury (I) chloride
$HgBr_2$ mercury (II) bromide
Hg_2Br_2 mercury (I) bromide

reason, we refer to the arrangement of New-lands as the *Law of Octaves*. Beyond calcium, the law of octaves breaks down.

TABLE 6.1						
Newlands' Law of Octaves						
Li	Be	B	C	N	O	F
Na	Mg	Al	Si	P	S	Cl
K	Ca					

6:3 Mendeleef's Classification

A more accurate arrangement, although still incomplete and imperfect, was proposed by Mendeleef, a Russian chemist, in 1869. Mende-leef's proposal, called the *Periodic Law**, states that the *properties of the elements are periodic functions of their atomic mass*. By the term "periodic functions", we understand the periodic recurrence of similar properties.

The great importance of the periodic law is that it shows clearly that the classification of the elements is completely natural. Simply arrange the elements in order of atomic mass or atomic number and the elements are also arranged in order of their properties. This is an amazing fact. To be able to classify the elements at all, other than in alphabetical order, is surprising enough. To discover that their atomic masses go up regularly, and indeed their atomic numbers go up one unit at a time, is equally surprising. But to show that both classifications really coincide! That was a truly remarkable discovery. The benefit to chemistry is easy to see. This organizes and simplifies the subject and makes it unnecessary to memorize a limit-less amount of detail. Mendeleef's arrangement of the elements is called the *Periodic Table*. A modern form of the table in which the elements discovered since 1869 are included, is presented in Fig. 6.1.

When Mendeleef proposed his classification of the elements, fewer than seventy elements had been discovered. Mendeleef had great faith in the periodic table. Rather than force an element incorrectly into a blank in the table where it did not belong, Mendeleef preferred to leave an empty space and to predict the properties of the element which he believed would someday be discovered to fit into the empty spot.

For example, Mendeleef predicted that an unknown element of atomic mass 72 lying between gallium and arsenic should eventually be found. Because it was in the same family as silicon, but belonged in the space below it, he named it "eka-silicon", meaning "beyond silicon". He predicted its properties solely on the basis of the position it would occupy in the

TABLE 6.2		
Properties of Germanium ("ekasilicon")		
Properties of the element	"Ekasilicon" (Predicted Values)	Germanium (Actual Values)
Atomic Mass	72 amu	72.3 amu
Density of the Element	5.5 g/cm^3	5.36 g/cm^3
Formula of the Oxide	EkO$_2$	GeO$_2$
Density of the Oxide	4.7 g/cm^3	4.70 g/cm^3
Formula and Properties of the Chloride	EkCl$_4$, boiling point a little under 100°C, density 1.9 g/cm^3	GeCl$_4$, boiling point 86°C, density 1.88 g/cm^3

*The modern statement of the *Periodic Law* is: *The properties of the elements are periodic functions of their atomic numbers.* The reasons behind this modification become clear when atomic structure is studied in chapters 15 and 16.

table. He averaged the properties of the elements surrounding it. Mendeleef lived to see his predictions confirmed with uncanny accuracy. In 1886, the German chemist, C. A. Winkler, discovered the element which fitted into that position in the periodic table. He named it germanium. This was triumphant proof of the validity of the periodic table. To see how closely the predictions were, compare the predicted and actual properties of germanium as shown in Table 6.2.

6:4 Characteristics of the Periodic Table

In the periodic table shown in Fig. 6.1, the elements are arranged in the order of increasing atomic numbers. The atoms of each succeeding element contain one more electron (and one more proton).

The elements with similar chemical and physical properties are placed under each other in a vertical column called a *group* or *family*. There are eight such main groups designated as groups I, II, III, IV, V, VI, VII, and VIII. The remaining ten vertical columns between groups II and III, represent the "transition" elements wherein resemblances tend to appear among succeeding elements in a horizontal row.

The seven horizontal rows are called *periods*. The first period contains two elements, hydrogen and helium. The second and third periods have eight elements each. The fourth and fifth periods contain eighteen elements each. The sixth period contains thirty-two elements.

Until 1940, the seventh period contained only six elements, ending with uranium. This element has an atomic number of 92, the highest atomic number among the naturally occurring elements. Today there are seventeen elements in the seventh period. The additional eleven elements have all been synthesized in about twenty years of research in the field of atomic

energy. More may be synthesized in the future.

The two large groups of elements placed at the bottom of the table fit into periods six and seven. They are called the lanthanides and the actinides. The elements within these groups have almost identical chemical properties.

The most metallic elements are found on the left-hand side of the periodic table while the most nonmetallic elements are on the right-hand side. As we move across a given period from left to right we notice a gradual decrease in the metallic nature of the elements.

6:5 The Noble* Gases: Structure and Chemical Stability

The elements forming group VIII of the periodic table have properties and atomic structures that can help us understand the chemical activity of other elements. The members of this chemical family are the rare or noble gases: helium (He), neon (Ne), argon (Ar), krypton (Kr), xenon (Xe), and radon (Rn).

Discovery of the Noble Gases

In 1892, the English scientist Ramsay became interested in the discovery that nitrogen obtained from the air had a slightly higher density than that prepared by chemical means. After many months of careful investigation, he concluded that the higher density must be due to the presence of an unknown gas. When he separated this gas from the air, he found that it was completely unreactive. He called it argon, the "idle" gas. He soon found also that this gas was really a mixture of gaseous elements, and he isolated helium, neon, krypton, and xenon as well as argon, from this mixture. This was a remarkable achievement when it is considered that these gases are colorless, odorless, and very inert chemically. For over fifty years it was believed that they would not combine with even

*The name Noble Gases is used in this book to describe these elements. They are sometimes called the Rare Gases and the Inert Gases. Since some of them are not rare, and others are not inert, these names were rejected here.

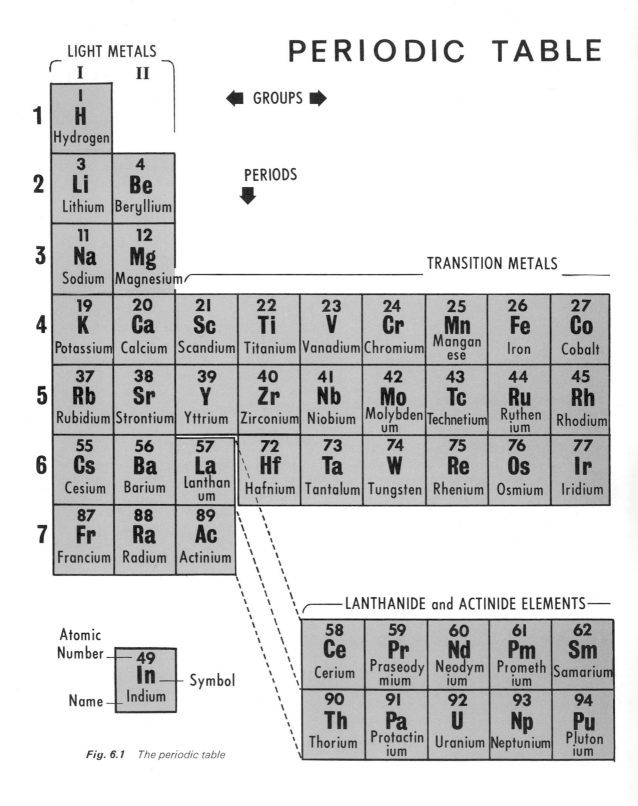

Fig. 6.1   *The periodic table*

OF THE ELEMENTS

								2 **He** Helium

NON—METALS

			III	IV	V	VI	VII	
			5 **B** Boron	6 **C** Carbon	7 **N** Nitrogen	8 **O** Oxygen	9 **F** Fluorine	10 **Ne** Neon
			13 **Al** Aluminum	14 **Si** Silicon	15 **P** Phosphorus	16 **S** Sulfur	17 **Cl** Chlorine	18 **Ar** Argon
28 **Ni** Nickel	29 **Cu** Copper	30 **Zn** Zinc	31 **Ga** Gallium	32 **Ge** Germanium	33 **As** Arsenic	34 **Se** Selenium	35 **Br** Bromine	36 **Kr** Krypton
46 **Pd** Palladium	47 **Ag** Silver	48 **Cd** Cadmium	49 **In** Indium	50 **Sn** Tin	51 **Sb** Antimony	52 **Te** Tellurium	53 **I** Iodine	54 **Xe** Xenon
78 **Pt** Platinum	79 **Au** Gold	80 **Hg** Mercury	81 **Tl** Thallium	82 **Pb** Lead	83 **Bi** Bismuth	84 **Po** Polonium	85 **At** Astatine	86 **Rn** Radon

63 **Eu** Europium	64 **Gd** Gadolinium	65 **Tb** Terbium	66 **Dy** Dysprosium	67 **Ho** Holmium	68 **Er** Erbium	69 **Tm** Thulium	70 **Yb** Ytterbium	71 **Lu** Lutetium
95 **Am** Americium	96 **Cm** Curium	97 **Bk** Berkelium	98 **Cf** Californium	99 **Es** Einsteinium	100 **Fm** Fermium	101 **Md** Mendelevium	102 **No** Nobelium	103 **Lw** Lawrencium

the most active substances. Today we know that at least one of them, xenon, combines with the highly reactive gas fluorine to form XeF_4, xenon tetrafluoride.

Some of the Properties and Uses of the Noble Gases

Helium is only one-seventh as heavy as air and therefore has considerable lifting power. Its inactivity makes it safer than hydrogen for use in weather balloons and in toy balloons. It is also used in low temperature research, because it has the lowest boiling point and freezing point of any substance known.

Because argon is an exceptionally good conductor of heat, it is often used in incandescent light bulbs and electronic tubes to conduct heat away from the filament. This permits the filament to be operated at a higher temperature which results in a more efficient bulb. Argon is also used in the welding of magnesium to provide a gaseous atmosphere that excludes oxygen, thereby preventing oxidation of the weld.

When a gas is placed in a tube at low pressure and a high voltage is applied, a spark jumps between the electrodes at each end of the tube, as the gas begins to conduct the electric current. When it does so, it also emits light. By this means neon gives an orange-red light, argon and xenon give a blue light, and helium a cream or pale orange light. The use of mixed gases and dyes in the glass tubes gives us the great variety of signs that are commonly seen today.

Structure and Chemical Stability

The greatest distinctive property of the noble gases is their almost total lack of chemical reactivity. Their inertness is associated with electronic structures that are particularly stable. We know that the outer shells of the noble gas atoms hold eight electrons (2 in the case of the helium atom) (Table 6.3). An atom with eight electrons in its outer shell displays a stable electronic structure. Since the outer shell of the

helium atom can hold a maximum of only two electrons, and the atom has two electrons, helium is also chemically inert.

TABLE 6.3

Electron Structures of the Noble Gases

Element	Atomic Number	Number of Electrons in the Electronic Shells					
		K	L	M	N	O	P
He	2	2					
Ne	10	2	8				
Ar	18	2	8	8			
Kr	36	2	8	18	8		
Xe	54	2	8	18	18	8	
Rn	86	2	8	18	32	18	8

How Sodium and Chlorine Atoms Combine

Sodium chloride, table salt, is a very stable chemical compound. The particles that make up the crystals of salt are the positive sodium ions and the negative chloride ions. These ions are present in the crystal in the ratio of one to one (Fig. 3.2). What accounts for the great chemical stability of sodium chloride?

Sodium has an atomic number of 11. Therefore, the neutral sodium atom has one more electron than the noble gas neon (atomic number 10) just preceding it. Chlorine on the other hand, with an atomic number of 17, has one electron less than the noble gas argon (atomic number 18) just following it.

In the stable compound sodium chloride, how many electrons do the sodium and chloride ions have? By losing one electron, the sodium atom acquires the stable electronic structure of its nearest noble gas neighbor, the neon atom:

$$Na^° \rightarrow Na^+ + 1e^-$$

By gaining one electron, the chlorine atom acquires the stable electronic structure of its nearest neighbor, the argon atom:

$$Cl° + 1e^- \rightarrow Cl^-$$

When sodium and chlorine combine, the sodium atom loses an electron to a chlorine atom. This electron transfer permits both atoms to acquire the stable electronic structures of the noble gases. The reaction between sodium and chlorine can be represented by the following:

$$Na° + \overset{..}{\underset{..}{Cl}} : \longrightarrow \overset{+}{Na} + \overset{..}{\underset{..}{:Cl:}}^-$$

6:6 A Family of Metals: The Alkali Metals

The elements of group I in the periodic table, called the alkali metals, are lithium (Li), sodium (Na), potassium (K), rubidium (Rb), cesium (Cs), and francium (Fr). The alkali metals are all solid elements at room temperature. Their melting and boiling points decrease with increasing atomic size. They are soft and may be cut with a knife. They have very low densities, whereas most metals have high densities. The physical properties of the alkali metals along with their electron configurations are summarized in Table 6.4.

Chemically, the alkali metals are extremely reactive. We have seen that sodium and chlorine react readily forming sodium chloride. The two

ions formed in the reaction, the sodium ion (Na^+) and the chloride ion (Cl^-), are held together in the crystal (Na^+Cl^-) by mutual electrical attraction. The behavior of sodium towards chlorine is typical of the alkali metals; they all form stable ionic solids with chlorine.

$$2Li_{(s)} + Cl_{2(g)} \rightarrow 2LiCl_{(s)} \text{ (lithium chloride)}$$
$$2Na_{(s)} + Cl_{2(g)} \rightarrow 2NaCl_{(s)} \text{ (sodium chloride)}$$
$$2K_{(s)} + Cl_{2(g)} \rightarrow 2KCl_{(s)} \text{ (potassium chloride)}$$
$$2Rb_{(s)} + Cl_{2(g)} \rightarrow 2RbCl_{(s)} \text{ (rubidium chloride)}$$
$$2Cs_{(s)} + Cl_{2(g)} \rightarrow 2CsCl_{(s)} \text{ (cesium chloride)}$$

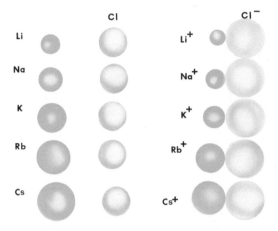

The alkali metals react vigorously with water liberating hydrogen and forming aqueous solutions of their hydroxides. These hydroxides,

TABLE 6.4

The Alkali Metals—Group I of the Periodic Table										

Element	Atomic Number	Electron Configuration						Boiling Point	Melting Point	Density g/cm³
		K	L	M	N	O	P	Q			
Lithium	3	2	1						1330°C	108°C	0.53
Sodium	11	2	8	1					892	97.8	0.97
Potassium	19	2	8	8	1				760	63.7	0.86
Rubidium	37	2	8	18	8	1			688	38.9	1.53
Cesium	55	2	8	18	18	8	1		690	28.7	1.90
Francium	87	2	8	18	18	32	8	1	—	(27)	—

LiOH, NaOH, KOH, RbOH, CsOH, and FrOH, are all strong bases. Typically the reaction of sodium and water is represented by the following equation:

$$2\ Na_{(s)} + 2\ H_2O_{(l)} \rightarrow 2\ NaOH_{(aq)} + H_2 \uparrow _{(g)}$$

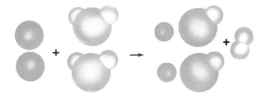

Because of its extreme reactivity, sodium must be kept entirely away from air and water; therefore, it is stored in kerosene. The reaction of sodium with water, and the resultant release of hydrogen may be demonstrated in the laboratory. The amount of sodium used must be very small. If the amount of sodium used is about the size of a match-head, the hydrogen thus given off may be ignited conveniently.

In all their compounds, the alkali metals exist as stable ions with a charge of 1+. Their atoms have a single electron in their outer shell (Table 6.4) which is removed with relatively little energy, and thus the alkali metals are extremely reactive. By losing one electron, a given alkali metal acquires the stable electron structure of its immediate noble gas neighbor (Fig. 6.2). The larger the atom, the easier it is to remove the outer electron. Furthermore, metals depend on the electrons in the outer shells for bonding or cohesion in the metal state. With only one outermost electron, the alkali metals are held together very weakly; therefore they are soft, and they have low melting and boiling points and low densities.

6:7   A Family of Non-Metals: The Halogens

Another group of elements with strong resemblances includes fluorine (F), chlorine (Cl), bromine (Br), iodine (I), and astatine (At).

VII	VIII	I
	2 He	3 Li
9 F	10 Ne	11 Na
17 Cl	18 Ar	19 K
35 Br	36 Kr	37 Rb
53 I	54 Xe	55 Cs
85 At	86 Rn	87 Fr

Fig. 6.2   *The noble gases and their neighbors*

Called the *halogens*, they form group VII of the periodic table. The word halogen means salt former and these five elements occur in nature as salts rather than as free elements. Their atoms have seven electrons in the outer shell (Table 6.5), and they readily gain another to become negatively charged ions. The resulting stable ions have the electron configuration of the noble gas atoms just following them. Their great chemical activity depends upon their attraction for electrons. The smaller the atom,

TABLE 6.5

The Halogens—Group VII of the Periodic Table

Element	Atomic Number	Electron Configuration						Boiling Point °C	Melting Point °C	Density* g/ml
		K	L	M	N	O	P			
Fluorine	9	2	7					−188	−220	1.11
Chlorine	17	2	8	7				−35	−101	1.56
Bromine	35	2	8	18	7			58	−7	3.12
Iodine	53	2	8	18	18	7		183	114	4.94
Astatine	85	2	8	18	32	18	7	—	—	—

*Densities for gaseous elements are for liquid at the boiling point

the more readily is the electron attracted. For this reason, fluorine has the greatest attraction for electrons and is the most active of the halogens.

The differences in properties of the halogens are themselves interesting, for they demonstrate how differences in size of atoms of similar structure produce gradual differences in other properties.

The melting and boiling points rise as the atomic number increases. At room temperature fluorine is a pale yellow gas, chlorine a greenish-yellow gas, bromine a deep red liquid, and iodine a steel-gray solid. Astatine exists only in trace amounts in nature.

In contrast to the noble gases which exist as single atoms, the halogens form diatomic molecules: F_2, Cl_2, Br_2, and I_2. Apparently, the halogen atoms acquire some of the stable structure of the noble gases by sharing electrons. If two atoms, say of chlorine, come close together, they might be able to share a pair of electrons:

In the Cl_2 molecule, the shared pair of electrons, may be thought of as belonging to both atoms.

The chemical reaction of chlorine with the alkali metals was noted in the preceding sections. The other halogens react with the alkali metals in a similar manner forming stable ionic compounds. For example:

$2Na_{(s)} + F_{2(g)} \rightarrow 2NaF_{(s)}$ (sodium fluoride)
$2Na_{(s)} + Cl_{2(g)} \rightarrow 2NaCl_{(s)}$ (sodium chloride)
$2Na_{(s)} + Br_{2(g)} \rightarrow 2NaBr_{(s)}$ (sodium bromide)
$2Na_{(s)} + I_{2(g)} \rightarrow 2NaI_{(s)}$ (sodium iodide)

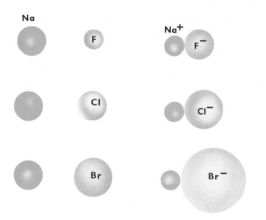

The halogens react with hydrogen at high temperature forming similar hydrides.

$H_{2(g)} + F_{2(g)} \rightarrow 2\,HF_{(g)}$ (hydrogen fluoride)
$H_{2(g)} + Cl_{2(g)} \rightarrow 2\,HCl_{(g)}$ (hydrogen chloride)
$H_{2(g)} + Br_{2(g)} \rightarrow 2\,HBr_{(g)}$ (hydrogen bromide)
$H_{2(g)} + I_{2(g)} \rightarrow 2\,HI_{(g)}$ (hydrogen iodide)

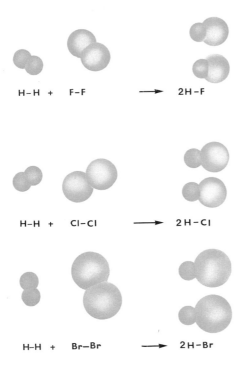

H–H + F–F ⟶ 2 H–F

H–H + Cl–Cl ⟶ 2 H–Cl

H–H + Br–Br ⟶ 2 H–Br

These hydrides are gases at room temperature and are highly soluble in water. When they dissolve in water, they also react with it to form strong acids.

Hydrogen

The chemistry of hydrogen resembles that of both the halogens and the alkali metals. For this reason, hydrogen does not fit well into any group. However because of its single electron, hydrogen is usually placed in group I with the alkali metals.

6:8 The Periodic Table and Atomic Structure

The strongest impression which the study of the periodic table leaves with us is that the atoms of the elements are somehow related despite their differences. If elements resemble one another it is safe to suspect that their atoms must have similar structures. If elements differ regularly in their combining capacity, it is probably because their atoms have structures which differ slightly. For this to be possible, the atoms themselves must be composed of still smaller particles. This suspicion likely arose in the minds of chemists when the periodic table was first suggested. It was confirmed with the discovery that all atoms have electrons, units of negative electric charge, and protons, units of positive electric charge. The number of such units, protons or electrons, in an atom is called the atomic number.

The atomic numbers serve to arrange the elements even better than do the atomic mass. Thus you can begin to see the great importance of electrons in chemistry. It is for this reason that we will turn our attention in chapter 14 to the story of electrons and their many interesting properties and contributions.

QUESTIONS

1. Sodium forms the following compounds: sodium oxide, Na_2O, and sodium hydroxide, NaOH. What would you expect the names and formulas of the corresponding compounds of potassium and rubidium to be?

2. State (a) the law of octaves; (b) the modern periodic law.

3. What is the difference between periods and groups in the periodic table?

4. Which of the following pairs of elements belong to the same family in the periodic table?
   (A) oxygen and fluorine
   (B) hydrogen and helium
   (C) sodium and neon
   (D) zinc and gold
   (E) helium and krypton

5. (a) List the elements of the second period.
   (b) How does the number of outer electrons vary from element to element?

6. Which of the following statements is true about the elements of a family in the periodic table?
   (A) They have similar chemical properties.
   (B) They have the same number of protons in their nuclei.
   (C) They have the same number of electron shells.
   (D) They have the same atomic mass.

7. (a) What led to the discovery of the noble gases?
   (b) What properties do these gases have in common?
   (c) List three uses of these gases.

8. To what do we attribute the lack of chemical activity of the noble gases?

9. What happens "electronically" when a sodium atom combines with a chlorine atom?

10. Draw an electron dot diagram to show how potassium and chlorine combine.

11. What is the relationship between the melting points of the alkali metals and the size of their atoms?

12. Which of the following statements about the elements of group I is *false?*
    (A) They produce ions having electronic structures similar to those of the noble gases.
    (B) They are called the alkali metals.
    (C) Their melting points show a rising trend with increasing atomic mass.
    (D) They have very low densities, compared to other metals.

13. Write the equations representing the reaction between (a) potassium and water; (b) lithium and water.

14. Why are sodium and potassium stored in oil?

15. Write equations representing the removal of one electron from each of the alkali metal atoms.

16. The larger the alkali metal atom, the easier it is to remove its outer electron. Suggest a logical explanation for this behavior.

17. (a) How can halogen atoms acquire noble gas electron configuration?
    (b) How can alkali metals acquire such configuration?

18. Which alkali ion and which halogen ion have an electron configuration similar to that of argon?

19. Write equations representing the gain of one electron by each of the halogen atoms.

7 Behavior of Gases and the Gas Laws

Matter exists in three states: gaseous, liquid, and solid. Of these, the gaseous state is the simplest to study. All substances in the gaseous state behave in many strikingly similar ways.

7:1 General Characteristics of Gases

(a) Expansion

Gases have no fixed volume. They expand indefinitely to occupy the entire volume available to them. Therefore, gases have no definite shape; they simply assume the shape of their containers.

(b) Compressibility

Gases are easily compressed into a fraction of their original volume. When the service station attendant "fills" the automobile tire, he is compressing air into the volume of the tire.

(c) Pressure

Confined gases exert a force on the walls of their container.

(d) Diffusion

When a gas is introduced into a vessel, it distributes itself throughout the entire volume. The process, called diffusion, takes place whether the vessel was originally empty or already occupied with another gas. A spray of perfume evaporates easily and soon occupies the entire room with its fragrance. The perfume diffuses throughout the entire space of the room. All gases diffuse readily through one another.

In the remaining sections of this chapter, we will investigate more intensively the properties of gases mentioned above.

7:2 Pressure and Its Measurement

Pressure is the force per unit area of surface that a gas or liquid exerts. Pressure may be expressed in g/cm², lb/in², or simply as a height of mercury in centimeters, millimeters, or inches.

The *Torr* is a unit of pressure, equal to $\frac{1}{760}$th of the normal atmosphere or to 1 mm of mercury. It is derived from the name of Torricelli, the Italian scientist who pioneered the study of atmospheric pressure.

The instrument used for measuring atmospheric pressure is the *barometer* (Fig. 7.1). A barometer is a glass tube about 80 cm long, sealed at one end, filled with mercury, and inverted in a vessel containing mercury. The mercury column in the tube falls until it exerts the same pressure as the atmosphere around it. As the pressure of the air changes, the level of

Fig. 7.1 *The barometer*

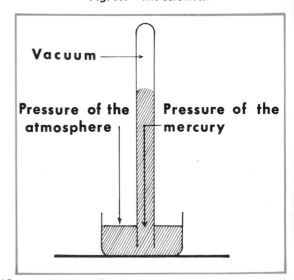

Vacuum

Pressure of the atmosphere

Pressure of the mercury

the mercury moves up or down correspondingly and thus shows the changes of atmospheric pressure. The average barometric reading is 76 cm or 760 mm of mercury at sea level. This is known as standard pressure or one atmosphere.

Expressed in inches, the standard atmospheric pressure is equivalent to a column of mercury about 30 inches high. If the column were one square inch in area, the mass of the mercury enclosed in it would be almost 15 pounds. Standard atmospheric pressure, therefore, is about 15 pounds per square inch at sea level. Sea level is specified because air pressure decreases with altitude.

The pressure of a gas can be measured with a *manometer* (Fig. 7.2). The gas whose pressure is to be measured is admitted into the left-hand column of the instrument. The curved section of the manometer contains mercury and the right-hand column is open to the atmosphere. Thus, atmospheric pressure is exerted on the right-hand mercury column, while the confined gas exerts pressure on the left-hand column of mercury. The pressure of the confined gas could be equal to, greater than, or less than the atmospheric pressure. If we let P_g, P_a, and h, stand for the pressure of the gas, the pressure of the atmosphere, and the difference in the heights of the columns of mercury, respectively, we obtain for the three illustrated cases (Fig.7.2):

(a) $P_g = P_a$ (b) $P_g = P_a + h$

(c) $P_g = P_a - h$

(a) Pressure of gas equals pressure of the atmosphere

(b) Pressure of gas is greater than atmospheric pressure by $+h$

(c) Pressure of gas is less than atmospheric pressure by $-h$

7:3 Boyle's Law

Robert Boyle was one of the first scientists to study the effect of pressure on the volume of a

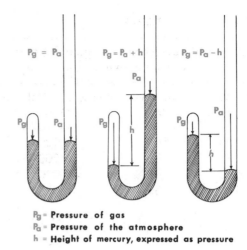

P_g = Pressure of gas
P_a = Pressure of the atmosphere
h = Height of mercury, expressed as pressure

Fig. 7.2   *The manometer*

gas. He observed that if the pressure of a gas is doubled while its temperature remains the same, its volume is decreased one-half; and if its pressure is tripled, its volume is decreased to one-third of the original. Such regularity was found to apply for a large range of pressure changes. Boyle summed up his findings in a statement known as *Boyle's Law: At constant temperature, the volume of a given mass of gas is inversely proportional to its pressure.* (Fig. 7.3).

Fig. 7.3   *The volume of a given mass of gas is inversely proportional to the pressure, at constant temperature.*

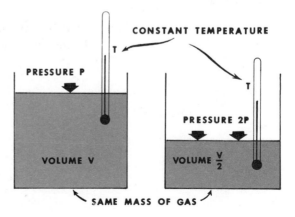

TABLE 7.1

Relationship Between Pressure and Volume at Constant Temperature

Pressure (P)	Volume (V)	Pressure × Volume (PV)
100	100	10,000
125	80	10,000
150	66⅔	10,000
200	50	10,000

Table 7.1 gives typical data obtained when a gas is subjected to changes in pressure. The first column lists the pressure readings in millimeters of mercury. The second column lists the volume of gas in milliliters. The temperature is kept constant.

Mathematically, Boyle's law may be expressed as

$$\text{Pressure} \times \text{Volume} = k, \text{ a constant}$$
$$\text{or} \qquad P \times V = k$$
$$\text{or} \qquad P_1V_1 = P_2V_2$$

where the subscripts 1 and 2 refer to the values of pressure and volume at any two readings during the experiment.

Example

The volume of a gas is 415 m*l* when the pressure is 500 mm of mercury. What will the volume be at 760 mm pressure if the temperature remains constant?

Solution 1

Boyle's law states that the volume of a given mass of gas is inversely proportional to its pressure if the temperature remains constant. Therefore, since the pressure has been increased in this problem, the volume will decrease. The new pressure is $\frac{760}{500}$ of the original pressure. Therefore, the new volume must be $\frac{500}{760}$ of the former volume.

Hence, the new volume will be $415 \text{ m}l \times \dfrac{500 \text{ mm}}{760 \text{ mm}} = 273 \text{ m}l$

Solution 2

The same result would be obtained by using the formula $P_1V_1 = P_2V_2$.

In this problem $P_1 = 500$ mm
$$V_1 = 415 \text{ m}l$$
$$P_2 = 760 \text{ mm}$$
$$V_2 \text{ is the unknown}$$

Solving for V_2,

$$V_2 = \frac{P_1V_1}{P_2}$$

Substituting, $V_2 = \dfrac{500 \text{ mm} \times 415 \text{ m}l}{760 \text{ mm}}$

$$= 273 \text{ m}l$$

7:4 Change in the Volume of a Gas with Temperature

Substances expand when heated and contract when cooled. Gases expand far more than liquids or solids.

A French scientist, Charles, who studied the effect of temperature on the volumes of gases, discovered that all gases expand by the same amount when heated and contract by the same amount when cooled if the pressure remains constant. Such behavior is in marked contrast to liquids and solids where each liquid and each solid expands at its own individual rate.

Consider the results of an experiment on the expansion of gases upon heating. For greatest simplicity, let us select a volume of 273 ml of a gas at 0°C. When the gas is heated to 1°C at constant pressure, its volume becomes 274 ml; at 2°C, its volume is 275 ml; at 100°C, the volume is 373 ml, and at 273°C, the volume reaches a value of 546 ml. When we cool the original volume of 273 ml from 0°C to −1°C, the new volume is found to be 272 ml; at −2°C, the volume is 271 ml and at −100°C, it is 173 ml. These data are reported in the first two columns of Table 7.2.

Charles found that the volume of a given sample of gas measured at 0°C increases by 1/273 of its value for every degree rise in temperature. If the gas is cooled, on the other hand, its volume decreases by 1/273 of its value at 0°C for every degree drop in temperature.

7:5 The Absolute Temperature Scale

If the volumes given in Table 7.2 are plotted against the temperatures, the graph shown in Fig. 7.4 is obtained. When the points representing the volumes are joined together, a straight line is obtained. By extending this line so that it intersects the temperature axis, the point of intersection is found to be −273°C. We can deduce that if a sample of gas at 0°C could be cooled to −273°C, it would shrink by 273/273 of its original volume; that is, it would occupy no volume at all! Of course, all gases condense into liquids before such a temperature is reached, and remember that liquids do not contract at the same rate as gases. Nevertheless, this temperature, −273°C, is believed to be the lowest possible limit of temperature, and is called the *absolute zero*.

For many practical reasons, it is useful to use a temperature scale that begins with absolute zero and has degrees which are the same size as Celsius degrees. Such a scale can be devised by adding 273 to the Celsius reading

$$°K = °C + 273$$

Readings on the absolute scale are represented by the symbol °K in honor of Lord Kelvin, who proposed the absolute scale.

7:6 Charles' Law

The absolute temperature scale enables us to see the relation between the volume and the temperature of a gas very simply (See Table 7.2 and Fig. 7.4). Charles' law states that the volume of the gas is proportional to the absolute temperature at constant pressure. For example,

TABLE 7.2

Volume of a Gas at Different Temperatures (constant pressure)

Temperature (°C)	Volume (ml)	Temperature (°K)
273	546	546
100	373	373
2	275	275
1	274	274
0	273	273
−1	272	272
−2	271	271
−100	173	173

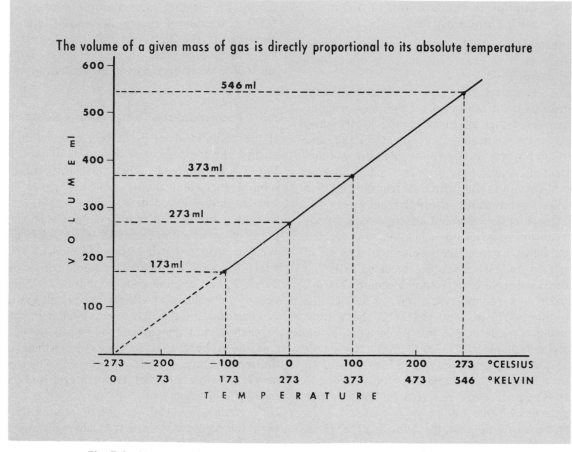

The volume of a given mass of gas is directly proportional to its absolute temperature

Fig. 7.4   *How the volume of a gas changes with temperature at constant pressure*

if the absolute temperature of a gas is doubled, the volume is doubled. When the absolute temperature is halved, so is the volume. This is *Charles' Law: At constant pressure, the volume of a given mass of gas is directly proportional to its absolute temperature.**

Charles' law may be expressed by the equation:

$$\frac{V_1}{V_2} = \frac{T_1}{T_2} \text{ (at constant pressure)}$$

where V_1 represents the original volume of a given mass of gas at a temperature T_1, and V_2 represents the new volume of the gas at a new temperature T_2.

Standard Conditions

In order to provide a uniform basis for comparing gases, we should observe them under similar conditions. Scientists have agreed to specify 0°C (273°K) as the *standard temperature* and 760 mm of mercury (1 atm), the *standard*

---

*So far we have assumed that Boyle's and Charles' laws are exact; they are nearly so for most gases under ordinary conditions of temperature and pressure. Deviations from the gas laws become important, especially at high pressures and at temperatures near the liquefaction point. Special corrections have to be made at such extreme conditions.

Example

The volume of a certain mass of gas is 150 m*l* at 27°C. What will its volume be at 127°C if the pressure remains constant?

Solution 1

Convert the temperature readings to absolute: the original temperature is 27°C or 300°K; the final temperature is 127°C or 400°K.

The absolute temperature changes in the ratio of $\frac{400}{300}$. Therefore, the volume will also increase in this ratio.

Hence the new volume will be 150 m*l* $\times \frac{400°K}{300°K} = 200$ m*l*.

Solution 2

The same result would be obtained by substitution in the formula $\frac{V_1}{V_2} = \frac{T_1}{T_2}$

In this problem $V_1 = 150$ m*l*
$T_1 = 300°K$
V_2 is the unknown
$T_2 = 400°K$

The expression for V_2 is: $V_2 = \frac{V_1 \times T_2}{T_1}$

Substituting, $V_2 = \frac{150 \text{ m}l \times 400°K}{300°K}$

$= 200$ m*l*

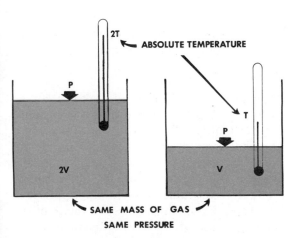

Fig. 7.5 *Charles' law*

pressure. These are known as *standard conditions* of temperature and pressure (STP).

7:7 When Both Pressure and Temperature Change

It is sometimes necessary to find the new volume of a gas when both the temperature and the pressure change. In that event, both temperature and pressure will be responsible for the change in volume, according to Boyle's law and Charles' law.

In mathematical symbols, the combined effect of pressure and temperature on volume may be expressed by the equation

$$\frac{P_1V_1}{T_1} = \frac{P_2V_2}{T_2}$$

where P_1, V_1, and T_1 represent the original pressure, volume, and temperature and P_2, V_2, and T_2 represent the final values. This is sometimes termed the combined gas law equation.

Example

The volume of a gas is 2.00 liters at 27°C and 600 mm pressure. What will the volume be at 227°C and 400 mm pressure?

Solution 1

The absolute temperature has gone up from 300°K to 500°K; therefore the volume will increase in that ratio. Hence we must multiply the original volume by $\frac{500}{300}$. The pressure has been decreased from 600 to 400 mm; therefore the volume will increase in the ratio of $\frac{600}{400}$.

The final volume will be: $2.00 \; l \times \frac{500°K}{300°K} \times \frac{600 \; mm}{400 \; mm} = 5.00 \; l$

Solution 2

The same result would be obtained by substitution in the formula $\frac{P_1V_1}{T_1} = \frac{P_2V_2}{T_2}$.

In this problem $P_1 = 600$ mm $\qquad$ $P_2 = 400$ mm
$\qquad\qquad\qquad$ $V_1 = 2.00 \; l$ $\qquad\qquad$ V_2 is the unknown
$\qquad\qquad\qquad$ $T_1 = 300°K$ $\qquad\qquad$ $T_2 = 500°K$

The new volume $V_2 = \dfrac{V_1P_1T_2}{P_2T_1}$

Substituting $\qquad V_2 = \dfrac{2.00 \; l \times 600 \; mm \times 500°K}{400 \; mm \times 300°K}$

$\qquad\qquad\qquad\quad = 5.00 \; l$

7:8   Partial Pressures of Gases

The presence of different gases in a mixture has no effect on the pressure that any particular gas in the mixture exerts. Each gas exerts the same pressure that it would if it were present alone in the same volume and at the same temperature as the mixture. Each gas contributes part of the total pressure of a mixture. Its contribution is termed the *partial pressure of that gas*. These facts are formulated in *Dalton's Law of Partial Pressures* which states: *In a mixture of gases, the total pressure exerted by the mixture is equal to the sum of the partial pressures exerted by the gases taken separately.* Dalton's law can be written:

$$P_{total} = P_1 + P_2 + P_3 \ldots$$

where the subscripts denote the partial pressures of the various gases in the mixture.

Correction for Water Vapor

An important application of Dalton's law of partial pressures is in reporting the pressure of a gas that is collected over water (Fig. 7.6). The total pressure of the system would be the sum of the partial pressure of the gas plus the pressure of the water vapor. The latter may be found from the table of water vapor pressures, (see Appendix 4) which gives the values of the vapor pressure of water at different temperatures. Hence, by knowing the temperature and the total pressure, we may find the pressure of the gas by subtracting the water vapor pressure from the total pressure.

Example

Find the volume of a dry gas at standard temperature and pressure if, when collected over water at 20°C and 780 mm pressure, it occupies 100 ml. The vapor pressure of water at 20°C is 17.5 mm.

Discussion and Solution

The pressure of 780 mm is the sum of the partial pressures of the gas and the water vapor. Now, by Dalton's law of partial pressures:

$$P_{total} = P_{dry\ gas} + P_{water\ vapor}$$

or

$$P_{dry\ gas} = P_{total} - P_{water\ vapor}$$

therefore,

$$P_{dry\ gas} = 780\ mm - 17.5\ mm = 762.5\ mm.$$

We need to calculate the volume of a gas at STP corresponding to 100 ml at an original pressure of 762.5 mm and a temperature of 293°K.

The new volume,
$$V_2 = \frac{V_1 P_1 T_2}{P_2 T_1}$$

Substituting,
$$V_2 = \frac{100\ ml \times 762^* mm \times 273°K}{760\ mm \times 293°K}$$

$$= 93.5\ ml.$$

Fig. 7.6 *Gas collected over water*

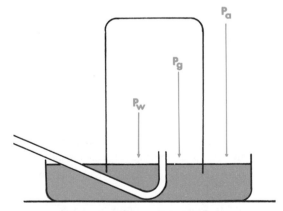

P_a

P_g

P_w

P_a = PRESSURE OF THE ATMOSPHERE

P_g = PRESSURE OF THE GAS

P_w = PRESSURE OF THE WATER VAPOR

$P_a = P_g + P_w$

*Rounded out to nearest significant figure.

7:9 Diffusion of Gases: Graham's Law

When two gases are brought together, they mix by themselves. This process is termed *diffusion*. Graham, a Scottish chemist, discovered that the lighter the gas, the faster it diffuses (Fig. 7.7). He studied the phenomenon carefully, and found that *the rate of diffusion of a gas is inversely proportional to the square root of its density*. This statement is called *Graham's Law of Diffusion*. Stated mathematically, Graham's law takes the following form:

$$\frac{u_1}{u_2} = \frac{\sqrt{d_2}}{\sqrt{d_1}}$$

where u_1 and d_1 represent the rate of diffusion and the density of one gas, and u_2 and d_2 the corresponding values for a second gas. Both gases must be measured under the same conditions of temperature and pressure.

When this formula is applied to find the relative diffusion rates of hydrogen and oxygen, we obtain:

$$\frac{u_1}{u_2} = \frac{\sqrt{d_2}}{\sqrt{d_1}} = \frac{\sqrt{1.429}}{\sqrt{0.089}} \frac{(\text{density of } O_2)}{(\text{density of } H_2)} \doteq \frac{4}{1}$$

The result obtained indicates that hydrogen diffuses four times as fast as oxygen when both gases are compared at the same temperature and pressure.

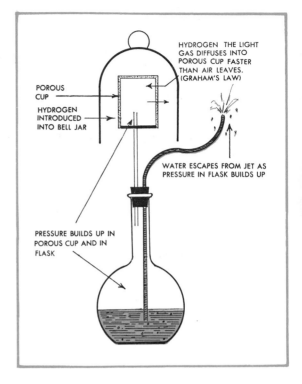

POROUS CUP

HYDROGEN INTRODUCED INTO BELL JAR

HYDROGEN THE LIGHT GAS DIFFUSES INTO POROUS CUP FASTER THAN AIR LEAVES. (GRAHAM'S LAW)

WATER ESCAPES FROM JET AS PRESSURE IN FLASK BUILDS UP

PRESSURE BUILDS UP IN POROUS CUP AND IN FLASK

Fig. 7.7 *Demonstrating the rapid diffusion of hydrogen*

QUESTIONS

1. (a) What is the difference between the expansion of a gas and diffusion?
   (b) Give an example to illustrate your answer.

2. Describe a manometer.

3. Sketch a mercury barometer showing how it operates.

4. What is *standard pressure?*

5. State Boyle's law.

6. Explain clearly what is meant by the statement that pressure of a given mass of gas multiplied by its volume equals a constant if the temperature remains the same.

7. A gas measures 1.00 *l* at a pressure of 790 mm of mercury. Find its volume at 500 mm pressure.

8. If a quantity of gas measures 800 m*l* at 1.20 atmospheres, find its volume at 6.00 atmospheres.

9. A volume of 400 m*l* of oxygen is collected at 700 mm pressure. Find its volume if the pressure changes to 1.00 atmosphere.

10. A volume of 4.00 *l* of hydrogen is measured at standard pressure. Find its volume at 780 mm.

11. A tire has a capacity of 2 cubic feet when inflated. Find the pressure in the tire if a volume of 8 cubic feet of air, measured at atmospheric pressure, is forced into it. Neglect the amount of air in the flat tire.

12. If a volume of 10.0 l of gas at 600 mm pressure is expanded to 12.0 l find the new pressure.

13. How are degrees Celsius changed to degrees Kelvin?

14. What is *absolute zero*?

15. If a gas expands, does its temperature remain constant automatically?

16. State Charles' law.

17. A gas has a volume of 687 ml at 17°C. Find its volume at 30°C.

18. A gas occupies a volume of 1200 ml at 227°C. Find its volume at −173°C.

19. A volume of gas measures 1200 ml at 100°C. To what temperature must it be cooled so that the volume becomes 800 ml?

20. A quantity of gas is measured at 20°C. To what temperature must it be heated so that its volume is doubled?

21. A gas has a volume 22.4 l measured at 20°C and 78.0 cm pressure. Find the volume at STP.

22. A gas has a volume of 800 ml at 25°C and 720 mm. Find its volume at 50°C and 800 mm.

23. A sample of helium measures 100 ml at STP. Find its volume at 125°C and 800 mm.

24. Some carbon dioxide at STP is cooled to 200°K. At the same time the pressure is doubled. If the initial volume of the gas was 4.00 l, find the new volume.

25. A gas has a volume 20 l at 20°C and 760 mm. To what temperature must it be heated so that the volume doubles and the pressure goes to 1440 mm?

26. (a) State Dalton's law of partial pressures.
    (b) Give an example of this law.

27. How is the partial pressure of a gas collected over water determined from the total pressure?

28. (a) If, on a day when the barometric pressure is 768 mm, some oxygen gas is collected over water whose vapor pressure is 19 mm, what is the partial pressure of the oxygen gas?
    (b) A volume of two liters of "wet" oxygen is collected at 768 mm with the water vapor pressure being 19 mm. What would the volume of the oxygen be if the water vapor were removed?

29. A 1.00 l sample of hydrogen is collected over water at 700 mm total pressure and 20°C. What would the volume of the dried hydrogen be at STP?

30. State Graham's law of diffusion.

31. Illustrate Graham's law by reference to the densities and diffusion rates of hydrogen and oxygen.

32. Find the relative rates of diffusion of two gases, sulfur dioxide and methane. Their densities are 2.86 g/l and 0.71 g/l respectively at STP.

33. If some hydrogen were introduced into one end of a glass tube 20 cm long, and some oxygen were introduced into the other end at the same time, where would the two gases meet in the tube?

34. If 1 l of hydrogen will diffuse through a hole in one hour, how long will it take 1 l of oxygen to diffuse through the same hole?

35. A sample of gas is confined to a sealed metal cylinder. Which of the following is *true* about the pressure exerted by the gas when the absolute temperature is doubled?
    (A) It is halved.   (C) It is tripled.   (E) It remains unchanged.
    (B) It is doubled.   (D) It is quadrupled.

36. In which of the following cases could the volume of a given mass of gas remain constant?
    (A) when the temperature is lowered and the pressure is increased
    (B) when the temperature is increased and the pressure remains the same
    (C) when the temperature is increased and the pressure is decreased
    (D) when both the temperature and pressure are increased

37. Which of the following represent standard conditions?
    (A) 0°C and 76 mm of Hg   (C) 0°K and 76 cm of Hg
    (B) 273°K and 760 mm of Hg   (D) 273°C and 760 mm of Hg

38. In which of the following groups are the gases correctly ranked in order of increasing diffusion rate?
    (A) oxygen, hydrogen, helium   (C) oxygen, helium, hydrogen
    (B) helium, oxygen, hydrogen   (D) hydrogen, helium, oxygen

8 The Kinetic Molecular Theory

8:1 Some Questions about Gases

The behavior and properties of gases makes one wonder about them. What is a gas? How does it exert pressure? How does it occupy the entire volume of any container in which it is placed? How does it expand so automatically when any external pressure is removed? Why is it possible to compress gases? How do gases diffuse among other gases? Their volumes are affected by temperature and pressure so uniformly that these effects can be expressed as scientific laws. Can this be explained? How does a gas expand when heated? Why do all gases expand by the same amount? Why does the absolute temperature scale express the rate of expansion of gases? What is the difference between a liquid and a gas? Why can a liquid be changed to a gas, and then the gas changed back to a liquid, by raising or lowering the temperature or pressure?

8:2 The Kinetic Molecular Theory of Gases

An attempt to answer these questions was made by proposing that gases consist of molecules in motion. Such an idea might be called a model, or a theory. Because of what it proposes, it is called the *Kinetic Molecular Theory*.

It has been very useful in explaining gas behavior, changes of state, and other important phenomena.

The main ideas of the kinetic molecular theory are the following:

1. Gases are made up of exceedingly small particles called molecules.

2. The distances between the molecules are very large compared with the size of the molecules themselves.

3. The molecules are in continuous motion in straight lines and in all directions.

4. The kinetic energy of the moving molecules is proportional to the absolute temperature of the gas.

This energy increases when the gas is heated and decreases when the gas is cooled. The average kinetic energy of the molecules of all gases is the same at a given temperature.

5. The molecules collide with each other and with the walls of their container.

6. The collisions of the molecules among themselves or with the walls of the container are perfectly elastic.

Any molecule that collides with the walls of the container rebounds at a speed that is exactly the same as its speed before collision. When molecules collide among themselves, they rebound with speeds whose sum is the same as that before the collision. Such collisions, in which there is no loss of total speed or momentum, are called elastic.

The reason for believing that molecular collisions are elastic is that gases may exist indefinitely, with collisions going on all the time. If the molecules gradually slow down, the gas ceases to exist, as we know it.

8:3 A Scientific Model

The above assumptions of the kinetic molecular theory provide us with a model which helps us to understand how a gas behaves. Such models are very useful and scientists use them often as an aid to form a mental picture of how some system "works". A model is often an oversimplification, and what it depicts is termed "perfect" or "ideal". The kinetic molecular theory simplifies the behavior of gases by ignoring any attraction between the molecules. Nevertheless, the assumptions of the theory may be applied to actual gases, especially at low pressure and high temperature, when intermolecular attraction is indeed negligible.

8:4   Explanation of Gas Behavior by the Kinetic Molecular Theory

The real test of a successful theory is its ability to explain facts. Let us see how the kinetic molecular theory explains the facts of gas behavior.

Expansion

The expansion of a gas is due to the straight line motion of the molecules, which causes them to "fill" any volume, no matter how large. Upon expansion, the spaces between the molecules become larger.

Compressibility

The compressibility of a gas is due to the large spaces between the molecules. When outside pressure is applied, the molecules simply crowd together in a smaller volume; the distances between them become smaller.

Pressure

Gas pressure is caused by molecular bombardment of the walls of a vessel by the gas enclosed in it. Since each molecule has mass and velocity, it gives an impulse to the wall upon collision. The total effect of all the collisions of all the molecules with the wall results in pressure.

Diffusion

Diffusion of gases may also be explained by molecular motion. As soon as a vessel contain-

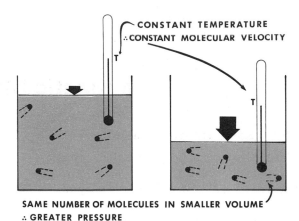

CONSTANT TEMPERATURE
∴CONSTANT MOLECULAR VELOCITY

SAME NUMBER OF MOLECULES IN SMALLER VOLUME
∴ GREATER PRESSURE

Fig. 8.1   *How the kinetic molecular theory explains Boyle's law*

ing gas is opened, some molecules escape from it into the adjacent atmosphere. At the same time, molecules of the adjacent air start to fly into the open container. In this way molecular motion causes diffusion and intermingling of gases.

Explanation of the Gas Laws by the Kinetic Molecular Theory

BOYLE'S LAW

If the volume of a gas is compressed, more molecules are present per unit volume (Fig. 8.1). The result is more collisions between the molecules of the gas and the walls of the vessel. Because such collisions are the cause of pressure, it is to be expected that a decrease in volume should produce a corresponding increase in pressure, and vice versa.

In this experiment the temperature should remain constant to ensure that the kinetic energy and hence the velocity of the molecules do not change.

CHARLES' LAW

The motion of the molecules of a gas depends on their kinetic energy. In turn, the kinetic energy depends on the absolute temperature of the gas. At a given temperature, the mole-

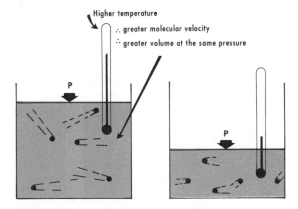

Fig. 8.2 *How the kinetic molecular theory explains Charles' law*

cules have a definite kinetic energy and move at a definite average speed. When the temperature is raised, the kinetic energy of the molecules is increased, and the molecules thus move faster than before. Hence, there will be more collisions with the walls of the vessel if the volume is kept the same, and this will cause an increase in pressure.

If the pressure is to be kept constant while the temperature is raised, the molecules must be given a larger volume in which to fly about, so that the number of collisions per unit of wall area will remain the same. Thus we see that the volume would increase at the same rate as the absolute temperature (Fig. 8.2).

DALTON'S LAW OF PARTIAL PRESSURES

So large are the spaces between the molecules of a gas, or a mixture of gases, that the presence of different kinds of molecules does not change the behavior of the molecules. The pressure of a gas depends on the number of molecules present and their average kinetic energy. These factors are not altered by the presence of molecules of various other gases. Fig. 8.3 illustrates this fact. The three containers shown have the same capacity. The molecules of gas present in container A exert a pressure of 20 mm of Hg, while the molecules of gas in container B exert a pressure of 10 mm. When both gases are transferred to the third container C, the combined pressure noted is 30 mm.

GRAHAM'S LAW OF DIFFUSION

The kinetic molecular theory assumes that the average kinetic energy of the molecules of gases is proportional to the absolute temperature. Furthermore, all gases at the same absolute temperature have the same kinetic energy. From physics, we learn that the kinetic energy of a body of mass m and velocity v is given by the equation K.E. = $\frac{1}{2}mv^2$. Different gases have different molecular mass. Therefore, if two gases are to have the same kinetic energy at a given temperature, they must have different velocities. The greater the mass of the molecules

Fig. 8.3 *Illustration of the law of partial pressures*

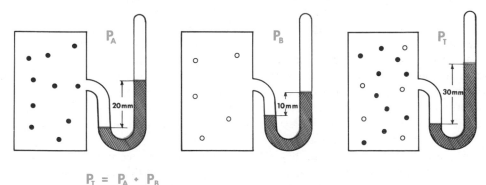

$$P_T = P_A + P_B$$

of one gas, the slower the speed and the rate of diffusion of that gas compared to another lighter gas.

8:5   The Kinetic Molecular Theory Applied to Liquids and Solids

The kinetic molecular theory can be related to liquids and solids provided slight modifications are made.

In a liquid, the molecules are closer together than in a gas. The molecules of a liquid have enough energy to slide past each other but not enough to overcome the forces of attraction between them.

When applying the kinetic molecular theory to solids, we must keep in mind that the particles making up the solid are not necessarily molecules. These particles can be molecules, atoms, or ions. They are arranged in fixed positions to produce the regular crystalline structure of solids. In all solids, whether molecular, atomic, or ionic, the particles do not move around freely but simply vibrate about their points of location in the crystal structure.

8:6   The States of Matter Viewed in terms of Molecular Motion

Whether a given substance exists as a gas, a liquid, or a solid, depends on whether the molecules are free to fly about, or are prevented from doing so by their mutual attraction. This explains why the temperature and pressure are such important factors in determining the state of a substance.

When the temperature is high and the pressure is low, the molecules have great kinetic energy with large spaces between them for flying about. These conditions favour the gaseous state. Here the kinetic energy of the molecules greatly outweighs the intermolecular attraction and the molecules move about freely as they fill the entire space of the container. Thus, gases have no definite volume and their densities are

relatively small. When the temperature is lowered, the kinetic energy of the molecules is less. They move at a greatly reduced speed. If, in addition, the surrounding pressure is high, the molecules come close together and this helps them attract each other. A point is reached where the force of attraction becomes so great as to outweigh the kinetic energy of the molecules. Low temperature and high pressure force the molecules to cling together and the gas condenses to a liquid.

In this state the average distance between molecules is less and the density is greater than in a gas. Furthermore, the liquid has a definite volume and shows an upper surface. The forces of attraction between molecules, termed *van der Waals' forces*, depend on the kind of molecules between which they are acting as well as the distance between the molecules. They are stronger between molecules of water than between those of hydrogen. Between sugar molecules they are stronger still. At a given temperature the average kinetic energy of all molecules is the same. Owing to the difference in the strength of the van der Waals' forces, however, hydrogen is a gas, water is a liquid, and sugar is a solid, when all three substances are at room temperature.

8:7   Changes of State in terms of Molecular Motion

It may happen that a certain molecule in a liquid receives more energy than the average through collisions with other molecules. Indeed, collisions may result in the accumulation of enough energy by a molecule to escape from the liquid and enter the air. Molecules of liquids evaporate in this manner. At any temperature, some molecules are able to leave a liquid in this way. As the temperature is raised, the number of collisions between molecules increases. More molecules reach the escape velocity, leaving the liquid as a vapor. Conversely, molecules of vapor may slow down and thus fall back into the liquid. The changes of state from liquid to gas and to liquid are readily explained.

If the temperature of a liquid or gas is lowered sufficiently, the substance will change to the solid state. The forces of attraction overcome the kinetic energy of the molecules. Conversely, when a solid has absorbed sufficient energy to overcome the attractive forces between the molecules, a process called *fusion* or *melting* occurs. The temperature at which this occurs is called the *melting point*.

In a large class of compounds which form solids, the particles are electrically charged atoms or groups of atoms called ions. These are the salts. Here the forces of attraction are even greater than the van der Waals' type. As a result, the melting points of salts are relatively high. Thus, the melting of solids to liquids and the freezing of liquids to solids are readily explained by the motion of molecules and ions, and the effect of temperature on such motion.

8:8   Critical Temperature and Critical Pressure

We have seen that if a gas is compressed, the molecules are brought closer together, thus enabling the intermolecular attraction to be more effective. In this way compression assists in liquefying gases. However, unless the kinetic energy of the molecules is below a certain value, compression alone cannot liquefy a gas. The temperature above which a gas cannot be liquefied, no matter how great the pressure is called the *critical temperature* of the gas. The pressure able to liquefy a gas at the critical temperature is called the *critical pressure*. Table 8.1 shows the critical temperatures and the critical pressures of a few common substances as well as the temperature at which they boil under atmospheric pressure.

8:9   The Liquefaction of Air

A gas such as air can be converted into a liquid by lowering the temperature and increasing the pressure. The method used to liquefy air is to compress it and then allow it to expand suddenly. This sudden expansion has a cooling effect whereby the temperature of the air drops. When the air expands, its molecules move farther apart and work is done in overcoming the forces of attraction between the molecules. This work takes heat away from the air and the kinetic energy of the molecules is lowered. The opera-

TABLE 8.1			
Some Critical Temperatures and Pressures			
Substances	Critical Temperature (°C)	Critical Pressure (atm)	Boiling Point (°C, 1 atm)
Ammonia, NH_3	133	115	−33
Carbon dioxide, CO_2	31	73	−78
Chlorine, Cl_2	146	94	−35
Helium, He	−268	2.75	−269
Hydrogen, H_2	−241	15	−253
Nitrogen, N_2	−146	33	−196
Oxygen, O_2	−118	50	−183
Water, H_2O	374	217	100

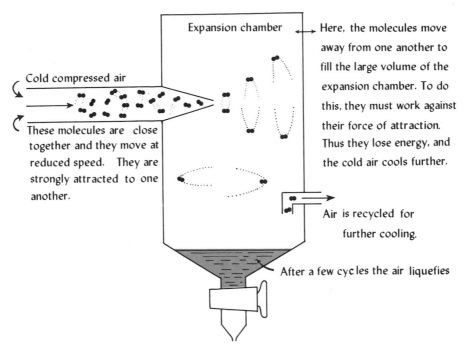

Expansion chamber

Here, the molecules move away from one another to fill the large volume of the expansion chamber. To do this, they must work against their force of attraction. Thus they lose energy, and the cold air cools further.

Cold compressed air

These molecules are close together and they move at reduced speed. They are strongly attracted to one another.

Air is recycled for further cooling.

After a few cycles the air liquefies

Fig. 8.4   *Liquefaction of air*

tion is repeated with the cooler gas, each time making it cooler still, until eventually it liquefies. The liquefaction of air is diagrammatically represented in Fig. 8.4.

Recently helium has been used as cooling agent to liquefy air. First the helium is compressed, and any heat produced is dissipated. Then it is allowed to expand, thus causing a large drop in its temperature. It becomes so cold that the air in an adjacent vessel in the apparatus is liquefied.

The Storage of Liquid Air

Because of the low temperature at which liquid air boils, it cannot be stored in an ordinary refrigerator. It can be stored for short periods in Dewar flasks, which are named after the man who first used them for this purpose. In a Dewar flask, there is a vacuum between the walls (Fig. 8.5) so that heat will not be conducted from the outside to the inside of the flask. The efficiency of the Dewar flask is further improved by silvering so that radiation may be reflected rather than absorbed. It is not possible, however, to stop the passage of all heat into the flask; so the liquid air slowly boils away. Liquid air containers must therefore not be stoppered, because the internal pressure caused by the vaporization of the air might burst the container.

Liquid Air: A Commercial Source for Oxygen

Since industry and hospitals need a large a-mount of oxygen, a method to produce an ample supply has been devised which separates the oxygen from the other gases of the air by first liquefying the air. Liquid air is a mixture of oxygen (boiling point, $-183°C$), and nitrogen

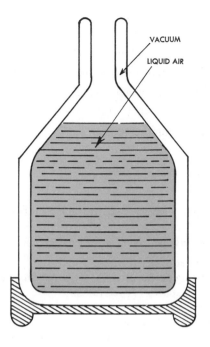

(boiling point, $-196°C$). To separate the gases, the more volatile nitrogen is allowed to boil off first; then the oxygen comes off as a gas and is led to steel cylinders. The separation just described is based on the fact that the liquids mixed have different boiling points. The process is called *fractional distillation*.

Fig. 8.5 *Dewar flask for storing liquid air*

QUESTIONS

1. Tabulate the main points of the kinetic molecular theory.

2. Suggest a reason why a real gas does not behave exactly as an ideal gas would.

3. In terms of the kinetic molecular theory explain why:
   (a) gases fill their containers;
   (b) gases are compressible;
   (c) gases exert pressure;
   (d) gases are miscible.

4. By means of the kinetic molecular theory, explain why:
   (a) letting air out of a tire reduces the pressure;
   (b) the pressure exerted by a gas increases as it is heated;
   (c) 2 g of oxygen gas in a given container exerts twice the pressure of 1 g of oxygen in the same container at the same temperature;
   (d) hydrogen diffuses faster than oxygen when the two gases are at the same temperature.

5. Do the molecules of two different gases at the same temperature have the same average velocity? Explain.

6. A container has a certain number of molecules of oxygen and three times as many molecules of nitrogen. The partial pressure exerted by the oxygen is 150 mm of Hg. If the pressure depends on the number of molecules, what is the total perssure exerted by the mixture of gases?

7. What would happen to a gas if the collisions between its molecules and the walls of its container were not perfectly elastic?

8. Why does the air under pressure in a tire become cool as it escapes?

9. Distinguish between gases, liquids, and solids, in terms of the kinetic molecular theory.

10. Under what conditions will a gas condense into a liquid?

11. Explain why condensation is a heat evolving process.

12. Suggest a reason why liquids are practically incompressible.

13. How do liquids evaporate?

14. What is meant by *critical temperature* and *critical pressure*?

15. Describe the preparation of liquid air.

16. (a) What properties of oxygen and nitrogen are used in separating them from liquid air?
    (b) Does such separation of the two gases involve chemical or physical change?

17. How does a Dewar flask maintain low temperature?

Questions 18, 19, 20, and 21 relate to the following points of the kinetic molecular theory:
1. Gases are made of molecules with large spaces between them.
2. The molecules move about at high speeds.
3. The collisions between molecules are perfectly elastic.
4. The molecules have kinetic energy which increases directly with absolute temperature.

Which of the above statements best explains:

18. Charles' law?
    (A) 1   (B) 2   (C) 3   (D) 4

19. why gases are compressible?
    (A) 1   (B) 2   (C) 3   (D) 4

20. how gases exert pressure?
    (A) 1   (B) 2   (C) 3   (D) 4

21. how gases diffuse?
    (A) 1   (B) 2   (C) 3   (D) 4

9 The Principle of Avogadro

9:1 The Molecule-Atom Problem

Physical changes, such as the compression and expansion of gases and changes of state, are explained by supposing that gases consist of molecules in motion, according to the kinetic molecular theory.

Chemical changes, such as the formation of compounds from the elements, are explained by supposing that the elements consist of atoms, according to the atomic theory. Both the atom and the molecule are so small that they cannot be seen. Are molecules and atoms the same, or are they different? If atoms combine to form molecules, how are we to find out how many atoms there are in a molecule? In what proportion do atoms combine in any given case? What evidence have we that in the water molecule, there are two atoms of hydrogen and one of oxygen? Why not one of hydrogen and one of oxygen?

A similar difficulty arises even in the case of certain elements. For example, since oxygen is a gas, the molecular theory maintains that it is composed of molecules. Since oxygen is an element, the atomic theory maintains that it is composed of atoms. Are the molecules of oxygen the same as the atoms of oxygen, or are they different? If they are different, what is the difference?

Even if we know that atoms combine in the ratio of one to one (or two to one) to form a certain molecule, how can we provide equal numbers of atoms to react with one another? Surely we cannot count them out one by one because they are not visible and they would be too numerous. There must be some other way to provide the required numbers of atoms and molecules in chemical reactions. How can such problems be solved?

9:2 A Clue Leading to the Solution of the Problem

At about the time that Dalton proposed the atomic theory, the French scientist Gay-Lussac became interested in a special feature of reactions between gases. As we have seen in Chapter 3, when water is decomposed by electrolysis, the volume of hydrogen obtained is exactly double that of the oxygen liberated at the same time. The volumes of hydrogen and oxygen evolved are in the simple ratio of 2:1. Similarly, when water is synthesized from hydrogen and oxygen, the volumes of these gases are in the same ratio of 2:1.

Gay-Lussac wondered whether this ratio was a feature of this chemical reaction alone, or whether it was true for all reactions involving gases. He found that when hydrogen and chlorine combine to form hydrogen chloride, the volumes of the hydrogen and chlorine are equal, and the volume of hydrogen chloride produced is exactly double that of either of the combining gases. Similarly, when carbon monoxide reacts with oxygen to form carbon dioxide, the volume of carbon monoxide required is twice that of the oxygen. The volume of carbon dioxide produced is the same as the volume of carbon monoxide used up. In similar experiments, he found that whenever gases react, the volumes are in a simple ratio of small whole numbers.

The chemical reactions described above can be summarized in the following equations:

(a) hydrogen   +   oxygen → steam
     (2 vol.)   (1 vol.)   (2 vol.)

(b) hydrogen   +   chlorine → hydrogen
     (1 vol.)   (1 vol.)   chloride
                                       (2 vol.)

(c) carbon monoxide + oxygen → carbon
     (2 vol.)   (1 vol.)   dioxide
                                            (2 vol.)

Gay-Lussac summed up his findings in the *Law of Combining Gas Volumes*, which states that *volumes of gases which combine or which are produced in chemical reactions are always in the ratio of small whole numbers.*

9:3   Avogadro's Principle

In 1811, the Italian scientist Avogadro realized that the law of combining gas volumes contained a clue to the problem of how to obtain more precise information about atoms and molecules. Here was a chance to discover the secret of the mass, the number, and the composition of molecules. There might even be some way of proving that the molecule of an element was not the same as an atom of that element. Avogadro suggested that the reason why the volumes of reacting gases are always in a simple ratio is that *equal volumes of all gases at the same temperature and pressure contain the same number of molecules.* This statement is termed Avogadro's Principle.

As you will see, the Avogadro principle accomplished much for chemistry:

1. It explained Gay-Lussac's law of combining gas volumes.

2. It distinguished between the idea of the atom and that of the molecule.

3. It proved that the molecules of some gaseous elements contained two atoms.

4. It provided a method for finding the mass of molecules and atoms.

5. With the aid of molecular and atomic mass, molecular formulas became possible.

6. With molecular formulas, chemical equations became possible.

Thus you can see why it is said that Avogadro helped to change chemistry, in the early years of that science, from a confusing mass of details into a quantitative study with its own exact and dependable language.

Nevertheless, despite its possibilities, Avogadro's principle remained unnoticed for nearly fifty years. In 1860 a congress of chemists was called to consider the confusing molecule-atom problem. Cannizzaro, another Italian chemist, revived Avogadro's ideas and proved beyond doubt the validity of the principle. A German chemist present at the congress remarked: "It was as if the scales fell from my eyes; doubt vanished, and was replaced by a feeling of peaceful clarity."

Let us see how reasonably the principle of Avogadro explains the law of combining gas volumes.

It is an experimental fact that one volume of hydrogen combines with one volume of chlorine to produce two volumes of hydrogen chloride gas (Fig. 9.1).

What must happen here, said Avogadro, is that each molecule of hydrogen reacts with one molecule of chlorine. The first molecule of hydrogen with the first of chlorine, the second with the second, the nth with the nth, the last with the last. Now all the molecules of hydrogen have reacted, each with a molecule of chlorine. The reaction is over. All the molecules are "used up". But so too are the equal volumes of hydrogen and chlorine. There must be some relationship between the equal numbers of reacting molecules and the equal volumes of reacting gases, thought Avogadro. The simplest possible connection is that equal volumes of all gases must have the same numbers of molecules at the same temperature and pressure.

WHAT IS SEEN EXPERIMENTALLY:

The volumes of hydrogen and chlorine are equal.   **The volume of hydrogen chloride is twice as great.**

Fig. 9.1   *The hydrogen-chlorine reaction*

What are we to conclude about the "double" volume of hydrogen chloride that was produced? It must contain twice as many molecules of hydrogen chloride as there were of hydrogen or of chlorine in *their* original "single" volume. The above ideas are shown in Fig. 9.2.

But why was it necessary to say that equal volumes of gases contained the same number of molecules and not of atoms? Would it not have been possible to give the above explanation in terms of atoms instead of molecules, keeping in mind that chemical reactions take place between atoms? The atomic theory maintains, for example, that hydrogen chloride is formed when atoms of hydrogen combine with atoms of chlorine.

Fig. 9.2   *Explanation of the hydrogen-chlorine reaction*

WHAT IS SEEN:

A volume of hydrogen reacts with an equal volume of chlorine to yield a double volume of hydrogen chloride

WHAT IS IMAGINED:

1. That the equal volumes of the gases contain equal numbers of molecules at the same temperature and pressure.

2. That each molecule of chlorine reacts with one molecule of hydrogen to yield two molecules of hydrogen chloride.

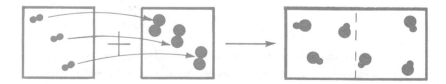

9:4 How the Difference between Molecules and Atoms was Established

In the reaction between hydrogen and chlorine, the volume of the hydrogen chloride produced is twice as great as that of either the hydrogen or the chlorine. Avogadro therefore assumed that twice as many molecules of hydrogen chloride were formed as there were of either hydrogen or chlorine originally. This would mean that *one molecule of hydrogen and one molecule of chlorine combine to form two molecules of hydrogen chloride.*

Each of the molecules of hydrogen chloride contains one atom of hydrogen and one of chlorine. Therefore, Avogadro concluded that each hydrogen particle had been split into two halves, one for each of the two molecules of hydrogen chloride. In the same way each of the particles of chlorine must have been split into two halves to supply the chlorine for the two hydrogen chloride molecules (Fig. 9.3).

Since atoms could not be divided by chemical means, Avogadro reasoned that *the particles that make up hydrogen gas could not be simple atoms but must contain two atoms. Such particles are the molecules of hydrogen.* Similarly, the particles that make up chlorine gas could not be simple atoms, but must also be molecules that contain two atoms. The *molecule* is the smallest particle that can exist physically and yet retain the composition of the original pure substance. The *atom* is the smallest particle of an element able to enter chemical reaction. "*I have shown,*" wrote Avogadro, "*that the physical molecule and the chemical atom are not the same.*"

9:5 The Molecules of Hydrogen, Chlorine, Oxygen, and Nitrogen Each Have Two Atoms

To prove that the molecules of hydrogen and chlorine have two atoms each, we noted that one volume of hydrogen combines with an equal volume of chlorine to form a double volume of hydrogen chloride. The same argument may be given to prove also that the molecules of oxygen and nitrogen have two atoms each.

Fig. 9.3   *Molecules of hydrogen and chlorine have two atoms each*

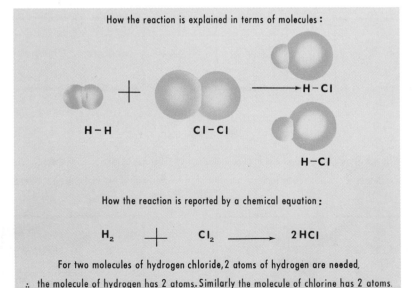

How the reaction is explained in terms of molecules:

H–H   Cl–Cl   ⟶   H–Cl

H–Cl

How the reaction is reported by a chemical equation:

$$H_2 + Cl_2 \longrightarrow 2HCl$$

For two molecules of hydrogen chloride, 2 atoms of hydrogen are needed,
∴ the molecule of hydrogen has 2 atoms. Similarly the molecule of chlorine has 2 atoms.

In the reaction between oxygen and hydrogen to form steam, one volume of oxygen gas is responsible for the formation of a volume of steam twice as great. According to Avogadro's

Fig. 9.4   *The hydrogen-oxygen reaction*

WHAT IS SEEN:

A double volume of hydrogen reacts with a single volume of oxygen to yield a double volume of steam.

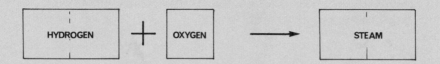

WHAT IS IMAGINED:

1. That there are twice as many molecules in the double volume of hydrogen as in the single volume of oxygen.

2. That each molecule of oxygen reacts with two molecules of hydrogen to yield two molecules of steam.

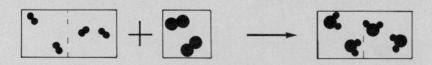

How the reaction is explained in terms of molecules:

H-H + O=O → H H O / H H O

How the reaction is reported by a chemical equation:

$$2H_2 + O_2 \longrightarrow 2H_2O$$

For two molecules of water, 2 atoms of oxygen are needed,

∴ the molecule of oxygen has 2 atoms.

principle, one molecule of oxygen helps to form two molecules of water vapor. The molecule of oxygen must have divided into two halves, one for each molecule of steam. This proves that the molecule of oxygen contains two atoms (Fig. 9.4).

Nitrogen combines with hydrogen to form ammonia. In this reaction, the volume of

Fig. 9.5 *The hydrogen-nitrogen reaction*

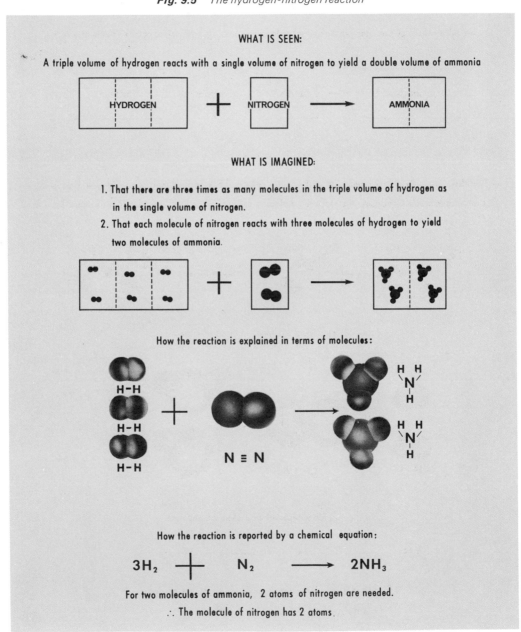

WHAT IS SEEN:

A triple volume of hydrogen reacts with a single volume of nitrogen to yield a double volume of ammonia

HYDROGEN + NITROGEN → AMMONIA

WHAT IS IMAGINED:

1. That there are three times as many molecules in the triple volume of hydrogen as in the single volume of nitrogen.
2. That each molecule of nitrogen reacts with three molecules of hydrogen to yield two molecules of ammonia.

How the reaction is explained in terms of molecules:

H-H
H-H   +   N ≡ N   →
H-H

How the reaction is reported by a chemical equation:

$$3H_2 \quad + \quad N_2 \quad \longrightarrow \quad 2NH_3$$

For two molecules of ammonia, 2 atoms of nitrogen are needed.

∴ The molecule of nitrogen has 2 atoms.

ammonia produced is twice as great as the volume of the original nitrogen used. Reasoning as before, the conclusion is reached that the molecule of nitrogen contains two atoms (Fig. 9.5).

9:6   Consequences of Avogadro's Principle

Avogadro's main purpose in suggesting that equal volumes of gases contained the same number of molecules was to explain the law of combining gas volumes in terms of the atomic and molecular theories. The principle did this very successfully, as we have seen. It also accomplished much more. It provided a clear distinction between the "physical molecules" and the "chemical atoms" by showing that even a simple molecule might be composed of two atoms.

Perhaps the most far-reaching result of the principle is that it gave to chemistry a method of finding the relative mass of the molecules and atoms. Thus it helped to make chemistry a quantitative science, as was mentioned before.

9:7   Avogadro's Number and Avogadro's Law

Since Avogadro's time, scientists have been able to determine the actual number of molecules in a given volume or mass of gas. Thirty-two grams of oxygen have been found to contain 6.02×10^{23} molecules. This number is called *Avogadro's Number*. It is also referred to as *one mole* of particles.

Two famous physicists, Perrin and Millikan, stated that it is possible to calculate the number of molecules in a gas as accurately as one can determine the population of a city like New York. Many chemists and physicists have worked on the calculation of Avogadro's number, and because their final results are in very close agreement, confidence has been established in the accuracy of this number. So great is this confidence that Avogadro's principle is now accepted as a law.

QUESTIONS

1. (a) State the law of combining volumes.
    (b) Apply this law to the decomposition of water and to the union of hydrogen and oxygen.
    (c) Discuss this law in reference to the reactions between (i) hydrogen and chlorine (ii) carbon monoxide and oxygen.

2. (a) State Avogadro's principle.
    (b) What led to the development of this principle?

3. Explain why the size of the molecules in a gas has little to do with its volume.

4. Outline a proof showing that the molecule of hydrogen and of chlorine each contains two atoms. Do the same for nitrogen.

5. Define the terms *atom* and *molecule*.

6. When may the terms "atom" and "molecule" be used interchangeably?

7. What is Avogadro's number? What does it signify?

8. What is a *mole* of particles?

9. How many molecules are there in 1 g of oxygen at STP?

10. What is the importance of Avogadro's principle?

CHAPTER

10 The Mole

Lord Kelvin, a famous English scientist, once said, "When you can measure something and express it in numbers, you know something about it; but when you cannot measure it, and you cannot express it in numbers, your knowledge is of a meagre and unsatisfactory kind." Kelvin might well have had chemistry in mind when he made this statement, for as long as theories about atoms and molecules were not quantitative, no real progress was made in the building of the science. When, however, a method was worked out for finding molecular and atomic mass, progress became very rapid indeed.

10:1 Method for Finding Molecular Mass of Gases

Weighing a single molecule or atom on a balance is impossible. It is a fairly simple matter, however, to weigh equal volumes of different gases at the same temperature and pressure. In effect, this is the same as weighing equal numbers of molecules of the various gases. Therefore, Avogadro's law spares us the need of having to weigh single molecules on a balance in order to find the relative mass of molecules.

If, for example, a certain volume of gas A contains x molecules, then an equal volume of gas B would also contain x molecules at the same temperature and pressure. Suppose it is found that gas A weighs twice as much as gas B. Then one molecule of A must weigh twice as much as one of B. This illustrates how Avogadro's law enables us to find the relative mass of molecules.

As a more realistic example, suppose a certain volume of oxygen at 0°C and 760 mm of pressure weighs 32 grams. The same volume of hydrogen under the same conditions weighs only two grams. If the number of molecules

Fig. 10.1 *Comparing equal volumes of gases*

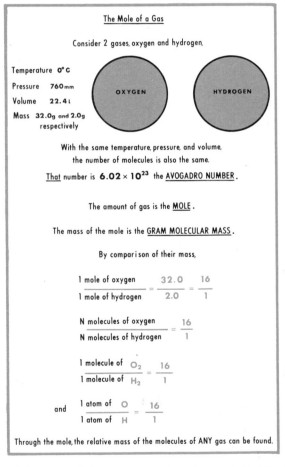

The Mole of a Gas

Consider 2 gases, oxygen and hydrogen,

Temperature 0°C
Pressure 760mm
Volume 22.4 l
Mass 32.0g and 2.0g respectively

OXYGEN   HYDROGEN

With the same temperature, pressure, and volume, the number of molecules is also the same.
That number is **6.02 × 10²³** the AVOGADRO NUMBER.

The amount of gas is the MOLE.

The mass of the mole is the GRAM MOLECULAR MASS.

By comparison of their mass,

$$\frac{1 \text{ mole of oxygen}}{1 \text{ mole of hydrogen}} = \frac{32.0}{2.0} = \frac{16}{1}$$

$$\frac{N \text{ molecules of oxygen}}{N \text{ molecules of hydrogen}} = \frac{16}{1}$$

$$\frac{1 \text{ molecule of } O_2}{1 \text{ molecule of } H_2} = \frac{16}{1}$$

and $$\frac{1 \text{ atom of } O}{1 \text{ atom of } H} = \frac{16}{1}$$

Through the mole, the relative mass of the molecules of ANY gas can be found.

*Both hydrogen and oxygen have small percentages of isotopes of different mass. These occur in such small amounts that the ratio of 1:16, in round figures, is not altered.

of oxygen is x, the number of hydrogen molecules also would be x. Since x molecules of oxygen weigh 16 times as much as x molecules of hydrogen, therefore, *one* molecule of oxygen weighs 16 times as much as *one* of hydrogen.

We have already seen that the molecules of oxygen and hydrogen have two atoms each. We may now conclude that the atom of oxygen weighs 16 times as much as the atom of hydrogen* (Fig. 10.1).

10:2   Standard for Atomic and Molecular Mass

The above idea has been used by chemists to find the relative mass of molecules of gases, and of the atoms which form such molecules. To apply the method, we choose an atom to which all other atoms and molecules could be compared. We have already indicated in sec. 4:9 that the atom of the most common isotope of carbon was chosen for this purpose.‡ It has been assigned a value of exactly 12.000 atomic mass units (amu). On the same scale, the atomic mass of oxygen is 16.00 amu to an accuracy of 99.996 per cent. For convenience, the atomic mass of oxygen will be taken as 16 amu and other atomic masses also will be rounded out.

10:3   The Atomic Mass Unit (amu)

The standard for atomic mass is the *carbon-12 isotope*. This most abundant isotope is assigned a mass of 12.000 atomic mass units (amu). Thus, *one amu* is 1/12 the mass of the "standard" isotope of carbon. With the atomic mass unit, we can assign units to the atomic and molecular mass of the elements and compounds. To illustrate, the atomic masses of oxygen and

hydrogen, in round numbers, are 16 and 1 amu respectively, while their molecular masses are 32 and 2 amu. The molecular mass of the water molecule is $(2 \times 1) + 16 = 18$ amu.

10:4   The Mole: A Practical Chemical Unit for Handling Atoms and Molecules

When we wish to carry out a reaction, we cannot weigh out individual atoms or molecules or count them because of their tiny size. Remember too, how numerous they are. What we need is some way to link up a number of molecules or atoms with mass. We can then simply weigh out our sample, and automatically know the number of particles in it. Our concern about knowing the number of molecules or atoms in a sample is easy to understand. Chemical reactions take place between one (or two, or three) atoms or molecules of reactant A, and one (or two, or three) of reactant B.

The chemical mass unit that always contains the same number of particles is the mole. If you wish to study a reaction between two substances, A and B, in which one particle of A combines with one of B, you would measure out one mole of A and one of B, or two moles of each, depending on the amount of product you wish to obtain. The moles of A and B are easy to measure for practical purposes because they can be weighed on a balance. The individual atoms or molecules of these substances cannot be handled in this way.

The *mole* of an element or compound is the mass represented numerically by the symbol or formula of the substance in gram amounts. For carbon, the symbol C represents one atom with a mass of 12 amu. Automatically, the mole

---

‡At one time H = 1 was the standard. It was found, though, that the relative masses of oxygen and hydrogen atoms were 16:1.008 rather than 16:1. This made it necessary to choose as a standard an element whose atomic mass is a whole number. Oxygen was then chosen, because it forms compounds with both metallic and nonmetallic elements, while hydrogen does not. In 1961, C = 12 was adopted as a standard because it is easier to obtain the pure isotope of carbon-12 than that of oxygen-16. Changes in standards of atomic masses do not alter the theory of how atomic masses were found; neither do they seriously change the numerical values of the atomic masses.

of carbon is 12 grams. Similarly, the formula for sulfur, S, represents 32 amu. The mole of sulfur weighs 32 grams. In 12 grams of carbon and in 32 grams of sulfur, the same number of atoms are present. This is so because the masses of the respective moles are in the same ratio as the masses of the respective atoms of carbon and sulfur.

10:5 What the Mole Represents

The mole of all substances contains the same number of particles. That number is very important and is named in honour of Avogadro, the scientist who gave chemistry its first method for finding molecular and atomic mass. The *Avogadro Number* is 6.02×10^{23} particles.

A mole of any pure substance has a mass in grams equal numerically to the atomic or molecular mass of the substance. When the atomic mass of an element is expressed in grams, it is called also the *gram-atomic mass* of the element. Similarly, the *gram-molecular mass* of a substance is its molecular mass expressed in grams. One mole of any pure substance contains 6.02×10^{23} particles.

The concept of the mole is one of the most important ideas in chemistry. It is widely used in the solution of problems about the mass of reactants and products in chemical changes.

Fig. 10.2   *The gram-molecular volume of gases at STP*

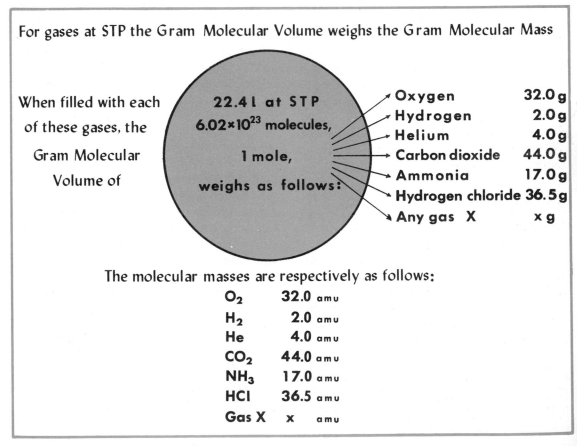

For gases at STP the Gram Molecular Volume weighs the Gram Molecular Mass

When filled with each of these gases, the Gram Molecular Volume of

22.4 l at STP
6.02×10^{23} molecules,
1 mole,
weighs as follows:

Oxygen	32.0 g
Hydrogen	2.0 g
Helium	4.0 g
Carbon dioxide	44.0 g
Ammonia	17.0 g
Hydrogen chloride	36.5 g
Any gas X	x g

The molecular masses are respectively as follows:

O_2	32.0	amu
H_2	2.0	amu
He	4.0	amu
CO_2	44.0	amu
NH_3	17.0	amu
HCl	36.5	amu
Gas X	x	amu

The mole represents:

a. the gram-atomic mass of an element;
b. the number of atoms in the gram-atomic mass;
c. the gram-molecular mass of any substance;
d. the number of molecules in a gram-molecular mass;
e. the gram-molecular volume (sec. 10.6) of a gaseous substance at STP;
f. the number of particles in the gram-molecular volume of a gaseous substance at STP.

"A mole of atoms" and "a mole of molecules" should not be confused. In a mole of oxygen gas, there are a mole of molecules and two moles of atoms. Unless specified, a mole of gas refers to the number of molecules.

10:6   The Gram-Molecular Volume

To simplify the task of finding the gram-molecular mass of a gas, the volume which this mass would occupy at STP is used. This volume can be calculated from the gram-molecular mass of oxygen and its density of 1.43 grams per liter at STP.

If 1.43 g of oxygen occupy 1 liter at STP,

then, 32.00 g of oxygen occupy: $\dfrac{1\,l}{1.43\,g} \times 32.00\,g$

$$= 22.4 \text{ liters}$$

This volume, *22.4 liters*, occupied by the gram-molecular mass (1 mole) of oxygen at STP is called the *gram-molecular volume*.

The gram-molecular volume of any gas at STP weighs the gram-molecular mass of that gas (Fig. 10.2). Since it is feasible to weigh 22.4 liters of a gas at STP, it is possible to find the gram-molecular mass, and from this, the molecular mass of that gas. In practice, it is not even necessary to weigh a volume of exactly 22.4 liters at 0°C and 760 mm of pressure. Any volume at any pressure and temperature will do, for the data can be converted to the standard values with the aid of the gas laws.

10:7   Examples

Example 1

The density of a hydrocarbon gas is 2.54 g/*l* at STP. Find its gram-molecular mass.

Solution

The gram-molecular mass of a gas is the mass of 22.4 liters at STP. Therefore,

the gram-molecular mass $= 2.54 \dfrac{\text{grams}}{\text{liter}} \times 22.4 \dfrac{\text{liters}}{\text{mole}}$

$$= 56.9 \dfrac{\text{grams}}{\text{mole}}$$

Note that the units of the gram-molecular mass are $\dfrac{\text{grams}}{\text{mole}}$ and of the gram-molecular volume are $\dfrac{\text{liters}}{\text{mole}}$.

Example 2

One liter of ammonia weighs 0.70 g at a pressure of 780 mm and a temperature of 27°C. Find its gram-molecular mass.

Solution

The first step is to calculate the volume that the gas would occupy at STP. Using the equation $\dfrac{P_1V_1}{T_1} = \dfrac{P_2V_2}{T_2}$ where the subscript 1 refers to the original conditions and the subscript 2 refers to the final standard conditions, we may solve for V_2:

Volume at STP, $V_2 = \dfrac{V_1P_1T_2}{P_2T_1}$

$$= 1.00 \; l \times \frac{780 \text{ mm}}{760 \text{ mm}} \times \frac{273°K}{373°K}$$

$$= 0.93 \; l$$

The next step is to calculate the mass of 22.4 l at STP.

Thus, the gram-molecular mass $= \dfrac{0.70 \text{ grams}}{0.93 \text{ liter}} \times 22.4 \dfrac{\text{liters}}{\text{mole}}$

$$= 17.0 \frac{\text{grams}}{\text{mole}}$$

Alternatively, keeping in mind how changes in pressure and temperature affect volumes according to Boyle's and Charles' laws, we may say:

The volume at STP $= \dfrac{\text{present}}{\text{volume}} \times \dfrac{\text{temperature}}{\text{change}} \times \dfrac{\text{pressure}}{\text{change}}$

$$= 1.00 \; l \quad \times \quad \frac{273°K}{300°K} \quad \times \quad \frac{780 \text{ mm}}{760 \text{ mm}}$$

$$= 0.93 \; l$$

The next step is to calculate the mass of 22.4 l at STP.

0.93 l at STP weighs 0.70 g

$\therefore$ 22.4 l at STP weighs $\dfrac{0.70 \text{ g}}{0.93 \; l} \times 22.4 \dfrac{l}{\text{mole}} = 17.0 \dfrac{\text{g}}{\text{mole}}$

Example 3

The molecular mass of carbon dioxide is 44.0 amu. Find the mass of 3.00 l of this gas at STP.

Solution

One mole (22.4 liters) of carbon dioxide weigh 44.0 g at STP. Therefore,

the mass of 3.00 $l = \dfrac{44.0 \text{ grams}}{22.4 \text{ liters}} \times 3.00 \text{ liters}$

$$= 5.90 \text{ g}$$

Alternatively

22.4 l of the gas weighs 44.0 g

$\therefore$ 3.00 l weighs $\dfrac{44.0 \text{ g}}{22.4 \; l} \times 3.00 \; l$

$$= 5.90 \text{ g}$$

10.8 The Ideal Gas Equation

From the laws of Boyle, Charles, and Avogadro, we learn that the volume of a gas depends on three factors, the pressure P, the absolute temperature T, and the number of molecules or the number of moles n. Thus,

Boyle's Law: $V \propto \dfrac{1}{P}$, (const T, n)

Charles' Law: $V \propto T$, (const P, n)

Avogadro's Law: $V \propto n$, (const T, P)

Combining these, $V \propto \dfrac{nT}{P}$

or $V = \text{constant} \times \dfrac{nT}{P}$

The constant in this equation is called the *gas constant* because it applies to all gases. It is represented by R. Now the equation becomes

$$V = \frac{RnT}{P}$$

$$\text{or}\ \ PV = nRT$$

This is called the *Ideal Gas Equation*.
To evaluate R, we may write

$$R = \frac{PV}{nT}$$

and then substitute values for P, V, n, and T. Thus, for any gas at STP,

If   n = 1.00 mole,

P = 1.00 atmosphere,

T = 273°K

then   V = 22.4 liters

Therefore $R = \dfrac{1.00 \times 22.4}{1.00 \times 273}$ or

$0.0821 \dfrac{\text{liter} \times \text{atmosphere}}{\text{mole} \times \text{degree}}$

Examples

(a) The volume of a gas measures 10.0 liters at 0.500 atmospheres and 27.0°C. How many moles of gas are present?

From   PV = RnT

$$n = \frac{PV}{RT}$$

Here, P = 0.500 atm, V = 10.0 liters, T = 300°K and

$$R = 0.0821 \frac{\text{liter} \times \text{atm}}{\text{mole} \times {}^\circ\text{K}}$$

Substituting, $n = \dfrac{0.500 \times 10.0}{0.082 \times 300} \times \dfrac{\text{atm} \times \text{liter}}{\dfrac{\text{liter} \times \text{atm}}{\text{mole} \times {}^\circ\text{K}}} \times {}^\circ\text{K}$

= 0.200 moles

(b) If the above gas weighed 15.0 grams, what is its molecular mass?

0.20 moles weigh 15.0 g

1 mole weighs $\dfrac{15.0}{0.20} = 75.0$

The molecular mass is 75.0 amu or 75.0 g/mole.

The use of the ideal gas equation PV = nRT to calculate molecular mass of gases: The number of moles n, of gas may be expressed by dividing the weight of gas w, by the molecular mass M.

$$n = \frac{w \text{ grams}}{M \text{ grams/mole}} = \text{moles}$$

When this value of n is substituted into the ideal gas equation, the result is

$$PV = \frac{wRT}{M}$$

and the molecular mass is given by

$$M = \frac{wRT}{PV}$$

This equation makes it possible to find the molecular mass in one calculation.

(c)   3.00 grams of gas is present in 2.50 liters at 27.0°C and 0.500 atm pressure. What is the molecular mass of the gas?

Using $M = \dfrac{wRT}{PV}$, where w = 3.00 g, T = 300°K, V = 2.50 liters

$R = 0.082 \dfrac{\text{liters} \times \text{atm}}{\text{moles} \times °K}$ and P = 0.500 atm

we obtain $M = \dfrac{3 \times 0.082 \times 300}{0.5 \times 2.50}$

approximately $M = \dfrac{3 \times 8 \times 3 \times 10^{-2+2}}{5 \times 2.5 \times 10^{-1}}$

$$= 6 \times 10^1$$

more accurately   59.0 amu or 59.0 grams/mole

Fig. 10.3   *The mass spectrograph analogy*

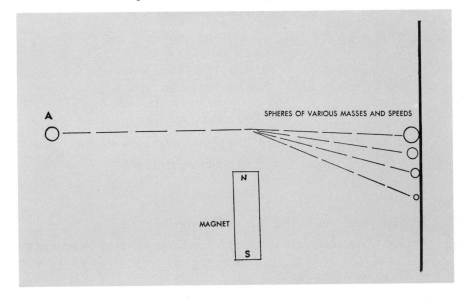

Overhead ✓

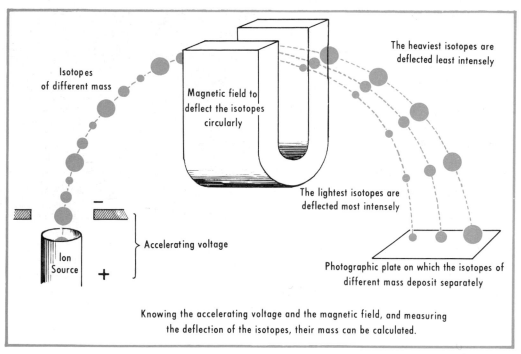

Isotopes of different mass

Magnetic field to deflect the isotopes circularly

The heaviest isotopes are deflected least intensely

The lightest isotopes are deflected most intensely

Accelerating voltage

Ion Source

Photographic plate on which the isotopes of different mass deposit separately

Knowing the accelerating voltage and the magnetic field, and measuring the deflection of the isotopes, their mass can be calculated.

Fig. 10.4 *Schematic diagram of a mass spectrograph*

10:9 The Mass Spectrograph

Chemical methods for finding the atomic mass of the elements were used successfully to establish the truth of the atomic theory in the early years of scientific chemistry. In the present century physicists have devised another method for finding atomic mass, based on the mass of the atom as a physical property. The instrument employed in this method is called the *mass spectrograph.*

To illustrate the idea of this method, imagine a few steel balls, each of slightly different mass, which are allowed to roll down a gentle incline. The balls would roll in a straight line from point A to point B. Suppose now, a magnet NS is placed near the path along which the balls roll. It would then be found that the magnetic attraction would cause the balls to be deflected from their paths. The heaviest ball would be deflected to the smallest extent, while the lightest ball would be deflected to the greatest extent by the attraction of the magnet (Fig. 10.3).

The spots where the balls strike the target could be noted, and the relative masses of the balls calculated from the extent of their deflection by the magnetic field.

The mass spectrograph works on a similar principle. Instead of steel balls, atoms carrying electrical charges are shot out by electrical energy. These are then deflected by a magnetic field. The atoms of different mass separate and come to rest at different points or lines on a film. From the extent of deflection and the strength of the magnetic field, it is possible to calculate the atomic mass (Fig. 10.4).

When the elements are examined with the spectrograph, it is found that not all the atoms of an element have the same mass. The atoms of chlorine, for example, have masses of 35 amu and 37 amu. Some elements have as many as 12 atoms of different mass. These atoms of the same element that have different mass are called isotopes (Chapter 5). The chemical atomic mass is the weight average of the atomic mass of the isotopes of a given element. The atomic mass is constant because any natural sample of an element always contains the same proportions of its isotopes.

Other methods for determining atomic mass exist and need to be applied in certain cases. Fortunately, all methods for finding atomic mass agree in their results.

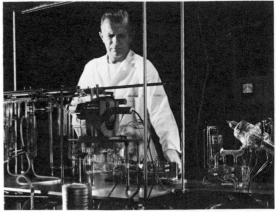

Courtesy Brookhaven National Laboratory

Fig. 10.5   *This photo shows a high sensitivity mass spectrometer. This instrument is able to detect as little as one billionth of a cubic milliliter of gas through the difference of the mass of its molecules. The magnet may be seen at the center of the photo.*

QUESTIONS

1. Explain clearly why the mass of identical volumes of different gases under the same conditions are in the same ratio as the mass of their individual molecules.

2. (a) Define the terms *atomic mass, atomic mass unit, molecular mass, gram-atomic mass, gram-molecular mass, mole.*
   (b) How many moles of nitrogen gas are there in 42 grams of the element?
   (c) How many grams are there in 0.52 moles of helium?

3. (a) Why was hydrogen originally chosen as the standard for atomic and molecular mass?
   (b) Why was it replaced by oxygen?

4. (a) What is the present standard for atomic mass?
   (b) Why was this standard chosen?

5. What can a mole represent?

6. Define the term *gram-molecular volume*. Explain its importance.

7. Outline the method used to calculate the gram-molecular mass of a gas.

8. Find the gram-molecular mass of a gas if 1 *l* of it weighs 0.09 g at STP.

9. If 340 m*l* of a gas weighs 0.70 g at STP, what is its gram-molecular mass?

10. Find the mass of 3.00 *l* of ammonia, NH_3, at STP.

11. Calculate the mass of 400 m*l* of oxygen at STP.

12. What volume would be occupied by 10.0 g of hydrogen at STP?

13. Find the volume occupied by 4.00 g of carbon dioxide, CO_2, at STP.

14. What is the gram-molecular mass of a gas if 200 m*l* of it at 20°C and 780 mm pressure weigh 0.28 g?

15. What is the mass of 300 m*l* of oxygen at 25°C and 750 mm?

16. Calculate the density (g/*l*) of methane gas, CH_4, at STP.

17. (a) Describe the operation of the mass spectrograph.
    (b) Of what value is this instrument?

18. (a) Define the term *isotope*, giving several examples.
    (b) Since isotopes are so common, explain why atomic masses are constant.

19. How are the atomic masses of the elements conclusive evidence for the atomic theory? Explain.

20. What mass of sulfur will combine with 10.0 g of oxygen to form sulfur dioxide, SO_2?

21. Calculate the number of atoms in (a) 5.00 g of carbon; (b) 5.00 g of oxygen.

22. How many moles of oxygen and carbon atoms are there in 10.0 g of carbon dioxide?

23. Find the mass in grams of (a) 0.50 moles of sodium; (b) 1.50 moles of silver.

24. How many grams of iron will combine with 12.0 g of sulfur to form iron (II) sulfide, FeS?

25. Using the Ideal Gas Equation, find the pressure exerted by 0.25 moles of gas in 6.25 liters at 127°C.

26. Solve problems 8 to 15 inclusive, using the Ideal Gas Equation.

CHAPTER

11 Chemical Formulas

11:1 Symbols

Each element is represented by a symbol which stands for the element, its atom, and its atomic mass (Chapter 3). Thus, C stands for carbon, for the atom of carbon, and for the atomic mass of 12. When speaking of the atom of carbon, its mass is in amu (C = 12 amu); when speaking of the mole of carbon, its mass is in grams $\left(\text{C} = 12 \, \dfrac{\text{grams}}{\text{mole}} \right)$

11:2 The Composition of Compounds

How can the composition of a compound be represented? We might report the mass of the elements in it. For instance, in the case of water, we can say that 1 g of hydrogen combines with 8 g of oxygen to form 9 g of water. Another way of reporting the composition of water is to say that it is 11.2% hydrogen and 88.8% oxygen. This method is termed *percentage composition*.

With the help of atomic symbols, the composition of a compound can be represented in a much more significant way; namely, by showing how many atoms of each element are present in the molecule. Even when atoms form ions, it is possible to show the ratio of atoms in the compound. The formula of a compound shows the atomic composition of its molecule, or, if the compound is ionic, the atomic composition of its ions.

11:3 Deriving the Molecular Formula

Let us derive the formula of water. The molecular mass of water is 18 amu and the percentage composition is 11.2% hydrogen and 88.8% oxygen. The atomic mass of its elements are H = 1 amu and O = 16 amu in round numbers. To find the molecular formula, the reasoning is as follows:

The molecule of water weighs 18 amu. Of this mass, hydrogen is 11.2%; therefore, the hydrogen in the molecule weighs 18×0.112 or 2 amu. Since the atom of hydrogen weighs 1 amu, there must be two atoms of hydrogen in the molecule of water.

TABLE 11.1				
The Molecular Formula of Water (18 amu)				
The elements in water	Percentage in compound	Mass in Molecule	Number of Atoms	
Hydrogen (1 amu)	11.2%	11.2% of 18 amu = 2 amu	$\dfrac{2 \text{ amu}}{1 \text{ amu}} = 2$	∴ formula H_2O
Oxygen (16 amu)	88.8%	88.8% of 18 amu = 16 amu	$\dfrac{16 \text{ amu}}{16 \text{ amu}} = 1$	

84

Oxygen makes up 88.8% of the mass of the molecule. The mass of oxygen in the molecule would be 18×0.888 or 16 amu. The atom of oxygen weighs 16 amu; therefore there is one atom of oxygen in the molecule of water. Thus the molecule of water consists of two atoms of hydrogen and one of oxygen. Hence, its formula is H_2O (Table 11.1).

In the case of methane, the molecular mass is 16 amu and the percentage compositon is 75% carbon and 25% hydrogen. The mass of carbon in the molecule is 75% of 16 amu which equals 12 amu, and since the mass of an atom of carbon is also 12 amu, there is one atom of carbon in the molecule of methane. The mass of hydrogen is 25% of 16 amu which equals 4 amu. Since the mass of hydrogen's atom is one amu, it is evident that there are four atoms of hydrogen in methane's molecule. With one atom of car-bon and four of hydrogen, methane has the molecular formula CH_4.

A general method for finding formulas may be worked out using these ideas.

11:4 Simplest and Molecular (or True) Formulas

Some compounds are composed of molecules, others are made up of ions. For molecular compounds, it is possible to find the number of the different kinds of atoms in the molecule and, thus, express the molecular, or true, formula. To do this, the percentage composition, atomic mass of its elements, and molecular mass of the compound are needed.

Ionic compounds, on the other hand, are represented by formulas which show only the ratio of the atoms in the compound. Such representation is called the *simplest formula*.

11:5 Examples

Example 1

Sodium chloride is 39.3% sodium and 60.7% chlorine. What is its simplest formula?

Solution

In 100 g of sodium chloride there are 39.3 g of sodium and 60.7 g of chlorine.

The number of moles of sodium is $\dfrac{39.3 \text{ g}}{23.0 \text{ g/mole}}$ or 1.71 moles

The number of moles of chlorine is $\dfrac{60.7 \text{ g}}{35.5 \text{ g/mole}}$ or 1.71 moles

The ratio of moles of sodium to chlorine is thus 1.71:1.71 or 1:1. This is also the ratio of their atoms in the compound; therefore, the formula is NaCl.

Example 2

A pure compound was found on analysis to contain 31.9% potassium, 28.9% chlorine, and 39.2% oxygen. Calculate its simplest formula.

Solution

From the percentage composition, it follows that 100 g of the compound contain 31.9 g of potassium, 28.9 g of chlorine, and 39.2 g of oxygen. To find the number of moles of each element in this sample, we divide the mass of each element by its atomic mass.

The number of moles of K $= \dfrac{31.9 \text{ g}}{39.1 \text{ g/moles}} = 0.815$ moles

The number of moles of Cl $= \dfrac{28.9 \text{ g}}{35.5 \text{ g/mole}} = 0.815$ moles

The number of moles of O $= \dfrac{39.2 \text{ g}}{16 \text{ g/mole}} = 2.45$ moles

The molar ratio of K to Cl to O is 0.815:0.815:2.45. To simplify this we divide all three of these numbers by the smallest.

$$K = \dfrac{0.815}{0.815} = 1, \qquad Cl = \dfrac{0.815}{0.815} = 1, \qquad O = \dfrac{2.45}{0.815} = 3$$

The simplest formula of the compound is, therefore, $KClO_3$.

Example 3

Ethane is 80.0% carbon and 20.0% hydrogen. Its molecular mass is 30.0 amu. What is its (a) simplest formula (b) molecular formula?

Solution

In 100 g of ethane there are 80.0 g of carbon and 20.0 g of hydrogen.

The number of moles of C $= \dfrac{80.0 \text{ g}}{12.0 \text{ g/mole}} = 6.66$ moles

The number of moles of H $= \dfrac{20.0 \text{ g}}{1.00 \text{ g/mole}} = 20.0$ moles

The molar ratio of C to H is 6.66:20.0 or 1:3. Therefore the simplest formula is CH_3. This has a formula mass of 15.0 amu.

The molecular mass of the compound is 30.0 amu; therefore, the molecular formula is $(CH_3)_2$ or C_2H_6.

Example 4

A certain organic compound contains 26.7% carbon, 2.24% hydrogen and 71.1% oxygen. Its molecular mass is 90.0 amu. What is its molecular formula?

Solution

In 100 g of the compound there are 26.7 g of carbon, 2.24 g of hydrogen and 71.1 g of oxygen. The number of moles of each element in this sample are:

$$\text{Carbon, } \dfrac{26.7 \text{ g}}{12.0 \text{ g/mole}} = 2.24 \text{ moles}$$

$$\text{Hydrogen, } \dfrac{2.24 \text{ g}}{1.00 \text{ g/mole}} = 2.24 \text{ moles}$$

$$\text{Oxygen, } \dfrac{71.1 \text{ g}}{16.0 \text{ g/mole}} = 4.45 \text{ moles}$$

Therefore the atomic ratio of C to H to O is 2.24:2.24:4.45. This is closest to 1:1:2. Therefore the simplest formula is CHO_2.

Since CHO_2 has a formula mass of $12 + 1 + 32 = 45$ amu and the organic compound one of 90.0 amu, the molecular formula is twice CHO_2 or $C_2H_2O_4$.

11:6 What the Chemical Formula Expresses

A great deal of information obtained by careful experimentation is represented in the chemical formula of a compound. The basic things expressed by the formula are:

(a) The atomic composition of molecules or ions:

The elements whose symbols appear in the formula are the only ones present in the compound. Their atoms have combined in the ratio shown in the formula.

(b) The composition by weight of the compound:

The formula reports the composition of the compound in terms of the number of atoms. But atoms have mass. Hence it is possible to calculate the composition by weight of the compound.

$\rightarrow$

(c) The molecular mass and the formula mass:

From the formula and the atomic mass, the molecular mass for molecular compounds and the formula mass for ionic compounds can be calculated. The terms *formula mass* or *gram-formula mass* are used when referring to ionic substances. Such compounds do not contain molecules. The mole of sodium chloride contains one mole of sodium ions and one mole of chloride ions. Its formula mass is the sum of Na, 23.0 amu, and Cl, 35.5 amu or 58.5 amu.

(d) The information to calculate gas volumes and weights:

In the case of gases, the gram-molecular mass fills the gram-molecular volume at STP. The molecular formula of a gas enables us to calculate what volume a certain mass of gas will occupy, or alternatively, how much a certain volume of a given gas will weigh.

11:7 Calculations Based on Formulas

Example 1

The molecular formula of butane is C_4H_{10}. What is its molecular mass?

Solution

The molecule is composed of four atoms of carbon and ten of hydrogen. These weigh $(4 + 12.0) + (10 \times 1.00) = 58.0$ amu. Therefore the molecular mass of butane is 58.0 amu.

Example 2

What is the percentage composition of butane?

Solution

The mass of carbon is 4×12.0 or 48.0 amu out of 58.0. The mass of hydrogen is

10×1.00, or 10.0 amu out of 58.0. The percentages of carbon and hydrogen are:

$$\text{Carbon} \quad \frac{48.0 \text{ amu}}{58.0 \text{ amu}} \times 100 = 82.8\%$$

$$\text{Hydrogen} \quad \frac{10.0 \text{ amu}}{58.0 \text{ amu}} \times 100 = 17.2\%$$

Example 3

What volume does 10.0 g of butane occupy at STP?

Solution

Because butane is a gas, the mole (58.0 g) occupies the gram-molecular volume at STP. The reasoning now is as follows:

$$58.0 \text{ g occupy } 22.4 \text{ liters}$$

$$10.0 \text{ g occupy } \frac{22.4 \, l}{58.0 \text{ g}} \times 10 \text{ g} = 3.94 \text{ liters}$$

Alternative Solution

Since the volume is proportional to the mass, we may find the new volume x by means of the ratio:

$$\frac{xl}{22.4 \, l} = \frac{10.0 \text{ g}}{58.0 \text{ g}}$$

$$\text{and } x = \frac{10.0 \text{ g}}{58.0 \text{ g}} \times 22.4$$

$$= 3.94 \, l$$

Example 4

What is the density of butane at STP?

Solution

As in Example 3, 22.4 liters of butane weigh 58.0 g. Therefore, one liter of butane weighs $\frac{58.0 \text{ g}}{22.4 \, l}$ or 2.58 g at STP.

Example 5

What is the formula mass of Na_2SO_4?

Solution

The formula mass, the sum of the mass of the atoms in the formula, would be

$$(2 \times Na) + (1 \times S) + (4 \times 0)$$

or $\qquad (2 \times 23.0 \text{ amu}) + (1 \times 32.2 \text{ amu}) + (4 \times 16.0 \text{ amu})$

which adds up to 142.2 amu.

11:8   Structural Formulas

While the molecular formula gives much information about the composition of a compound, it does not show how the atoms are linked to each other. The structural formula does this. The difference between a molecular formula and a structural formula is important. To draw an analogy, it is not enough to describe a car by reporting how much steel, glass, rubber, and plastic it contains; we want to know how these are arranged in the finished car. In other words, we are interested in the "structure" of the car. Similarly, we are interested in knowing the structure of molecules, and structural formulas

have been devised to attempt to show how the atoms are linked together to form the molecule.

The structural formulas for some simple compounds are:

```
     H                H  H              H  H  H
     |                |  |              |  |  |
  H–C–H            H–C–C–H           H–C–C–C–H
     |                |  |              |  |  |
     H                H  H              H  H  H

  Methane           Ethane             Propane
```

Structural formulas, like molecular formulas, are based on experimental evidence.

QUESTIONS

For atomic mass refer to the table.

1. List three things which a chemical symbol represents.

2. Define the terms: (a) *simplest formula;* (b) *molecular formula.*

3. Report the composition of benzene, C_6H_6, as
   (a) a ratio of the mass of the elements involved;
   (b) a percentage composition;
   (c) a ratio of atoms present in the molecule.

4. Is NaCl a molecular formula? Give reasons for your answer.

5. What information is required to calculate the simplest formula of a compound?

6. Find the simplest formula of a salt whose composition is 85% silver and 15% fluorine.

7. Calculate the simplest formula of a salt with composition 27.4% sodium, 1.2% hydrogen, 14.2% carbon, and 57.2% oxygen.

8. What is the simplest formula of a compound composed of 32.4% sodium, 22.5% sulfur, and 45.1% oxygen?

9. Calculate the simplest formulas of the compounds whose percentage compositions are listed below:
   (a) 29.5% calcium, 23.5% sulfur, 47.0% oxygen;
   (b) 26.5% potassium, 35.4% chromium, 38.1% oxygen.

10. What minimum information is required to calculate the molecular formula of a compound?

11. The simplest formula of a compound is CH_2O, and its molecular mass is 180 amu. Find its molecular formula.

12. (a) Calculate the simplest formula of a compound consisting of 47.48% sulfur and 52.52% chlorine.

(b) If the molecular mass of this compound is 135 amu, find its molecular formula.

13. Calculate the molecular formula of a compound that is composed of 27% carbon and 73% oxygen with molecular mass 44 amu.

14. A compound contains 92.25% carbon and 7.75% hydrogen. What is its molecular formula, if 1.0 l of its vapor at STP weighs 3.48 g?

15. The composition of a compound is 2% hydrogen, 33% sulfur, and 65% oxygen; its molecular mass is 98 amu. Find its molecular formula.

16. Calculate the molecular mass or the formula mass of the following:
(a) H_2SO_4 (b) H_3PO_4 (c) NaOH   (d) $Ca(OH)_2$ (e) $Al(OH)_3$
(f) $Ca_3(PO_4)_2$ (g) $C_6H_{12}O_6$ (h) $C_{12}H_{22}O_{11}$ (i) O_3 (j) $MgSO_4.7\,H_2O$

17. How many atoms are there in each of the formulas represented in question 16?

18. Find the percentage composition of calcium carbonate, $CaCO_3$.

19. Find the percentage composition of sodium sulfate, Na_2SO_4.

20. What is the percentage of chromium in chrome alum, $KCr(SO_4)_2.12\ H_2O$?

21. What is the percentage of water in gypsum, $CaSO_4.2H_2O$?

22. Determine the maximum mass of mercury that could be obtained from 10.0 kg of cinnabar, assuming that it is 100% pure HgS.

23. Find the volume occupied by 6.0 g of hydrogen at STP.

24. Find the volume occupied by 6.0 g of carbon dioxide, CO_2, at STP.

25. At STP, 2.20 g of a gaseous compound occupies 1100 ml. Find its molecular mass.

26. At STP, 2.8 l of sulfur dioxide weigh 8.0 g. Find the gram-molecular mass of sulfur dioxide.

27. Find the mass of 6.0 l of hydrogen measured at STP.

28. What is the mass of 10.0 l of carbon dioxide measured at STP?

29. How much aluminum could be obtained from 100 pounds of bauxite that contains 80% of pure alumina, Al_2O_3?

30. Find the mass of 3×10^{23} molecules of chlorine.

31. Find the mass of 1.5 moles of nitrogen gas.

32. The density of nitric oxide, is 1.34 g/l at STP. Find its molecular mass. Given that the ratio of nitrogen to oxygen atoms in nitric oxide is 1:1, what is its molecular formula?

33. Find the density of sulfur dioxide, SO_2, at STP.

CHAPTER

12 Elements, Compounds, and Chemical Equations

The chemist represents elements and compounds by means of symbols and formulas. Chemical reactions are also summarized in expressions called chemical equations. In this chapter, we will investigate methods for writing correct formulas easily and for setting up chemical equations. We will also explore the relationships among weights and volumes of reactants and products shown in chemical equations.

12:1 Common Ions and Their Charges

It would be a difficult task to memorize the formulas of thousands of compounds. However the study of a number of experimentally determined formulas reveals that elements have a definite combining power. For example, sodium, magnesium, aluminum, and tin combine with chlorine forming the compounds:

$NaCl$	$MgCl_2$	$AlCl_3$	$SnCl_4$
sodium chloride	magnesium chloride	aluminum chloride	tin (IV) chloride

Obviously the combining capacities of these metallic elements are different. The sodium atom combines with only one chlorine atom, while the magnesium atom can combine with two. Aluminum and tin can combine with three and four atoms of chlorine respectively.

This combining ability that atoms have is associated closely with their electronic structures. When atoms combine, they may gain, lose, or share electrons. Since electrons are negatively charged, their gain or loss results in the electrical charges associated with ions.

We have already mentioned (Chapter 6) that the alkali metals with one electron in their outer shell readily form stable ions with a

Fig. 12.1 *Group number vs ionic charge*

Periodic Table of the Elements Showing Group Number and Charge

I 1+	II 2+											III 3+	IV 4+	V 5+ 3−	VI 2−	VII 1−	VIII 0
H																	He
Li	Be											B	C	N	O	F	Ne
Na	Mg	GENERALLY 2+ OR 3+										Al	Si	P	S	Cl	Ar
K	Ca	Sc	Ti	V	Cr	Mn	Fe	Co	Ni	Cu	Zn	Ga	Ge	As	Se	Br	Kr
Rb	Sr	Y	Zr	Nb	Mo	Tc	Ru	Rh	Pd	Ag	Cd	In	Sn	Sb	Te	I	Xe
Cs	Ba	La	Hf	Ta	W	Re	Os	Ir	Pt	Au	Hg	Tl	Pb	Bi	Po	At	Rn
Fr	Ra	Ac															

charge of $1+$: Li^+, Na^+, K^+, Rb^+, Cs^+, and Fr^+. The halogens on the other hand readily gain an electron, forming stable ions with a charge of $1-$: F^-, Cl^-, Br^-, I^-, and At^-.

We can refer to the periodic table to generalize our ideas on the formation of ions. The elements of groups I, II, and III have 1, 2, and 3 electrons respectively in the outer shell of their atoms. If we assume that these atoms may lose their electrons, the resulting ions will have charges of $1+$, $2+$, and $3+$ (Fig. 12.1). The atoms of the nonmetallic elements of groups V, VI, and VII may acquire 3, 2, and 1 electrons respectively. The ions formed will then have charges of $3-$, $2-$, and $1-$. When the transition metals lose electrons they commonly form ions with a charge of $2+$ or $3+$. It is uncommon for atoms to gain or lose larger numbers of electrons.

A number of elements form more than one

TABLE 12.1

COMMON IONS AND THEIR CHARGES

Ammonium	NH_4^+	Barium	Ba^{2+}	Aluminum	Al^{3+}
Copper (I)	Cu^+	Calcium	Ca^{2+}	Antimony	Sb^{3+}
Hydrogen, hydronium H^+,	H_3O^+	Chromium (II)	Cr^{2+}	Bismuth	Bi^{3+}
Lithium	Li^+	Copper (II)	Cu^{2+}	Chromium (III)	Cr^{3+}
Mercury (I)	Hg^+	Iron (II)	Fe^{2+}	Iron (III)	Fe^{3+}
Potassium	K^+	Lead	Pb^{2+}		
Silver	Ag^+	Magnesium	Mg^{2+}		
Sodium	Na^+	Mercury (II)	Hg^{2+}		
		Zinc	Zn^{2+}		
Acetate	CH_3COO^-	Carbonate	CO_3^{2-}	Nitride	N^{3-}
Bromide	Br^-	Chromate	CrO_4^{2-}	Phosphate	PO_4^{3-}
Chlorate	ClO_3^-	Dichromate	$Cr_2O_7^{2-}$		
Chloride	Cl^-	Oxide	O^{2-}		
Chlorite	ClO_2^-	Sulfate	SO_4^{2-}		
Fluoride	F^-	Sulfide	S^{2-}		
Hydrogen carbonate ion, bicarbonate	HCO_3^-	Sulfite	SO_3^{2-}		
Hydrogen sulfate ion, bisulfate	HSO_4^-				
Hydrogen sulfite ion, bisulfite	HSO_3^-				
Hydroxide	OH^-				
Hypochlorite	ClO^-				
Iodide	I^-				
Nitrate	NO_3^-				
Nitrite	NO_2^-				
Perchlorate	ClO_4^-				
Permanganate	MnO_4^-				

type of ion depending on what reactions take place. For example, copper, mercury, chromium, and iron may form the following ions: Cu^+, Cu^{2+}, Hg^+, Hg^{2+}, Cr^{2+}, Cr^{3+}, Fe^{2+}, and Fe^{3+}.

In many compounds, there are groups of atoms bonded together, carrying an electric charge. The group behaves as single atoms in chemical reactions. Examples of such groups, called *polyatomic ions*, are: the ammonium ion, NH_4^+; the hydroxide ion, OH^-; the nitrate ion, NO_3^-; the carbonate ion, CO_3^{2-}; the sulfate ion, SO_4^{2-}. A list of common ions and their charges is shown in Table 12.1.

12:2   Valence

Valence was once regarded as the study of how atoms combine. With rapid growth of our knowledge of atomic structure, the ideas of valence have also changed rapidly. So extensive is the modern study of atomic bonding, that it is best to use more meaningful words than valence to describe particular aspects of bonding. Three ideas stand out in a definition of valence:

(a)   The capacity of an atom to combine with other atoms.

(b)   The electrical charges which some atoms may obtain.

(c)   The bond between atoms.

Valence as Combining Capacity:

As was seen in section 12:1, elements have different combining capacities. This must relate to combining ability of atoms. What was true in the formation of chlorides, is also seen as atoms of various elements combined with different numbers of hydrogen atoms. This may be seen from the formulas of the following compounds:

| HCl | H_2O | NH_3 | CH_4 |
| Hydrogen Chloride | Water | Ammonia | Methane |

In the molecule of hydrogen chloride, an atom of chlorine is combined with only one atom of hydrogen. In the other molecules shown, the atoms of oxygen, nitrogen, and carbon are combined with two, three, and four hydrogen atoms, respectively. So it is apparent that the combining abilities of chlorine, oxygen, nitrogen, and carbon differ.

From this point of view, the "valence" of an element is the number of hydrogen or chlorine atoms with which one atom of that element will combine. This definition stresses valence as combining capacity.

Valence as electrical charge:

This is due to the gain or loss of electrons. Since electrons are negatively charged, their gain or loss results in the electrical charges that are commonly associated with valence. *Ionic charge* is a better term than valence to describe this electrical property of ions.

Valence as a bond:

Atoms may be bonded together by sharing electrons. The shared electrons are referred to as "*chemical bond*", and this form of bonding is called *covalence*. Covalent bonds between atoms are oriented in certain directions. Therefore, molecules formed by atoms united through covalent bonds have definite shape, as discussed in Chapter 19.

In this book, the terms combining capacity, ionic charge, and chemical bonding will be used, rather than the vague term "valence".

12:3   Writing Formulas of Compounds

Formulas for many compounds can be correctly written using our knowledge of the charges of the ions listed in Table 12.1. When a positive metallic ion is combined with a negative non-metallic ion, the total positive charges must equal the total negative charges, so that the algebraic sum of the charges in the compound is zero. It is customary to place the symbol of the metallic element first when writing the formula. A few examples will illustrate these practical rules.

The formula for sodium chloride is NaCl; the single positive charge of the sodium ion just balances the single negative charge of the chloride ion. However, two chloride ions are needed to equal the charge of a calcium ion; therefore, the formula for calcium chloride is $CaCl_2$. Aluminum sulfate is composed of aluminum ions, Al^{3+}, and sulfate ions, SO_4^{2-}. The total positive charges of two aluminum ions will be balanced by the total negative charges of three sulfate ions: $Al_2(SO_4)_3$. Notice that when a polyatomic ion is taken more than once, it is enclosed in parentheses and the proper subscript is placed just outside to the right. Since iron may form two different ions, Fe^{2+} and Fe^{3+}, two different compounds will result when chlorine reacts with iron: iron (II) chloride, $FeCl_2$, and iron (III) chloride, $FeCl_3$.

The above rules permit us to write the formulas of compounds by inspection. Remember that formulas must be checked by experiment. What is so gratifying about the rules is that the formulas they predict always check with experimental results.

12:4 Naming Compounds

Compounds containing two elements are called binary and those with three elements are ternary.

Binary Salts

Binary salts consist of a metallic and a non-metallic element combined together. The name of a binary salt is made up of the name of the metal followed by the name of the non-metal whose ending is changed into -ide.

NaF, sodium fluoride
$ZnCl_2$, zinc chloride
PbS, lead sulfide
Mg_3N_2, magnesium nitride

Oxides

Oxides are binary compounds containing the element oxygen. They are named in a similar fashion to binary salts.

BaO, barium oxide
CO, carbon monoxide
CO_2, carbon dioxide
FeO, iron (II) oxide (ferrous oxide)
Fe_2O_3, iron (III) oxide (ferric oxide)
SO_2, sulfur dioxide

Notice that prefixes are sometimes used to indicate the number of atoms present. The prefixes mono-, di-, tri-, tetra-, penta-, etc., indicate that 1, 2, 3, 4, 5, etc. atoms of a given element are present. When metallic elements exhibit different ionic charges, these are indicated by a Roman numeral placed in brackets after the name of the metal. For example, iron in FeO and Fe_2O_3 exhibits a charge of 2+ and 3+ respectively. The names of these two oxides are therefore iron (II) oxide and iron (III) oxide. Older names for these are still used: ferrous oxide and ferric oxide. The suffixes -ous and -ic refer to the lower and higher charges respectively.

Peroxides

Some oxides possess one more oxygen atom than ordinary oxides. The prefix per- is used to designate such substances.

H_2O_2, hydrogen peroxide
Na_2O_2, sodium peroxide
BaO_2, barium peroxide
K_2O_2, potassium peroxide

Binary Acids

All binary acids consist of hydrogen along with another element. Therefore, the name of a binary acid consists of the prefix *hydro-* for the hydrogen, a short form of the name of the element with which the hydrogen is combined in the acid, and the ending *-ic*. When these compounds are in the gaseous state their names end with -ide.

gaseous compounds

HF, hydrogen fluoride
HCl, hydrogen chloride
HBr, hydrogen bromide
HI,   hydrogen iodide
H_2S, hydrogen sulfide

acid solutions

HF, hydrofluoric acid
HCl, hydrochloric acid
HBr, hydrobromic acid
HI,   hydriodic acid
H_2S, hydrosulfuric acid

Ternary Acids

These compounds contain hydrogen, oxygen, and a third element. They are always named after this third element. The common ternary acids end with -ic. Sometimes other acids exist that have one more oxygen atom than the -ic acid; the prefix per- is then added. Other acids still, may have one or two atoms of oxygen less than the common -ic acid. The -ic ending is then changed into -ous in one case and both the suffix -ous and the prefix hypo- are used in the other case.

HNO_3, nitric acid
$HClO_3$, chloric acid
H_2SO_4, sulfuric acid
H_3PO_4, phosphoric acid
H_2CO_3, carbonic acid
$HClO_4$, perchloric acid
$HClO_3$, chloric acid
$HClO_2$, chlorous acid
$HClO$, hypochlorous acid

Ternary Salts

Salts can be considered as the products formed when a metallic element replaces the hydrogen of an acid. The names of the ternary salts are derived from the names of the corresponding acids. An -ic acid gives an -ate salt. An -ous acid

gives an -ite salt, etc. The following examples illustrate these rules:

$NaNO_3$, sodium nitrate
$NaClO_3$, sodium chlorate
Na_2SO_4, sodium sulfate
Na_2CO_3, sodium carbonate
Na_3PO_4, sodium phosphate
$NaClO$, sodium hypochlorite
$NaClO_2$, sodium chlorite
$NaClO_3$, sodium chlorate
$NaClO_4$, sodium perchlorate

Bases

Common bases contain the hydroxide (OH^-) ion. They are all called hydroxides:

$NaOH$, sodium hydroxide
NH_4OH, ammonium hydroxide
$Ca(OH)_2$, calcium hydroxide
$Al(OH)_3$, aluminum hydroxide

Acid Salts

An acid salt is formed when only part of the replaceable hydrogen of an acid is displaced by a metal. Here are a few examples of such salts and their names:

$NaHSO_4$, sodium hydrogen sulfate or sodium bisulfate
$KHCO_3$, potassium hydrogen carbonate or potassium bicarbonate

12:5 Chemical Equations

Chemical equations are so important in the study of chemistry that they had to be introduced near the very beginning of the course (Chapter 3) and have had to be used in nearly every chapter since. We are now in a position to appreciate their meaning and use more thoroughly,

In the chemical equation, the left-hand side shows the substances that react. These are termed the reactants. The right-hand side shows the new substances resulting from the change, and these are termed the products.

Perhaps you have noticed the following points about the chemical equations used thus far:

1. A chemical equation represents a reaction that really takes place. The mere writing of symbols and formulas does not make up a chemical equation unless they report an actual chemical reaction.

2. Every chemical equation is "balanced", which means that there are the same number of atoms of each element on both sides of the equation. This is done because every chemical reaction complies with the law of conservation of mass.

12:6   Writing and Balancing Chemical Equations

A chemical equation is more than a mathematical exercise. Make it a policy to understand the chemical reaction when you write its equation. To write and balance a chemical equation correctly, we must:

1. Know what substances react and are produced during the reaction;

2. Know the correct formulas of all the substances involved;

3. Account for every atom before and after the reaction.

To illustrate the method for writing and balancing equations, let us consider a few common reactions.

Example 1

The reaction between magnesium and oxygen may be reported by the word or name equation:

Magnesium + oxygen → Magnesium oxide
(Rule *a*)

If we use the chemical formula for each substance instead of the name, we obtain the beginnings of a chemical equation:

$$Mg + O_2 \rightarrow MgO \text{ (Rule } b)$$

We thus observe the second rule about chemical equations. We must use formulas which represent the substances correctly. Thus Mg, the symbol for magnesium, stands for the atom of that metallic element. This is justified because metals consist of atoms rather than molecules. O_2 is the true formula for oxygen, an element which occurs as molecules with two atoms. MgO is the simplest formula for magnesium oxide. This is an example of a compound where we can report only that the ratio of magnesium atoms to oxygen atoms is 1:1. Magnesium oxide does not form molecules so that a true molecular formula is not possible.

In a chemical reaction there is no loss or gain in the total number of atoms involved (Rule c). Since each molecule of oxygen is known to contain two atoms, it follows that for every molecule of O_2 used up, two "molecules" of MgO will be formed. For these, two atoms of Mg will be required. The balanced chemical equation is thus:

$$2Mg + O_2 \rightarrow 2MgO$$

Indeed this equation is valid because it is *both* balanced and correct. The formulas represent the composition of the substances.

To write $Mg + O \rightarrow MgO$ is unacceptable despite the fact that the equation is balanced. Oxygen occurs as O_2 not as O.

Similarly $Mg + O_2 \rightarrow MgO_2$ is no better. The formula for magnesium oxide is MgO, not MgO_2.

Example 2

It can easily be established experimentally that zinc reacts with hydrochloric acid to produce zinc chloride and hydrogen gas. Experiments have also proved that the formula for hydrochloric acid is HCl and for zinc chloride, $ZnCl_2$. Of course, we would arrive at the same formulas by applying the generalizations made in the earlier sections of this chapter concerning the ions and their charges. We know that hydrogen gas exists as diatomic molecules. With this information, we are ready to set up the following skeleton equation:

$$Zn_{(s)} + HCl_{(aq)} \rightarrow ZnCl_{2(aq)} + H_2 \uparrow_{(g)}$$
(not balanced)

This skeleton equation may be read: solid zinc reacts with hydrochloric acid to produce zinc chloride that remains in solution and hydrogen that escapes as a gas. This skeleton equation, however, does not satisfy the law of conservation of mass. Two atoms of chlorine and two atoms of hydrogen are shown on the right-hand side while only one atom of each of these elements are represented on the left-hand side. If we could tamper with the formulas for zinc chloride and hydrogen gas, we might write $ZnCl$, and H for these substances. This is not permissible because it would contradict experimental facts. We can simply "balance" the equation by doubling the number of molecules of HCl, thus doubling the number of hydrogen and chlorine atoms represented on the left-hand side:

$$Zn_{(s)} + 2HCl_{(aq)} \rightarrow ZnCl_{2(aq)} + H_2 \uparrow_{(g)}$$

We see that an equation can be balanced by adjusting the coefficients placed in front of the formulas of the substances involved in order to obtain the same number of atoms of each element on each side of the equation.

Example 3

When potassium chlorate is strongly heated it is decomposed into potassium chloride and oxygen gas. The skeleton equation with formulas only representing this reaction is:

$$KClO_{3(s)} \rightarrow KCl_{(s)} + O_2 \uparrow_{(g)}$$
(not balanced)

In the equation, three atoms of oxygen are present in $KClO_3$, and two atoms of oxygen are present in O_2. The lowest common multiple of three and two is six. Three divides into six twice, and two divides into six three times. Two

becomes the coefficient of $KClO_3$, and three becomes the coefficient of O_2. KCl, according to the same reasoning, receives the same coefficient as $KClO_3$. Thus the equation is written:

$$2KClO_{3(s)} \rightarrow 2KCl_{(s)} + 3O_2 \uparrow_{(g)}$$

In many equations, there are certain atoms or ions which are more significant than the rest. These are helpful in balancing the equation, since the problem becomes one of finding the lowest common multiple for those on both sides of the equation. This point was illustrated with oxygen in the above equation.

Example 4

The following equation is also instructive:

$$NaOH + H_2SO_4 \rightarrow Na_2SO_4 + 2H_2O$$
(not balanced)

This illustrates the difficulty of attempting to balance an equation without knowing the chemistry that it represents. Without such knowledge, the equation looks strange, and balancing it is more or less pointless. If, however, we recognize that this reaction is the neutralization of a base, NaOH, by an acid, H_2SO_4, then we readily see that the OH^- of the base and the $H+$ of the acid are the "significant reactants".

Since NaOH provides one OH^-, and H_2SO_4 provides two $H+$, we obtain the lowest common denominator of one and two, namely two. Thus the coefficient of NaOH is two, and that of H_2SO_4 is one, and the equation is balanced accordingly:

$$2NaOH_{(aq)} + H_2SO_{4(aq)} \rightarrow Na_2SO_{4(aq)} + 2H_2O_{(l)}$$

12:7 The Quantitative Meaning of Equations

In addition to reporting a chemical change, the chemical equation states what masses and volumes of substances react and how much product is formed. The importance of such relationships becomes apparent when we realize that they enable the chemist to calculate the actual amounts of reactants required to produce a desired amount of a product.

Let us consider an example to see how many facts are implied in a chemical equation. The products of combustion when methane gas burns are carbon dioxide and water:

$$CH_{4(g)} + 2O_{2(g)} \rightarrow CO_{2(g)} + 2H_2O_{(l)}$$

Besides stating qualitatively that methane combines with oxygen producing carbon dioxide and water, this equation may be interpreted quantitatively as follows:

a. 1 molecule of methane combines with 2 molecules of oxygen forming 1 molecule of carbon dioxide and 2 molecules of water;

b. 1 mole of methane combines with 2 moles of oxygen forming 1 mole of carbon dioxide and 2 moles of water;

c. 16 grams of methane combine with 64 grams of oxygen forming 44 grams of carbon dioxide and 36 grams of water;

d. 22.4 l (STP) of methane combine with 44.8 l (STP) of oxygen forming 22.4 l (STP) of carbon dioxide and 36 grams of water.

Note that water cannot be reported as a gaseous volume here because it would be either a liquid or a solid (ice) at STP.

These facts are conveniently summarized below.

12:8   Calculations Based on Equations

The quantities of reactants and products of a chemical reaction can easily be found from the equation. Problems about such quantities can easily be solved if a few simple steps are observed.

1. Make sure that all formulas in the equation are correct and that the equation is balanced.

2. Think and reason through what is required and what is given in the problem. These quantities must be in the same ratio as that represented by the equation.

3. From the equation, note how many moles of each reactant and product are involved. From this information, the mass of reactants and products may be found.

4. The ratio and proportion of the various quantities used will be seen more easily if these are written directly below and above the equation.

	CH_4 $_{(g)}$	+	$2O_2$ $_{(g)}$	$\rightarrow$	CO_2 $_{(g)}$	+	$2H_2O$ $_{(l)}$
(a).	1 molecule (16 amu)	+	2 molecules (64 amu)	$\rightarrow$	1 molecule (44 amu)	+	2 molecules (36 amu)
(b).	1 mole (6×10^{23} molecules)	+	2 moles (12×10^{23} molecules)	$\rightarrow$	1 mole (6×10^{23} molecules)	+	2 moles (12×10^{23} molecules)
(c).	16 grams	+	64 grams	$\rightarrow$	44 grams	+	36 grams
(d).	22.4 l (STP)	+	44.8 l (STP)	$\rightarrow$	22.4 l (STP)	+	36 grams

12:9   Mass Relationships in Chemical Reactions

Example

What weight of oxygen is needed for the complete combustion of 25.0 grams of methane?

Solution

We will solve the problem by following the steps mentioned in the previous paragraph.

Step 2:   25.0 g   x g
Step 1: CH_4 + $2O_2$ → CO_2 + $2H_2O$
Step 3:   16.0 g   64.0 g

From the equation, we know that 16.0 g of methane require 64.0 g of oxygen for complete combustion. Then, 25.0 g of methane will require $\dfrac{25.0}{16.0}$ times as much oxygen. Therefore,

Step 4:   Mass of oxygen = $\dfrac{25.0\ g}{16.0\ g}$ × 64.0 g = 100.0 g

Alternate Solution

In 25.0 grams of methane there are $\dfrac{25.0\ g}{16.0\ g/mole}$ = 1.56 moles of the gas. We can then write:

Step 2:   1.56 moles   x moles
Step 1: CH_4 + $2O_2$ → CO_2 + $2H_2O$
Step 3:   1 mole   2 moles

Since 1 mole of methane requires 2 moles of oxygen, then 1.56 moles of methane will require 3.12 moles of oxygen. Because 1 mole of oxygen weighs 32.0 g, the mass of oxygen needed in grams is:

Step 4:   Mass of oxygen = 32.0 g/mole × 3.12 moles = 99.8 g

12:10   Mass-Volume Relationships in Chemical Reactions

In many reactions the reactants and/or the products are in the gaseous state. Remember that in such cases, the formula of a gaseous compound shown in an equation represents not only the gram-molecular mass of the substance but also the gram-molecular volume, i.e., 22.4 *l* at STP occupied by one mole of the gas. This fact enables us to solve problems involving volumes of gases in chemical reactions.

Example

What volume of oxygen measured at 27°C and 750 mm is required for the complete combustion of 25.0 grams of methane?

Solution

Since we are interested in a *volume* of oxygen we will let the formula for oxygen in the equation stand for a volume and we will calculate the volume needed at STP.

Step 2: 25.0 g   x*l*(STP)
Step 1: CH_4 + $2O_2$ → CO_2 + $2H_2O$
Step 3: 16.0 g   2 × 22.4 *l* (STP)

We see that 44.8l of oxygen measured at STP are needed for the combustion of 16.0 g of methane. For the combustion of 25.0 g of methane, $\frac{25.0}{16.0}$ times as much oxygen will be needed. The volume of oxygen obtained at STP can then be converted, by applying the gas laws, into the volume it would occupy at 27°C and 750 mm of Hg.

$$\text{Volume of oxygen at STP} = \frac{25.0 \text{ g}}{16.0 \text{ g}} \times 44.8 \text{ } l = 70.0 \text{ } l$$

$$\text{Volume at 27°C and 750 mm} = V_2 = \frac{V_1 P_1 T_2}{P_2 T_1} = \frac{70.0 \text{ } l \times 760 \text{ mm} \times 300°\text{K}}{750 \text{ mm} \times 273°\text{K}} = 78.0 \text{ } l$$

12:11   Volume–Volume Relationships in Chemical Reactions

When gaseous volumes only are involved, the problems are simplified by the fact that single moles of all gases at the same conditions of temperature and pressure occupy the same volume.

Example

What volume of carbon dioxide measured at STP will be formed if 50.0 liters of methane, measured at STP, are completely burned?

Solution

The equation reveals that 1 mole of methane produces 1 mole of carbon dioxide. The volumes of these two gases are in the ratio of 22.4:22.4 or 1:1. That is, at any temperature and pressure the volume of carbon dioxide formed is always equal to the volume of methane consumed when both gases are measured under the same conditions.

Step 2: 50.0 l x l
Step 1: CH_4 + 2O_2 → CO_2 + 2H_2O
Step 3: 22.4 l 22.4 l
        (1 vol)   (1 vol)

$$\text{Step 4: Volume of carbon dioxide at STP} = \frac{50.0 \text{ } l}{22.4 \text{ } l} \times 22.4 \text{ } l = 50.0 \text{ } l$$

QUESTIONS

1. What is the meaning of the terms *copper* (*I*) and *copper* (*II*)?

2. What "rule" must be observed when a formula for a compound made of a metallic ion and a nonmetallic ion is written?

3. What is meant by the term *polyatomic ion*? Give a few examples of such ions.

4. Write the formula and the name for the compound formed when each of the following

pairs of ions combine:

(a) K^+ and CO_3^{2-} (f) Cu^{2+} and Cl^-
(b) Ca^{2+} and NO_3^- (g) NH_4^+ and SO_3^{2-}
(c) Al^{3+} and O^{2-} (h) Ba^{2+} and OH^-
(d) Mg^{2+} and SO_4^{2-} (i) Zn^{2+} and PO_4^{3-}
(e) K^+ and MnO_4^- (j) Ag^+ and Cl^-

5. Name the following compounds:

(a) $MgBr_2$ (f) $KClO$ (k) $KClO_3$
(b) H_2SO_4 (g) KOH (l) $NaHCO_3$
(c) H_2SO_3 (h) HCl (m) HgO
(d) $Al(NO_3)_3$ (i) Na_2S (n) $MgSO_3$
(e) K_2O_2 (j) Na_2SO_4 (o) CO

6. Give the formulas for the following:

(a) magnesium oxide   (f) carbonic acid
(b) sulfur trioxide   (g) calcium hydroxide
(c) nitric acid   (h) hydrogen iodide
(d) zinc sulfate   (i) iron (II) sulfide
(e) sodium hydroxide   (j) potassium hydrogen sulfate

7. Distinguish between *reactants* and *products*.

8. What do upward and downward-pointing arrows used in chemical equations signify?

9. Outline a method of writing and balancing a chemical equation.

10. Balance each of the following equations:

(a) Fe $+ O_2$ $\rightarrow Fe_2O_3$
(b) $AgNO_3$ $+ MgCl_2$ $\rightarrow AgCl\downarrow$ $+ Mg(NO_3)_2$
(c) HgO $\rightarrow Hg$ $+ O_2\uparrow$
(d) Na $+ H_2O$ $\rightarrow NaOH$ $+ H_2\uparrow$
(e) Mg $+ O_2$ $\rightarrow MgO$
(f) Zn $+ HCl$ $\rightarrow ZnCl_2$ $+ H_2\uparrow$
(g) Fe $+ H_2O$ $\rightarrow Fe_2O_3$ $+ H_2\uparrow$
(h) Na_2SO_4 $+ BaCl_2$ $\rightarrow BaSO_4\downarrow$ $+ NaCl$
(i) $C_{10}H_{16}$ $+ Cl_2$ $\rightarrow HCl\uparrow$ $+ C$
(j) CaO $+ H_2O$ $\rightarrow Ca(OH)_2$

11. One volume of hydrogen combines with one volume of fluorine to produce two volumes of hydrogen fluoride.

(a) Write the equation for this reaction.
(b) How many moles of fluorine are necessary to produce 4 moles of hydrogen fluoride?
(c) How many molecules of hydrogen are required in the formation of 4 molecules of hydrogen fluoride?

12. Sodium reacts with chlorine producing sodium chloride.

(a) Write the equation for this reaction.
(b) How many moles of sodium chloride will be formed from one mole of sodium?
(c) How many grams of sodium chloride will be formed from 23 grams of sodium?

13. From the reaction $CH_{4(g)} + 2O_{2(g)} \rightarrow CO_{2(g)} + 2H_2O_{(l)}$, calculate:

(a) the number of moles of water produced from 5 moles of methane;

(b) the volume of carbon dioxide at STP produced from 5 moles of methane;

(c) the number of grams of oxygen necessary for the combustion of 5 moles of methane.

14. Find the weight of magnesium oxide formed from the complete oxidation of 6.25 g of magnesium according to the equation:

$$2Mg_{(s)} + O_{2(g)} \rightarrow 2MgO_{(s)}$$

15. Zinc reacts with sulfuric acid according to the following equation:

$$Zn_{(s)} + H_2SO_{4(aq)} \rightarrow ZnSO_{4(aq)} + H_2\uparrow_{(g)}$$

What weight of zinc sulfate will be formed when 2 moles of zinc react with excess acid?

16. How many grams of calcium oxide will be produced by heating 75.0 g of calcium carbonate according to the following equation?

$$CaCO_{3(s)} \rightarrow CaO_{(s)} + CO_2\uparrow_{(g)}$$

17. How many moles of hydrogen chloride will be formed when 12 moles of hydrogen combine with excess chlorine?

18. In an electrolysis experiment 9.0 g of water were electrolyzed by a current producing hydrogen and oxygen.

(a) What volume of hydrogen measured at STP was produced?

(b) What volume would this hydrogen occupy at 27°C and 38 cm of Hg?

19. How many moles of carbon dioxide are produced by the complete combustion of 660 g of carbon?

20. Potassium chlorate decomposes into potassium chloride and oxygen when heated: $2KClO_{3(s)} \rightarrow 2KCl_{(s)} + 3O_2\uparrow_{(g)}$. What volume of oxygen measured at STP can be obtained when 49.0 grams of potassium chlorate is strongly heated?

21. Find the weight of sodium carbonate that is required to prepare 50.0 liters of carbon dioxide measured at STP. The equation for this reaction is:

$$Na_2CO_{3(s)} + 2HCl_{(aq)} \rightarrow 2NaCl_{(aq)} + H_2O_{(l)} + CO_2\uparrow_{(g)}$$

22. What volume of hydrogen will combine with 33.6 liters of oxygen in the synthesis of water? What will be the weight of the water formed?

23. The complete combustion of acetylene is represented by the following equation:

$$2C_2H_{2(g)} + 5O_{2(g)} \rightarrow 4CO_{2(g)} + 2H_2O_{(l)}$$

(a) What volume of oxygen is needed for the combustion of 100 l of acetylene, both gases being measured at STP?

(b) What volume of carbon dioxide measured at 23°C and 742 mm pressure is produced?

CHAPTER

13 Hydrogen and Oxygen

Hydrogen is the most abundant element in the universe and oxygen makes up nearly half of the earth's crust. The abundance of these gases and the numerous compounds they form makes their study important. Their presentation will give us an opportunity to introduce a number of useful terms and concepts. The chapter is divided into two parts for convenience.

PART I — HYDROGEN

13:1 Discovery and Occurrence of Hydrogen

The English scientist Cavendish is usually regarded as the discoverer of hydrogen because he was the first to prepare it in the pure state (in 1766), describing its properties and recognizing it as an element. He found that a gas is set free when acids react with metals, and that the gas burns to form water. Lavoisier named the gas hydrogen, meaning water-former.

Hydrogen occurs commonly combined with other elements in water, in all plant and animal tissues, and in hydrocarbons which constitute the greater part of natural gas and petroleum. It is not present as a free gas in the atmosphere of the earth at sea level. If it were present in the pure state, there would be an explosion whenever someone struck a match, but luckily, we are spared this hazard. Free hydrogen is present, however, in outer space, and in the sun and the other stars. Astronomers believe that it is the most common element in the universe.

13:2 Preparation of Hydrogen

Because hydrogen does not exist in the free state to any appreciable extent, it must be prepared from one of its compounds. The principal sources used are water, acids, and hydrocarbons.

(a) The Electrolysis of Water

The decomposition of water by the passage of an electric current has been described in section 3:8.

(b) The Action of Very Active Metals with Water

Some metals are so extremely reactive that they can liberate hydrogen even from cold water. Sodium is such a metal. Because of its extreme reactivity, sodium must be kept entirely away from air and water; it is therefore stored in kerosene. Sodium is so soft that it can be cut with a knife and so light that it floats on the water while reacting with it.

In the reaction between sodium and water, hydrogen is liberated from water as one atom of sodium takes the place of one atom of hydrogen in the molecule of water. This may be represented by the equation:

$$2Na_{(s)} + 2HOH_{(l)} \rightarrow 2NaOH_{(aq)} + H_2\uparrow_{(g)}$$

Sodium hydroxide may be obtained as a white crystalline solid by evaporating the water from the solution formed in the above experiment.

(c) The Action of Carbon on Steam

Hydrogen can be produced inexpensively on a commercial scale by passing steam over strongly heated carbon:

$$C_{(s)} + H_2O_{(g)} \rightarrow CO\uparrow_{(g)} + H_2\uparrow_{(g)}$$

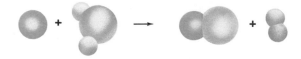

The resulting mixture of carbon monoxide and hydrogen, called water gas, can be used as a cheap industrial fuel. The mixture can be further treated and its components separated; thus, it represents an important source of commercial hydrogen.

(d) The Action of Metals on Acids

The most convenient method of preparing hydrogen for laboratory study is a reaction between a metal and an acid. Metals differ in their ability to react with acids to liberate hydrogen and it is this which partly determines wheth-er a metal is known as reactive or inert. Zinc and hydrochloric acid are used most frequently to prepare hydrogen, because their reaction liberates a good yield of the pure gas. Some of the other acids react with metals to liberate gases other than hydrogen.

To prepare hydrogen, granulated or mossy zinc is put into an Erlenmeyer flask, and dilute hydrochloric acid is added through a thistle tube. Hydrogen begins to come off almost immediately. The first bit of gas is discarded since it probably has some air mixed with it, but the remainder is collected through the downward displacement of water (Fig. 13.1). The chemical reaction may be represented by the following equation:

$$Zn_{(s)} + 2HCl_{(aq)} \rightarrow ZnCl_{2(aq)} + H_2\uparrow_{(g)}$$

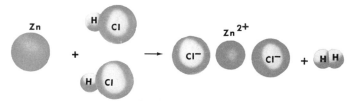

Fig. 13.1   *A laboratory preparation of hydrogen*

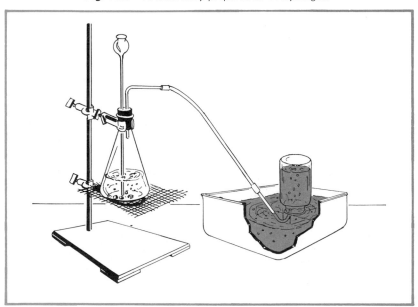

Although it might appear that the zinc has dissolved in the acid this is not the case. A chemical reaction has taken place in which the original reactants were changed into entirely different substances. The zinc chloride that forms is a salt and does not have any of the properties of the original zinc.

13:3 The Displacement Series

In the reaction described in the last section between zinc and hydrochloric acid, the hydrogen gas is said to have been displaced by the zinc.

Can all metals displace hydrogen from acids and water? By experimenting with various metals, chemists have found that some metals cannot do so. Copper is an example of a metal that cannot displace hydrogen from acids.

The metals which can displace hydrogen from acids or water vary in their level of activity. Potassium and sodium displace hydrogen violently from cold water while lithium and calcium react with water more slowly. Magnesium reacts only with hot water or steam while iron displaces hydrogen only at bright red heat as steam is passed over it. By experimenting with acids and salt solutions, the order of activity of metals and hydrogen may be found. By performing similar experiments with combinations of metals, the order in which the metals displace one another is revealed.

A list of metals and hydrogen arranged in the order of their activity is called the *Displacement Series* or the *Activity Series* (Table 13.1). The most reactive metals are at the top of the list, and the least reactive are at the bottom. Any metal will displace those below it from their compounds in solution. For example, a strip of iron dipped into a solution of copper (II) sulfate becomes covered with metallic copper:

$$Fe_{(s)} + CuSO_{4(aq)} \rightarrow FeSO_{4(aq)} + Cu_{(s)}$$

The chemical activity of metals is due to their outer electrons: the more reactive a metal is, the easier it is to remove its outer electrons. Hence, this list is also called the *Electromotive Series*.

TABLE 13.1	
The Displacement Series*	
Lithium	Li
Potassium	K
Calcium	Ca
Sodium	Na
Magnesium	Mg
Aluminum	Al
Zinc	Zn
Iron	Fe
Tin	Sn
Lead	Pb
Hydrogen	H
Copper	Cu
Mercury	Hg
Silver	Ag
Platinum	Pt
Gold	Au

13:4 Physical Properties of Hydrogen

Hydrogen gas is colorless, odorless, tasteless, and practically insoluble in water. It is the lightest of all gases, its density (0.089 g/l) being 1/16 that of oxygen, and 1/14 that of nitrogen. Hydrogen has an extremely low boiling point, and it was a major scientific achievement to produce liquid hydrogen. This was done by Dewar, in 1898, by cooling the gas to a very low temperature and then subjecting it to high pressure. The normal boiling point is $-253°C$. The

*It must be noted that the rate of reaction of a metal with water and acids is not always an accurate measure of its chemical activity. For example, lithium and calcium are placed above sodium in the displacement series in spite of the fact that they react with water somewhat more slowly than sodium does. Another method for determining the chemical activity of metals will be explained in Chapter 41.

density of liquid hydrogen is extremely low, only about 1/14 that of water.

13:5 Chemical Properties and Uses of Hydrogen

(a) Hydrogen-Oxygen Reaction

Hydrogen burns with a hot, pale blue flame as it combines chemically with oxygen to form water.

$$2H_{2(g)} + O_{2(g)} \rightarrow 2H_2O_{(l)}$$

It is apparent that oxygen and hydrogen could not be present in the atmosphere for any great length of time without reacting violently. The extremely inflammable nature of hydrogen makes it dangerous to have a mixture of hydrogen and oxygen (or air) near an open flame.

(b) Hydrogen-Nitrogen Reaction

Direct combination of hydrogen and nitrogen under pressure is the industrial method for making ammonia (Chapter 33):

$$3H_{2(g)} + N_{2(g)} \rightarrow 2NH_3\uparrow_{(g)}$$

Ammonia has many important uses in the laboratory and in industry.

(c) Hydrogen-Chlorine Reaction

When a mixture of hydrogen and chlorine is ignited or exposed to direct sunlight, the gases react to form hydrogen chloride, also a gas:

$$H_{2(g)} + Cl_{2(g)} \rightarrow 2HCl\uparrow_{(g)}$$

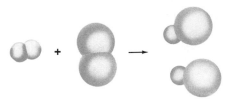

Direct combination of hydrogen and chlorine is the industrial method for making hydrogen chloride gas. When dissolved in water, hydrochloric acid is formed. This acid has many important uses in the laboratory and industry.

(d) Hydrogenation Reactions

The hydrogenation of oils is an important use of hydrogen. For example, cotton-seed and soya bean oils are combined with hydrogen to produce the more desirable solid shortening, oleomargarine, and fats. Nickel is used as a catalyst in this reaction.

$$\text{Cottonseed or soya bean oil} + H_2 \xrightarrow{\text{Ni catalyst}} \text{solid fat}$$

The hydrogenation of carbon monoxide is used to make methanol, a raw material used in the making of plastics. A similar process is used in the petroleum industry to enrich gasoline.

$$CO_{(g)} + 2H_{2(g)} \rightarrow CH_3OH_{(l)}$$

(e) Reduction with Hydrogen

Reference was made in section 3.8 to the fact that hydrogen can remove oxygen from some oxides such as copper (II) oxide and iron (III) oxide:

$$CuO_{(s)} + H_{2(g)} \rightarrow H_2O_{(l)} + Cu_{(s)}$$

$$2Fe_2O_{3(s)} + 6H_{2(g)} \rightarrow 6H_2O_{(l)} + 4Fe_{(s)}$$

In the examples above, oxygen is removed from the oxides; they are said to be *reduced*. The hydrogen is termed the *reducing agent*. The hydrogen itself is being *oxidized* since it combines with oxygen. The oxides are called *oxidizing agents*. Oxidation-reduction will be discussed more fully in chapter 20.

(f) Chemical Test for Hydrogen

If the gas being tested burns when ignited and forms water only, it is hydrogen.

PART II — OXYGEN

13:6 Discovery and Occurrence of Oxygen

Oxygen was discovered independently by the young Swedish chemist Scheele and the English clergyman Priestley, about the year 1774. Scheele probably prepared the gas first, but Priestley was the first to report his discovery and to describe some of the properties of the gas.

Priestley discovered oxygen by heating a red powder called "calx of mercury" now known to be mercury (II) oxide, in apparatus of the type shown in Fig. 13.2. He collected the gas that was given off, and on testing it, found that a candle burned in the gas with a much brighter flame than in air.

Lavoisier, a contemporary of Priestley, studied the properties of the newly discovered gas. It was he who named the gas oxygen, meaning acid-former, because he erroneously thought that the properties of acids were due to its presence.

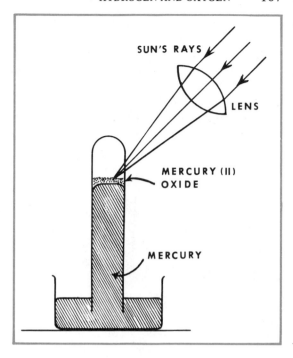

Fig. 13.2 *Priestley's method for preparing oxygen*

In studying the properties of oxygen, Lavoisier arrived at the conclusion that burning was a chemical change involving oxygen and a combustible substance. He also proved that no destruction of mass occurs in burning. The methods used by Lavoisier involved accurate weighings and calculations. His work marks the opening of a new era in chemistry. He is often called the father of experimental chemistry.

Oxygen is the most abundant of all the elements in the earth's crust. By weight it makes up nearly half of the earth's crust, including the oceans and the air. Air is 21% oxygen by volume and water is 88.8% oxygen by weight. The human body is about two-thirds by weight of oxygen in the combined state.

13:7 Preparation of Oxygen

(a) Decomposition of Mercury (II) Oxide

If a little mercury (II) oxide is placed in a pyrex

test tube and heated over a Bunsen flame, two results will be noted: droplets of mercury are seen to form on the inside of the tube and a gas evolves. If this gas is tested with a glowing splint, the latter bursts into flame. These results are due to the fact that mercury (II) oxide undergoes decomposition according to the following equation:

$$2HgO_{(s)} \rightarrow 2Hg_{(l)} + O_2\uparrow_{(g)}$$

This is essentially the method Priestley used when he discovered oxygen. Since mercury (II) oxide is an expensive substance and yields little oxygen, this is not an economical method of preparing oxygen in the laboratory.

(b) Decomposition of Potassium Chlorate

Potassium chlorate also gives off oxygen when heated. It is cheaper than mercury (II) oxide and contains a greater percentage of oxygen. As a result, potassium chlorate is often chosen as the source of oxygen in the laboratory preparation of the gas.

One of the interesting features of the decomposition of potassium chlorate by heat is that the presence of some manganese dioxide makes possible the liberation of the oxygen at lower temperatures than would be needed in its absence. When the experiment is over, the manganese dioxide is still present in the same quantity as at the beginning. Substances like manganese dioxide, which alter the speed of a chemical reaction without themselves being permanently changed, are called *catalysts*. Catalysis will be more fully discussed in Chapter 26.

Potassium chlorate is mixed with about one-quarter its weight of manganese dioxide and placed in a pyrex test tube fitted with a stopper and delivery tube, as shown in Fig. 13.3. Gas bottles are made ready to receive the gas by filling them with water and inverting them in a trough containing water.

The mixture of potassium chlorate and manganese dioxide is heated, and the first few bubbles of gas are allowed to escape, since they are not pure oxygen. Soon, the pure gas may be collected by leading the outlet of the delivery tube to the first gas bottle where the incoming oxygen displaces the water. The delivery tube is then led into the other bottles in turn. The equation for this reaction is:

$$\overset{MnO_2}{2KClO_{3(s)} \rightarrow 2KCl_{(s)} + 3O_2\uparrow_{(g)}}$$

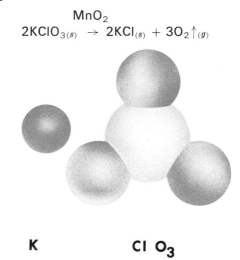

K   **Cl O₃**

Notice that the presence of the catalyst does not affect the equation.

(c) The Electrolysis of Water

See section 3:8.

(d) Distillation of Liquid Air

This is by far the cheapest method of preparing oxygen on a large scale. Air is first liquefied and its components are then separated by fractional distillation, taking advantage of their differ-

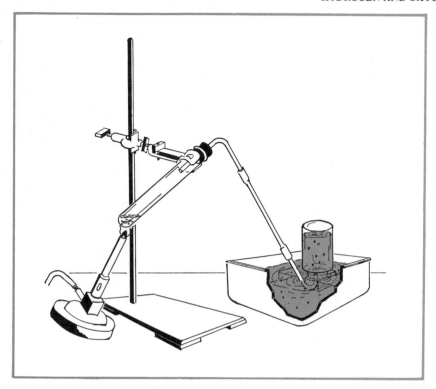

Fig. 13.3 *Preparation of oxygen from potassium chlorate*

ence in boiling points. The liquefaction of air and its subsequent distillation were discussed in section 8:7.

13:8 Physical Properties of Oxygen

Oxygen is a colorless, odorless, and tasteless gas. Its density is 1.43 grams per liter at 0 °C and one atmosphere of pressure. Oxygen is only slightly soluble in water; about 5 ml dissolve in 100 ml of water. The amount that does dissolve, however, is of great natural importance because it supports the respiration of nearly all life existing in water. The gills of a fish, for example, are so constructed that they may extract the dissolved oxygen from water.

13:9 Chemical Properties of Oxygen

Oxygen is only moderately active at lower temperatures but much more so at higher temper-

atures. In many of its reactions with other substances at higher temperatures, heat and light are produced. A chemical change involving the production of heat and/or light is often termed *combustion*. Oxygen supports combustion but does not burn itself. Indeed, the *test for oxygen* is the insertion of a glowing splint into the gas. If the splint bursts into flame, the gas is oxygen. No other odorless gas behaves in this way.

13:10 Oxides

Compounds of oxygen with another element are called *oxides*. These are further subdivided into oxides of metals and oxides of non-metals.

(a) Oxides of Metals

Oxygen combines with almost all metals. Three examples of metallic oxides are:

$$4Fe_{(s)} + 3O_{2(g)} \rightarrow 2Fe_2O_{3(s)}$$

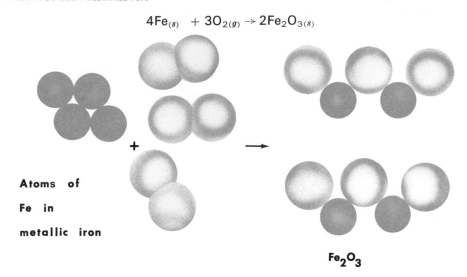

Atoms of

Fe in

metallic iron

Fe₂O₃

$$2Mg_{(s)} + O_{2(g)} \rightarrow 2MgO_{(s)}$$

Atoms of Mg

and O in solid

MgO

$$2Ca_{(s)} + O_{2(g)} \rightarrow 2CaO_{(s)}$$

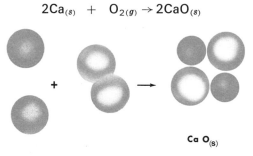

Ca O₍ₛ₎

The metals with which oxygen does not easily combine are called the *noble metals*, and these are gold, silver, and platinum.

The oxides of metals are called *basic anhydrides* (bases without water), because they react with water to form compounds known as *bases*. Some of these compounds contain hydrogen and oxygen combined to form what is known as the *hydroxide group*. In a base the hydroxide group is combined with a metal.

$$CaO_{(s)} + H_2O_{(l)} \rightarrow Ca(OH)_{2(aq)}$$

$$MgO_{(s)} + H_2O_{(l)} \rightarrow Mg(OH)_{2(aq)}$$

In solutions, bases may be recognized by their effect on natural dyes such as litmus, which turns blue on contact with a base. Bases have a bitter taste and feel slippery to the touch.

(b) Oxides of Non-Metals

Oxygen combines with non-metals, such as sulfur, carbon, and phosphorus, as shown by the following examples:

$$P_{4(s)} + 5O_{2(g)} \rightarrow P_4O_{10(s)}$$

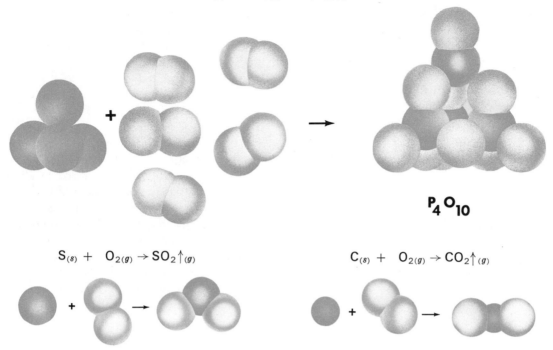

P_4O_{10}

$$S_{(s)} + O_{2(g)} \rightarrow SO_2\uparrow_{(g)}$$

$$C_{(s)} + O_{2(g)} \rightarrow CO_2\uparrow_{(g)}$$

The oxides of the non-metals are called *acidic anhydrides* (acids without water), because they unite with water to form *acids*.

$$P_4O_{10(s)} + 6H_2O_{(l)} \rightarrow 4H_3PO_{4(aq)}$$
(phosphoric acid)

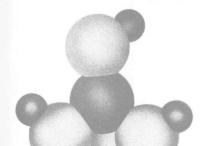

H_3PO_4

Acids in solution may be recognized by their effect on litmus, which turns red on contact with them. Acids have a sour taste and can neutralize

$$SO_{2(g)} + H_2O_{(l)} \rightarrow H_2SO_{3(aq)} \text{ (sulfurous acid)}$$

$$CO_{2(g)} + H_2O_{(l)} \rightarrow H_2CO_{3(aq)} \text{ (carbonic acid)}$$

bases. A more complete discussion of acids and bases will be given in Chapter 25.

Many carbon compounds, such as those found in coal, fuel gases, fuel oils, and gasoline, burn readily in air and even more vigorously in oxygen. Such compounds, which contain carbon, hydrogen, and possibly other elements, are called *organic compounds*. The complete combustion of many organic compounds produces water and carbon dioxide. For example:

$$CH_{4(g)} + 2O_{2(g)} \rightarrow CO_2\uparrow_{(g)} + 2H_2O_{(l)}$$
methane

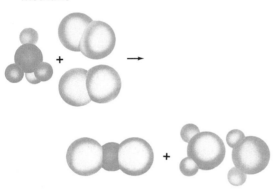

$$2C_2H_{2(g)} + 5O_{2(g)} \rightarrow 4CO_2\uparrow_{(g)} + 2H_2O_{(l)}$$
acetylene

acetylene

13:11   The Oxyacetylene Torch

If a stream of oxygen is mixed with acetylene and ignited, as in an oxyacetylene torch, the temperature reaches nearly 6000°F, and the carbon contained in the acetylene is all burned. The terrific heat produced by this torch can be used for cutting and welding metals. A great part of the commercial oxygen produced is used for this purpose.

13:12   The Bunsen Burner

The Bunsen burner works on a principle similar to that of the acetylene torch, but does not produce nearly so much heat. In the Bunsen burner, gas is admitted through a small jet to the mixing barrel and air enters at the base of the mixing barrel through adjustable holes. The mixture is ignited and burns at the top of the barrel.

If the air holes of a Bunsen burner are closed, the flame becomes luminous. This is due to glowing particles of carbon caused by the incomplete combustion of the gas. With a proper amount of air, the flame is non-luminous (gives off little light), and contains certain well-defined zones, as shown in Fig. 13.4. In the outer zone oxygen is abundant and combustion is complete; in the area of rapid combustion the flame may be luminous; the inner cone consists of unburned gas and air. The hottest part of the

Fig. 13.4   *Bunsen burner and flame*

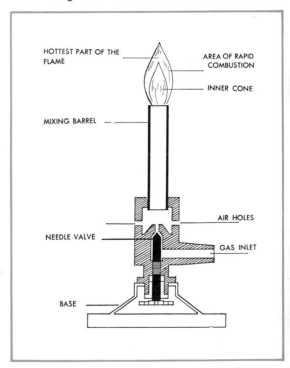

flame is just about the tip of the inner cone, where combustion is most intense.

The lowest temperature at which a material will start to burn and continue to burn is known as its *kindling temperature*. Any material must first be heated to its kindling temperature in order to burn. This may be illustrated by holding a wire gauze above a Bunsen burner, turning on the gas, and then igniting the gas above the gauze. It will be observed that the flame does not readily pass through the gauze. This is because the gauze conducts the heat away quickly from the base of the flame so that the gas beneath the gauze is not heated to its kindling temperature.

For combustion to occur, a combustible substance must be present together with a supporter of combustion. The latter may be the oxygen of the air. Thus the control of a fire is possible by:

(a) removing the fuel,
(b) cutting off the supply of the supporter of combustion,
(c) lowering the temperature below the kindling point.

13:13 Rapid and Slow Combustion

A vigorously burning fire is an example of rapid combustion. Respiration, on the other hand, illustrates slow combustion. In most cases combustion is a chemical reaction involving union with oxygen. For this reason, such reactions are called oxidations.*

Any reaction that instantaneously produces large quantities of gas and heat results in an *explosion*.

Hydrogen and oxygen, and natural gas and oxygen, are examples of explosive mixtures. If combustible materials in the air are very finely divided, they present so much surface to oxygen that combustion, once started, results in an explosion. The ignition of grain and coal dust particles suspended in the air of grain elevators and coal mines has resulted in many disastrous explosions and fires.

Many combustions occur slowly. In fact, it may not be noticeable that heat is being evolved. The rusting of iron and the drying of linseed oil are good examples of slow combustion. Rags containing oils that oxidize readily should never be bundled together. The heat produced in the oxidation of the oil cannot escape readily. Gradually the bundle of oily rags accumulates heat because of poor conductivity and poor ventilation until the kindling temperature of the oil is reached; then fire breaks out. Oily dust mops, cloths used in painting, damp hay, and large piles of soft coal are all potential sources of spontaneous combustion.

Respiration is a slow combustion of organic compounds in living tissue. Oxygen is used medically to help the body respire in cases of asphyxiation, severe injury, pneumonia, and cardiac conditions. The oxygen used medically generally contains about 7 per cent carbon dioxide to stimulate respiration.

Decay is a form of slow combustion of organic material brought about by bacteria or other organisms, such as moulds. The organisms digest the host material, and their respiration oxidizes it.

13:14 Exothermic and Endothermic Reactions

When heat is evolved in a reaction, the chemical change is known as *exothermic* (*exo* = outside, *therme* = heat). When, for example, oxygen combines with carbon, sulfur, iron, or magnesium, heat is given out; therefore the reactions are exothermic.

In other cases, heat must be added to make the reaction proceed. Such reactions are called *endothermic* (*endo* = within, *therme* = heat). The decomposition of potassium chlorate to

*The term oxidation has a more specific meaning discussed in Chapter 20.

oxygen and potassium chloride is an illustration of an endothermic reaction.

13:15   Ozone

You may have noticed that in the neighborhood of an electrical device, there is often a characteristic acrid odor. This odor is caused partly by a form of oxygen known as ozone. This is an example of the ability of an element to exist in more than one form in the same state. This property, which is common to many of the elements, is called *allotropy*. The forms are called *allotropic forms;* ozone is an allotropic form of oxygen.

Ordinary oxygen consists of two atoms of oxygen bonded together in the molecule. Ozone consists of molecules with three atoms of oxygen. The formula for ozone is O_3. Ozone may be prepared by passing an electrical discharge through air or oxygen. Ultraviolet light also produces some ozone in the atmosphere, mostly at high altitudes.

Ozone has about the same chemical properties as oxygen, except that it is more active. It decomposes into ordinary oxygen on standing:

$$2O_{3(g)} \rightarrow 3O_2\uparrow_{(g)}$$

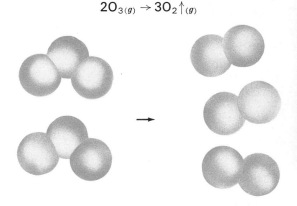

Ozone is a good bleaching and disinfecting agent, and it is sometimes used in very small amounts to purify water. It should be noted, however, that ozone is poisonous, and excessive amounts must be avoided.

QUESTIONS

1. Who first studied hydrogen in detail? Who named this gas?

2. Write a note on the occurrence of hydrogen.

3. What would be a plausible reason for the presence of only a small amount of hydrogen in the atmosphere?

4. (a) List the different methods of preparing hydrogen.
   (b) Write an equation to illustrate each method.

5. What weight of zinc is required to produce 56.0 liters of hydrogen measured at STP?

6. What weight of sodium hydroxide can be obtained by the reaction of 60.0 grams of sodium on water?

7. Complete the equations for the reactions that take place between each of the following pairs of reactants:
   (a) $Ca_{(s)} + H_2O_{(l)} \rightarrow$
   (b) $Mg_{(s)} + HCl_{(aq)} \rightarrow$
   (c) $Al_{(s)} + H_2SO_{4(aq)} \rightarrow$

8. Define the displacement series.

9. Which of the following reactions will occur? When a reaction is predicted, complete and balance it:

(a) $Fe_{(s)}$ + $CuSO_{4(aq)} \rightarrow$
(b) $Li_{(s)}$ + $H_2O_{(l)} \rightarrow$
(c) $Cu_{(s)}$ + $HCl_{(aq)} \rightarrow$
(d) $Mg_{(s)}$ + $H_2SO_{4(aq)} \rightarrow$
(e) $K_{(s)}$ + $H_2O_{(l)} \rightarrow$

10. What is the chemical test for hydrogen?

11. Find the volume of hydrogen that combines with 10.0 liters of chlorine to form hydrogen chloride. What volume of hydrogen chloride is formed? (All gases are measured at the same conditions.)

12. (a) Calculate the volume of hydrogen, measured at STP, which combines with 0.5 mole of nitrogen to form ammonia.
    (b) Find the volume of ammonia formed at STP.

13. (a) What volume of hydrogen is needed to combine with 3.0 liters of oxygen to form water?
    (b) If the 3.0 liters of oxygen are measured at 110°C, and this temperature is maintained after the reaction, find the volume of steam formed.

14. Hydrogen can remove oxygen from hot copper (II) oxide. In the light of this fact, which of the following is a correct conclusion?
    (A) Hydrogen is an oxidizing agent.
    (B) Oxidation need not be accompanied by reduction.
    (C) Hydrogen has a great affinity for oxygen.
    (D) The density of hydrogen is smaller than that of oxygen.

15. How many liters of hydrogen measured at STP are required to reduce completely 2.0 moles of copper (II) oxide, CuO?

16. Give an account of the discovery of oxygen.

17. Who named oxygen? Why was it so called?

18. Write a note on the occurrence of oxygen.

19. List the methods for the preparation of oxygen described in this chapter.

20. What is observed when mercury (II) oxide is heated in a test tube? Write the equation representing this reaction.

21. Determine the percentage of oxygen in (a) mercury (II) oxide; (b) potassium chlorate.

22. What weight of potassium chlorate is required to produce 100 grams of oxygen?

23. What is the test for oxygen?

24. What is a *catalyst*?

25. Contrast the properties of hydrogen and oxygen with regard to the following properties: (a) physical state; (b) color; (c) odor; (d) density; (e) solubility in water; (f) rate of diffusion.

26. Define the term *oxide*.

27. (a) Why are the oxides of metals called "basic anhydrides"?
    (b) Why are the oxides of the non-metals called "acidic anhydrides"?

28. List three properties of acids and bases.

29. Write the equations for the combination of oxygen with: (a) magnesium; (b) calcium; (c) iron; (d) sulfur; (e) carbon; (f) phosphorus. Give the name of the product formed in each case.

30. Write the equation for the combination of water with (a) magnesium oxide; (b) calcium oxide; (c) sulfur dioxide; (d) carbon dioxide. Give the name of the product formed in each case.

31. Write the equations for the complete combustion of methane, CH_4, and of ethane, C_2H_6.

32. Define the terms *kindling temperature* and *combustion*.

33. How can the luminous (yellow) flame of a Bunsen burner be made non-luminous?

34. Why does pouring cold water on a burning building help put out the fire?

35. What is the purpose of wrapping a person whose clothes are on fire in a fire blanket?

36. Define *spontaneous combustion* and give some examples of it.

37. How may rusting be prevented?

38. List as many uses of oxygen as you can.

39. Which of the following is an example of an exothermic reaction?
    (A) the decomposition of mercury (II) oxide;
    (B) the electrolysis of water;
    (C) the decomposition of potassium chlorate;
    (D) the reaction of sodium with water.

40. Define *allotropy*.

41. How may ozone be prepared?

42. How is ozone different from oxygen?

CHAPTER

14 Chemistry and Electrons

14:1 Unanswered Questions

During the first 150 years of scientific chemistry, from about 1750 to 1900, much information about elements and compounds was collected. A number of laws and theories were proposed, but on the whole, many questions could not be answered, such as: Why do atoms combine? Why are certain elements similar to each other? What is an electric current? How does an electric current have the ability to cause chemical change? What is the relationship between matter and electricity?

The answers to these and many other questions came with the discovery that atoms contain electrons. It is really these electrified particles which are responsible for the properties and behavior of the atoms. Even the electric current was seen to be a stream of electrons. How did this knowledge come about?

14:2 Static and Current Electricity

About 2,500 years ago, the Greeks discovered that when amber was rubbed with cloth it attracted small pieces of cotton and straw. The force of attraction was called electricity after the Greek name for amber, *electron*. Later it was found that whenever two different substances are rubbed together, both acquire electrical charges. Such charges are referred to as *static electricity*.

We can show that electrical charges are of two kinds. If we suspend a glass rod rubbed with silk, it is repelled when a second rod similarly charged is brought near (Fig. 14.1).

Fig. 14.1 *Electrostatic attraction and repulsion*

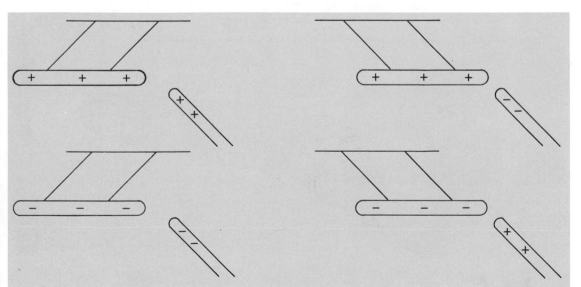

However, if a hard rubber rod is rubbed with fur and held near the suspended glass rod, the latter is attracted. Two charged rubber rods repel each other. We can thus formulate a simple law: *like charges repel while unlike charges attract.*

Around 1750, Benjamin Franklin, an American statesman and scientist, studied the nature of electricity. He suggested that the two kinds of electricity observed be called *positive* and *negative.*

Then about 1800, Volta and Galvani, two Italian scientists, learned how to produce a continuous electrical current. This was a major discovery, not only in the science of electricity but also in the history of man. With the discovery of current electricity, man's level of knowledge in many fields and, indeed, his very way of life began to change rapidly.

Later, it was shown that the electrical charges are due to the particles that make up the atoms themselves. The negative charges arc due to electrons and the positive charges are due to protons. *Electric current* is the flow of electrons

along a metal conductor such as a copper wire or the flight of electrons from the cathode to the anode in a vacuum tube. By knowing the properties of electrons, we learn how to control their motion and how to harness their energy. With the aid of this knowledge we build the hundreds of useful electric appliances so familar to us.

14:3   The Properties of Electrons

The properties of electrons were first studied in the cathode tube from which the television screen is developed. In the picture tube of the television set, electrons travel from a cathode located at the far end, towards an anode placed near the screen. Their motion, controlled through their charge, forms the picture as they strike the screen (Fig. 14.2).

The cathode tube is a glass vacuum tube fitted with two electrodes. A high voltage is applied to the electrodes to give energy to the electrons as they fly from the cathode to the anode; hence the name, *cathode tube.* Thomson, an English

Fig. 14.2   *The television picture tube*
The television screen is a modified cathode ray tube, in which direct evidence was first obtained that an electric current is a flow of electrons and that electrons are present in all atoms.

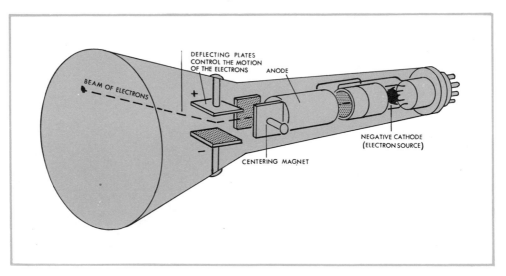

physicist, and other scientists, found that electrons had the following properties:

1. They carry a negative charge.

2. Their mass is very small. The mass of the hydrogen atom is about 1840 times as great as that of the electron.

3. They are present in the atoms of all the elements.

14:4 The Voltaic Cell

The voltaic cell consists of two different metal electrodes, such as copper and zinc, immersed in an acid solution. A wire is attached to each electrode so that they can make contact. When they do, an electric current flows through the wires (Fig. 14.3).

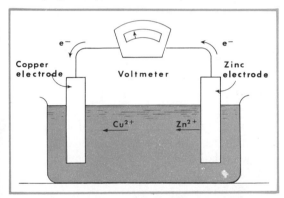

Fig. 14.3 *A simple voltaic cell*

It is interesting to examine the voltaic cell in the light of the idea that the electric current is the flow of electrons.

As a result of chemical action between the acid and the metals, electrons flow through the metal wire from the zinc electrode to the copper electrode. The circuit is completed by the movement of the ions through the solution between the plates.

14:5 Some Electric Terms and Units

In the voltaic cell, the driving force is the difference with which the atoms of the electrodes attract electrons. The driving force behind the flow of current is called the *voltage* which can be defined as the energy with which electric charge is conducted throught a circuit.

An amount of electric charge could be reported as a number of electrons. However, it is customary to express a quantity of charge in coulombs. One *coulomb* represents 6.24×10^{18} electrons.

The intensity of the electric current, that is, the rate of flow, is measured in amperes. The intensity of the current is one *ampere* when one coulomb passes a given point in the circuit in one second.

Table 14.1 presents a comparison between the flow of water in a pipe and the flow of electricity in a conductor. Pressure must be available to force a certain amount of water through a pipe in a given time. Similarly, a definite amount of electricity can be forced through a conductor in a given time only if a sufficient voltage is available.

TABLE 14.1		
Analogy Between a Water System and an Electric Current		
Quantity Measured	Units used with Water	Units used with Electricity
Amount	gallons	coulombs
Rate of flow	gallons/second	amperes (coulombs/ second)
Driving force (pressure)	pounds/inch²	volts

14:6 Electrons in Electrolysis

The passage of a current through a solution can cause a chemical reaction. This process is termed *electrolysis*. We have already seen one such reaction, namely the electrolysis of water (Chapter 3).

Electroplating is an important application of electrolysis. Let us consider silver plating, a process used to cover the surface of a metallic article with a thin coat of silver. The article to be plated is connected to the negative terminal of the battery and a strip of metallic silver is connected to the positive terminal. These two electrodes (the article and the strip) are immersed into a silver salt solution (Fig. 14.4). When a current is passed through the solution, silver atoms from the silver strip give up electrons and enter the solution as silver ions:

$$Ag^0{}_{(s)} \rightarrow Ag^+{}_{(aq)} + 1e^-$$

These electrons are "pumped" by the battery through the external circuit to the spoon where they are taken up by the silver ions of the solution. Each silver ion gains one electron to become a neutral atom of silver:

$$Ag^+{}_{(aq)} + 1e^- \rightarrow Ag^0{}_{(s)}$$

It is an experimental fact that to deposit 108 g of silver, the gram-atomic mass, or the mole of silver, requires 96,500 coulombs. Since the mole of silver is the Avogadro number of

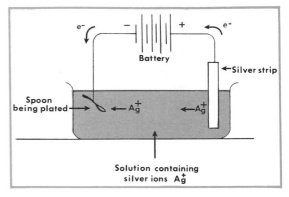

Fig. 14.4 *Silver plating*

silver atoms or ions, and since each ion of silver requires one electron to be electrolyzed, therefore, one Avogadro number of electrons is required for the deposit of 108 g of silver atoms. Thus one Avogadro number of electrons is present in 96,500 coulombs.

14:7   The Charge on the Electron

Millikan, an American scientist, is credited with the first accurate determination of the Avogadro number. A simplified version of his apparatus is shown in Fig. 14.5. His general procedure was as follows: he sprayed droplets of oil between charged plates of an electrical apparatus. By

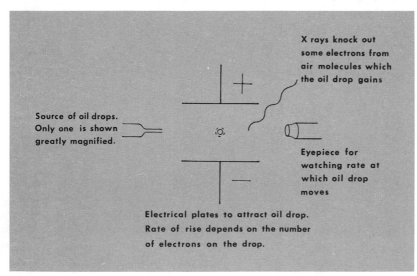

Fig. 14.5 *Millikan's oil drop experiment*

watching their rate of fall, he determined their mass. He charged the upper plate of the apparatus positively and the lower one negatively while at the same time, he placed a negative charge on the oil droplets. Thereupon the droplets rose to the upper plate. From the rate of rising he calculated the charge on the droplets.

For a specific measurement, he focused on one droplet. He first determined its mass. He then caused it to gain a negative charge and observed the rate at which it rose to the upper plate. From these data he calculated the charge on the single oil droplet. He found that the charges on the oil droplets were always multiples of the same fundamental value. This he calculated to be 1.60×10^{-19} coulombs. When charged, the oil droplets acquire one, or two, or three, or some other whole number, of these units. No exception to this rule was found in over 2000 experiments in more than 5 years by Millikan and his students. Such experiments have been repeated many times since by other scientists, and the results are confirmed. Hence the conclusion that this value must be the charge of one single electron.

$$1e^- = 1.60 \times 10^{-19} \text{ coulombs}$$

14:8 How the Avogadro Number was First Found

To find the Avogadro number, we use the fact that the charge on one Avogadro number of electrons is 96,500 coulombs. If N is the Avogadro number, we may write an equation:

$$N \times e^- = 96,500$$

$$N = \frac{96,500}{e^-}$$

Since $e^- = 1.60 \times 10^{-19}$

we have $N = \frac{96,500}{1.60 \times 10^{-19}}$

$$= \frac{9.65 \times 10^4}{1.60 \times 10^{-19}}$$

$$= 6.02 \times 10^{23}$$

This calculation represents one of the most important methods for determining the Avogadro number.

14:9 X rays

About the same time that Thomson was studying cathode rays and electrons (1893-5), Roentgen, a German physicist, discovered an unusual form of radiation. Using higher voltages than usual, thereby producing a flow of electrons of high energy, Roentgen found that rays coming out of his apparatus were able to pass through paper, wood, and even flesh, but not as readily through metal and bone. He named this radiation *X rays*.

X rays resemble light in that they are electrically neutral and travel at the same speed as light. They differ from light by having a shorter wave length and therefore greater frequency and energy. They are important in surgery, medicine, and industry.

The fact that X rays originate in the motion of electrons in the atoms is of great importance to the scientist. Indeed, the wave length and the frequency of the X rays emitted by an element are important clues to the number of electrons in the atom of that element (Chapter 15).

14:10 Radioactivity

Shortly after the discovery of X rays came an even more dramatic disclosure. In 1896, the French physicist Becquerel found that a certain mineral containing uranium gave off extremely powerful radiations even without the application of any energy. Marie Curie, a Polish student working with Becquerel, investigated this phenomenon further and called it *radioactivity*. Working with her husband Pierre Curie, she succeeded in isolating two new elements, radium and polonium, that were even more radioactive than uranium.

Lord Rutherford, a New Zealand physicist, while working at McGill University in Montreal, investigated the radiations emitted by the radioactive elements. He found that three different rays were being emitted. One ray was a stream of positively charged helium atoms, later to be identified as the nuclei of helium atoms. This beam was called the *alpha ray*, and the nuclei of the helium atoms were termed *alpha particles*. Another ray was a stream of electrons; this beam was called the *beta ray*. The third ray, called the *gamma ray*, was identified as powerful short-wave X rays. In view of the radiations emitted by the radioactive materials, Rutherford came to the conclusion that *in radioactivity certain atoms were in the process of breaking up*. As they broke up they emitted the various particles observed and thereby changed to atoms of another element.

In the course of his further work on radioactivity, particularly on alpha particles, Rutherford came upon evidence that helped him to form a theory about the structure of the atom.

The discovery of radioactivity in 1896 was the dawn of the nuclear age in which we now live. Similarly, the structure of the atom, suggested by the evidence from radioactivity, marks the beginning of the modern period in chemistry and physics.

Fig. 14.6   *Chemists with molecular model*

Courtesy Canadian Industries Limited

QUESTIONS

1. What is the origin of the word electron?

2. (a) What is *static electricity*?
   (b) How can static electricity be produced?

3. (a) What two kinds of electrical charges can be given to a body?
   (b) State the law concerning the attraction and repulsion of electrical charges.

4. What are the fundamental differences between positively and negatively charged bodies?

5. A glass rod is rubbed with silk and becomes positively charged. Do you think that the silk also aquires a charge? If so, what would be the nature of this charge?

6. What produces the image seen on a TV screen?

7. List three properties displayed by electrons.

8. What transformation of energy takes place in a voltaic cell?

9. Describe the mechanism of electric conduction of a voltaic cell, pointing out the difference between conduction in the wires and in the solution.

10. Distinguish between the terms *coulomb* and *ampere*.

11. Calculate the number of electrons passing through a given point in a wire in which the current is 5.0 amperes.

12. How does a voltaic cell differ from an electrolytic cell?

13. When fused sodium chloride, NaCl, is electrolyzed, metallic sodium forms at the negative electrode and chlorine gas forms at the positive electrode. Draw a simplified diagram representing this electrolysis and write the ionic equations for the reactions that take place at the anode and at the cathode.

14. What mass of silver can be electrolyzed by the passage of 24,125 coulombs?

15. What mass of silver can be electroplated by a current of 3.0 amperes passing through a solution for one hour?

16. (a) How many electrons are needed for the electrolysis of one copper ion, Cu^{2+}?
    (b) How many electrons are required for the electrolysis of 1 mole of copper ions?
    (c) Your answer in (b) represents how many coulombs?

17. Why is the charge on the oil droplet in Millikan's experiment always a certain value or some simple multiple of it?

18. How were X rays discovered?

19. What are some characteristics of X rays?

20. What is *radioactivity*?

21. Name three types of rays emitted as a result of radioactivity and give the principal characteristics of each.

22. What would you consider to be the most important result of the study of radioactivity?

15 The Structure of the Atom

15:1   The Nuclear Atom

How do electrons, protons, and neutrons make up the atom and how many of each kind of these fundamental particles are present in the atom? Where are they located? How are they arranged? These questions were first answered by Rutherford, Moseley, and Bohr. So important is atomic structure in the study of chemistry that ideas about it were introduced as early as Chapter 5. These ideas will now be developed in greater detail.

As mentioned in the last chapter, radioactive atoms are in the process of disintegrating. In this process, some radioactive atoms emit positively charged alpha particles, which are the nuclei of helium atoms. Rutherford wished to determine how alpha particles pass through metal. In 1911 he performed an experiment in which alpha particles from a radioactive source were directed against a thin sheet of gold foil. The alpha particles were detected by means of a screen coated with zinc sulfide, placed around the gold foil. A zinc sulfide screen emits light when struck by an alpha particle, thus showing their whereabouts (Fig. 15.1).

This experiment showed that most of the

Fig. 15.1 *Rutherford's experiment on the scattering of alpha particles*

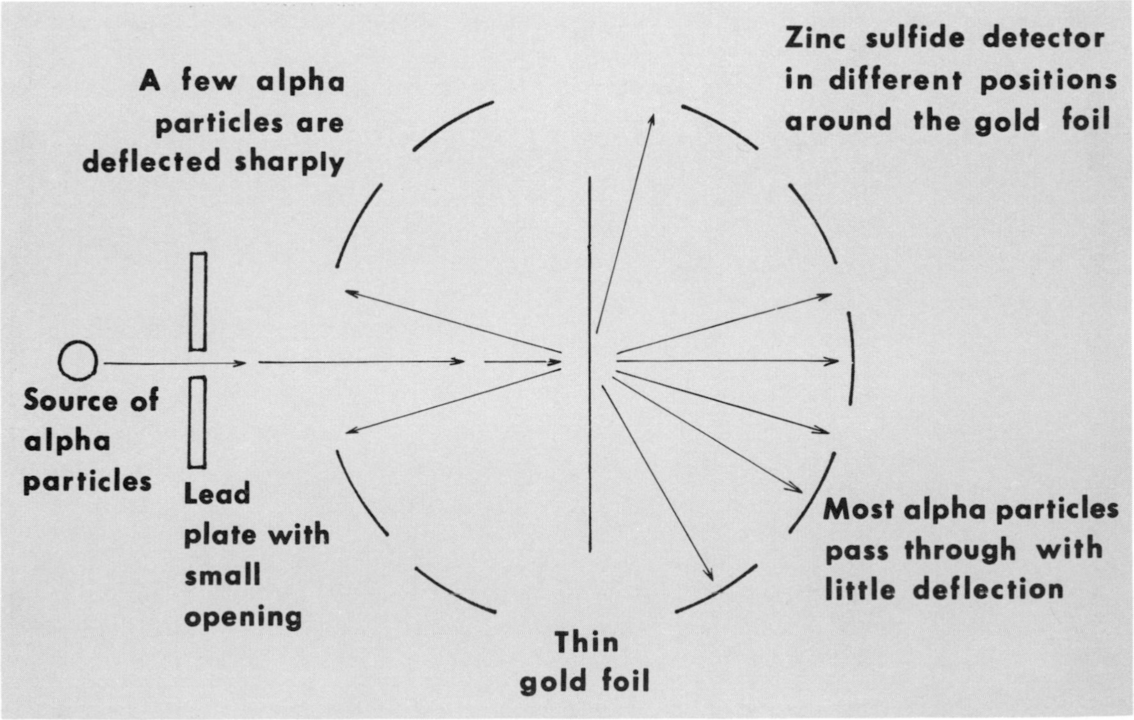

A few alpha particles are deflected sharply

Zinc sulfide detector in different positions around the gold foil

Source of alpha particles

Lead plate with small opening

Most alpha particles pass through with little deflection

Thin gold foil

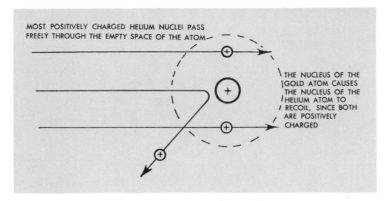

MOST POSITIVELY CHARGED HELIUM NUCLEI PASS
FREELY THROUGH THE EMPTY SPACE OF THE ATOM

THE NUCLEUS OF THE
GOLD ATOM CAUSES
THE NUCLEUS OF THE
HELIUM ATOM TO
RECOIL, SINCE BOTH
ARE POSITIVELY
CHARGED

Fig. 15.2 *Diagram to explain how alpha particles were scattered*

alpha particles passed through the gold foil. A few, however, were reflected back into the direction from which they came – a surprising result. Rutherford described it by saying that it was "almost as if you had fired a 15-inch shell at a piece of tissue paper and it came back and hit you". There was only one possible explanation for the phenomenon: the atom must be largely empty space through which most of the alpha particles could pass easily, but a small heavy nucleus with a positive charge must be present in the centre of the atom. The repulsion between the positive charges on the alpha particle and the atomic nucleus caused the scattering of the alpha particles that was seen (Fig. 15.2).

The idea that the atom consists of a small, dense, and positively charged nucleus surrounded by electrons at relatively great distances is known as the *theory of the nuclear atom*.

15:2   Atomic Numbers

From the scattering of alpha particles, Rutherford was able to prove that the atom consists of a nucleus of positive charge surrounded by electrons, but he did not know how many electrons were present in the atoms of any particular element. This number, called the *atomic number* of the element, was determined by Moseley in 1912. Moseley's method was based on the fact that when an atom is bombarded by high energy cathode rays or electrons, it emits X rays (Fig. 15.3). Moseley found that the frequency of the X rays emitted by an element was related to its atomic number. Since the frequency of the X rays could be found experimentally, the atomic number of an element could be calculated from experimental data.

The number of electrons in an atom is important but their arrangement is even more significant for chemistry. Evidence about the arrangement of electrons in atoms was first deduced from the study of the spectra of the elements.

15:3   Evidence for Electron Shells or Energy Levels

It has been known for a long time that atoms can absorb or emit light and other forms of radiant energy. When energy is introduced by heating the element to a high temperature, by radiation, or by electrical energy, the atoms absorb energy. When the source of energy is removed, the atoms emit the energy they have absorbed. In some cases, emission occurs while the energy source is still present, as in the case of the light emitted when a high voltage is

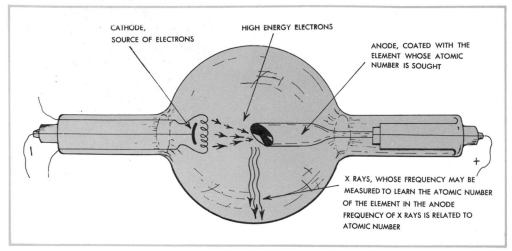

Fig. 15.3   *X rays and atomic numbers*

applied to carbon electrodes, producing an electric arc (Fig. 15.4).

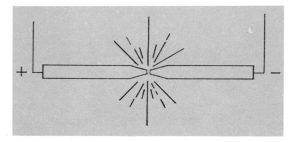

Fig. 15.4   *Electric arc producing light and other forms of radiant energy*

A familiar form of such radiation is light. The light that any atom emits is called its *spectrum*, and the study of this phenomenon is known as *spectroscopy*. The instrument used in spectroscopy, called a *spectroscope*, separates light into its component wave lengths. The different wave lengths are then focused as lines on a screen or a film (Fig. 15.5). This is the reason for the name, the *line spectrum*.

Each line corresponds to light of a certain wave length emitted by a particular element.

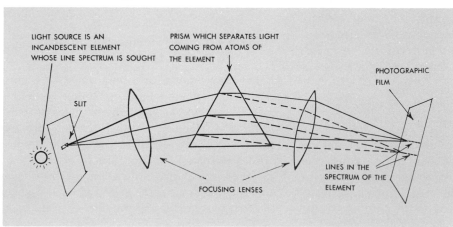

Fig. 15.5   *The line spectrum*

OPTICAL SPECTRA

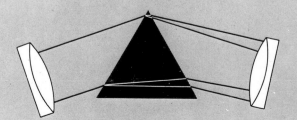

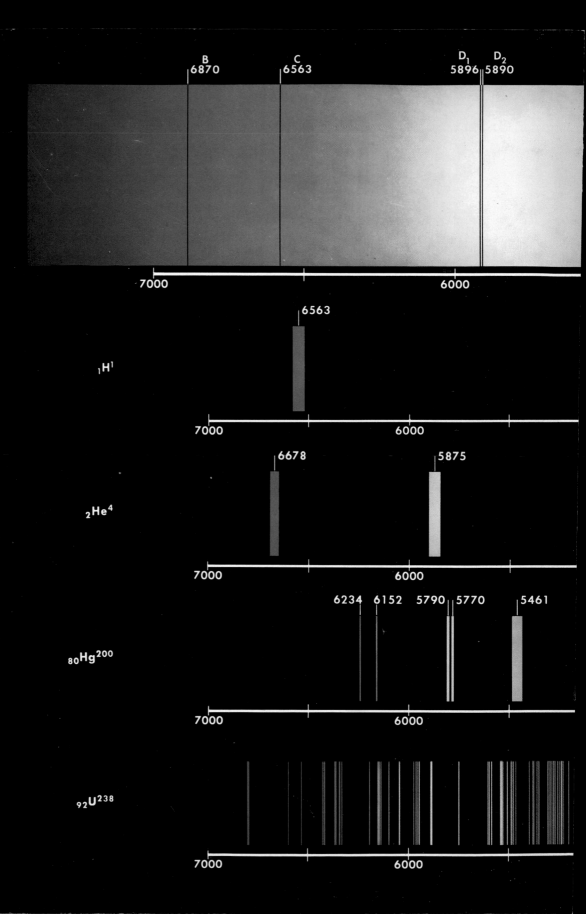

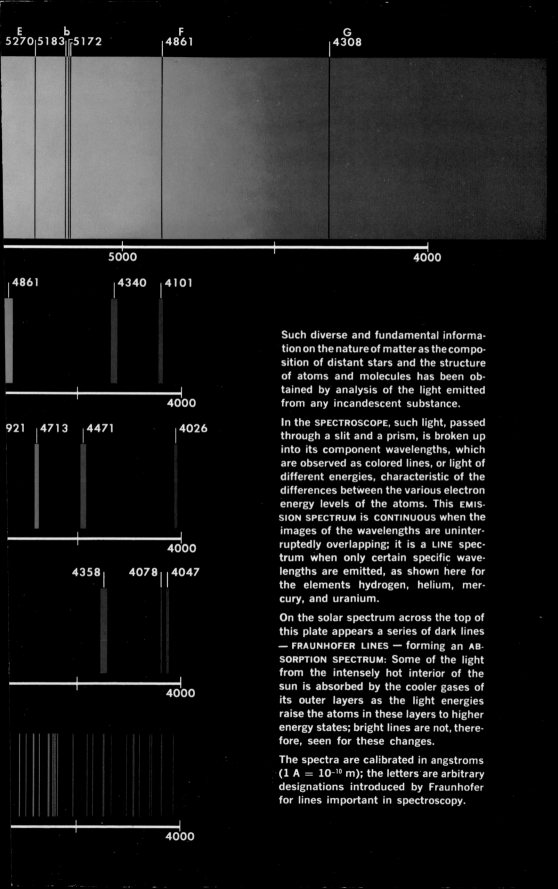

E 5270 | b 5183 | 5172 | F 4861 | G 4308

5000   4000

4861   4340   4101

4000

921 | 4713 | 4471   4026

4000

4358   4078 | 4047

4000

4000

Such diverse and fundamental information on the nature of matter as the composition of distant stars and the structure of atoms and molecules has been obtained by analysis of the light emitted from any incandescent substance.

In the SPECTROSCOPE, such light, passed through a slit and a prism, is broken up into its component wavelengths, which are observed as colored lines, or light of different energies, characteristic of the differences between the various electron energy levels of the atoms. This EMISSION SPECTRUM is CONTINUOUS when the images of the wavelengths are uninterruptedly overlapping; it is a LINE spectrum when only certain specific wavelengths are emitted, as shown here for the elements hydrogen, helium, mercury, and uranium.

On the solar spectrum across the top of this plate appears a series of dark lines — FRAUNHOFER LINES — forming an ABSORPTION SPECTRUM: Some of the light from the intensely hot interior of the sun is absorbed by the cooler gases of its outer layers as the light energies raise the atoms in these layers to higher energy states; bright lines are not, therefore, seen for these changes.

The spectra are calibrated in angstroms (1 A = 10^{-10} m); the letters are arbitrary designations introduced by Fraunhofer for lines important in spectroscopy.

Spectroscopists have learned how to measure the wave lengths of spectral lines with great precision. They have established beyond doubt that every element absorbs and emits only certain wave lengths.

A familiar example of the emission of a particular color or wave length of light is the reddish light of neon. The gas is placed at low pressure in glass tubes of desired shape. When voltage is applied, thereby introducing electrical energy, the gas glows, giving off the red color of the neon sign.

Spectroscopists studied the line spectra of atoms with the hope of understanding how atoms can radiate light.

15:4   Light and Quanta

What is light? It is a form of radiant energy. Other forms of radiant energy include X rays, infrared rays, radio waves, and microwaves used for television reception. All forms of radiant energy travel in a wavelike manner. Their waves differ in size, or *wave length*, and in the number of waves per second, or *frequency*, but all travel at the same velocity of 186,000 miles per second. The colors of light have different wave lengths and frequencies. Red has the longest wave length and violet has the shortest.

It had always been assumed without question that energy could be present in any amounts in any system. This also meant that energy could be added to, or removed from, a system in any amounts – large, small, or intermediate. The older idea about energy was that it was continuous. But is light continuous? To Bohr, the fact that the elements absorb or emit light of only certain wave lengths was a contradiction of the "continuous" nature of light. He maintained instead, that atoms absorb or emit light and other forms of radiation in units. These units may be imagined as packets of energy such that the atoms of an element absorb them and emit them entirely or else not at all.

If they are not the right "size", the atom must simply pass them up.

The units of radiation that an atom absorbs are called *quanta* (singular, *quantum*). The quantum theory maintains that when atoms, molecules, ions, or electrons absorb or emit energy they do so only in quanta. This theory had been proposed to explain other phenomena than spectral lines, but it seemed to Bohr that a combination of the ideas of the nuclear atom and the quantum theory might explain how electrons are distributed in atoms.

Waves and Particles

In suggesting that radiation was a stream of quanta, the new theory did not reject entirely the older idea that radiation was also of the wave form; rather the quantum theory brought these two aspects of radiation together by proving that the size of a quantum of energy was proportional to the *frequency* of the radiation. Frequency is a characteristic of wave motion, representing the number of waves per second.

15:5   The Quantum Theory Applied to Atomic Structure

How might electrons be distributed in atoms so that they absorb or emit energy as quanta? To answer this question, Bohr suggested that the electrons must be in orbits of a certain size and moving at a certain speed. The electron would then have a certain energy. If it absorbed energy, the electron would move to an orbit of higher energy further from the nucleus. If it lost energy, the electron would move to another orbit nearer the nucleus.

Thus the quantum theory led to the idea of orbits. The electrons in the orbits had certain amounts of energy, or, in other words, the electrons were said to be at certain *energy levels*. Radiation was due to electrons changing from a higher energy level to a lower one.

Bohr applied these ideas to the hydrogen atom and derived mathematically what the frequency of the radiation emitted by hydrogen should be. This was a great triumph. The new theory succeeded in explaining a difficult phenomenon, which the older idea, that light was continuous, could not even begin to explain.

Unfortunately, however, Bohr's theory did not work as well with elements whose atoms are more complex than those of hydrogen.

The New Quantum Theory

Some scientists believed that Bohr's theory became unwieldy with atoms larger than hydrogen because it assumed too much about the electron. The Bohr theory maintained that the electron, supposedly a particle, is at a certain place in the atom and moves at a certain speed. Perhaps, suggested these scientists, the best to be hoped for is an account of where the electrons of any atom or molecule are most likely to be.

As an analogy, the traffic department of a large city could not be expected to know where each individual car is at any moment. Nor is this necessary. It is more concerned with the flow of traffic and the points where traffic is likely to be heaviest at certain times.

Fortunately, to describe the approximate whereabouts of electrons in atoms and molecules proved easier than to establish the exact location of any particular one. It turned out that the location of electrons can be depicted graphically in terms of waves and numerically in terms of simple numbers, called *quantum numbers*, soon to be discussed.

As a result of theoretical and experimental work, a picture of the structure of the atom has been developed which explains chemical phenomena in a satisfactory way.

15:6 Energy Levels of Atoms and Electrons

Electrons revolving about the nucleus of an atom possess energy because of their motion and position. For the atom to be stable, that is, for the electrons to remain in the outer shells of the atom, the energy of the electron must correspond to certain values. These are the energy levels of the atom itself or of the electrons within it.

When the atom has the least amount of energy it can have, it is said to be in its *ground state*. In this state the atom may absorb energy from light or radiation. When it does, an electron in the atom goes from one energy level to a higher one. The atom is then in an *excited state*. The energy absorbed by an electron when passing from a lower energy level to a higher one is termed a *quantum of energy*. An atom emits the same quantum of energy when an electron falls back to the lower energy level.

15:7 The Four Quantum Numbers

The energy levels of an electron may be described by four numbers, called the quantum numbers. Of these, three are whole numbers, and they are related to one another in the values they may assume. The fourth is either $+\frac{1}{2}$ or $-\frac{1}{2}$.

The First Quantum Number n

This corresponds to the energy level in which the electron is found. It may have values of 1, 2, 3 ... and up. Thus, if a given electron is in the first or lowest energy level possible within an atom, its *first quantum number* has the value of one ($n = 1$). Similarly, for the second possible energy level, n has the value of two ($n = 2$), and so on (Fig. 15.6).

The Second Quantum Number l

An electron may go through different types of motion at a given energy level. Such differences necessitate the second quantum number *l*. The shape of the electron cloud is inferred from the second quantum number *l*.

The higher the energy level, the greater is the variety of electronic motion. Different electronic motions may be expressed by giving different values to *l*, according to this simple

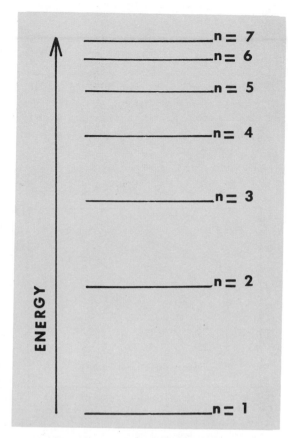

Fig. 15.6   *The energy levels in an atom*

rule: *l* may have values of 0, 1, 2, . . . up to n − 1.

An electron whose energy level contains a zero value for *l* is called an *s electron*. An electron whose energy level contains the value of *l* = 1 is called a *p electron*. When *l* = 2, the electron is termed *d*, and when *l* = 3, the electron is termed f.*

The second quantum number *l* also shows how many sublevels there are in each electron shell. Indeed, the term *sublevel* may be defined as a number of orbitals (Chapter 5) having the same value for *l*. When *l* has only 1 value, there is only 1 sublevel; when *l* has 2 values, there are two sublevels and so forth (Table 15.1).

The Third Quantum Number m

As the atom becomes larger, the electronic motion might be about different axes. Such differences have been revealed in the spectra of atoms taken in a strong magnetic field. These differences in orientation are described by the third quantum number m which may have values of *l*, *l* − 1, *l* − 2, . . . 0 . . . −(*l* − 2), −(*l* − 1), −*l*.

The *third quantum number m* shows how many orbitals there are in each sublevel. When m has only one value, there is only one orbital in the sublevel. When m has three values there are three orbitals in the sublevel and so on (Table 15.2 and Fig. 15.7).

The Fourth Quantum Number s

Finally, all electrons spin on their axes and are

TABLE 15.1				
The Energy Sublevels				
The value of n	The value of *l*	The number of values of *l*	The number of of sublevels	The names of the sublevels
1	0	one	one	s
2	0 and 1	two	two	s and p
3	0, 1, and 2	three	three	s, p, and d
4	0, 1, 2, and 3	four	four	s, p, d, and f

*The terms s, p, d, and f originated with the earlier spectroscopic notation for sharp, principal, diffuse, and fundamental. No significance is attached to this connection to-day.

TABLE 15.2

The Number of Orbitals in Each Sublevel

Value of l	Name of Sublevel	Values of m	Number of Values of m	Number of Orbitals	Name of Orbitals
0	s	0	one	one	s
1	p	1, 0, −1,	three	three	p
2	d	2, 1, 0, −1, −2,	five	five	d
3	f	3, 2, 1, 0, −1, −2, −3	seven	seven	f

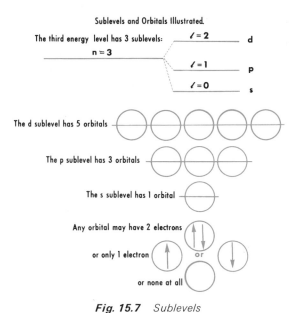

Sublevels and Orbitals Illustrated.

The third energy level has 3 sublevels: $l = 2$ d

n = 3

$l = 1$ p

$l = 0$ s

The d sublevel has 5 orbitals

The p sublevel has 3 orbitals

The s sublevel has 1 orbital

Any orbital may have 2 electrons

or only 1 electron   or

or none at all

Fig. 15.7   *Sublevels*

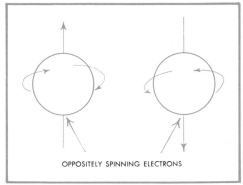

OPPOSITELY SPINNING ELECTRONS

Fig. 15.8   *Oppositely spinning electrons*
Two electrons must have opposite spins in order to occupy the same orbital.

TABLE 15.3

Values of Quantum Numbers

Values of n	Values of l	Values of m	Values of s
1 (K shell)	0	0	± ½
2 (L shell)	0	0	± ½
	1	1, 0, −1	± ½
3 (M shell)	0	0	± ½
	1	1, 0, −1	± ½
	2	2, 1, 0, −1, −2	± ½

distinguished by their spins (Fig. 15.8). The different spins are marked by the values for the *spin quantum number* of $+\frac{1}{2}$ and $-\frac{1}{2}$.* (Do not confuse the letter s used for the spin quantum number with the same letter when used to describe an orbital of spherical shape.)

*The spin quantum numbers of $+\frac{1}{2}$ and $-\frac{1}{2}$ arise from the conditions that there must be unit difference between their values, and their sum must be zero. If the spins are represented by s^+ and s^-

then $s^+ + s^- = 0$
and $s^+ - s^- = 1$

$2s^+ = 1$ or $s^+ = +\frac{1}{2}$
$2s^- = -1$ or $s^- = -\frac{1}{2}$

Table 15.3 sums up the relations between the quantum numbers.

While it is not possible to know the motion of electrons exactly, a general idea is given by the four quantum numbers. This may help us form a mental model of the atom. It should be kept in mind, however, that this is only an approximation.

15:8   Electronic Motion in Atoms

The s orbitals

The first two electrons of an energy level fly about in much the same way as a satellite would. The orbit always changes slightly, and the satellite may be at different distances from the earth. Yet, over a period of time, such a satellite would be visible in all the cities of the world. If a large number of photographs were taken and superimposed on one another, it would appear as if the satellite moved in a spherical region with no sharp boundaries with the earth at the center of this region.

Electrons moving in this way are said to be located in a sphere about the nucleus of the atom and are termed *s electrons*. Their motion is so rapid that it is impossible to describe their location at any instant. The best description that can be expected is of a blur. In the case of the electron, this effect is called an *electron cloud*.

To remember the name s electrons, keep in mind that their movement produces the effect of a *spherical cloud* around the core of the atom.

The region in space that an electron moves through is called an *orbital*. Spherical motion of the type described forms an *s orbital*. For such orbitals, the quantum number l has the value of zero.

The first energy level (n = 1) is filled when it contains two s electrons. Additional electrons must be at the second and higher levels. At such levels the first two electrons move about the nucleus in the manner already described; that is, such levels also have s electrons, and they are

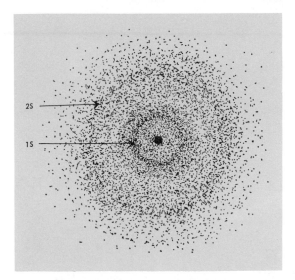

Fig. 15.9   *Spherical 1s and 2s electron clouds*

represented by 2s, 3s, 4s, and so on, depending on the energy level (Fig. 15.9).

The p orbitals

In addition, these levels have electrons that move about the nucleus in another way. Their motion can be about certain axes. There are three such directions, all perpendicular to one another; up and down, left and right, to and fro. They are termed the X, Y and Z (Fig. 15.10) axes or directions. The electrons move in elliptical orbitals about these three perpendicular directions. An orbital would lie entirely about one axis. Since there are three axes at right angles to one another, three orbitals are possible. There are two electrons spinning in opposite directions in each, or six electrons in all. Such electrons are termed *p electrons*. This symbol may be remembered by the fact that the axes of the electron clouds are *perpendicular* to each other. When it is necessary to distinguish between p orbitals of different axes, they are described as p_x, p_y and p_z. The quantum number l of such orbitals has a value of one. There are three p orbitals at every energy level beginning

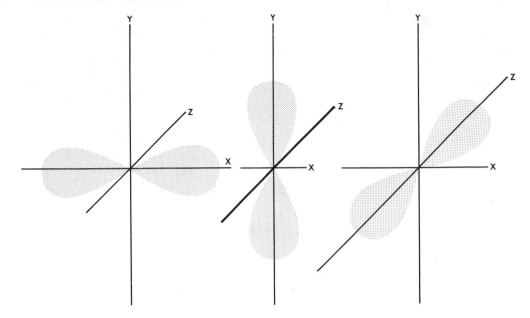

The 3 orientations of the p orbitals

Fig. 15.10   *The three p orbitals*

with the second (n = 2); and these orbitals are represented by 2p, 3p, 4p, and so forth.

The d and f orbitals

The third and higher energy levels contain s and p orbitals but in addition they also contain other orbitals termed d and f. Orbitals whose quantum number *l* equals 2 are called d orbitals, and those for which *l* equals 3 are termed f orbitals.

The third level (n = 3) has d orbitals; the higher levels (n = 4, 5 . . .) have both d and f.

When *l* is equal to 2, m may have five values of 2, 1, 0, −1, −2; and when *l* is equal to 3, m may have seven values of 3, 2, 1, 0, −1, −2, −3. Thus, there is room for 10 electrons, in 5 pairs, among the d, and 14, in 7 pairs, among the f orbitals.

15:9   Pauli's Exclusion Principle

With the four quantum numbers and the relationships that exist between them, it is possible to state an important rule which describes the electronic make-up of the atoms of all the elements. This is known as *Pauli's Exclusion Principle.*

All the electrons within the atoms of the elements are in energy levels described by the four quantum numbers. All such energy levels are eventually filled by electrons. No two electrons in an atom can be at energy levels having the same four quantum numbers. The filling of all the possible energy levels results in the periodic table of the elements as discussed in the next chapter.

15:10   An Analogy for Quantum Numbers and Orbitals

The use of the following loose analogy may help in understanding the idea of quantum numbers.

In the city of Freetown, Main Street runs east and west, and the houses are numbered

1, 2, 3 . . . East and 1, 2, 3 . . . West, the numbers starting from the centre of the city. A typical address would be: 100 West Main, Freetown. By this analogy, quantum number 1 would be Freetown; quantum number 2 would be Main; quantum number 3 would be "100"; and quantum number 4 would be West. Furthermore, if the houses are numbered in perfect sequence, there is a four-point address for every house in this city, and there is a house for every four-point address.

100 West Main Street is called an address. The four quantum numbers of an orbital also represent "an address". The orbital stands for a region which may have two electrons, or may have only one electron plus room for another, or may be empty, despite its capacity for two electrons.

QUESTIONS

1. (a) Describe Rutherford's experiment in which he caused alpha particles to bombard a thin sheet of gold.
   (b) Why were some of the alpha particles repelled in this experiment?
   (c) What did this experiment prove?

2. What is meant by the term *atomic number*?

3. Explain briefly how atomic numbers were determined.

4. How did Bohr explain that the energy emitted or absorbed by atoms is in certain definite wave lengths only?

5. List three ways by which atoms can absorb energy.

6. (a) What is meant by the term *line spectra*?
   (b) What information about electrons can be obtained from the study of line spectra?

7. How did Bohr explain the line spectrum of hydrogen?

8. Why could the Bohr model of the hydrogen atom not be applied successfully to other atoms?

9. Explain how electrons in atoms possess both potential and kinetic energy.

10. Explain the term *energy level*.

11. (a) When is an atom said to be in an excited state?
    (b) How can such an atom return to its ground state?

12. What do the four quantum numbers, n, *l*, m, and s, taken individually, represent?

13. (a) What values may the quantum number n have?
    (b) To what do these values correspond?

14. (a) What values may the quantum number *l* have?
    (b) What rule determines the number of values *l* may have?

15. (a) What values may the quantum number m have?
    (b) What rule determines the number of values m may have?

16. (a) What values may the spin quantum number have?
    (b) Why are there only two values for the spin quantum number?

17. (a)   What is an *atomic orbital*?
    (b)   What types of orbitals are present at each level?
    (c)   How many of each are found in each of the first four energy levels?

18. Distinguish between the motion of s and p electrons.

19. What values of *l* denote the motion of (a) an s electron? (b) a p electron? (c) a d electron? (d) an f electron?

20. Why does the quantum number m have three values for p electrons?

21. What values may m have when *l* is equal to 2? to 3?

22. Why is it possible to find only two electrons in each orbital?

23. State Pauli's exclusion principle.

CHAPTER

16 The Periodic Table (II)

In the previous chapter, a new model of the atom was discussed. It suggested that the electrons of an atom are in shells at definite energy levels. The latter could be described by four quantum numbers.

Can this model of atomic structure account for what is perhaps the most important phenomenon in chemistry – the classification of the elements in the periodic table? Can it explain why the table takes the form it does? Why are the numbers of elements in a period limited to 2, 8, 18, and 32?

16:1 The Quantum Numbers Explain the Periodic Table

The elements of the periodic table result from the filling up of the electronic orbitals in the order of their increasing energies. The combinations of quantum numbers give an account of the energy levels and the vacancies at each level. The electrons fill these vacancies by going into the lowest energy level first and then into progressively higher ones. When one level is filled, additional electrons must go to a higher energy level. Eventually the entire periodic table results.

16:2 The Atoms of 1s (n = 1, l = 0): Hydrogen and Helium

The first electron of the first atom, hydrogen, is in the orbital whose first quantum number is equal to 1 (n = 1). Such an orbital is of the lowest possible energy. When n = 1, l has the value of 0, and the electron is termed a 1s electron. The presence of only one such electron is represented by the notation $1s^1$ (Fig. 16.1).

When n = 1, two sets of quantum numbers are provided as shown in Table 16.1.

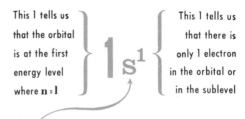

This l tells us that the orbital is at the first energy level where $n = 1$

$$1s^1$$

This l tells us that there is only 1 electron in the orbital or in the sublevel

The S tells us that the orbital is spherically shaped
For such orbitals, the quantum number l always equals zero, $l = 0$.

Fig. 16.1 *The electron configuration of hydrogen*

TABLE 16.1			
The Quantum Numbers of 1s			
n	l	m	s
1	0	0	$+\frac{1}{2}$
1	0	0	$-\frac{1}{2}$

Hydrogen has the first of these and helium has both. The helium atom is represented by $1s^2$. These are sufficient for two, but not more than two, electrons.

The Arrow Notation

An orbital is often represented by a circle ◯. Significantly, the orbital may be vacant and then the circle is empty. It may have one electron and this is shown by an arrow drawn in the circle ⊕ or ⊕. It may have two electrons if they are of opposite spin. The filled orbital is then shown as ⊕. The orbitals of hydrogen and helium are shown as:

Hydrogen $1s^1$ (↑) Helium $1s^2$ (↑↓)

135

The Dot Notation

Often, the electrons, particularly those in the outer shell are represented simply by dots. While this is a useful notation, it tells us only the number of electrons present in the outer shell. However, this information is often quite enough, and thus the electron dot symbol is used frequently,

Hydrogen H·   Helium He:

16:3   The Atoms of 2s (n = 2, l = 0): Lithium and Beryllium

In any atom beyond helium in the periodic table, the first shell (n = 1) is filled. The additional electrons go into the second shell (n = 2), or an even higher one still (n = 3, 4 . . . and up). With atom number three, lithium, the first two electrons fill the 1s orbital, and the third electron enters the second energy level, (n = 2).

When n = 2, l may have two values, 0 and 1. When l = 0, m may have only one value, zero, while the spin may be plus or minus ½. Thus, once again, quantum numbers for a sublevel with only one orbital are provided. The orbital thus formed is that of 2s. As usual, this orbital may have two electrons at most (Table 16.2).

TABLE 16.2

The Quantum Numbers of 2s

n	l	m	s
2	0	0	+½
2	0	0	−½

Lithium, atomic number three, has one of these electrons in the 2s orbital. It is represented by $1s^2 2s^1$ and it is shown as:

Beryllium, atomic number four, has both electrons of 2s. It is represented by $1s^2 2s^2$ and it is shown as:

The electron dot notation is:

Lithium   Li·   Berylium   Be:

Only the electrons of the outer second shell are shown by the symbolic dots.

16:4   The Atoms of 2p (n = 2, l = 1): Boron to Neon

Any atom beyond beryllium has both 1s and 2s orbitals filled with the two allowed electrons each. Boron, the atom with five electrons, has its fifth electron in a sublevel with the higher quantum numbers of n = 2, l = 1. Now the third quantum number m, may for the first time, have three values of +1, 0, and −1. This provides for three orbitals in this sublevel. For each of these the spin may be +½ or −½. This provides for six electrons, and automatically, for six elements (Table 16.3).

TABLE 16.3

The Quantum Numbers of 2p

n	l	m	s
2	1	1	+½
2	1	1	−½
2	1	0	+½
2	1	0	−½
2	1	−1	+½
2	1	−1	−½

The elements formed are boron, carbon, nitrogen, oxygen, fluorine, and neon. They have the atomic numbers five, six, seven, eight, nine, and ten, respectively. Boron has the first of these six electrons, carbon the second, and so on until neon has them all.

When $l = 1$, the letter p is used to describe the electrons, the orbitals, and the sublevel they occupy. There are three p orbitals and the six electrons fill them as shown in Table 16.4.

TABLE 16.4

The Notation for the Six Elements of 2p

Elements	Dot Notation	Orbitals		
		Already filled		Now filling
		1s	2s	2p
Boron	·Ḃ·	(↑↓)	(↑↓)	(↑)( )( )
Carbon	·Ċ·	(↑↓)	(↑↓)	(↑)(↑)( )
Nitrogen	·N̈·	(↑↓)	(↑↓)	(↑)(↑)(↑)
Oxygen	·Ö·	(↑↓)	(↑↓)	(↑↓)(↑)(↑)
Fluorine	:F̈·	(↑↓)	(↑↓)	(↑↓)(↑↓)(↑)
Neon	:N̈e:	(↑↓)	(↑↓)	(↑↓)(↑↓)(↑↓)

For neon, the electron configuration would be $1s^2 2s^2 2p^6$, showing that there are now 2 electons in 1s, 2 electrons in 2s, and 6 electrons in 2p. All orbitals possible up to this point are now filled. The second period of the periodic table is closed having reached this stage:

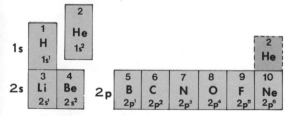

Fig. 16.2 *The first 10 elements placed in the periodic table*

16:5 The Atoms of the Third Energy Level

Any atom beyond neon in the periodic table has its first two shells filled with two and eight electrons respectively. The next set of atoms are in a shell whose first quantum number is 3.

With n = 3, l may have values of 0, 1, and 2.

When $l = 0$, m = 0, and s = $+\frac{1}{2}$ and $-\frac{1}{2}$. Two sets of quantum numbers result, and, therefore, two atoms, sodium and magnesium. Their orbital notation is shown in Table 16.5

TABLE 16.5

The Notation of the Two Elements of 3s

Elements		Orbitals			
		1s	2s	2p	3s
Sodium	Na·	(↑↓)	(↑↓)	(↑↓)(↑↓)(↑↓)	(↑)
Magnesium	Mg:	(↑↓)	(↑↓)	(↑↓)(↑↓)(↑↓)	(↑↓)

When $l = 1$, m may have three values of $+1$, 0, and -1 while s may be the usual $+\frac{1}{2}$ or $-\frac{1}{2}$ for each value of m. Again the six combinations of quantum numbers provide for the six p electrons at this sublevel. The six atoms from aluminum to argon result. The notation for their electron configurations are shown in Table 16.6.

TABLE 16.6

The Notation of the Six Elements of 3p

Elements		Orbitals		
		Already Filled		Now Filling
			3s	3p
Aluminum	·Äl·		(↑↓)	(↑)( )( )
Silicon	·S̈i·		(↑↓)	(↑)(↑)( )
Phosphorus	·P̈:	Neon Core $1s^2 2s^2 2p^6$	(↑↓)	(↑)(↑)(↑)
Sulfur	:S̈:		(↑↓)	(↑↓)(↑)(↑)
Chlorine	:C̈l:		(↑↓)	(↑↓)(↑↓)(↑)
Argon	:Är:		(↑↓)	(↑↓)(↑↓)(↑↓)

The periodic table has now reached the stage shown in Fig. 16.3.

This, however, is not the end of the third

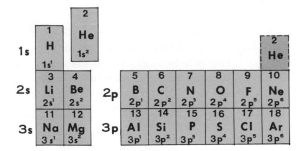

Fig. 16.3 *The first 18 elements placed in the periodic table*

energy level. When n = 3, *l* may be 2 as well as 0 and 1. At this value of *l* = 2, *m* may have five values: 2, 1, 0, −1, and −2. Thus five orbitals become possible. These are the five orbitals of the 3d sublevel. When *l* = 2, the electrons are termed "d". As usual, for each value of the other quantum numbers, the spin may be +½ or −½. This provides enough quantum numbers for 10 electrons, two electrons per orbital, or 10 electrons for the five orbitals of 3d. Automatically, 10 elements can now be accounted for. These are the elements which begin with scandium (#21) and end with zinc (#30) in the periodic table as shown in Fig. 16.4.

If you locate these elements in the table, you will notice that the elements potassium (#19) and calcium (#20) precede them. The properties of potassium and calcium resemble those of sodium and magnesium, the elements of 3s. Potassium and calcium are thus the elements of 4s. Evidently the 4s sublevel comes before the 3d sublevel, and the purely numerical order of filling orbitals has been upset.

16:6 The Sequence of Sublevels in the Periodic Table

To explain the sequence of sublevels remember that the quantum numbers represent energy levels of electrons. The lower the energy level, the more readily it is filled. Of the four quantum numbers, n and *l* make the most important contributions to the energy of the electron. The higher the values of n and *l*, the higher the energy of the electron. Thus, an energy level described by n = 2 is higher than that for which n = 1. Similarly, *l* = 1 refers to a higher energy sublevel than *l* = 0.

In view of these energy relations, consider that for potassium n = 4, *l* = 0. The sum of n + *l* is 4 + 0 or 4. For scandium, n = 3 and *l* = 2. The sum of n + *l* for this element is

Fig. 16.4 *The first 30 elements placed in the periodic table*

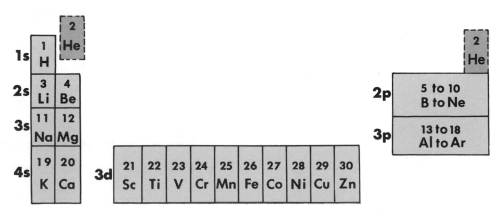

3 + 2 or 5. The occurrence of potassium before scandium in the periodic table suggests that an energy sublevel described by n = 3, l = 2 with a sum of 5 is higher than one described by n = 4, l = 0 with a sum of only 4.

It is safe to say that *throughout the periodic table the sublevels whose sum of n and l is lowest occur first*. This rule enables us to show the sequence of the sublevels in the periodic table in a diagram, as in Fig. 16.5. In the diagram, the vertical axis is scaled off according to values for n and the horizontal axis of the diagram is scaled off according to values for l, along with the s, p, d, and f symbols.

It is possible to follow the order of elements by means of the arrows as shown. It is readily seen that the 4s sublevel comes before the 3d. Similarly, 5s precedes 4d. The order in which the orbitals and sublevels increase in energy is shown in Fig. 16.6.

The periodic table in Fig. 16.7 emphasizes

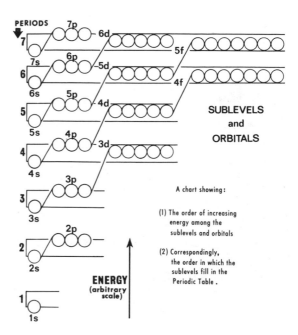

Fig. 16.6   *The energy sequence of sublevels and orbitals in the periodic table*

the orbital of the "last electron" in the case of each element. In the two columns, on the left, the "last electron" of the atom enters an s orbital. Of these, there are 1s, 2s, 3s . . . up to 7s. On the right there are six columns where the "last electron" enters a p orbital. Of these, there are 2p, 3p, 4p, 5p, and 6p. In the center are the 10 columns wherein the last electron enters a d orbital. Finally, at the very bottom of the table are two rows, each with 14 columns of the 4f and 5f orbitals respectively.

It is thus apparent that the model of the atom which teaches that electrons have energy levels described by four quantum numbers give a detailed explanation of the periodic table. When it is remembered that this table classifies all the elements, and that the elements are the building blocks out of which the entire universe is built, one can appreciate what a remarkable and useful achievement our knowledge of atomic structure is!

Fig. 16.5   *The sequence of sublevels and orbitals in the periodic table*

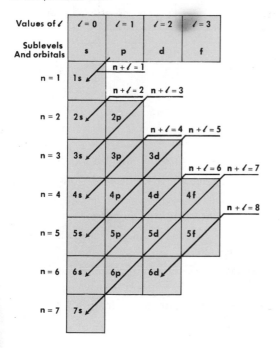

PERIODIC TABLE AND ORBITALS

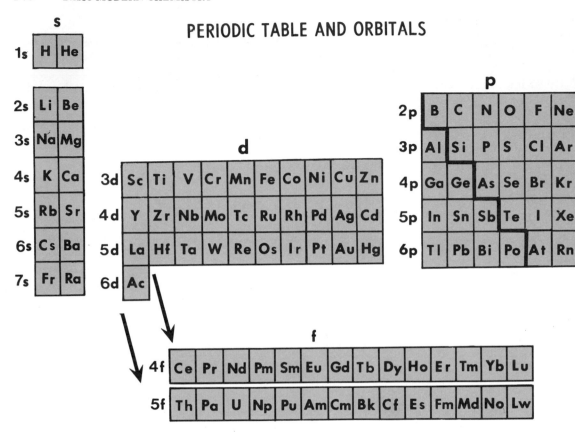

Fig. 16.7 *Periodic table showing orbitals being filled*

QUESTIONS

1. What different values may the quantum number n have?

2. Relate the values of the quantum number *l* to the quantum number n.

3. What values may the spin quantum number have? Give a reason for your answer.

4. (a) Explain why only two elements are possible when the quantum number n equals 1.
   (b) Name these two elements and give their electron configuration.

5. (a) Why are eight elements possible when n equals 2? Name the eight elements.
   (b) Give the orbital notation for these elements.

6. Referring to suitable Tables of this chapter, give the electron configuration for the following elements: Al, P, Mg, Si, S.

7. Account for the presence of s, p, and d electrons in an energy level in which n = 3.

8. When *l* = 3, how many values of m are possible?

9. Explain clearly why potassium precedes scandium in the periodic table.

10. State the rule determining the sequence of sublevels being filled in the atoms in the periodic table from the values of n and l.

11. Do the sublevels in the periodic table follow increasing values of n consistently? Explain.

12. The periodic table results from the filling of orbitals of ever increasing energy. What are the elements whose last electron, or pair of electrons, reaches the following orbital and have the given electron configuration: (a) $3s^1$, (b) $3p^4$, (c) $3d^1$, (d) $4s^2$, (e) $4d^1$?

13. Using the periodic table give the electron configuration for elements 34, 38, 54, 57.

14. Show the number of electrons in the orbitals of the (i) halogen elements (ii) alkali metals.

15. Explain why there are exactly ten elements in the first transition series beginning with scandium (#21) and ending with zinc (#30).

17 Four Important Periodic Properties

The elements have many physical and chemical properties. A few of these are density, melting point, boiling point, hardness, and chemical reactivity. Some of these properties permit quantitative measurements and from these, it can be seen that the properties tend to recur as suggested by the periodic law.

In this chapter four properties that in some fundamental way underlie all the others will be presented: atomic size, ionization energy, electron affinity, and electronegativity.

17:1 Atomic and Ionic Size

From what has been said about electronic motion and electron cloud in atoms, it can be seen that it is impossible to define exactly the size of a single isolated atom.

When atoms are linked to other atoms, atomic radius may be defined as the distance between an atomic nucleus and its boundary. True, the latter is rather indefinite. Various experimental methods have been used to find such distances. The atomic radii derived from such findings generally agree. For example, the atomic radius of carbon has been found to be 0.77 Å while that of chlorine is 0.99 Å. Carbon and chlorine, in turn, form a bond which when measured is found to be 1.77 Å. This is in good agreement with the sum of atomic radii of carbon and chlorine, $0.77 + 0.99 = 1.76$ Å. An error of 2 per cent is not unreasonable in this type of work. Scientists have also measured the distance between atomic nuclei in crystals and in the molecules of gaseous elements and compounds.

If a bond has a length smaller than the sum of the atomic radii, it is caused by one of two factors. (1) The bond consists of two or three pairs of electrons instead of only one pair of electrons. Such are termed double or triple bonds. (2) The bond is ionic. Bonds are discussed in Chapter 18.

Four interesting points stand out when atomic and ionic radii are examined:

1. Atomic radii decrease in going from left to right across the periodic table. This is contrary to what one would expect. The regular addition of an electron to the successive atoms does not result in atoms of larger size necessarily.

2. Within a group of the periodic table, atoms increase in size with increasing electron shells. The changes in atomic size with the successive addition of electrons is shown in Fig. 17.2.

3. The size of a cation, or positive ion, is less than that of the corresponding neutral atom. This is explained by the extra positive charge on the nucleus attracting the electrons closer to itself.

4. The size of an anion, or negative ion, is greater than that of the neutral atom. This is explained by the increased repulsion of the electrons from one another in an overall electron cloud carrying an extra negative charge.

17:2 Ionization Energy

As already mentioned, because of its energy the electron does not fall into the nucleus. The addition of energy to the atom causes the electron to go into shells further removed from the nucleus. It is possible to add an amount of

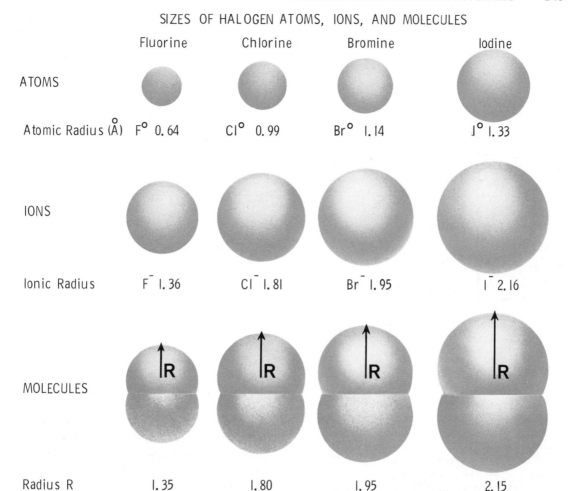

Fig. 17.1 *Sizes of atoms, ions, and molecules of the halogens*

energy that would cause the electron to leave the atom entirely, thus forming an electrically charged particle called an ion. This process may be shown by an equation:

$$A + \text{energy} \rightarrow A^+ + e^-$$

where A is an atom losing one electron. The energy that can remove an electron from the atom to form the ion is termed the *ionization energy*.

Elements differ greatly in their ionization energies. This means that to remove one or more electrons from the atoms of certain elements is easy, but to remove them from others is difficult. The ease with which electrons may be removed is in accordance with the chemical properties of these elements. For this reason, the ionization energy is a valuable guide to the chemical properties of the elements.

Tables 17.1 and 17.2 show how the ionization energy changes within a group or a period. Obviously, as the atom increases in size, it becomes easier to remove an outermost electron. Going from left to right across a period,

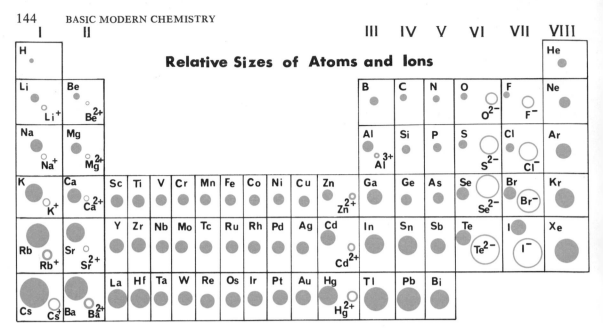

Fig. 17.2   *Atomic and ionic sizes*

it becomes more difficult to remove such an electron.

Note the high values for the Noble Gases and the low values for the alkali metals. Fig. 17.3 shows the variations in the ionization energies needed to remove one electron from the atoms as the atomic number increases.

TABLE 17.1

Ionization Energies of the Elements of Group I

Elements	Electrons in Shells	Ionization Energy in Electron-volts*
Lithium	2, 1	5.4
Sodium	2, 8, 1	5.1
Potassium	2, 8, 8, 1	4.3
Rubidium	2, 8, 18, 8, 1	4.2
Cesium	2, 8, 18, 18, 8, 1	3.9
Francium	2, 8, 18, 32, 18, 8, 1	?

TABLE 17.2

Ionization Energy of the Elements of Period 2

Elements	Outermost Electrons' Configuration	Ionization Energy in Electron-volts
Lithium	$2s^1$	5.4
Beryllium	$2s^2$	9.3
Boron	$2s^22p^1$	8.3
Carbon	$2s^22p^2$	11.3
Nitrogen	$2s^22p^3$	14.5
Oxygen	$2s^22p^4$	13.6
Fluorine	$2s^22p^5$	17.4
Neon	$2s^22p^6$	21.6

17:3   Electron Affinity

Atoms may gain electrons, and the energy released when this occurs is called *electron affinity*. The process may be shown by the equation:

*The electron-volt is a unit of energy. It represents the work done when one electron is raised one volt in potential.

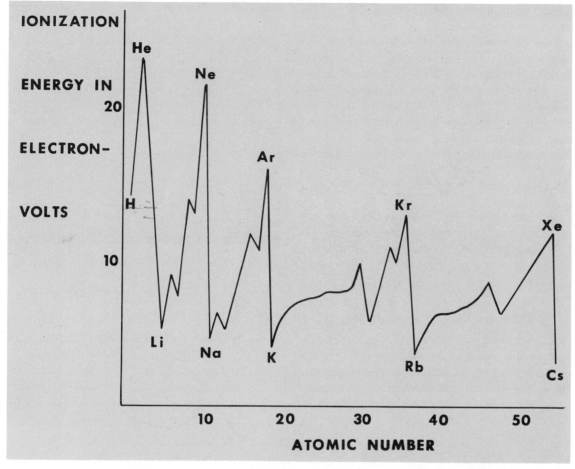

Fig. 17.3 *How atomic size and ionization energies change periodically with increasing atomic number of elements*

$$A + e^- \rightarrow A^- + energy$$

where A stands for the atom gaining an electron. The energy being liberated represents the electron affinity of the atom. Certain atoms show this property very readily, while others hardly show it at all. When an atom gains electrons, it becomes a negatively charged ion. The halogens of group VII are the best example of elements with high electron affinities because the addition of one electron to their atoms gives them a stable outer shell similar to the octet of a noble gas atom. The electron affinities of the atoms are rather difficult to determine and have been calculated for only a few elements.

17:4 Electronegativity

The *electronegativity* of an atom is a measure of its attraction for the electrons in the bond between itself and another atom. Atoms with a strong attraction for electrons have a high electronegativity. Fluorine, the smallest atom of group VII of the periodic table, has the highest electronegativity of all the elements; francium, the largest atom of group I, has the lowest. Numerically, electronegativity values range from 4.0 for fluorine to below 1.0 for most of the alkali metals.

The electronegativity scale (Table 17.3) was derived by taking into account the energy required to remove an electron from an atom, the ionization energy, and the energy change when an electron is added to an atom, the electron affinity. The scale is used to predict and explain the type of bond that forms between a particular pair of atoms. If we examine Table 17.3 the following points are readily observed:

1. The highest electronegativities are shown by the most reactive non-metallic elements. These are the halogens of group VII of the periodic table.

2. The lowest electronegativities are shown by the most active metallic elements. These are the alkali metals of group I.

3. Within a period, electronegativities generally increase from left to right. In the first short periods, the values increase one-half unit with each group. For example, the electronegativities of Li, Be, B, C,

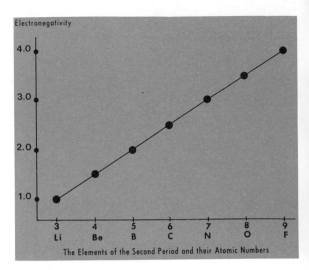

Fig. 17.4 *The electronegativities in the second period, Li to F*

N, O, F, and Ne are 1.0, 1.5, 2.0, 2.5, and so forth (Fig. 17.4).

4. Within a vertical column, electronegativity is usually greatest in the smallest atom and decreases with an increase in atomic size. Among the heavy metals, electronegativity values apparently do not follow

TABLE 17.3

The Electronegativities of Elements in the Periodic Table

2.1 H																	He
1.0 Li	1.5 Be											2.0 B	2.5 C	3.0 N	3.5 O	4.0 F	Ne
0.9 Na	1.2 Mg											1.5 Al	1.8 Si	2.1 P	2.5 S	3.0 Cl	Ar
0.8 K	1.0 Ca	1.3 Sc	1.5 Ti	1.6 V	1.6 Cr	1.5 Mn	1.8 Fe	1.8 Co	1.8 Ni	1.9 Cu	1.6 Zn	1.6 Ga	1.8 Ge	2.0 As	2.4 Se	2.8 Br	Kr
0.8 Rb	1.0 Sr	1.2 Y	1.4 Zr	1.6 Nb	1.8 Mo	1.9 Tc	2.2 Ru	2.2 Rh	2.2 Pd	1.9 Ag	1.7 Cd	1.7 In	1.8 Sn	1.9 Sb	2.1 Te	2.5 I	Xe
0.7 Cs	0.9 Ba	1.2 Lu	1.3 Hf	1.5 Ta	1.7 W	1.9 Re	2.2 Os	2.2 Ir	2.2 Pt	2.4 Au	1.9 Hg	1.8 Tl	1.8 Pb	1.9 Bi	2.0 Po	2.2 At	Rn
0.7 Fr	0.9 Ra																

this rule rigorously but are more or less constant.

5. Electronegativity values for the noble gases of group VIII are not readily available. For a long time it was believed that these elements formed no compounds; therefore, the concept of electronegativity did not apply to them. This belief will probably change now that xenon tetrafluoride has been synthesized.

17.5 Electronegativity Difference

When two atoms, A and B, combine, electrons may be shared between them or transferred from one to the other. If A and B have about equal affinity for electrons, they will form a bond by sharing electrons more or less equally:

$$A\cdot\ +\ \circ B\ \longrightarrow\ A\,{}^{\circ}_{\bullet}\,B$$

Such a bond is referred to as a non-polar *covalent bond*. When the two atoms have sufficiently different electron-attracting power, the electrons they share are displaced toward the atom that draws them more strongly. This unequal sharing of electrons causes one atom to be slightly negatively charged and the other positively charged. When this occurs, the bond is termed *polar covalent*. If atom B has greater ability to attract electrons than A, the bond can be represented as follows:

$$A\cdot\ +\ \circ B\ \longrightarrow\ A\,{}^{\circ}_{\bullet}\,B\ \text{or}\ A\,{}^{\bullet}_{\circ}\,B$$

If atoms have greater differences still in their electronegativity values, electrons may be transferred from one atom to the other. Such a transfer results in the formation of an *ionic bond*. For example, if B has a much stronger attraction for electrons than A, electrons may be transferred from A to B, and two ions are thus formed:

$$A\cdot\ +\ \circ B\ \longrightarrow\ A^{+}\ +\ {}^{\bullet}_{\circ}B^{-}$$

The electronegativity difference between two elements can thus help to describe the bonds formed between their atoms. Of course, since all gradations of polarity are possible, it is difficult in some cases to draw a clear distinction between ionic and covalent bonds. Table 17.4 was drawn up by chemists to express the nature of a chemical bond as *"percentage of ionic character"* based on electronegativity differences. In this tabulation, we see that a dif-

TABLE 17.4

Effect of Electronegativity on the Nature of Bonds

Electro-negativity Difference	Per Cent of Ionic Character	Type of Bond
0.2	1	Non-polar covalent
0.4	4	
0.6	9	... Polarity, if present, is not significant
0.8	15	Polar covalent
1.0	22	
1.1	26	
1.2	30	
1.3	34	
1.4	39	
1.5	43	
1.6	47	
1.7	50	50% ionic, 50% covalent
1.8	55	Ionic
1.9	59	
2.0	63	
2.2	70	
2.4	76	
2.6	82	
2.8	86	
3.0	89	
3.2	92	

ference of 1.7 in electronegativity is sufficient to cause an ionic bond to form between the atoms involved.

The value of 1.7 corresponds to about 50 per cent ionic character and 50 per cent covalent character. An electronegative difference greater than 1.7 means that the bond formed is more ionic than covalent while an electronegative difference smaller than 1.7 represents a bond more covalent than ionic. Many applications of electronegativity to bonding between atoms and to the chemical nature of compounds formed will be found in the study of the elements and their compounds.

QUESTIONS

1. Why may two combined atoms have a shorter bond length than the sum of the two atomic radii?

2. Offer an explanation as to why a cation is smaller and an anion is larger than the atom from which they are formed.

3. (a) Define the term *ionization energy*.
   (b) Name two factors that determine the magnitude of the ionization energy of an element.

4. Suggest a reason why it becomes more difficult to remove one outer electron as one goes from left to right across a period.

5. The ionization energy for sodium given in Table 17.1 is 5.1 electron-volts. This is sometimes called the first ionization energy, that is the energy to remove one electron. The second ionization energy, that is the energy to remove a second electron from a sodium atom, has a value of 47.3 electron-volts. Why should this second value be so much higher than the first?

6. Define the term *electron affinity*.

7. Write an ionic equation representing a fluorine atom becoming a fluoride ion.

8. How many angstroms are there in 1 cm?

9. Define *electronegativity*.

10. (a) Name the elements that have the highest electronegativity.
    (b) Name the elements that have the lowest electronegativity.

11. Relate atomic size to electronegativity.

12. How can the trend of electronegativity values of the elements within period 3 be explained?

13. (a) What is meant by a *non-polar covalent bond*?
    (b) When does a non-polar covalent bond form?

14. (a) What is a *polar covalent bond*?
    (b) Under what conditions will a polar covalent bond form?

15. (a) What is an *ionic bond*?
    (b) When does such a bond form?

16. Atom M whose electronegativity is 1.0 combines with atom N whose electronegativity is 3.5. Which of the following equations best represents this combination?

    (A)   M· + ₒN ⟶ M ⁰₀ N

    (B)   M· + ₒN ⟶ M⁻ ⁰₀N⁺

    (C)   M· + ₒN ⟶ M⁺ ⁰₀N⁻

    (D)   M· + ₒN ⟶ M⁻ᵒ N⁺

17. Discuss what is meant by *percentage ionic character.*

18. Of what significance is an electronegativity difference of 1.7 between two atoms?

19. Account for the fact that the carbon-hydrogen bond is covalent while the fluorine-hydrogen bond is ionic.

20. List five covalent bonds formed with hydrogen.

21. List five covalent bonds formed with oxygen.

22. List five ionic bonds formed with oxygen.

23. Suggest a reason why hydrogen does not form a strong bond with many metals.

24. Re-arrange the following pairs of elements in the order of decreasing bond polarity: (a) hydrogen-bromine; (b) hydrogen-chlorine; (c) hydrogen-iodine; (d) hydrogen-fluorine.

25. Give the per cent ionic character and predict the type of bond formed between the following atoms:

    (a) C − H   (f) Mg − O   (k) C − N
    (b) Cl − Cl   (g) S − O   (l) K − F
    (c) Fe − O   (h) K − Cl   (m) H − O
    (d) N − H   (i) I − O   (n) Li − Br
    (e) Cl − O   (j) C − O

18 Chemical Bonds

18:1 Chemical Bonds

Chemical change is the combining and the separating of atoms. But how do atoms combine, and what holds them together? Why is there a definite limit to the number of atoms that combine with each other in molecules or ions? The answers to these questions are given by the electronic structure of the atom. *Chemical combination is due to the attraction of atoms for the electrons of other atoms toward their unfilled orbitals.* If the attraction is great enough, the electrons leave their original atoms to fill the orbitals of another atom. If the attraction is not so great, the electrons may be shared by two atoms as a bond. The electronegativity of an element indicates the power of its atoms to attract electrons. Generally atoms gain, lose, or share electrons to assume the filled pattern of the atoms of the nearest noble gas in the periodic table.

18:2 Ionic Bonds

Ions form when only a small number of electrons needs to be gained or lost by the atoms in order to form stable electronic patterns. *Positive ions* result from the loss of electrons, and *negative ions* result from the gain of electrons. An ionic bond results from the force of attraction between the positive and negative ions. Positive ions are called *cations* because they are attracted to the cathode during electrolysis; negative ions are called *anions*, because they move to the anode.

The atoms of metals may lose one, two, or three electrons, thus forming positively charged cations. The atoms of non-metals, either singly or in groups, may gain one, two, or three electrons, thus forming negatively charged anions.

Sodium atoms have only one electron in the 3s orbital; this electron is easily removed as shown by its relatively low ionization energy. Chlorine atoms have seven electrons in their outer shell, 2 in the 3s orbital and 5 in the 3p orbitals. Energy is released when an eighth electron is added as shown by the electron affinity of chlorine. When sodium and chlorine react, the sodium atom loses its single electron from the 3s orbital and the chlorine atom adds it to its half-filled 3p orbital. The reaction may be represented in terms of the orbital or dot notations

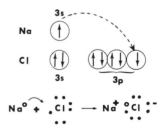

The electronegativities of sodium and chlorine are 0.9 and 3.0. The difference of 2.1 is large enough for the bond to be ionic.

18:3 The Formation of an Ionic Compound

The formation of crystalline sodium chloride involves three steps. In the first, an electron is removed from the sodium atom. This requires an amount of energy called the ionization energy. Such a reaction is endothermic since the above absorbs energy.

$$Na^0 + energy \rightarrow Na^1 + e^-$$

In the second step, this electron is added to the chlorine atom. This reaction releases an amount of energy called the electron affinity. Such a reaction is termed exothermic because it releases energy.

$$Cl^0 + e^- \rightarrow Cl^- + energy$$

In the third step, the positive sodium ions and the negative chloride ions attract each other and move toward one another. As they take up position next to each other, they form the sodium chloride crystal. This process also releases energy since particles with mutual attraction have come closer together. Thus, step three is exothermic.

The sum of the energy released in the second and third steps is greater than the energy required for the first. Hence, the formation of sodium chloride is exothermic. This is typical of the formation of all ionic compounds.

In the formation of an ionic compound, an important change occurs in the sizes of the atoms involved. The metal atom becomes an ion of smaller size as its nucleus attracts the electron clouds closer, now that the positive charge on the nucleus exceeds the negative charge of the electrons. The non-metallic atom, in gaining electrons, becomes an ion of larger size as the electron clouds, now with an excessive negative charge, repel each other. This is shown with sodium and chlorine in Fig. 18.1.

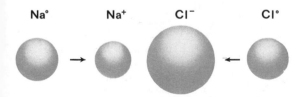

Fig. 18.1 *Changes of size when atoms form ions*

18:4   Properties of Ionic Compounds

Ionic compounds are combinations of positive and negative ions. The forces of attraction between ions of opposite charge are strong, and, at ordinary temperatures, the ions are held in close contact in regular crystal patterns. Ionic substances are always solids at room temperature and usually have high melting points. NaCl melts at 800°C, LiF at 870°C, and MgF_2 at 1400°C. Many ionic salts dissolve in water because the polar water molecules (Chapter 21) form weak bonds with the cations and the anions. The formation of such bonds releases energy. Such energy can overcome the force of attraction between the ions of the solid salt, and also between the molecules of water. Solutions of ionic compounds display interesting electrical and chemical properties. These will be discussed in Chapter 24.

18:5   Covalence

Atoms of equal of slightly different electro-negativity may form molecules by sharing one or more pairs of electrons. This is called *covalence*, and the bond formed is known as a *covalent bond*.

Some elements and compounds whose molecules are formed by covalent bonds between their atoms include H_2, Cl_2, O_2, HCl, H_2O, NH_3, and CH_4. Indeed, the majority of numerous compounds containing carbon are composed of covalent molecules.

Molecules which contain covalent bonds have definite structures. Some simple examples of such structures will be discussed in the remainder of this chapter and in the next. Since the structure of molecules determine to a large extent the properties of their compounds, references to structure will be made frequently throughout the study of chemistry.

18:6   Covalence in H_2

In the molecule of hydrogen, H_2, a covalent bond is formed between the hydrogen atoms. Each atom has one electron which it shares

$$H^\circ + \cdot H \longrightarrow H^\circ_\cdot H$$

with the other atom to form the covalent bond.

Let us attempt to picture how a covalent bond forms in terms of electron clouds.

The hydrogen atom has one electron in the 1s orbital. This electron has a certain spin in addition to its rapid motion about the nucleus. Through its rapid motion, it forms a spherical electron cloud.

When two hydrogen atoms approach, the electron clouds merge or overlap if the electrons are of opposite spin. The two hydrogen atoms are now held together firmly by the overlap of the two electron clouds. A molecule of hydrogen is thus formed with a covalent bond between the hydrogen atoms (Fig. 18.2).

The formation of the covalent bond in the hydrogen molecule can also be represented by the following orbital notation:

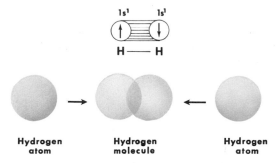

Fig. 18.2 *The formation of a molecule of hydrogen by electron cloud overlap*

18:7   The Chlorine Molecule

In the molecule of chlorine, Cl_2, a covalent bond is formed between the chlorine atoms. Each atom has seven outer electrons in the third shell. Two of these electrons fill the 3s

Fig. 18.3   *The p orbitals of the chlorine atom*

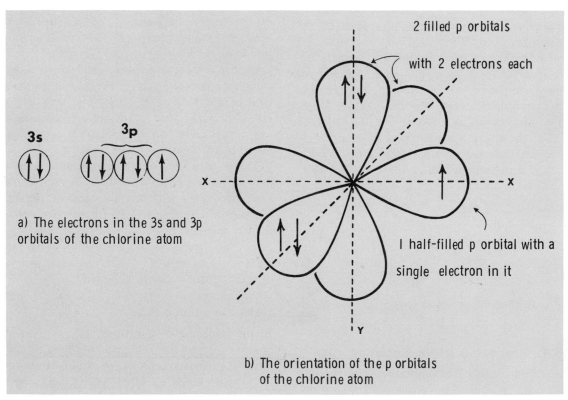

3s

3p

a) The electrons in the 3s and 3p orbitals of the chlorine atom

2 filled p orbitals

with 2 electrons each

I half-filled p orbital with a

single electron in it

b) The orientation of the p orbitals of the chlorine atom

orbital. The remaining five enter the orbitals of 3p. Two of these orbitals are thus filled completely with two electrons each. The last remaining orbital of 3p is left with only a single electron in it (Fig. 18.3).

When two chlorine atoms approach, they do so along the axes of the half-filled p orbitals, each having an electron of the opposite spin. In this manner, their electron clouds overlap and the covalent bond which holds the atoms together forms (Fig. 18.4).

The above is represented also by the orbital and dot notations:

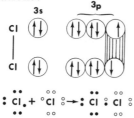

18:8   The Oxygen Molecule

Each oxygen atom has six electrons in the second shell. Two are in the 2s orbital and the remaining four are in the three orbitals of the 2p sublevel as follows:

$$\begin{array}{ccc} & & \overset{2p}{\overline{}} \\ \overset{1s}{} & \overset{2s}{} & \\ \uparrow\downarrow & \uparrow\downarrow & \uparrow\downarrow\ \uparrow\downarrow\ \uparrow \end{array}$$

When two oxygen atoms approach, they do so along the axes of half-filled p orbitals, each having a single electron with a different spin. Their electron clouds overlap and the covalent bond which holds the atoms together forms. Thus far, the oxygen atoms behave as do the atoms of chlorine. However, there is an important difference at this point. Each oxygen atom still has a half-filled p orbital containing single electrons of opposite spin. Their electron clouds may also overlap if given the chance. For this

Fig. 18.4   *Electron cloud overlap in the chlorine molecule*

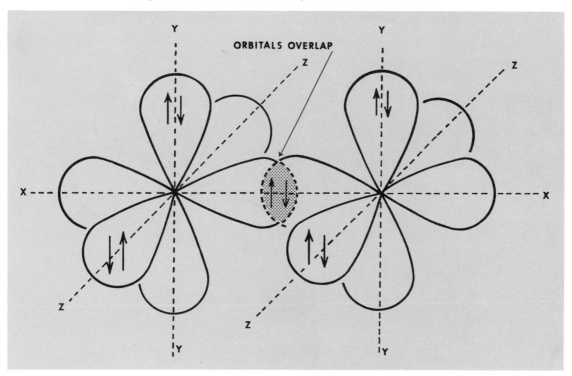

to happen, the atoms rotate around their common axis until the second pair of p orbitals find themselves parallel. Now the electron clouds are as close as they can ever be. The atoms stop rotating as a second bond forms by the overlap of the parallel p electron clouds (Fig. 18.5).

The above is represented also by orbitals and dots as follows:

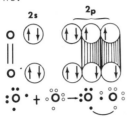

The single electrons in the pair of parallel p orbitals of Fig. 18.5 are shown as a dot and a circle in the atoms of the oxygen molecule above.

18:9   Covalence between Unlike Atoms

In the molecule of hydrogen chloride, HCl, a bond has formed between an atom of hydrogen and one of chlorine. As already mentioned, hydrogen has one electron in 1s and chlorine has seven electrons at the third energy level, 2 in the 3s orbital, and 5 in the 3p orbitals. It is, therefore, not surprising that the two atoms share their single electrons, as shown here in their orbital and dot notations:

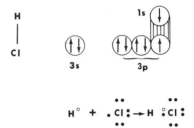

Fig. 18.5   *Covalence in oxygen*

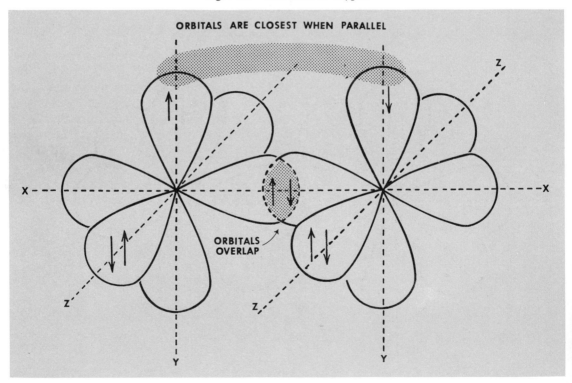

The electron clouds of the two atoms are different. That of hydrogen is spherical while that of chlorine is elliptical. Once again, there is overlap of the electron clouds as the covalent bond forms. The elliptical shape of chlorine's electron cloud is modified somewhat in such a reaction. This is the result of the electrons shifting toward the chlorine atom (Fig. 18.6).

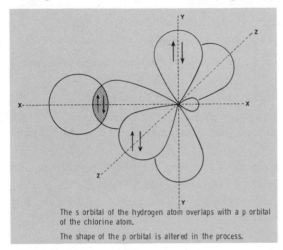

The s orbital of the hydrogen atom overlaps with a p orbital of the chlorine atom.

The shape of the p orbital is altered in the process.

Fig. 18.6 *The electron cloud overlap in hydrogen chloride*

It should be remembered that the actual chemical formation of hydrogen chloride results from molecular hydrogen, H_2, reacting with molecular chlorine, Cl_2. The equation for this reaction is

$$H_2 + Cl_2 \rightarrow 2HCl$$

18:10 Polar Covalent Bonds

Since the electronegativities of H and Cl are 2.1 and 3.5, with a difference of 1.4, the electrons in the bond are shared unequally but are not transferred. Thus the bond in HCl is covalent unlike that in ionic NaCl. Neither the hydrogen nor the chlorine atom can remove the electron completely from the other.

The electronegativity difference is great enough for the molecule of HCl to be polar with a positive pole near the hydrogen atom and a negative one near the chlorine (Fig. 18.7).

$\delta+$ $\delta-$

$\delta+$ $\delta-$

H — Cl

Fig. 18.7 *The polar covalent bond in HCl*

Two other polar covalent bonds of frequent occurrence are the OH and the NH, found most commonly in water and ammonia respectively. The oxygen and nitrogen atoms are more electronegative than the hydrogen. As a result the electrons in these bonds shift toward the oxygen and the nitrogen, and thus, polar bonds form:

$\delta+$ $\delta-$
H — N

$\delta+$ $\delta-$
H — O

QUESTIONS

1. (a) What is the origin of the charge on a negative ion?
   (b) What is the origin of the charge on a positive ion?

2. Using the electronegativity concept, explain why sodium and chlorine combine so readily.

3. Potassium and chlorine combine together forming potassium chloride. Represent this reaction (a) by an ordinary balanced chemical equation; (b) using the dot notation; (c) using the orbital notation of circles with arrows.

4. Repeat question 3 for the combination of magnesium and fluorine.

5. What common properties are shown by ionic compounds?

6. Explain covalence. Illustrate your answer by reference to the bond found in the molecule of hydrogen.

7. Why is the following reaction, $He + He \rightarrow He_2$, not likely to occur?

8. Using the electron dot notation show how: (a) 2 atoms of fluorine combine; (b) 2 atoms of chlorine combine; (c) 2 atoms of bromine combine; (d) 2 atoms of iodine combine.

9. Explain why chlorine atoms form molecules by sharing one pair of p electrons, and oxygen atoms form molecules by sharing two pairs of p electrons.

10. Give (a) the electron dot notation and (b) the orbital notation representing the formation of the hydrogen fluoride molecule.

11. (a) What is meant by the term *electron cloud*?
    (b) What is meant by the expression *s and p cloud overlap* used to describe the bond between two given atoms?

12. Account for the fact that some covalent bonds are polar while others are non-polar.

CHAPTER

19 Molecular Architecture

19:1 Introduction

As long as there are only two atoms in a molecule, the structure is that of a line joining two points. The presence of a third atom in the molecule poses the question of the shape or architecture of the molecule. Is the three-atom molecule still a straight line? or is it an angle or a triangle?

Early evidence about molecular architecture came from the chemical properties and the chemical reactions of the compounds. This is not surprising because the structure of a molecule has chemical significance. A chemical reaction involves the breaking and making of bonds between atoms. Since the structure of a molecule shows its bonds it also suggests what reactions the compound would be expected to undergo. The structure of a molecule has physical significance as well. The structure of a molecule will determine such physical properties as the melting and boiling points, density, conductivity, and solubility of the substance. It will also explain the radiation the compound will absorb or emit under suitable conditions.

Indeed, the most rapid and precise modern methods for finding molecular structures are based on observing how substances absorb or emit radiation. Such methods have enabled chemists to learn how the atoms of a molecule are linked together, how great is the distance between the atoms, and how large is the angle between the bonds. Scientists can also tell how strong the bonds are, how free the atoms are to vibrate, and other such fine detail. This chapter will be a brief introduction to this great field of study. Some of the ideas involved can be learned with the aid of the molecules of water, ammonia, and methane.

19:2 The Molecule of Water, H_2O

This molecule consists of one oxygen and two hydrogen atoms. Each hydrogen is bonded to the oxygen atom and thus there are two O-H bonds in the molecule. Experiment shows that the angle between these bonds is 104.5°.

The atom of oxygen has two half-filled p orbitals. From this, one might draw two conclusions:

(a) that the oxygen atom can combine with two atoms of hydrogen:

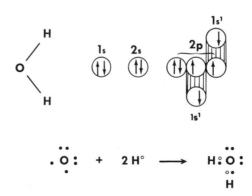

157

(b) that the bonds should be at right angles to one another since p orbitals are perpendicular to each other. This is not quite borne out experimentally since the angle between the bonds is 104.5° instead of 90°.

case of the water molecule this is not quite borne out experimentally. One begins to suspect that the orbital model needs a slight modification to explain the facts. The structure of the methane molecule sheds some light on this problem.

19:3   The Molecule of Ammonia, NH$_3$

This molecule consists of one nitrogen and three hydrogen atoms. Each hydrogen is bonded to the nitrogen atom and thus there are three N-H bonds in the molecule. Experiment shows that the angle between the bonds is 107.5°.

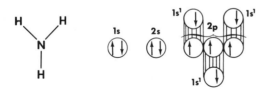

The atom of nitrogen has three half-filled p orbitals. From this one might conclude that:

(a) Nitrogen can combine with three hydrogen atoms.

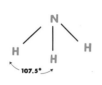

$$\cdot \overset{\cdot}{\underset{\cdot\cdot}{N}} \cdot \; + \; 3H° \longrightarrow H \overset{\cdot\cdot}{\underset{\cdot\cdot}{N}} \overset{H}{\underset{°}{°}} H$$

(b) the bonds should be at right angles to one another since p orbitals are perpendicular to one another. Again, as in the

19:4   The Molecule of Methane, CH$_4$

In this molecule, one carbon atom is attached to four hydrogens. There are four C-H bonds.

$$\cdot \overset{\cdot}{\underset{\cdot}{C}} \cdot \; + \; 4H° \longrightarrow H \overset{\overset{\displaystyle H}{\cdot\cdot}}{\underset{\underset{\displaystyle H}{\circ\circ}}{C}} H$$

Experiment shows that these bonds are at an angle of 109.5° with respect to each other.

In its ground state, the carbon atom has single electrons in only two half-filled p orbitals. Therefore, it should combine with two hydrogen atoms to form CH$_2$. Actually, such a molecule, if it forms at all, is highly reactive and next to impossible to collect. The common compound with one carbon atom in its molecule contains four and not two hydrogen atoms. Furthermore, the angle between the bonds is 109.5° and not 90° as the orbital model suggests.

There is still another important fact about the four C-H bonds in the methane molecule which experiment reveals. The four bonds are directed *symmetrically in space. It is as if the four electron pairs which make up the four bonds, repel one another to the utmost.* They are as far away from one another as they can possibly be, providing that they remain within the molecule. This is the reason the bonds orient themselves as they do.

To appreciate what the bonds have achieved through their mutual repulsion, think of a perfect cube in which diagonals are drawn (Fig. 19.1).

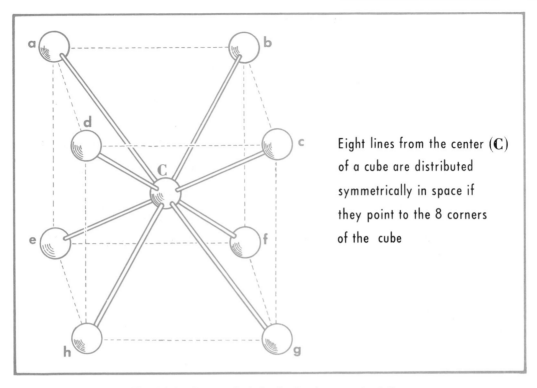

Eight lines from the center (**C**) of a cube are distributed symmetrically in space if they point to the 8 corners of the cube

Fig. 19.1   *Symmetrical distribution in space for 8 lines*

Fig. 19.1 shows a perfect cube with its diagonals intersecting at center C. The eight lines joining center C to each of the 8 corners are distributed symmetrically in space.

In the case of the carbon atom, there are only four bonds coming from the central point, and *they* are to be distributed symmetrically in space. Their orientation must be toward every *second* corner of the cube (Fig. 19.2).

By measurement or calculation, we find that the angle between any pair of lines such as Cc and Ca is 109.5°. This is the very same angle as that found experimentally between any pair of bonds in the methane molecule. That molecule must have the structure shown in Fig. 19.2. This is a significant conclusion, and we now proceed to develop it further.

To obtain a simpler and clearer picture of what that structure must be, join every second corner of the cube. The structure that results is a *tetrahedron* (Fig. 19.3). This is a pyramid with four faces, each an equilateral triangle (Figs. 19.3 and 19.4).

We have thus arrived at the conclusion that the shape or architecture of the methane molecule is that of a tetrahedron. The carbon atom is at the center and the hydrogen atoms are at the corners distributed symmetrically in the space around it.

In the vast majority of cases wherein one atom is joined to four others, the molecule assumes this shape. Illustrations of some of the more familiar molecules and ions which have this tetrahedral structure appear following (Figs. 19.5 and 19.6).

Can the orbital model be modified to explain the capacity of the carbon atom to bond with four hydrogen in the molecule of methane? The

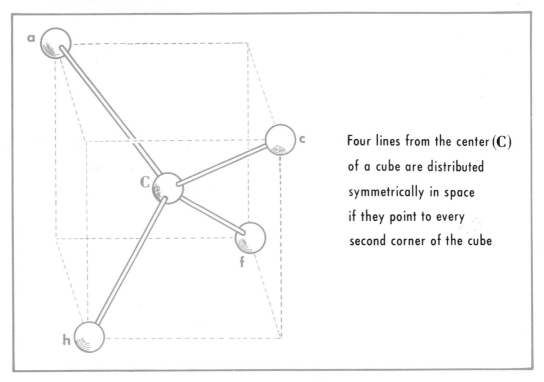

Four lines from the center (**C**)
of a cube are distributed
symmetrically in space
if they point to every
second corner of the cube

Fig. 19.2   *Symmetrical distribution in space for 4 lines*

modified model should also account for the fact that the four bonds are identical and distributed symmetrically in space. Let us reconsider the outermost electron shell of the carbon atom to find a clue. The orbitals of this shell are of two kinds, s and p, and they are filled up as follows:

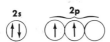

Four orbitals, all perfectly identical, can be obtained by mixing the 2s together with the three 2p orbitals. The new orbitals are termed sp^3:

sp³   sp³   sp³   sp³

The process by which the mixing is achieved

is called *hybridization*. The four *hybrid* orbitals are all exactly the same and point to the corners of an imaginary tetrahedron.

Carbon's combining capacity of four can also be explained by hybridization. The 2 electrons of 2s separate to become single electrons along with the other two single electrons of 2p; four electrons are now available one to each of the four new sp^3 orbitals. Thus the carbon atom will have a combining capacity of four.

The formation of methane can now be shown as follows:

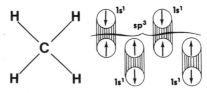

The sp³ orbitals are at a slighly higher energy

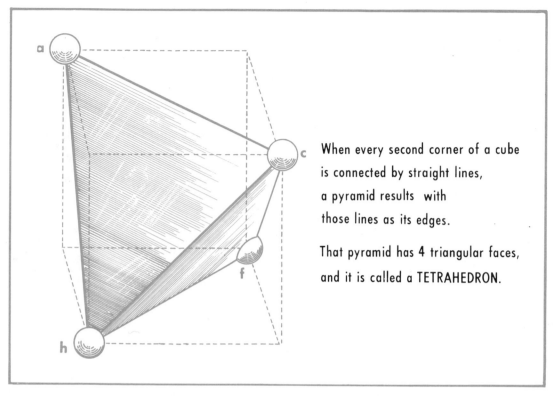

When every second corner of a cube
is connected by straight lines,
a pyramid results with
those lines as its edges.

That pyramid has 4 triangular faces,
and it is called a TETRAHEDRON.

Fig. 19.3 *The tetrahedron within a cube*

level than the s orbitals. Therefore the s electrons are said to be promoted as they hybridize with the p electrons to form sp³ orbitals. The energy needed for this promotion is supplied mainly by the bonding of the atoms.

The phenomenon of hybridization is quite common. To explain the bond angles of 104.5° and 107.5° in water and ammonia, it is assumed that the orbitals of oxygen and nitrogen also hybridize in the same way as do those of carbon, to provide the structures of the water and ammonia molecules (Fig. 19.7 a and b).

19:5 Bond Energy

The formation of bonds liberates energy, while the breaking of bonds requires energy. The amount of energy needed to separate the atoms of a bond is called the *bond energy*.

When one Avogadro Number of hydrogen molecules is dissociated into H atoms, the energy required is 104.2 kilocalories. This is called the bond energy of the H—H bond. The equation may be written as follows:

$$H_2 + 104.2 \text{ kcal} \rightarrow 2H$$

Similar values for other pairs of atoms are known (See Table 19.1).

In using bond energies, the assumption is made that each bond has a definite amount of energy associated with it, and this energy is not affected by neighboring atoms and bonds. This assumption is only approximately true, so that bond energies are merely the best average values obtainable for a large number of cases. They are

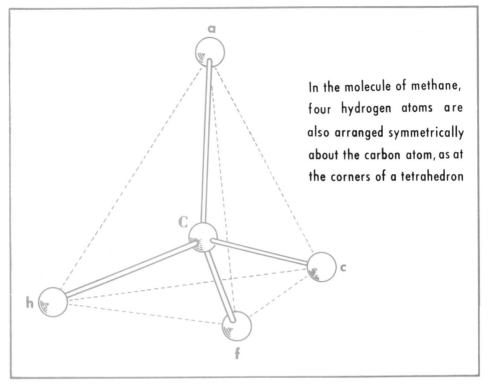

In the molecule of methane, four hydrogen atoms are also arranged symmetrically about the carbon atom, as at the corners of a tetrahedron

Fig. 19.4   *Four symmetrical lines in a tetrahedron*

TABLE 19.1

Bond Energies

Bond	Kilocalories per mole
H═H	104.2
Cl—Cl	58.0
O═O	118.3
O—O	33.0
C—C	80.0
H—O	109.4
H—Cl	103.0
H—C	99.0
C—Cl	78.0
C—O	79.0
C═C	145.0

not perfect and the error in their value is about five per cent.

Bond energies enable us to calculate the heat of a reaction. To do this, the energy needed to break the bonds in the reactants on the left-hand side of the equation is computed, then the energy released is computed for the bonds formed in the products on the right-hand side of the equation. Finally, the difference is taken. Thus,

heat of reaction = energy of bonds formed in products minus energy of bonds broken in reactants.

Example

What is the heat of reaction for

$$CH_4 + Cl_2 \rightarrow CH_3Cl + HCl \,?$$

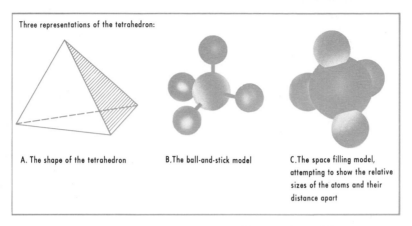

Three representations of the tetrahedron:

A. The shape of the tetrahedron

B. The ball-and-stick model

C. The space filling model, attempting to show the relative sizes of the atoms and their distance apart

Fig. 19.5 *The tetrahedron and its atomic model*

Fig. 19.6 *Examples of tetrahedral structure*

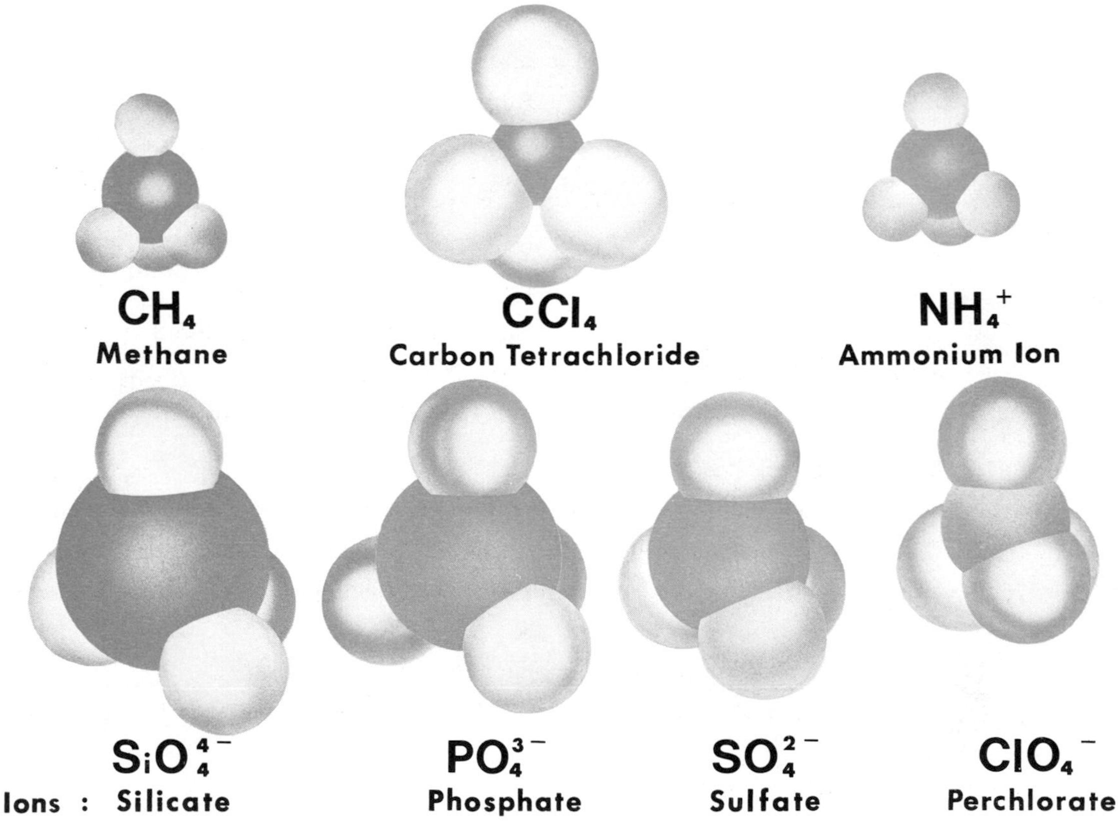

CH_4
Methane

CCl_4
Carbon Tetrachloride

NH_4^+
Ammonium Ion

SiO_4^{4-}
Ions : **Silicate**

PO_4^{3-}
Phosphate

SO_4^{2-}
Sulfate

ClO_4^-
Perchlorate

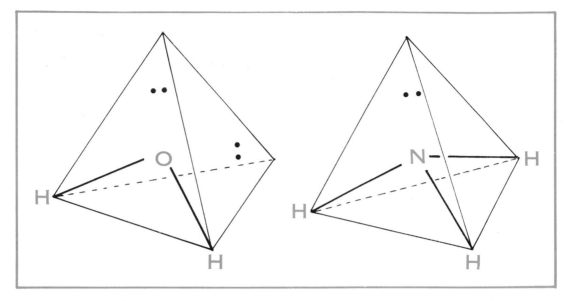

Fig. 19.7a *The water molecule*   *b*   *The ammonia molecule*

Solution

Structurally,

$$H—\overset{\overset{H}{|}}{\underset{\underset{H}{|}}{C}}—H + Cl—Cl \rightarrow H—\overset{\overset{H}{|}}{\underset{\underset{H}{|}}{C}}—Cl + H—Cl$$

Bonds Broken:

$$4 \times C—H = 4 \times 99.0 = 396.0$$
$$1 \times Cl—Cl = 1 \times 58.0 = \underline{58.0}$$
$$454.0$$

Energy required: 454.0 kcal

Bonds Formed:

$$3 \times C—H = 3 \times 99.0 = 297.0$$
$$1 \times C—Cl = 1 \times 78.0 = 78.0$$
$$1 \times H—Cl = 1 \times 103.2 = \underline{103.2}$$
$$478.2$$

Energy liberated: 478.2 kcal

Heat of reaction: 478.2 − 454.0 = 24.2 kcal

Since the energy liberated exceeds the energy absorbed, this reaction is exothermic.

QUESTIONS

1. Draw a diagram to show the arrangement of electrons in the methane molecule.
2. Describe clearly the shape of a tetrahedron. Use a diagram to illustrate.
3. Explain hybridization. Use carbon united with hydrogen as an illustrative example.
4. What is meant by sp³ orbitals?
5. Describe the structure of the water and the ammonia molecules.
6. Using Table 19.1, calculate the overall heat evolved or absorbed in the following reactions
   (a) $H_{2(g)} + Cl_{2(g)} \rightarrow 2HCl_{(g)}$
   (b) $2H_2O_{(g)} \rightarrow 2H_{2(g)} + O_{2(g)}$

CHAPTER

20 Oxidation-Reduction

20:1 Some Examples of Oxidation-Reduction

When oxygen reacts with magnesium, magnesium oxide is the product.

$$2Mg + O_2 \rightarrow 2MgO$$

The original oxygen molecules and atoms are neutral. In the final product, the oxygen atoms have acquired a charge of 2– because two electrons have been transferred to each oxygen atom. The original magnesium atoms carry no charge, while the resulting magnesium ions in magnesium oxide have a charge of 2+. Therefore, in this reaction oxygen attracts electrons from magnesium. Since oxygen has an electronegativity of 3.5 and magnesium of 1.2, it is not surprising that such an electron transfer occurs.

There are many reactions in which one substance attracts electrons from another. In some cases, the attraction leads to outright transfer of electrons from one atom to another and this results in the formation of ions. In other cases, the attraction leads only to a partial shift of electrons from one atom to another and this results in the formation of polar covalent bonds. In either case, the substance which attracts the electrons is called the *oxidizing agent*, and the substance which loses the electrons is called the *reducing agent*. Such substances may be atomic, molecular, or ionic.

Examples of oxidizing agents and the reactions they undergo when they accept electrons are the following:

Oxygen	O_2	$+ 4e^- \rightarrow 2O^{2-}$
Chlorine	Cl_2	$+ 2e^- \rightarrow 2Cl^-$
Sulfur	S	$+ 2e^- \rightarrow S^{2-}$
Silver ion	Ag^+	$+ 1e^- \rightarrow Ag^0$

Copper (II) ion $Cu^{2+} + 2e^- \rightarrow Cu^0$

Examples of reducing agents and the reactions they undergo when they donate electrons are the following:

Sodium	Na^0	$\rightarrow Na^+ + 1e^-$
Zinc	Zn^0	$\rightarrow Zn^{2+} + 2e^-$
Chloride ions	$2Cl^-$	$\rightarrow Cl_2 + 2e^-$

20:2 Some Terms

The processes of oxidation and reduction go on simultaneously. When electrons are transferred from reducing agents to oxidizing agents, the reducing agent is oxidized and the oxidizing agent is reduced. Thus, when Mg^0 loses electrons to oxygen and becomes Mg^{2+}, it is said to have been *oxidized*, or to have undergone *oxidation*.

In the same reaction, the oxygen has gained electrons and its electrical condition changed from 0 to 2–. It is said to have been *reduced*, or to have undergone *reduction*.

An oxidizing agent oxidizes another substance, but is itself reduced.

A reducing agent reduces another substance, but is itself oxidized.

Thus oxidation and reduction are opposite reactions which take place simultaneously. The overall reaction involving both the loss and the gain of electrons is termed an *oxidation-reduction reaction*.

20:3 Oxidation-Reduction Reactions

If the oxidizing agent gains electrons and the reducing agent loses electrons, a chemical reaction might be expected when they are brought together. This does occur, provided the energy liberated when the oxidizing agent gains

165

electrons is great enough to remove the electrons from the reducing agent. Systems in which such a chemical reaction proceeds are called electrical cells or batteries (Fig. 20.1). These are used to provide electrical energy in cars, airplanes, and in many other types of vehicles and devices.

20:4   The Car Battery

The car battery consists of plates of lead and lead dioxide, PbO_2. The lead acts as the reducing agent:

$$Pb \rightarrow Pb^{2+} + 2e^-$$

The lead dioxide acts as the oxidizing agent:

$$PbO_2 + 4H_3O^+ + 2e^- \rightarrow Pb^{2+} + 6H_2O$$

The chemical changes that the reducing agent and oxidizing agent undergo are shown separately. Each change is termed a *half-reaction* and both half-reactions constitute the overall reaction. Each electrode is termed a *half-cell* and both half-cells make up the complete cell.

The reducing half-reaction shows electrons being given off. The oxidizing half-reaction shows them being taken on. The equations for both half-reactions are balanced for atoms and charges.

The H_3O^+ in the oxidizing equation shows that the reaction requires an acid medium.

Sulfuric acid is used for this purpose. The overall chemical reaction is:

$$\overset{0}{Pb} + \overset{4+}{PbO_2} + 2H_2SO_4 \underset{charge}{\overset{discharge}{\rightleftharpoons}}$$

$$\overset{2+}{2PbSO_4} + 2H_2O$$

The reaction of the car battery, which is typical of oxidation-reduction reactions, proceeds in either direction – forward while it is delivering power to the ignition and other circuits in the car, and reverse as it is re-charged by the car generator.

20:5   Oxidation Numbers

How can one recognize an oxidation-reduction reaction? As was discussed, such reactions can be used to generate the electric current in cells and batteries as the electrons pass from the atoms losing electrons (reducing agent) to the atoms gaining them (oxidizing agent). For the purpose of writing equations, however, such reactions can be recognized with the aid of *oxidation numbers. The oxidation number of an atom is the electrical charge it appears to have when calculated by arbitrary rules.* These rules make it possible to calculate the oxidation numbers for the reactants and products of a chemical

Fig. 20.1   *Oxidation and reduction in an electric cell*

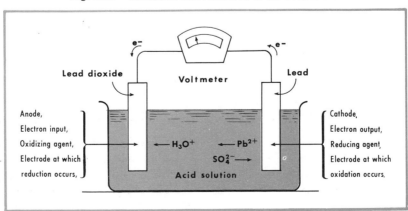

change. If a substance has gained or lost electrons, this fact would be reflected in a change in the oxidation number.

Rule 1. The oxidation number of an atom of an uncombined element is zero. This is often shown by a zero written above the element to the right of its symbol:

$$Na^0, Cl_2^0, Mg^0, O_2^0, P_4^0$$

Rule 2. When a single atom becomes an ion by gaining or losing electrons, its oxidation number is the same as its charge. Thus, the oxidation numbers of Na^+, Mg^{2+}, Al^{3+}, Cl^-, are the same as the charges, namely $1+, 2+, 3+, 1-$.

Rule 3. The algebraic sum of the oxidation numbers of all the atoms in the formula of a compound is zero. Thus for NaCl, the sum would be $1+$ for Na^+ and $1-$ for Cl^- or zero. For MgF_2, it would be $2+$ for Mg^{2+} and $2 \times 1-$ for the two fluoride ions. Again the sum is zero.

Rule 4. When electrons are shared in covalent bonds between two unlike atoms, they are counted as negative charges in the more electronegative of the atoms.

This would cause the charge on oxygen to be two minus $(2-)$ and that on the hydrogen one plus $(1+)$ in practically all of their compounds.*

Considering what was said about oxidation numbers, a practical definition of oxidation and reduction can now be given. An oxidation is a reaction in which the oxidation number of an atom is increased. Conversely, a reduction is a reaction in which the oxidation number of an atom is decreased:

$$
\begin{array}{c c c}
& 4+ & \\
& 3+ & \\
& 2+ & \\
& 1+ & \\
\text{oxidation} & 0 & \text{reduction} \\
& 1- & \\
& 2- & \\
& 3- & \\
& 4- & \\
\end{array}
$$

For example, in the reaction between magnesium and oxygen, $2Mg^0 + O_2^0 \rightarrow 2MgO$, the oxidation number of magnesium increases from 0 to $2+$; this is an oxidation. The oxidation number of oxygen decreases from 0 to $2-$; this is a reduction.

20:6 Examples

Calculate the oxidation numbers of sulfur in (a) H_2S, hydrogen sulfide; (b) SO_2, sulfur dioxide; (c) Na_2SO_4, sodium sulfate.

Solutions

(a) In hydrogen sulfide, one atom of sulfur is combined with two atoms of hydrogen whose oxidation number is $1+$. If the oxidation number of sulfur is x, we may write the equation:

$$2x(1+) + x = 0$$

since the sum of the oxidation numbers in a molecule is zero.

$$\therefore \qquad x = 2-$$

In H_2S, the oxidation number of sulfur is $2-$.

*In peroxides such as H_2O_2, the oxidation number of oxygen is $1-$ instead of the usual $2-$. Bonding between the oxygen atoms permits the presence of two of them in the molecules of peroxides. The rules about oxidation numbers do not reflect all structural facts about molecules or ions.
In LiH, the oxidation number of hydrogen is $1-$ because its electronegativity is greater than that of lithium.

(b)   In sulfur dioxide, one atom of sulfur is combined with two atoms of oxygen whose oxidation number is $2-$. If the oxidation number of sulfur is y, we may write the equation:

$$2x(2-) + y = 0$$
$$\therefore \qquad y = 4+$$

In SO_2, the oxidation number of sulfur is $4+$.

(c)   In Na_2SO_4, two sodium atoms contribute two positive charges, since each has an oxidation number of $1+$. The four oxygen atoms contribute $8-$, since each has an oxidation number of $2-$. If the oxidation number of sulfur is z, then,

$$2x(1+) + 4(2-) + z = 0$$
$$\text{or} \quad z = 6+$$

We may interpret the results of these calculations as follows:

In H_2S, the sulfur atom is more electron attracting or more electronegative than the hydrogen. It forms polar covalent bonds with the hydrogen atoms in which the electrons are attracted to the sulfur.

In SO_2 and Na_2SO_4, the sulfur atom is less electron attracting than the oxygen. It forms polar covalent bonds with the oxygen atoms in which the electrons are attracted to the oxygen. Four electrons are thus attracted in the case of SO_2, 6 in the case of Na_2SO_4.

20:7   Balancing Oxidation-Reduction Equations

In some cases, oxidation-reduction reactions require equations with large coefficients. There is a need for a method that will help to balance such equations.

Essentially, to balance an oxidation-reduction equation, it is necessary to make sure that the number of electrons gained by the oxidizing agent is equal to the number lost by the reducing agent. How this can be achieved will be illustrated by the reaction commonly used to prepare chlorine gas.

Suppose it is necessary to balance

$$MnO_2 + HCl \rightarrow MnCl_2 + Cl_2\uparrow + H_2O$$

This is a reaction in which MnO_2 is the electron acceptor, gaining electrons from chloride ions of hydrochloric acid. When the chloride ions lose electrons, they form chlorine atoms, which pair up to form molecules of chlorine gas.

Let us determine the oxidation numbers of the manganese and the chlorine in their compounds.

Originally, in MnO_2, the oxidation number of Mn is $4+$, being combined with two oxygen atoms, each $2-$. Finally, in $MnCl_2$, the oxidation number of Mn is $2+$, being combined with two chloride ions, each $1-$. Thus the oxidation number of the manganese changes from $4+$ to $2+$. Its oxidation number decreases, proving that Mn in MnO_2 accepts two electrons. This confirms its behavior as the oxidizing agent.

Originally, in HCl, the oxidation number of Cl is $1-$, being combined with one hydrogen atom whose oxidation number is $1+$. Finally, some chlorine is given off as a gas, $Cl_2^0\uparrow$. For the chlorine thus evolved, the oxidation number is zero (Rule 1). Thus the oxidation number of the molecular chlorine has changed from $1-$ to 0 indicating the loss of one electron per ion thus transformed. This confirms the behavior of the chloride ion as a reducing agent.

In the above reaction, each atom of Mn gains two electrons, while each molecule of chlorine forms through the loss of two electrons. Therefore, both Mn^{2+} and Cl_2^0 will have the same coefficient, thus ensuring that the number of electrons gained will equal the number lost. To each is assigned a coefficient of one (which is understood but not expressed).

$$\begin{array}{cccc} 4+ & 1- & 2+ & 0 \\ MnO_2 & + HCl \to MnCl_2 & + Cl_2^0\uparrow & + H_2O \end{array}$$

$$1 \times 2e^- \quad = \quad 1 \times 2 \times 1e^-$$

With a coefficient of 1 for MnO_2, there will also be a coefficient of 1 for $MnCl_2$. Inspection now shows that 4 chlorine atoms are required by the right hand (or product) side; therefore, a coefficient of 4 is needed for HCl:

$$MnO_2 + 4HCl \to MnCl_2 + Cl_2^0\uparrow + H_2O$$

Four hydrogen atoms are now available, enough for 2 molecules of water. Hence, a coefficient of 2 is needed for H_2O:

$$MnO_2 + 4HCl \to MnCl_2 + Cl_2^0\uparrow + 2H_2O$$

With these coefficients, the oxygen atoms are also balanced and thus the entire equation is balanced.

In this reaction, some chloride ions, Cl^-, lost one electron to become Cl^0, others remained unchanged. In the above equation, Cl^0, the reducing agent, appears in HCl, $MnCl_2$, and Cl_2^0. The Cl's of $MnCl_2$ represent chloride ions, Cl^-, and thus they have not lost any electrons. It would be incorrect to place the arrow at this point to show electron loss.

The Cl's of HCl include those which *did* lose electrons to become Cl_2 as well as those which *did not*. It would be misleading to place the arrow at this point to show electron loss.

The Cl's of Cl_2^0 are indeed the result of electron loss. Therefore this was the point at which the arrow was placed.

QUESTIONS

1. (a) Define in electronic terms: *oxidation, reduction, oxidizing agent; reducing agent.*
   (b) Explain each of the above by reference to the reaction $2Mg + O_2 \to 2MgO$.

2. Give three examples of oxidizing agents and three examples of reducing agents. In each case, show the number of electrons gained or lost in a reaction you select.

3. What is an *oxidation number*?

4. What are the rules for calculating oxidation numbers?

5. Indicate the oxidation number of each element in the following compounds:
   (a) AgI   (e) Na_2S (i) $BiCl_3$
   (b) NaBr   (f) Mg_3N_2 (j) $ZnBr_2$
   (c) $FeCl_2$ (g) CaF_2
   (d) $FeCl_3$ (h) Al_2O_3

6. Indicate the oxidation number of each element in the following compounds:
   (a) H_2O (f) $KMnO_4$ (k) H_2SO_4
   (b) K_2CO_3 (g) $BaSO_4$ (l) SO_3
   (c) $KClO_3$ (h) CuS   (m) CuO
   (d) CO   (i) NH_4OH (n) $MnCl_2$
   (e) CO_2 (j) $CuCrO_4$ (o) MnO_2

7. Determine the oxidation number of chlorine in each of the following compounds:
   (a) NaCl (b) NaClO (c) $NaClO_2$ (d) $NaClO_3$ (e) $NaClO_4$

8. Explain how oxidation-reduction reactions might liberate electrical energy.

9. Write the overall reaction taking place in a car battery. Show clearly how this is an oxidation-reduction reaction.

10. Identify the following as oxidations or reductions:
    (a) $Cu^{2+} + 2e^- \rightarrow Cu^0$
    (b) $Br_2^0 + 2e^- \rightarrow 2Br^-$
    (c) $Mg^0 \rightarrow Mg^{2+} + 2e^-$
    (d) $Zn^0 \rightarrow Zn^{2+} + 2e^-$
    (e) $Cl_2^0 + 2e^- \rightarrow 2Cl^-$

11. When the electrolysis of fused sodium chloride is carried out, chlorine gas forms at the positive electrode (anode) and metallic sodium forms at the negative electrode (cathode). Tell which of these reactions is an oxidation and which is a reduction. Represent the reactions separately by means of equations showing the electrons involved.

12. What is the significance of oxidation-reduction in terms of change in oxidation numbers?

13. Indicate which of the following are oxidation-reduction type reactions, and label the substances oxidized, the substances reduced, the oxidizing agents, and the reducing agents.
    (a) $Fe^0 + S^0 \rightarrow FeS$
    (b) $NaOH + HCl \rightarrow NaCl + H_2O$
    (c) $2FeCl_2 + Cl_2^0 \rightarrow 2FeCl_3$
    (d) $CuO + H_2^0 \rightarrow H_2O + Cu^0$
    (e) $2Fe_2O_3 + 6H_2^0 \rightarrow 6H_2O + 4Fe^0$
    (f) $Zn^0 + 2HCl \rightarrow ZnCl_2 + H_2^0$
    (g) $2H_2^0 + O_2^0 \rightarrow 2H_2O$
    (h) $NaCl + AgNO_3 \rightarrow AgCl + NaNO_3$
    (i) $2Al^0 + 3H_2SO_4 \rightarrow Al_2(SO_4)_3 + 3H_2^0$
    (j) $H_2S + SO_2 \rightarrow H_2O + S^0$

14. (a) What is the basic procedure in balancing oxidation-reduction equations?
    (b) Balance the following equations using this method.
        (i) $Cu^0 + HNO_3 \rightarrow Cu(NO_3)_2 + NO_2 + H_2O$
        (ii) $NH_3 + O_2^0 \rightarrow NO + H_2O$
        (iii) $H_2S + SO_2 \rightarrow H_2O + S^0$
        (iv) $KMnO_4 + H_2SO_3 \rightarrow K_2SO_4 + MnSO_4 + H_2SO_4 + H_2O$

CHAPTER

21 Liquids

21:1 The Kinetic Molecular Theory Applied to Liquids: Intermolecular Attraction

The model used to explain the behavior of gases suggested that they consist of molecules in motion. The energy of motion of the molecules is their kinetic energy, and when heat energy is added, that kinetic energy increases. When heat is removed, the kinetic energy of the molecules decreases and the molecules move more slowly. Eventually as the gas is cooled, the speed is reduced more and more and the intermolecular attraction causes the molecules to condense to a liquid.

The intermolecular forces of attraction are called *van der Waals' forces*, after the chemist who studied the behavior of gases being cooled, compressed, and liquefied. Although the van der Waals' forces are powerful enough to hold the molecules together in the liquid state, they are not as strong as the chemical bonds that exist between atoms.

For chemically similar liquids, the bigger the molecules of a liquid, the larger the van der Waals' forces they exert on one another. This fact is illustrated by the liquids listed in Table 21.1. Their boiling points increase with their molecular mass.

21:2 The Intermolecular Attraction in Water

In addition to van der Waals' forces, which are present in all liquids, there are at least two other forces of attraction between the molecules of water. These cause water to be an unusual liquid in many respects. These forces arise because

TABLE 21.1		
Boiling Points vs Molecular Masses		
Liquid	Molecular Mass (amu)	Boiling Point (°C)
Hexane, C_6H_{14}	86	69
Heptane, C_7H_{16}	100	98
Octane, C_8H_{18}	114	126

(a) water molecules are polar, and (b) the oxygen and hydrogen atoms in different water molecules exert a special attraction, called hydrogen bonding, on one another (sec. 21.3).

Water molecules are polar for two reasons. First, the oxygen and hydrogen atoms differ in their ability to attract electrons, oxygen being the more electronegative of the two. Therefore, the bond between oxygen and hydrogen in the water molecule is a polar covalent bond. Second,

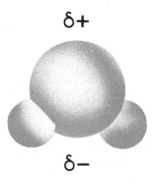

$\delta+$

$\delta-$

the water molecule has the shape of an angle of about 105 degrees:

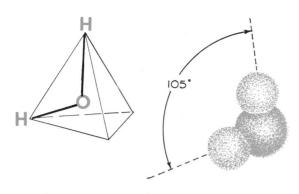

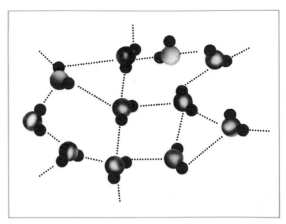

Fig. 21.1 *Schematic diagram of hydrogen bonding Hydrogen bonds between water molecules are shown by dotted lines.*

Because the water molecule has this shape, the oxygen atom is a negative pole, while the region between the hydrogen atoms is a positive pole. Thus the water molecule consists of poles of positive and negative electricity, respectively. For this reason, it is termed a *dipole* (di-pole, two poles).

A liquid composed of polar molecules is called a *polar liquid*. In such a liquid, the molecules attract each other more strongly than in a non-polar liquid. The attraction between two dipoles takes place because the positive pole of one molecule attracts the negative pole of another.

21:3   Hydrogen Bonding

In the case of water, the polarity gives rise to an intermolecular force whose power is unique. The oxygen atom in a water molecule is not only bonded to two hydrogen atoms, but it is attracted to hydrogen atoms belonging to other molecules as well (Fig. 21.1).
As a result, the force of intermolecular attraction is unusually powerful in water.

Hydrogen bonding is a powerful intermolecular force present in compounds containing —OH and —NH groups, as well as in hydrogen fluoride, HF.

What evidence is there for hydrogen bonding? The simplest and most convincing proof for hydrogen bonding is found by comparing the boiling points of water and the compounds resembling water. Two ideas, illustrated in Table 21.1, are essential to the proof. First, the higher the boiling point of a compound, the greater is the force of attraction between the molecules. Second, large molecules attract each other more strongly than small molecules, other things being equal. With these thoughts in mind, compare the boiling points of water H_2O, hydrogen sulfide H_2S, hydrogen selenide H_2Se, and hydrogen telluride H_2Te. These compounds resemble water in the sense that oxygen, sulfur, selenium, and tellurium are elements of group VI of the periodic table. Since they are compounds of hydrogen with another element, they are called *hydrides*. Their boiling points and molecular mass are given in Table 21.2 and shown graphically in Fig. 21.2.

Note that the boiling point of water is much higher than that of even hydrogen telluride. This is true despite the fact that the molecule of water is the smallest and lightest of the four. True to form, the boiling points of the three other compounds decrease as the molecules become smaller (Fig. 21.2).

TABLE 21.2

The Boiling Points of the Hydrides of Group VI

Elements of Group VI and their Atomic Mass		Their Hydrides and Molecular Mass		Boiling Points °C
Oxygen	(16)	H_2O	(18)	+100
Sulfur	(32)	H_2S	(34)	−60
Selenium	(79)	H_2Se	(81)	−40
Tellurium	(128)	H_2Te	(130)	0

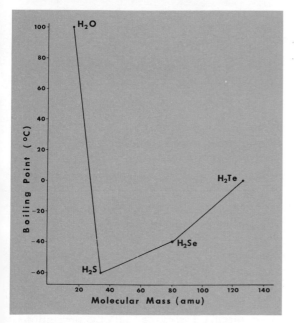

Fig. 21.2 *Evidence for hydrogen bonding
The unusually high boiling point of water is due to
hydrogen bonding between its molecules.*

21:4 Liquids Have a Definite Volume

Because of the intermolecular forces of attraction, liquids retain their own volume and do not distribute themselves throughout the whole space of the containing vessel, as gases do. Since the molecules of a liquid still have the freedom to glide past each other, the liquid takes the shape of the vessel it occupies.

21:5 The Vapor Pressure of Liquids

A liquid gradually evaporates if it is left in an open vessel. In *evaporation*, the molecules of the liquid pass into the air in the form of a gas or vapor. In order to be able to do so, the molecules must have enough energy to overcome the intermolecular attractive forces. At any one time, only a relatively small fraction of all the molecules have this amount of energy. These molecules escape into the air and do not return to the liquid, and the liquid thus evaporates.

If the liquid is in a closed vessel, the process of evaporation still goes on since the molecules escape from the liquid as before. Now the molecules have only a limited space in which to fly about. Soon they must fall back into the liquid. This is called *condensation*. Two processes are now going on in the closed vessel, evaporation and condensation. These processes go on at equal rates, thus establishing a *dynamic equilibrium* (Fig. 21.3).

In such a condition, no change appears to be taking place, but in reality two opposite changes are going on at equal rates. Some molecules leave the liquid to enter the vapor, while others leave the vapor to return to the liquid.

The pressure that the molecules in the vapor above the liquid exert is called the *vapor pressure*, and it depends on the temperature only. The size, shape, or fullness of the vessel do not alter the vapor pressure of a liquid.

Since the vapor pressure depends on the escape of the molecules from a liquid, the more powerful the force of intermolecular attraction, the smaller the vapor pressure of the liquid will be. The vapor pressure of water is less than that of a non-polar liquid of the same molecular mass.

21:6 Boiling Point

When a liquid is heated, the heat energy makes the molecules move more rapidly as their energy increases. This causes more molecules to over-

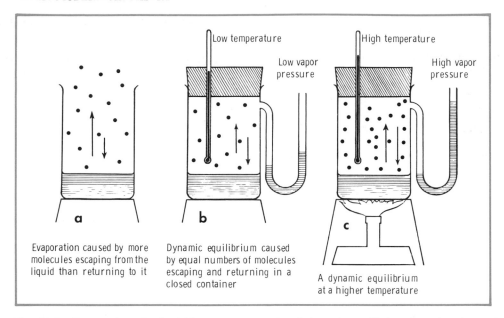

Fig. 21.3   *Evaporation of a liquid in an open vessel and dynamic equilibrium in a closed vessel*

come the molecular attraction and escape from the liquid as vapor. Thus the vapor pressure of a liquid increases rapidly as its temperature is raised (Fig. 21.4). A point is reached where the vapor pressure becomes as great as the atmospheric pressure. It is then that the liquid begins to boil. The temperature at which the vapor pressure of a liquid becomes 760 mm, the standard pressure of the atmosphere, is called the *normal boiling point* of the liquid. The greater the molecular attractive forces in a liquid, the higher will be its boiling point (Fig. 21.4).

21:7   Heat of Vaporization

When a liquid changes to its vapor, the molecules need to be separated from one another. To do this, the forces of intermolecular attraction must be overcome, and this requires work. The energy for this work is called the *heat of vaporization*. When a liquid changes to a vapor, the heat of vaporization must be supplied to the liquid, but when the vapor re-condenses to the liquid state, the same amount of energy is

liberated. As a general rule, *heat is required when matter passes from a state where the particles are closer, or are held more rigidly together, to a state where they are further apart, or are held less rigidly*. Such is the case in vaporization and melting. When the opposite occurs, that is, when matter passes from a state where the particles are held loosely to a state where they are held more firmly, heat is given out. Such is the case in condensation and freezing.

As would be expected, in liquids of stronger intermolecular forces the heat of vaporization is greater than in liquids of weaker forces. Thus, the heat of vaporization of water is 540 calories per gram, while the heat of vaporization of octane is about 140 calories per gram.

21:8   Freezing Point

If a liquid is cooled, the loss of heat means a lowering of molecular energy and molecular motion. Upon continued cooling, a point is reached where the molecules move so slowly

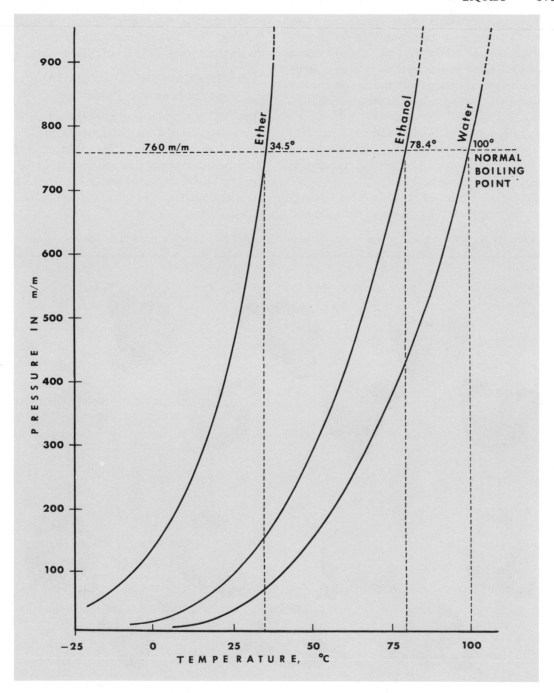

Fig. 21.4 *Graph showing how the vapor pressure of a liquid changes with temperature*

that the intermolecular forces cause the molecules to assume certain positions in a geometrical pattern called a *crystal*. The substance is thus *solidified* or *frozen*. The solid is usually in the form of rigid crystals, and any molecular motion that does remain is limited to vibration only.

As in the case of boiling and condensation, freezing is a reversible process which occurs at a definite temperature. The reverse process is called *melting* or *fusion*.

A definite amount of heat is needed to overcome the intermolecular forces in the solid and to permit the molecular motion needed for melting. This is called the *heat of fusion*. When the liquid freezes, the heat of fusion is liberated.

21:9 The Unusual Behavior of Water at its Freezing Point

The density of water is greater than that of ice. There is greater mass per unit volume in the liquid than in the solid. This means that there must be more molecules per unit volume after the crystal of ice is broken down by melting than while it was still intact. How can this be explained?

Fig. 21.5   *The crystal structure of ice, showing molecules of water held rigidly by hydrogen bonds*

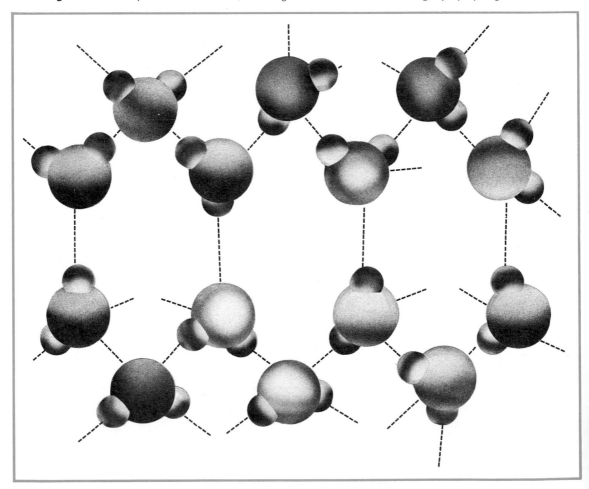

The water molecules exert special attraction on each other by hydrogen bonding. In the liquid state, the molecules are free to glide past each other. In the solid state, free molecular motion from point to point is eliminated. The hydrogen bonds become the cohesive force that helps to form the crystal of ice. Each oxygen atom is now attached, not merely attracted, to four hydrogen atoms – two combined chemically, two held by hydrogen bonding. The resulting ice structure is relatively uncrowded; that is, there is much space between the molecules, owing to the rigidity of the hydrogen bonds (Fig. 21.5).

When ice melts, some of the hydrogen bonds break and the molecules of water crowd together as the ice structure collapses. As a result, the molecules take up less space and the liquid has a greater density than the ice (Fig. 21.6).

From 0°C to 4°C, the volume continues to decrease as more hydrogen bonds break. Meanwhile, thermal agitation drives the molecules further apart. Above 4°C, the expanding effect of thermal agitation exceeds the crowding effect caused by the continuing breakage of hydrogen bonds. This explains why 4°C is the temperature of maximum density. In ice, the hydrogen bonds hold the molecules in an "open" crystal

Fig. 21.6 *Expansion and contraction of water on freezing and melting*

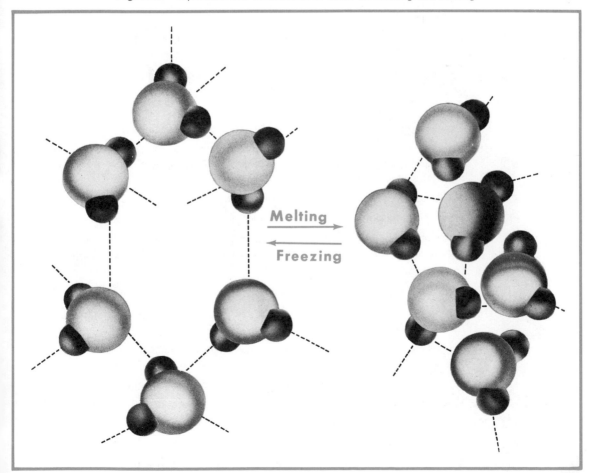

Melting →

← Freezing

lattice. Freezing causes expansion of volume. In water, the hydrogen bonds are not rigid, and the molecules come closer together. Melting causes contraction in volume.

It should be noted that hydrogen bonds remain an attractive force between water molecules in the liquid state, and even to a certain extent, in the gaseous state.

QUESTIONS

1. Why does lowering the temperature of a gas cause it to condense to a liquid?

2. What are van der Waals' forces?

3. Why is the water molecule polar? Draw a diagram to illustrate your answer.

4. Draw a graph similar to that shown in Fig. 21.2. Plot on the graph the normal boiling points of hydrogen iodide, HI ($-35°C$), hydrogen bromide, HBr ($-67°C$), hydrogen chloride, HCl ($-84°C$), and hydrogen fluoride, HF ($19°C$). Label and join the four points obtained by straight lines. Draw conclusions concerning intermolecular forces of attraction present in these compounds.

5. Octane, C_8H_{18}, is said to be a non-polar liquid. Explain clearly what is meant by this statement.

6. Explain why the density of water (18 amu) is greater than that of octane (114 amu) in spite of the fact that octane has a greater molecular mass.

7. Explain dynamic equilibrium by reference to an evaporating liquid in a closed container.

8. What is meant by the term *vapor pressure*?

9. How is vapor pressure related to the force of intermolecular attraction?

10. Consider Fig. 21.3 b and c in which dynamic equilibrium exists between the liquid phase and the vapor phase. Compare these from the point of view of the number of molecules leaving the liquid and returning to it.

11. Relate boiling point to atmospheric pressure.

12. How is boiling point related to the forces of intermolecular attraction in a liquid?

13. Referring to Fig. 21.4, determine the temperature at which water boils under the following pressures: (a) 400 mm Hg (b) 200 mm Hg (c) 100 mm Hg (d) 500 mm Hg.

14. What is *heat of vaporization*?

15. Why is the heat of vaporization of octane less than that of water?

16. Why is heat absorbed when the particles of matter making up a substance are forced further apart?

17. Why is energy given up when a liquid changes to a solid?

18. (a) What is *heat of fusion*?
    (b) The heat of fusion of water is 80 cal/g. What does this mean?

19. How many calories are required to convert 10 g of water at 100°C to steam at 100°C?

20. Describe the structure of ice.

21. Why does water expand upon freezing?

22. Explain carefully why the maximum density of water is at 4°C.

22 Solids

22:1 The Kinetic Molecular Theory Applied to Solids

A solid is rigid; it has a definite shape with enough mechanical strength to resist changes in its shape. An examination of many solids shows that their structure has a definite geometrical form. They are said to be *crystalline*. Although the particles of a solid do not wander freely, they vibrate back and forth about their fixed positions. When the solid is heated sufficiently, the vibrations of its particles, atoms, molecules, or ions, become great enough to break the bonds that hold them in the crystal and the solid melts.

22:2 The External Structure of Crystals

A crystal is always bounded by flat surfaces or planes which meet at right angles or at some other characteristic angles. Crystals can be classified according to their geometrical forms. The structures of crystals are best described in terms of imaginary axes drawn through their centers and parallel to the planes. All crystals that have been studied belong to one or other of six fundamental arrangements of axes. These six *crystallographic systems* are illustrated in Fig. 22.1. The study of the structure of crystals is called *crystallography*.

22:3 The Internal Structure of Crystals

The external shape of a crystal is the result of the spatial arrangement of the particles that make up the crystal. This three-dimensional, ordered array of particles is called the *crystal lattice*. The lattice may be considered to be made up of *unit cells* which are each the smallest portion of the crystal lattice.

To get an idea of how the unit cell recurs throughout a crystal, think of displays of spherically shaped fruit in a food store. Oranges and grapefruit are often arranged carefully in rows forming a layer; other rows are then fitted into the spaces formed by the spheres of the level below (Fig. 22.2).

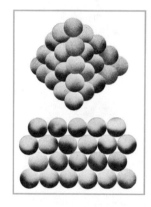

Fig. 22.2 *The regular spacing of ions or atoms in a crystal*

The shape of the unit cell, and therefore of the whole crystal, depends on the force of attraction between the particles, on whether the particles are the same or different, and, if they are different, on their relative sizes.

The unit cell of a given crystallographic system may be one of a few types with the same shape. For example, in the cubic system alone, there are three common types. The lattice may be made up of *simple cubic, face-centered cubic,* or *body-centered cubic* cells (Fig. 22.3).

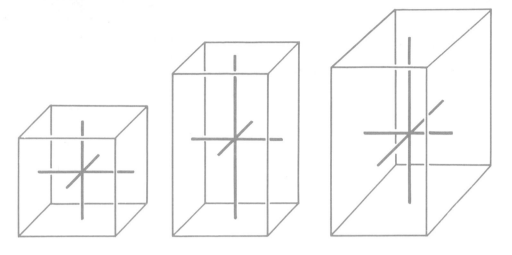

a. Cubic

3 equal axes all at right
angles to one another

b. Tetragonal

2 equal axes and 1 axis
of different length; all at
right angles to one another

c. Orthorhombic

3 unequal axes all at right
angles to one another

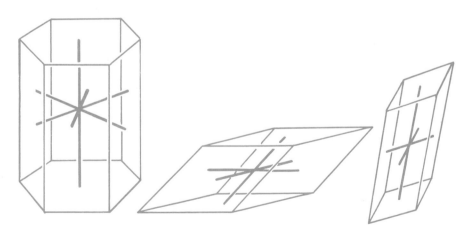

d. Hexagonal

3 equal axes and a 4th of
different length; 3 at 60°
to one another and the 4th
at right angles to the other 3

e. Monoclinic

3 unequal axes, 2 at right
angles to each other; the
3rd is at right   angles to
one but not to the other

f. Triclinic

3 unequal axes,
no two at right
angles to the others

Fig. 22.1   *The six crystallographic system*

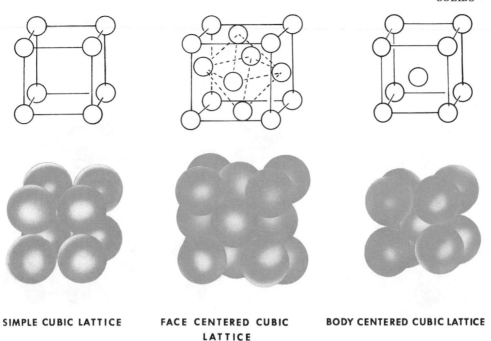

SIMPLE CUBIC LATTICE   **FACE CENTERED CUBIC LATTICE**   **BODY CENTERED CUBIC LATTICE**

Fig. 22.3   *Unit cells of the cubic system*

22:4   Types of Solids

Knowledge about crystal structure makes it possible to relate important physical properties of solids to their crystalline structure. In addition to the above classification, crystals can be classified also according to the chemical nature of their particles. This yields four types of solids: covalent, ionic, molecular, and metallic. Table 22.1 lists for each type, the nature of the particles occupying the lattice points, the nature of the bonds involved, a few characteristic properties, and some examples.

(a) *Covalent Atomic Solids*

In *covalent solids* the points of the crystal lattice are occupied by atoms which share electrons with their neighbors. These covalent bonds extend in fixed directions and bind the crystal in a giant interlocking structure. The covalent bonds are quite strong and as a result the solids are quite hard, have a high melting point, and are poor conductors of electricity.

The classical example of this type of solid is diamond, in which all the carbon atoms are held together in a lattice by covalent bonds. Each atom is joined to four others at exactly the same distance from one another. Any atom may be considered to be at the center of a tetrahedron with four atoms at the corners. This pattern repeats itself throughout the entire crystal which becomes a giant molecule (Fig. 22.4).

In graphite, on the other hand, each atom is joined to only three others by covalent bonds. The three covalent bonds lie in the same plane with an angle of 120 degrees between them. In this way, the carbon atoms arrange themselves at the corners of adjacent hexagons, forming planes. The atoms in a given plane are held together by strong covalent linkages, but the forces between the planes are weak. As a result,

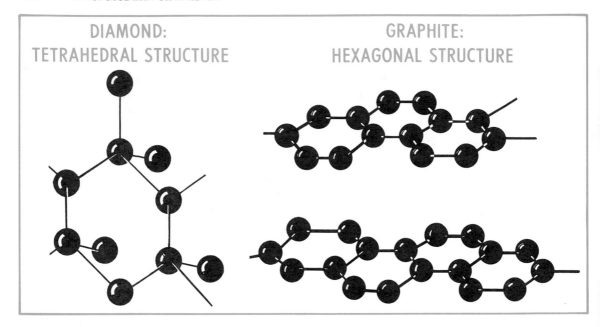

Fig. 22.4   *Crystal structure of diamond and graphite*

the planes can glide readily past one another. This causes graphite to be soft and flake-like. Furthermore, this structure requires only three of the electrons of the carbon atoms to form strong covalent bonds. One electron is relatively free to move, giving graphite its power to conduct electric current, a property that diamond does not have.

(b) *Ionic Solids*

The particles that occupy the lattice points in an *ionic solid* are positive and negative ions. The binding forces that hold the crystal together are the fairly strong electrostatic attractions between the ions of opposite charge. Therefore, these solids have rather high melting points, are hard and brittle, and are poor conductors of electricity. Examples of ionic solids include sodium chloride, $NaCl$, potassium nitrate, KNO_3, and sodium sulfate, Na_2SO_4.

Fig. 3.2 shows the lattice of sodium chloride, which, like all ionic salts, exists only in the ionic, not in the molecular condition. In the lattice, every sodium ion has six chloride ions as nearest neighbors; one to the right and one to the left, one above and one below, one in front and one behind. Similarly, every chloride ion has six sodium ions as immediate neighbors.

(c) *Molecular Solids*

In *molecular solids* the lattice points are occupied by molecules. The forces of attraction between the molecules of such solids can be of two kinds. The relatively weak van der Waals' attractions are present in all molecular solids. If the molecules of the solid are polar, additional forces act between the poles of opposite charges. However, these forces are not very strong when compared to covalent or ionic bonds. Thus, molecular crystals have low melting points, are usually quite soft and do not conduct the electric current. Iodine crystals, I_2, dry ice, CO_2, and ordinary ice, H_2O, are examples of molecular solids.

(d) *Metallic Solids*

The crystal lattice of *metallic solids* consists of atoms in which the outer electrons are free to move from atom to atom under the slightest electrical stimulus. In reality, because their outer electrons are free to move about in the metal lattice, the particles that make up the metallic crystal are positively charged ions, rather than atoms. The mobile electrons belong to the crystal as a whole and are the cohesive force in the metal. This mobility of electrons gives the metals their high electrical conductivity. The number of free electrons available for bonding varies from group to group in the

TABLE 22.1

Types of Solids

Types	Covalent	Ionic	Molecular	Metallic
Particles occupying lattice points	atoms	positive and negative ions	molecules	positive ions
Binding force between particles	shared electrons	electrostatic attraction	van der Waals' and dipole-dipole intermolecular attraction	electrical attraction between positive ions and negative electrons
Strength of binding force	very strong	fairly strong	weak	dependant on the number of mobile electrons
Properties	hard, high melting point, non-conductors	hard, brittle, medium melting point, non-conductors	soft, low melting point, non-conductors	wide range of hardness and melting point, good conductors
Examples	diamond, C quartz, SiO_2 carborundum, or silicon carbide, SiC	sodium chloride, NaCl potassium nitrate, KNO_3	iodine, I_2 ice, H_2O dry ice, CO_2	sodium aluminum iron
Pictorial representation	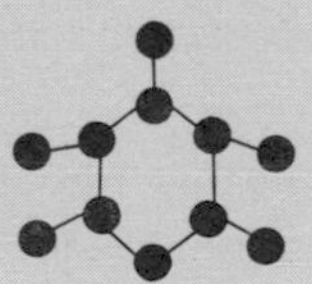	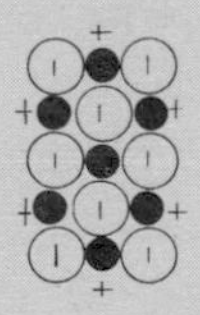	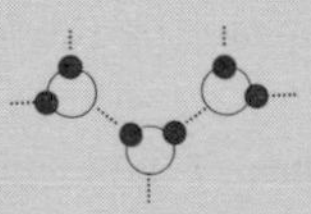	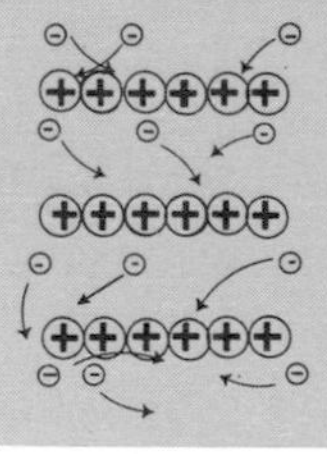

periodic table. This partly explains why the properties of metals vary as they do. Some are better conductors than others; their melting points and their degree of hardness vary over a wide range. Potassium melts at 62°C while iron melts at 1535°C. Sodium is so soft that it can be cut with a knife. Tungsten is a hard metal used to make alloys that can cut steel.

22:5   Efflorescence and Deliquescence

Theoretically, molecules might escape from solids as they do from liquids. If this occurred, the solid would then have a vapor pressure. Thus molecules of carbon dioxide escape readily from dry ice, solid carbon dioxide. Most solids, however have only a negligible vapor pressure.

A certain class of salts, containing *water of hydration*, have a definite vapor pressure at any particular temperature due to the evaporation of some of the molecules of water of hydration. If these salts are placed in an area where the humidity is so high that the water vapor pressure in the air is greater than that of the salt, then some water might condense on the salt. This phenomenon, called *deliquescence*, con-

tinues until the rate of condensation on the salt and evaporation from the salt become equal.

If, on the other hand, the humidity is so low that the vapor pressure of the salt is greater than that of the environment, then the water of hydration evaporates. This phenomenon, called *efflorescence*, also continues until evaporation and condensation go on at equal rates.

Sodium sulfate is an example of a salt with 10 molecules of water of hydration per formula unit of salt. In this form, the hydrate would be represented by $Na_2SO_4 \cdot 10H_2O$. The loss of water, and the condensation of water may be represented by the equation:

$$\overset{\text{efflorescence}}{\underset{\text{deliquescence}}{Na_2SO_4 \cdot 10H_2O \rightleftharpoons Na_2SO_4 + 10H_2O}}$$

(solid)   (solid)   (vapor)

If the hydrated salt is placed in an environment where the vapor pressure of water is less than that of the salt, the latter steadily loses its water of hydration, thus becoming a lower hydrate, or completely anhydrous. The reverse occurs if the vapor pressure of the environment is greater than that of the anhydrous salt or of the lower hydrate.

QUESTIONS

1. What is a *crystalline solid*?

2. In terms of the kinetic molecular theory, explain why: (a) solids are practically incompressible; (b) solids expand when heated; (c) solids have a definite shape.

3. Why must a solid absorb heat in order to melt?

4. What is meant by the following terms: (a) *crystallographic systems*; (b) *crystal lattice*; (c) *unit cell*?

5. What types of cubic cells occur? Illustrate your answer with diagrams.

6. List the six main crystalline systems and give the distinguishing characteristics of each.

7. What explanation can be given for the hardness of diamond?

8. Why is graphite so much softer than diamond?

9. Account for the fact that graphite will conduct an electric current while diamond will not.

10. Describe the crystalline structure of sodium chloride.

11. Account for the fact that ionic solids do not conduct the electric current even though they are made of positive and negative ions?

12. Atom A belongs to group I of the periodic table and atom B belongs to group VII. What type of solid results when the two atoms combine to form compound AB? Predict the general properties of compound AB with regard to hardness, melting point, conductivity in the solid state, and conductivity in the liquid state.

13. Describe the crystalline structure of metals.

14. Why are metals good conductors of electricity?

15. What is the main cohesive force in metals?

16. What is a *hydrate*?

17. What is the percentage of water of hydration in sodium sulfate decahydrate, $Na_2SO_4 \cdot 10H_2O$?

18. How many pounds of anhydrous copper (II) sulfate can be obtained from 100 pounds of copper (II) sulfate pentahydrate $CuSO_4 \cdot 5H_2O$?

CHAPTER

23 Solutions

23:1 Nature of Solutions

Solutions have been defined in section 3:6 as homogeneous mixtures. Because solutions are of widespread importance in chemistry, they are discussed somewhat more intensively in the present chapter. Their importance is apparent when it is realized that the majority of chemical reactions that occur in nature as well as in the chemical industries take place in solution. For example, unless food is in solution, it cannot be absorbed by the blood.

A solution is usually formed when a gas, a liquid, or a solid is dissolved in a liquid, called the *solvent*; but gases and even solids may act as solvents (Table 23.1). The substance dissolved is called the *solute*. A *solution* may be redefined as a homogeneous mixture of solute and solvent.

23:2 Solubility

Ethanol and water mix with one another in all

proportions to form a solution. Such liquids are said to be perfectly *miscible*. On the other hand, oil and water are *immiscible*; they do not mix in one another.

In many cases, there is a limit to the amount of solute A that will dissolve in a given amount of solvent B under specified conditions. When this amount, called the *solubility* of A in B, is exceeded, the undissolved excess is called a *precipitate*. For example, 36 g of sodium chloride dissolve in 100 g of water at 20°C. When the solubility of a solute is determined at various temperatures, the results can be shown as a *solubility curve* (Fig. 23.1).

When enough solute is added to a solvent so that the limit of solubility is reached, the solution is said to be *saturated*. If more solute is added, a precipitate of undissolved solute forms. The saturated solution will be in equilibrium with the undissolved solute. In this condition, the solute enters and leaves the solution at the

TABLE 23.1		
Types of Solutions		
Solute	Solvent	Examples
solid	liquid	brine (sodium chloride in water)
liquid	liquid	antifreeze (alcohol in water)
gas	liquid	soda water (carbon dioxide in water)
solid	gas	naphthalene in air (sublimation of moth balls)
liquid	gas	humid air (water vapor in air)
gas	gas	air (oxygen in nitrogen)
solid	solid	brass (zinc in copper)
liquid	solid	amalgams (gold in mercury)
gas	solid	hydrogen in platinum

186

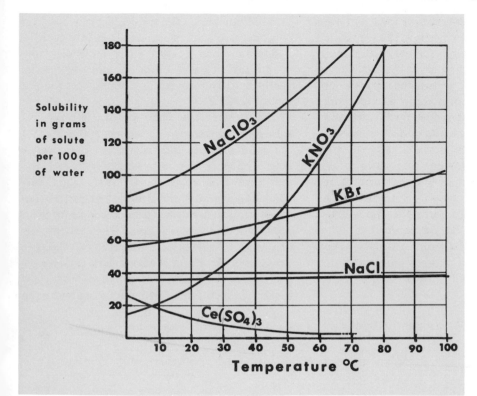

Fig. 23.1 *Solubility curves*

same rate. If the solution contains less solute than it is capable of dissolving at a given temperature, it is *unsaturated*.

With certain solutes such as sodium thiosulfate, $Na_2S_2O_3$, and sodium acetate, CH_3COONa, it is possible to prepare solutions which contain more of the dissolved solute than the normal saturation quantity. Such solutions are *supersaturated* and can be prepared by cooling saturated solutions or by evaporation. These solutions are unstable and crystallize easily when jarred or when a crystal of the solute is added to them.

Factors Affecting Rate of Solution of Solids in Liquids

The solubility curve for potassium nitrate indicates that about 55 g dissolve in 100 g of water at room temperature, about 20°C. If this amount is simply added to the water, consider-

able time may be required for it to dissolve completely. The process of dissolving may be speeded up by agitation or stirring, by reducing the size of the crystals, and by heating the solution. These three methods increase the rate of dissolving by favoring the contact between solute and solvent.

23:3 The Process of Dissolving

As is well known, certain solvents readily dissolve certain solutes, but not others. While we are still unable to predict perfectly what solute will dissolve in what solvent or the extent of any given solubility, nevertheless, we may learn a great deal about the process of dissolving by considering the intermolecular or interionic forces that come into play.

When solute A dissolves in solvent B, the intermolecular or interionic forces of A and of B both have to be overcome. The solute must be broken down to its molecules or ions, and even the solvent molecules need to be separated somewhat to make room for the molecules or ions of the solute. To separate the particles of solute requires energy, as does the separation of a solid in melting or of a liquid in vaporizing. Such energy might be provided by the formation of bonds between the solute and the solvent.

When salt dissolves in water, the powerful interionic forces between the sodium and chloride ions, as well as the hydrogen bonds between the water molecules, both have to be overcome. The energy needed to break these bonds is supplied by the new bonds formed between the ions and the water molecules. Such bonds are referred to as *ion-dipole bonds*, the ions being Na^+ and Cl^-, while the dipoles are the water molecules.

When an ionic compound, such as sodium chloride, is placed in water, the partly positive hydrogen atoms of the water molecules surround the negative chloride ions, while the partly negative oxygen surrounds the sodium ions (Fig. 23.2).

The formation of these ion-dipole bonds releases enough energy to separate the ions of the solid salt and the molecules of the water (Fig. 23.3).

Experiments have shown that when surrounded by water, the force of attraction between electrically charged bodies is reduced to 1/80 of its normal strength. This property is described by saying that water has a *dielectric constant* of 80. Water is also able to dissolve organic compounds containing hydroxide groups (—OH) in their molecules by forming hydrogen

Fig. 23.2   *How polar water molecules are attracted to ions in the process of dissolving salts*

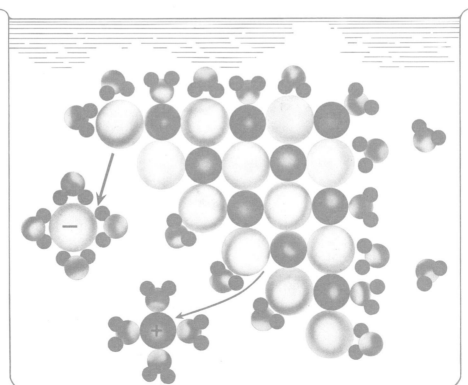

bonds with these groups. Such organic compounds include alcohol and sugar.

When, by contrast, oil is added to water, no bonds form between the non-polar molecules of oil and the polar molecules of water; therefore, no energy is released for breaking the powerful hydrogen bonds of the water. As a result, oil cannot dissolve in water; nor can water dissolve in oil. Similarly, when salt is added to an oil, there is no possibility of bonds forming between the ions of the salt and the molecules of oil. Thus, no energy is provided for breaking the interionic bonds of the salt, and, as a result, salt cannot dissolve in oil.

Again, the intermolecular forces in non-polar liquids are not very strong. When, therefore, one non-polar compound is added to another, it is easy for the solute and solvent molecules to be separated. For this reason non-polar substances readily dissolve in one another.

23:4 Factors Affecting Solubility

The concentration of a given saturated solution depends on the nature of the solvent, the nature of the solute, the temperature, and the pressure.

(a) The Nature of Solvent and Solute

As was pointed out in the previous section, sodium chloride dissolves in water but does not dissolve in oil. Some gases are extremely soluble in water while other gases are only slightly soluble. The dissolving mechanism of sodium chloride in water revealed that the formation of new bonds between solvent and solute made the reaction possible. No doubt, as knowledge about the structure of matter improves, better explanations for solubility will be possible.

(b) Effect of Temperature

As a general rule, gases dissolve in liquids to a larger extent at low temperatures than at high

Fig. 23.3 *Hydrated ions in a solution*

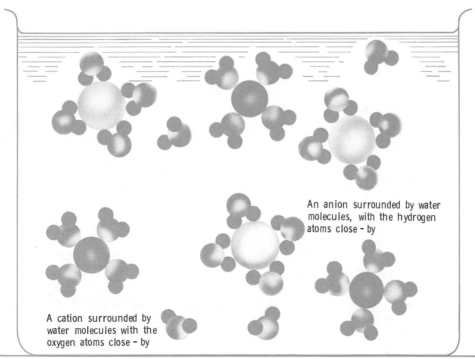

An anion surrounded by water molecules, with the hydrogen atoms close - by

A cation surrounded by water molecules with the oxygen atoms close - by

temperatures, while liquids and solids show opposite behavior. This may be explained by considering the effect of temperature on the solute and solvent in each case. The addition of heat increases the kinetic energy of all the particles of the solution. Such increased motion results in a greater tendency of gas molecules to escape from the solution; hence, the lower solubility of gases. The increased motion of the molecules of liquids and the particles of solids helps to break the bonds between them. This explains the higher solubility of liquids and solids.

(c) Effect of Pressure

Changes in pressure have practically no effect on the solubility of solids and liquids. However, gases are more soluble in liquids as pressure is raised. A familiar example is furnished by carbonated beverages. The gaseous solution is bottled under pressure. When the cap is removed, the pressure on the solution is reduced and the carbon dioxide gas escapes, causing the effervescence observed.

23:5   Concentration of Solutions: Molarity

A solution containing a large amount of solute is termed *concentrated* whereas one containing a small amount is called *dilute*. These terms do not give information about the exact amounts of solute present in a solution. Knowing the amount of solute is important to the chemist. The concentration of a solution may be expressed in a number of ways.

The concentration is sometimes reported on a percentage basis. This could be a percentage by weight or a percentage by volume. *Percentage by weight* represents the number of grams of solute present in 100 grams of solution. Thus a 5% solution of sugar in water contains 5 g of sugar in 100 g of solution. *Percentage by volume* shows how many milliliters of solute are present in 100 milliliters of solution. For instance, a 3%

solution of hydrogen peroxide contains 3 ml of H_2O_2 per 100 ml of solution.

Molarity

Units of concentration that indicate the relative number of solute molecules or ions present in a solution are called *chemical units*. An example of a useful chemical unit is the *molarity* (M) which expresses the number of moles of solute present in one liter of solution. The number of moles of a substance may be found by dividing its mass by its atomic or formula mass.

The reason for using molarity is to indicate how many particles of solute are present in the sample of the solution. Such information is more important than merely the mass or volume of solute because chemical reactions occur among the molecules or ions of the dissolved reactants.

23:6   Physical Properties of Solutions

When a non-volatile solute is dissolved in a liquid, the vapor pressure of the liquid is lowered because some of the solvent molecules collide with the solute particles near the surface of the liquid, thus preventing their escape. Since the vapor pressure of a liquid is due to the number of molecules escaping, the vapor pressure is lowered (Fig. 23.4).

The more solute particles there are, the greater is the number of interfering collisions and the greater is the drop in vapor pressure. Attraction between solute and solvent particles also makes it more difficult for solvent to escape. These considerations explain what is actually observed experimentally, namely, that the drop in the vapor pressure depends on the number of solute particles present in unit mass of solvent.

The lowering of the vapor pressure of a solution automatically causes its boiling point to be higher than that of the solvent. A liquid normally boils at the temperature at which its vapor pressure is equal to 760 mm or 1 atmosphere. The addition of a non-volatile solute

Example

What is the molarity of a solution of hydrochloric acid, HCl, (molecular mass 36.5 amu) containing 20.0 g of HCl in 500 ml of solution?

Solution

Since molarity is the number of moles of solute per liter of solution, molarity may be found by dividing the number of moles of solute (n) by the volume in liters (v) of the solution.

Mathematically,

$$\text{Molarity} = \frac{\text{moles of solute}}{\text{liters of solution}} = \frac{n}{v}$$

where   n, the number of moles of HCl in 20.0 grams, is $\frac{20.0 \text{ g}}{36.5 \text{ g}}$ moles

and   v, the number of liters of solution, is 0.50 liter

$\therefore$ $$\text{Molarity} = \frac{n}{v} = \frac{20.0 \text{ moles}}{36.5 \times 0.50 \text{ liters}}$$

$$= 1.10 \frac{\text{moles}}{\text{liters}} \text{ or } 1.10 \text{ molar or } 1.10 \text{ M}$$

This 1.10 M solution contains 1.10 moles of solute per liter of solution.

Fig. 23.4   *Lower vapor pressure of a solution compared to a pure solvent*

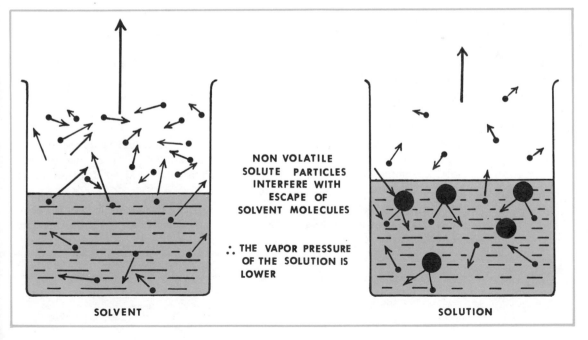

NON VOLATILE
SOLUTE PARTICLES
INTERFERE WITH
ESCAPE OF
SOLVENT MOLECULES

$\therefore$ THE VAPOR PRESSURE
OF THE SOLUTION IS
LOWER

SOLVENT   SOLUTION

lowers the vapor pressure of the solution below that of the solvent. Therefore, at the normal boiling temperature, the vapor pressure of the pure solvent is 760 mm, but that of the solution is less. The solution is not yet at its boiling point. To cause the solution to boil, it must be heated until its vapor pressure will also be equal to 760 mm. The additional temperature to which it must be heated for this reason is called the *rise in the boiling point* (Fig. 23.5). By similar reasoning, the solution freezes below the normal freezing temperature of the solvent.

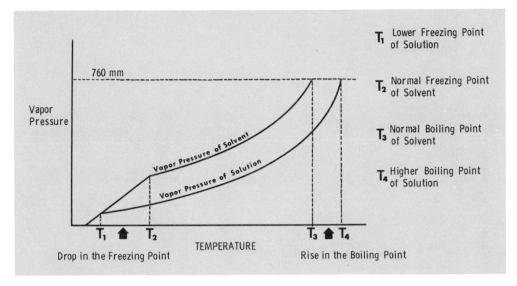

Fig. 23.5   *Vapor pressure, boiling and freezing points of a solvent and a solution*

QUESTIONS

1. Define *solution*, *solute*, and *solvent*. Give an example of each.

2. What is the importance of solutions?

3. What is meant by *miscible liquids*? Give an example.

4. Define *solubility* and *precipitate*.

5. Using the data available in Fig. 23.1, give the approximate solubility for the following salts at the given temperatures: (a) sodium chlorate at 20°C; (b) potassium nitrate at 10°C; (c) potassium bromide at 90°C; (d) sodium chloride at 90°C; (e) potassium bromide at 100°C.

6. The solubility of silver nitrate at various temperatures was determined in the laboratory. Draw on a graph the solubility curve of silver nitrate using the data obtained and shown below.

Temperature (°C)	0	10	20	30	40	50	60	70	80	90	100
Solubility (g of AgNO$_3$ per 100 g water)	115	160	215	270	335	400	470	550	650	760	910

7. Explain what happens when a crystal of the solute is dropped into: (a) an unsaturated solution; (b) a saturated solution; (c) a supersaturated solution.

8. How can the dissolving of sugar in water be speeded up?

9. Describe what forces need to be overcome in forming a solution.

10. Why does the formation of a solution require energy?

11. What are *ion-dipole bonds*?

12. Describe how water dissolves a salt like sodium chloride.

13. What is meant by the statement that "the dielectric constant of water is 80"?

14. How does water dissolve compounds containing hydroxide groups?

15. Why does water not dissolve oil?

16. Why does oil not dissolve salt?

17. What mass of sodium chloride would be required for 150 grams of solution 5% by weight NaCl?

18. Why do two oil-like substances usually mix?

19. What factors affect solubility?

20. Why does a rise in temperature decrease the solubility of a gas but usually increase the solubility of a solid?

21. When a glass of cold water is left standing in a warm room, bubbles of gas appear on the inside walls of the glass. Explain why.

22. Is a saturated solution necessarily a concentrated solution? Explain.

23. In what ways may the concentration of a solution be expressed?

24. What is *molarity*?

25. Describe how a molar solution of sodium chloride would be prepared.

26. What mass of nitric acid, HNO_3, is present in 1 liter of 0.1 M solution?

27. Calculate the number of grams of each of the following compounds required to prepare 1 liter of solution: (a) 1.0 M KNO_3; (b) 2.0 M H_2SO_4; (c) 0.5 M $KClO_3$; (d) 0.1 M $C_{12}H_{22}O_{11}$; (e) 3.0 M HNO_3.

28. Calculate the number of grams of solute needed to make the solutions listed below:
    (a) 1000 ml of 0.5 M NaCl; (d) 2000 ml of 0.09 M $AgNO_3$;
    (b) 200 ml of 1.5 M KCl;   (e) 250 ml of 3.1 M $BaCl_2$.
    (c) 100 ml of 0.3 M HCl;

29. Calculate the molarity of a solution containing 10 g of each of the following in 1 liter of solution: (a) H_2SO_4; (b) HCl; (c) $Ca(OH)_2$; (d) NaOH; (e) $CaCl_2$.

30. Give two reasons why the addition of a non-volatile solute to a liquid lowers the vapor pressure.

31. How does the non-volatile solute raise the boiling point?

24 Electrolytes and Non-Electrolytes

24:1 Conductance

Salt and sugar, two familiar compounds that look alike, are both soluble in water; but close examination reveals that their solutions behave quite differently. Each is typical of a class of solutions of different electrical, physical, and chemical properties. The two classes of solutions are termed electrolytes and non-electrolytes respectively.

Fig. 24.1 shows an electric bulb connected in series with two electrodes that dip into a solution. A switch enables a current to be turned on or off. If the liquid in the beaker conducts an electric current, the bulb will glow; otherwise it will not. By means of this apparatus, it can be shown that water solutions of such substances as sugar, methanol, and glycerol are non-conductors and, hence, *non-electrolytes*.

Similarly, water solutions of other substances such as sodium chloride, sodium hydroxide, and hydrochloric acid are good conductors. These are typical *electrolyte* solutions. Also, different electrolytes of the same concentration conduct current to a different extent. Consequently, electrolytes are further classified as *strong* and *weak*, depending on their ability to conduct an electric current.

The passage of direct current through electrolyte solutions may decompose them. Such decomposition, termed *electrolysis* (sec. 14:6), results in the liberation of hydrogen or a metallic element at the cathode and oxygen or other gases at the anode. In some cases the metallic anode may disintegrate during electrolysis.

Electrolyte solutions may also be used to generate electric voltage, thus acting as an electric cell or battery. Electricity is generated when two different metals are placed in an electrolyte solution and connected externally (sec. 14:4).

24:2 Physical Properties of Electrolytes

When a solid is dissolved in a liquid, it causes the vapor pressure of the liquid to decrease. This, in turn, raises the boiling point of the solution above that of the solvent and lowers

Fig. 24.1 *Conductivity of electrolytes*

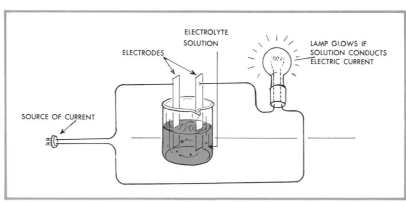

the freezing point of the solution below that of the solvent (sec. 23:6).

Experiment shows that in the case of non-electrolytes, one mole of solute dissolved in one kilogram* of water causes the boiling point to become 0.52°C higher and the freezing point 1.86°C lower than the normal values for pure water. The interesting point is that the same changes in the boiling and freezing point of water are produced by one mole of any non-volatile dissolved compound, provided the resulting solution is a non-electrolyte. Since one mole of any non-electrolyte compound always represents the same number of particles, it may be stated that the rise in the boiling point and the drop in the freezing point of a solution depend only on the number of particles of solute present in the solution per unit mass of solvent.

For electrolytes, on the other hand, the rise in the boiling point or drop in the freezing point is greater than for non-electrolyte solutions of the same concentration. Many electrolytes raise the boiling point and lower the freezing point almost twice as much as non-electrolytes do for the same concentration. An aqueous solution of sodium chloride behaves in this way. Other electrolytes raise the boiling point and lower the freezing point to a greater or lesser extent than does sodium chloride.

24:3   Chemical Properties of Electrolytes

The properties of an aqueous electrolyte solution consist of the properties of its cations, its anions, and the solvent – water. Thus, every electrolyte has two sets of chemical properties due to its solute, and still another due to its solvent. These properties are independent of one another. An electrolyte has similar properties to any other having an ion in common. Thus, all solutions which contain the hydronium

ion, H_3O^+, have a set of properties in common; they are called by a common name – acids. Similarly, all the solutions with at least moderate amounts of hydroxide ions, OH^-, have properties in common, and are called bases. In the same way, all electrolytes containing other ions in common, such as the sodium ion, would show the properties typical of that ion. The chemical properties of electrolytes and their solutions make it easy to classify them as acids, bases, and salts.

Electrolytes are chemically active, reacting more rapidly than non-electrolytes. For example, when an acid is added to a base, the neutralization reaction occurs readily. When silver nitrate is added to sodium chloride, both in solution, precipitation of silver chloride promptly takes place. Acetic acid reacts instantly with sodium hydroxide, NaOH, but very slowly with ethanol, C_2H_5OH. Both sodium hydroxide and ethanol have the OH group; but sodium hydroxide is an electrolyte while ethanol is not.

24:4   The Electrolytic Dissociation of Substances in Solution

Among the several theories advanced to explain the properties of electrolyte solutions, one proposed by a Swedish chemist, Arrhenius, in 1885, was fairly successful. His theory, known as the *Theory of Electrolytic Dissociation*, has evolved as more knowledge about the structure of the atom has accumulated. Consequently, modern theories about electrolytes are refinements of the older ones.

The following is a summary of the modern ideas about electrolytes and ions.

1. Ionic solids, such as salts and strong bases, consist of ions. When these compounds dissolve, the molecules of water weaken

*A solution formed by dissolving one mole of a substance in 1000 g of solvent is said to be a 1 molal (1 m) solution. Molality, represented by the symbol m, should not be confused with molarity whose symbol is M.

the attraction between their cations and anions, and soon these ions are free and separate.

2. Some covalent compounds furnish ions by reacting chemically with water or other solvents. Such reactions cause the formation of hydronium ions, H_3O^+, and other ions. Acids and weak bases behave in this way. For example, the reaction between hydrogen chloride and water and that between ammonia and water can be represented, using electron-dot formulas, as follows:

$$H\!:\!\overset{\cdot\cdot}{\underset{H}{O}}\!:\quad +\quad H\!:\!\overset{\cdot\cdot}{\underset{\cdot\cdot}{Cl}}\!:\quad \longrightarrow\quad \left[H\!:\!\overset{\cdot\cdot}{\underset{H}{O}}\!:\!H\right]^{+}\quad +\quad \left[:\!\overset{\cdot\cdot}{\underset{\cdot\cdot}{Cl}}\!:\right]^{-}$$

Hydronium   Chloride
Ion   Ion

$$H\!:\!\overset{\cdot\cdot}{N}\!:\!H\ +\ H\!:\!\overset{\cdot\cdot}{\underset{H}{O}}\!:\ \rightleftharpoons\ \left[H\!:\!\overset{H}{\underset{H}{N}}\!:\!H\right]^{+}\ +\ \left[:\!\overset{\cdot\cdot}{\underset{H}{O}}\!:\right]^{-}$$

Ammonium   Hydroxide
Ion   Ion

3. The number of positive charges equals the number of negative charges in an electrolyte solution.

4. The ionization of weak electrolytes is a reversible reaction. A dynamic equilibrium exists between the process of molecules dissociating into ions and that of the reassociation of the ions into molecules. If the number of ions present at any time is relatively small in this reversible reaction, the electrolyte is termed *weak*. For example, when a 0.1 M acetic acid solution, CH_3COOH, is prepared, about 1% of the molecules react with the water to form acetate and hydronium ions:

$$CH_3COO\!:\!H\ +\ :\!\overset{\cdot\cdot}{\underset{H}{O}}\!:\!H\ \rightleftharpoons$$

Acetic Acid

In some electrolyte solutions, on the other hand, practically all the solute particles in solution exist as ions. Solutes of this type are the *strong* electrolytes. The terms strong and weak electrolytes refer to the *degree of ionization* these substances undergo when dissolved in water.

24:5 Explanation of Conductance and Electrolysis

To explain conductance and electrolysis, a simple case will now be discussed, namely, the electrolysis of a concentrated copper (II) chloride solution.

Copper (II) chloride consists of copper (II) ions, Cu^{2+}, and chloride ions, Cl^-. When water comes in contact with copper (II) chloride, the small polar water molecules surround the copper (II) and the chloride ions, thereby dissolving the salt and liberating its ions from the crystal lattice:

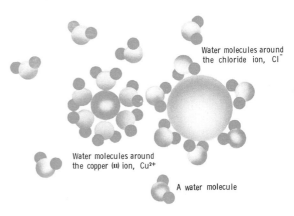

Water molecules around the chloride ion, Cl^-

Water molecules around the copper (II) ion, Cu^{2+}

A water molecule

If two inert electrodes (carbon or platinum) are introduced into a concentrated solution and a voltage is applied to them, the positive copper (II) ions migrate to the negative cathode while the negative chloride ions migrate to the

$$H\!:\!\overset{\cdot\cdot}{\underset{H}{O}}\!:\!H^{+}\quad +\quad CH_3COO\!:^{-}$$

Hydronium   Acetate
Ion   Ion

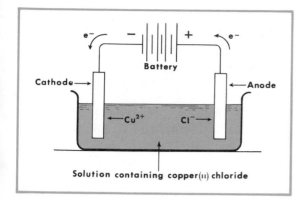

Fig. 24.2   *Electrolysis of copper (II) chloride*

anode (Fig. 24.2). At the cathode, each copper (II) ion gains two electrons and is reduced to an atom of copper:

$$Cu^{2+} + 2e^- \rightarrow Cu^0$$

Thus, copper metal is deposited on the cathode. Similarly, at the anode, each chloride ion gives up one electron and is oxidized to an atom of chlorine. Two such atoms form a molecule of chlorine and, in this way, chlorine gas is liberated at the anode:

$$Cl^- \rightarrow Cl^0 + 1e^-$$
$$2Cl^0 \rightarrow Cl_2^0\uparrow$$

The reactions taking place at the electrodes are referred to as *half-reactions* because they take place simultaneously and can be combined into a single over-all reaction:

cathode half-reaction:	$Cu^{2+} + 2e^- \rightarrow Cu$
anode half-reaction:	$2Cl^- \rightarrow Cl_2^0 + 2e^-$
over-all reaction:	$Cu^{2+}_{(aq)} + 2Cl^-_{(aq)} \rightarrow$ $Cu_{(s)} + Cl_2^0\uparrow_{(g)}$

During electrolysis, electrons have been removed from the cathode and returned to the anode. Thereby, the solution has effectively transferred electrons from cathode to anode. In this manner the solution acts as a conductor of the electric current.

Notice the difference in the way electrolyte solutions on the one hand, and metal conductors on the other, conduct the electric current. In ionic or electrolytic conduction, it is the *motion of the ions* to the electrodes, and their *reactions* at the electrodes, which results in the conductance of the current. In electronic or metallic conduction, the *electrons themselves move* from one electrode to the other.

24:6   Explanation of How a Voltaic Cell Generates Electric Current

If a zinc strip is dipped into a copper sulfate solution, it becomes copper plated. In this reaction, zinc atoms are *oxidized* to zinc ions by losing electrons. Copper ions are *reduced* to copper atoms by gaining those electrons:

$$Zn^0_{(s)} + Cu^{2+}_{(aq)} \rightarrow Zn^{2+}_{(aq)} + Cu^0_{(s)}$$

It is possible to use this oxidation-reduction reaction to generate an electric current. In a properly constructed cell, the two half-cells function in separate compartments so that electrons can flow from one to the other through an external wire.

In the cell shown in Fig. 24.3, the strips of

Fig. 24.3   *The Cu-Zn voltaic cell*

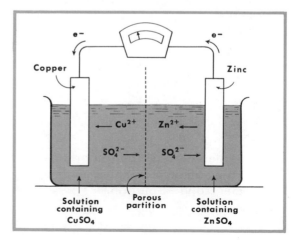

copper and zinc are placed in solutions containing their respective ions. The two solutions are separated by a porous partition which permits the diffusion of ions. Zinc loses electrons more easily than does copper. This is in keeping with the statement that zinc is above copper in the electromotive series (Table 13.1), or that the electronegativity of zinc is less than that of copper. When the two metals are connected externally a current flows through the wire at a certain voltage as shown by the voltmeter.

The cell operates as follows. At the zinc electrode, zinc atoms undergo oxidation by losing electrons and enter the solution as zinc ions:

$$Zn^0_{(s)} \rightarrow Zn^{2+}_{(aq)} + 2e^-$$

These electrons move through the wire to the copper electrode where reduction occurs. Copper ions from the solution gain the electrons and are deposited as atoms on the copper strip:

$$Cu^{2+}_{(aq)} + 2e^- \rightarrow Cu^0_{(s)}$$

The circuit is completed inside the solution by the movement of the positive ions towards the copper strip and the negative ions towards the zinc strip. The reaction goes on until either the zinc atoms or the copper ions are depleted.

It should be noted that an oxidation-reduction reaction is used to produce an electric current. This is exactly the opposite of what happens during electrolysis where an electric current is used to cause an oxidation-reduction reaction.

24:7   Explanation of the Abnormal Freezing and Boiling Points of Electrolyte Solutions

As noted earlier, the change in the boiling and freezing point produced by adding solute to solvent depends only on the number of solute particles, and not on their kind. One mole of any non-electrolyte furnishes 6.02×10^{23} solute particles in solution. When electrolytes are dissolved in water, they furnish ions to the solution in one way or another. Such ions are more numerous than the undissociated molecules would be. For example, one mole of sugar dissolved in 1000 g of water furnishes one mole of molecules of sugar, but one mole of sodium chloride supplies two moles of ions, that is, one mole of Na^+ ions and one mole of Cl^- ions. The excessive number of ions is responsible for the excessive rise in the boiling point or drop in the freezing point.

24:8   Explanation of the Chemical Activity of Electrolytes

Since ions have an electrical charge, it may be assumed that oppositely charged ions attract each other and collide much more quickly and directly than in reactions involving non-electrolytes.

The reactions that ions undergo in solution are best studied by noting only the ions involved in the chemical change. For this reason, their equations are often written in the ionic form. For example, in the reaction between solutions of sodium chloride and silver nitrate (Fig. 24.4), only the chloride ions and the silver ions come together to form an almost insoluble precipitate. The sodium ions and the nitrate ions take no part in the reaction and remain in the solution as free ions; they are merely spectator ions. The *ionic equation* representing this reaction is:

$$Cl^-_{(aq)} + Ag^+_{(aq)} \rightarrow AgCl_{(s)} \downarrow$$

This equation represents the reaction between any solution containing chloride ions with any solution containing silver ions.

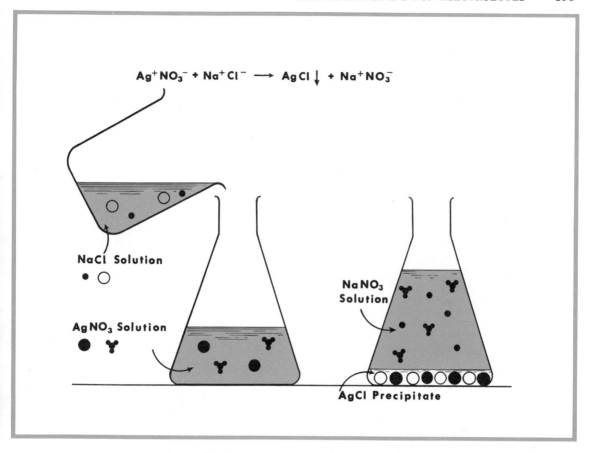

Fig. 24.4   *Reaction between Na+Cl⁻ and Ag+NO⁻₃*

QUESTIONS

1. Define *electrolyte, non-electrolyte, anion,* and *cation.* Give three examples of each.

2. When the two electrodes of an apparatus used for testing the conductivity of a substance are placed in granular sodium chloride, the bulb does not glow, but if the salt is heated until it melts, then the light shines. Explain these observations.

3. Compare electrolytes and non-electrolytes from the point of view of the following general properties: (a) electrical conductance; (b) effect on the boiling point of water; (c) effect on the freezing point of water; (d) speed of reaction.

4. Copper (II) sulfate $CuSO_4$, copper (II) nitrate $Cu(NO_3)_2$, and copper (II) chloride $CuCl_2$, all produce blue solutions when dissolved in water. Suggest a reason for this phenomenon.

5. Into what classes of compounds may electrolytes be divided?

6. How do water molecules cause ionic substances to dissociate during the solution process?

7. How do water molecules cause some covalent substances to form ions during the solution process?

8. Why is an electrolyte solution electrically neutral?

9. Why is there a marked difference between the conduction of an electric current in a solution of sodium chloride and in a solution of acetic acid of the same molar concentration?

10. Pure hydrogen chloride in the liquid state is considered to be a non-electrolyte. However, HCl is a strong electrolyte in aqueous solution. Why?

11. Why would it be better to write the formula of sodium chloride as Na^+Cl^- rather than NaCl?

12. Explain the electrolysis of a concentrated solution of hydrochloric acid, considered to be hydronium ions, H_3O^+ and chloride ions, Cl^-. Give equations representing the reactions taking place at the anode and at the cathode.

13. Distinguish between the terms *metallic conduction* and *electrolytic conduction*.

14. Calculate the number of electrons needed to liberate 10.0 g of copper metal from copper (II) chloride by electrolysis.

15. (a) What mass of hydrogen and oxygen would be obtained by the electrolysis of 10.0 g of water?
    (b) What volume would this hydrogen occupy at $-10°C$ and 750 mm of pressure?

16. What mass of water would be decomposed by electrolysis to yield 10.0 *l* of oxygen recovered at 20°C and 780 mm pressure?

17. Calculate the number of electrons released by a bar of silver, if 20.0 g of it go into solution during an electroplating process (review of sec. 14:6 should help you solve this problem).

18. Consider the following diagram representing the set up of a voltaic cell:

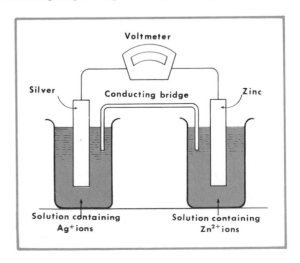

(a)   In which direction will the electrons flow?

(b)   Write the half-reaction taking place in beaker A.

(c)   Write the half-reaction taking place in beaker B.

(d)   Write the over-all reaction in ionic form.

19.   Why are electrolytes generally more active chemically than non-electrolytes?

20.   Which aqueous solution has the lower vapor pressure, a 1.0 M solution of sugar, $C_{12}H_{22}O_{11}$, or a 1.0 M solution of sodium chloride, NaCl? Explain.

21.   Solution X contains 100 g of sugar, $C_{12}H_{22}O_{11}$, dissolved in 1000 g of water and solution Y contains 100 g of ethyl alcohol, C_2H_5OH, dissolved in 1000 g of water. Which solution has the lower freezing point? Why?

22.   Which of the following substances is likely to cause the greatest lowering of the freezing point of water when a mole of it is dissolved in 1 kg of water?
(A) $C_{12}H_{22}O_{11}$ (C) NaCl
(B) $CuCl_2$ (D) CH_3COOH

23.   Re-write the following equations in their simple ionic form:
(a) $Zn_{(s)}$ $+ CuSO_{4(aq)}$ $\rightarrow ZnSO_{4(aq)} + Cu_{(s)}$
(b) $NaOH_{(aq)} + HCl_{(aq)}$ $\rightarrow H_2O_{(l)}$ $+ NaCl_{(aq)}$
(c) $KCl_{(aq)}$ $+ AgNO_{3(aq)}$ $\rightarrow KNO_{3(aq)} + AgCl\downarrow_{(s)}$
(d) $Fe_{(s)}$ $+ CuSO_{4(aq)}$ $\rightarrow FeSO_{4(aq)} + Cu_{(s)}$
(e) $BaCl_{2(aq)}$ $+ H_2SO_{4(aq)}$ $\rightarrow BaSO_4\downarrow_{(s)} + 2HCl_{(aq)}$

CHAPTER
25 Acids, Bases, and Salts

25:1 Acid-Base Phenomena

Long before chemistry had become a quantitative science, it had been observed that many substances had certain properties in common. Those with a sour taste were called acids (Latin acidus—sour). When chemists studied acids and their solutions, they found that the substances showed other common properties as well. Litmus, a vegetable dye, turns a pinkish red when it comes in contact with an acid. When acids react with certain metals, hydrogen is liberated.

Another group of compounds, also found to have common properties, taste bitter; their solutions feel slippery; they reverse the color effect that the acids produce on dyes. They are called bases.

The most interesting property of acids is their reaction with bases and, conversely, that of bases is their reaction with acids, in the course of which the properties of both the acids and the bases disappear. Hence the reaction is termed neutralization (Latin neuter–neither). The products of this reaction are water and a salt.

Since phenomena like the above were observed relatively early in chemical history, it is not surprising that the theories offered to explain them have grown in depth with the passing of time. Lavoisier (1770) believed that acid properties were caused by the presence of oxygen. Indeed, the name oxygen means "the producer of acids", but, substances were soon found which had acid properties even though they did not contain oxygen. One such compound is hydrogen chloride, HCl, which forms hydrochloric acid when dissolved in water.

25:2 Arrhenius Theory of Acids and Bases: The Water Definitions

In (1885), Arrhenius proposed the idea that an acid was a substance that liberated "hydrogen ions" to its water solution, while a base furnished hydroxide ions. This theory was successful in explaining many important facts. Any substance that could furnish hydrogen ions or hydroxide ions to its water solution would show the properties of acids or bases respectively. Furthermore, the removal of the H^+ and OH^- by their formation of water would explain how acids and bases neutralize one another:

$$H^+ + OH^- \rightarrow HOH$$

So successful was Arrhenius in explaining acid-base behavior that we still often use his definitions of acids and bases, although they have certain shortcomings.

With the establishment of the modern knowledge of the structure of the atom, it became apparent that the hydrogen ion was the proton. In essence then, the Arrhenius theory suggested that there were free protons in aqueous solutions. There is no evidence for the presence of free protons in solutions, just as there is no evidence for the presence of free electrons in any solution. Therefore, a modified theory of acid-base behavior was needed. Two such theories were proposed around 1923.

25:3 The Bronsted-Lowry Theory of Acids and Bases: The Proton Definitions

An acid is a substance whose molecules or ions can donate protons in a chemical reaction, while *a base* is a substance whose molecules or ions can accept protons in a chemical reaction. An acid is a *proton donor;* a base is a *proton acceptor.*

Since HCl is a proton donor, it is an acid according to this theory. Under certain conditions, the ammonium ion, NH_4^+ is a proton donor, as in the following reaction:

$$NH_4^+ + OH^- \rightarrow NH_3 + HOH$$

According to the Bronsted-Lowry theory, NH_4^+ is also an acid in such reactions. The older theory did not apply the term acid to such ions. Similarly, OH^- is a proton acceptor, but so too is ammonia, NH_3, when the above reaction is reversed. The latter also would be called a base by the Bronsted-Lowry theory.

When an acid donates its proton, the remainder of the acid can act as a base, and it is called the *conjugate base* of the original acid. Under suitable conditions, the base may recombine with a proton to re-form the acid. Examples are:

Acid $\quad$ = Proton + Conjugate base
HCl $\quad$ = $\quad H^+ \quad$ + $\quad Cl^-$
$NH_4^+ \quad$ = $\quad H^+ \quad$ + $\quad NH_3$
HOH $\quad$ = $\quad H^+ \quad$ + $\quad OH^-$

The ionization of an acid or a base is itself a chemical reaction between the acid or the base and the solvent. For example, the ionization of hydrochloric acid is a reaction between hydrogen chloride and water:

$$HCl + H_2O \rightarrow H_3O^+ + Cl^-$$

The hydrogen chloride donates a proton to the water. Therefore, the hydrogen chloride acts as acid, or proton donor, while the water acts as base, or proton acceptor. When hydrogen chloride donates its proton, the chloride ion is left. Therefore, the chloride ion is the conjugate base of hydrogen chloride.

Similarly, the hydronium ion may lose its proton under certain conditions. It then becomes the water molecule. Thus the water

molecule is the conjugate base of the hydronium ion.

The Arrhenius theory presented the ionization of HCl as:

$$HCl \rightarrow H^+ + Cl^-$$

The Bronsted–Lowry theory presents the ionization of HCl as a reaction between an acid and a base, producing another acid and base:

Acid 1 + Base 2 → Acid 2 + Base 1
HCl $\quad$ + $H_2O \quad$ → $H_3O^+ \quad$ + Cl^-

In the reaction between ammonia and water, we have a similar acid–base exchange:

Acid 1 + Base 2 → Acid 2 + Base 1
$H_2O \quad$ + $NH_3 \quad$ → $NH_4^+ \quad$ + OH^-

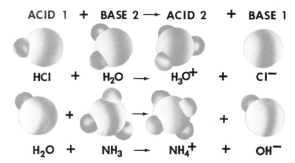

Fig. 25.1 *Bronsted theory of acids and bases*

In this last reaction, water acts as a proton donor while ammonia acts as a proton acceptor. Therefore, water is the acid in the reaction, while ammonia is the base.

When the water molecule loses its proton, the hydroxide ion remains. Therefore, the hydroxide ion, OH^-, is the conjugate base of the water molecule, H_2O.

In some reactions, the ammonium ion donates protons and thus acts as an acid. Upon donation of the proton, the ammonia molecule remains. Therefore, the ammonia molecule is the conjugate base of the ammonium ion, NH_4^+.

The equation may be written as:

Acid 1 + Base 2 → Base 1 + Acid 2
NH_4^+ + OH^- → NH_3 + HOH

In the reaction with hydrogen chloride, HCl, water acts as a base, or proton acceptor. In the reaction with ammonia, NH_3, water acts as an acid, or proton donor. A substance that can act as either an acid or a base is called *amphoteric*.

25:4   Electronic Explanation of Acid–Base Behavior

To determine if there are any electronic features in the molecules or ions that behave as acids or bases, the formulas of the above substances may be written to show their outer electrons.

As was discussed in chapter 19, the oxygen atom has six outer electrons and forms two covalent bonds with two hydrogen atoms in forming the water molecule. This may be represented thus:

$$\overset{\bullet\bullet}{\underset{\bullet}{\cdot O \colon}} + 2H^\circ \longrightarrow H \colon \overset{\bullet\bullet}{\underset{\circ\circ}{O}} \colon H$$

Note that the water molecule has two free electron pairs.

Similarly, the nitrogen atom has five outer electrons and forms three covalent bonds with hydrogen atoms in the ammonia molecule. This may be represented by:

$$\cdot \overset{\bullet}{\underset{\bullet\bullet}{N}} \cdot + 3H^\circ \longrightarrow H \overset{H}{\underset{\bullet\bullet}{\colon N \colon}} H$$

Note that the ammonia molecule has one free electron pair.

When the water and ammonia molecules react, a proton of the water molecule becomes attached to the ammonia molecule at the free electron pair. This results in the formation of the ammonium ion from the ammonia molecule, leaving the hydroxide ion as the remainder of the water molecule.

$$H \colon \overset{\bullet\bullet}{\underset{\circ\circ}{N}} \colon H + H \colon \overset{\bullet\bullet}{\underset{\circ\circ}{O}} \colon \rightleftharpoons \left[H \colon \overset{H}{\underset{\bullet\bullet}{N}} \colon H \right]^+ + \left[\colon \overset{\bullet\bullet}{\underset{\circ\circ}{O}} \colon \right]^-$$

Ammonium Ion   **Hydroxide Ion**

Similarly, when water and hydrogen chloride molecules react, protons from the hydrogen chloride attach themselves to the water molecules at one of the pairs of unshared electrons in those molecules:

$$H \colon \overset{\bullet\bullet}{\underset{\circ\circ}{O}} \colon + H \colon \overset{\bullet\bullet}{\underset{\bullet\bullet}{Cl}} \colon \longrightarrow \left[H \colon \overset{H}{\underset{\circ\circ}{O}} \colon H \right]^+ + \left[\colon \overset{\bullet\bullet}{\underset{\bullet\bullet}{Cl}} \colon \right]^-$$

Hydronium Ion   **Chloride Ion**

This reaction results in the formation of the hydronium and the chloride ions.

In every case, a new covalent bond is formed by the proton attaching itself to a pair of electrons.

25:5   The Lewis Theory of Acids and Bases: The Electronic Definitions

The Lewis theory defines a base as any substance that has one or more pairs of electrons for the formation of bonds. A Lewis base is an *electron-pair donor* while a Lewis acid is an *electron-pair acceptor*.

In all the above examples, the proton would be the acceptor of the electron pair. There are other substances that do not contain protons but may, nevertheless, accept a pair of electrons. Such substances would be Lewis acids. Similarly, there are many substances other than the hydroxide ion that can donate pairs of electrons for the formation of bonds. They should be considered as bases.

Boron trifluoride, BF_3, is a Lewis acid because it is an electron pair acceptor. The boron atom has three electrons in its outer shell. It forms three covalent bonds with electrons from three fluorine atoms:

$$\overset{\circ}{\underset{\circ}{B}}\circ + 3 \colon \overset{\bullet\bullet}{\underset{\bullet\bullet}{F}} \colon \longrightarrow \colon \overset{\overset{\bullet\bullet}{\colon F \colon}}{\underset{\bullet\bullet}{F \colon B \colon F}} \colon$$

There is still one vacant orbital in the outer shell of the boron atom, causing it to be an electron pair acceptor, or Lewis acid. Because of this property, it is valuable as a catalyst in the petroleum industry for the production of enriched high power gasoline.

25:6 A Comparison of the Three Acid–Base Theories

The Bronsted–Lowry theory is superior to Arrhenius' theory for several reasons:

1. It eliminates the need for believing that there are free protons in solution, a belief for which there is no evidence.

2. It explains how such substances as the ammonium ion show acid properties under certain conditions. Even though these substances do not furnish "hydrogen ions" to their water solutions, they react with hydroxide ions by donating protons to them. Hence, they are called acids by the Bronsted-Lowry theory, but not by the Arrhenius theory.

3. It shows that there are many substances other than hydroxides that may be considered as bases.

The Lewis theory of acids and bases is more general than the other theories.

1. It explains acid behavior in terms of electrons rather than protons. Since electrons are seen to be responsible for bonding generally, it is desirable to explain all chemical change in terms of electrons, rather than have a major field of chemistry in which protons, rather than electrons, are interchanged by the reacting substances.

2. It draws attention to the compounds that do not have hydrogen and which show acid–base properties.

25:7 Neutralization

Neutralization is the reaction between acid and base. A common example is the reaction between hydrochloric acid and sodium hydroxide:

$$HCl + NaOH \rightarrow NaCl + HOH$$

This neutralization goes practically to completion because the hydrochloric acid and sodium hydroxide are a strong acid and base respectively and the water hardly ionizes at all. Neutralization may be used to find the concentration of acids and bases. Such measurements are called *acidimetry* (measurement of acid), and *alkalimetry* (measurement of base). These are carried out by *titration*, a process of reacting volumes of solutions until a color change occurs in an added indicator. Titration is a *volumetric method of analysis* and is both convenient and rapid.

The apparatus used in titration consists of a *burette* and a *pipette*. The burette is a straight tube graduated in tenths of milliliters, with a stopcock or pinch clamp at the bottom through which the solution is run out drop by drop. The pipette is a straight tube used for drawing a definite volume of solution.

A *standard solution*, one whose concentration is known accurately, must be used. Both acidic and alkaline standard solutions are prepared by the analytical chemist. The standard acid is used for titrating the unknown base, and vice versa. A measured volume of the acid is added by means of the pipette into a beaker or flask. A few drops of indicator, usually phenolphthalein, are added. (This indicator is colorless in acid and pink in base). Alkaline solution is then added from the burette, and the mixture is stirred continuously. As the *end point* approaches, a pink color appears briefly. This a signal for the solution to be added drop by drop, a procedure which is continued until the first permanent color appears. The reaction has then reached its end point. The volume of solution run out of the burette is observed and the data are ready to be used in titration calculations.

25:8 Titration Calculations

Titration is usually carried out for a definite purpose; namely, to determine the concentration of an acid or a base. The end point is reached when the number of hydronium ions provided by the acid is equal to the number of hydroxide ions provided by the base. For this reason it is important to know how many hydronium and hydroxide ions are present per liter of solution.

Such information is provided by the molarity of the solutions of acids and bases.

To illustrate, the gram-molecular mass of HCl, 36.5 g, furnishes one Avogadro number of hydronium ions, but the gram-molecular mass of H_2SO_4, 98.0 g furnishes two moles of hydronium ions. This is because the molecule of H_2SO_4 has two protons. The mass of H_2SO_4 which furnishes one Avogadro number of hydronium ions is $\dfrac{H_2SO_4}{2}$ or $\dfrac{98.0}{2}$, or 49.0 grams.

25:9 Examples

Example 1

What mass of aluminum hydroxide, $Al(OH)_3$, will supply one mole of OH^-?

Solution

Since aluminum hydroxide furnishes three OH^- ions per molecule, the gram-molecular mass furnishes three Avogadro numbers of hydroxide ions per mole. Therefore, the mass of $Al(OH)_3$ that will supply one mole of OH^- ions is one third of the gram-formula mass of $Al(OH)_3$,

$$= \frac{Al(OH)_3}{3}\ g$$

$$= \frac{78.0}{3}\ g$$

$$= 26.0\ g$$

Example 2

What is the molarity of a solution containing 6.5 grams of H_2SO_4 in 500 ml of solution?

Solution

$$Molarity = \frac{moles\ of\ solute}{liters\ of\ solution} = \frac{n}{v}$$

For H_2SO_4, the gram-molecular mass is $2.0 + 32.0 + 64.0 = 98.0$ g and the number of moles n of H_2SO_4 in 6.5 g is $\dfrac{6.5\ g}{98.0\ g/mole}$

Therefore, the molarity (M) is

$$M = \frac{n}{v} = \frac{\dfrac{6.5 \text{ g}}{98.0 \text{ g/mole}}}{\dfrac{500 \text{ ml}}{1000 \text{ ml//}}}$$

$$= 0.13 \frac{\text{mole}}{\text{liter}} \text{ or } 0.13 \text{ M}$$

Example 3

What is the concentration of hydrogen ions in the above solution? Assume complete ionization.

Solution

Since by assumption, each molecule of H_2SO_4 provides two hydrogen ions, the number of moles of hydrogen ions is double the number of moles of H_2SO_4. As a result, the concentration of hydrogen ions will be double the molar concentration of H_2SO_4. The concentration of

$$H^+ = 2 \times 0.13$$

$$= 0.26 \frac{\text{moles}}{\text{liter}}$$

Example 4

What is the molarity of a sample of HCl solution if a volume of 24.5 ml of 0.10 M NaOH is required for the neutralization of 20.0 ml of the acid?

Solution

Since HCl and NaOH react in the molar ratio of 1 to 1, the number of moles of HCl will be equal to the number of moles of NaOH in the completed neutralization. The number of moles, n, may be found from the equation

$$\text{molarity} \qquad M = \frac{n}{V}$$

$$\text{therefore} \qquad n = MV$$

At the end point,
the number of moles of A = the number of moles of B
that is, $n_A = n_B$
or $M_A V_A = M_B V_B$

where subscripts A and B refer to acid and base respectively; we have these values:

$$M_A = \text{unknown}$$
$$V_A = 20.0 \text{ ml}$$
$$M_B = 0.10 \frac{\text{moles}}{\text{liter}}$$
$$V_B = 24.5 \text{ ml}$$

Substituting,

$$M_A = \frac{M_B V_B}{V_A}$$

$$= \frac{0.10 \, \frac{\text{moles}}{\text{liter}} \times 24.5 \text{ ml}}{20.0 \text{ ml}}$$

$$= 0.12 \text{ M}$$

Since both V_A and V_B are expressed in milliliters, it is unnecessary to change them to liters.

25:10 Free Hydronium Ions

An important property of any water solution is the number of free hydronium ions it contains. In pure water, as well as in all water solutions, both hydronium and hydroxide ions are present.

In pure water, the number of hydronium ions and hydroxide ions are equal. This is easily explained by the way these ions form. Since water is both proton donor and proton acceptor, at any time there will be a few water molecules which have donated protons to others:

or $2H_2O \quad \rightleftharpoons \quad H_3O^+ + OH^-$

As a result of this reaction, one liter of pure neutral water contains one ten-millionth of an Avogadro number of hydronium ions and hydroxide ions. To simplify, one ten-millionth is expressed as 10^{-7}, and the symbol [ ] is used to express the concentration of the ions in the solution. This symbol stands for the number of moles of solute per liter of solution. Thus, $[H_3O^+]$ stands for the moles of hydronium ions per liter of solution. We may report the above experimental fact about pure water by writing:

$$[H_3O^+] = 10^{-7}$$

The number of hydroxide ions is exactly the same as that of hydronium ions since they originate from the same dissociated molecules in the ratio of one to one. With an equal number of hydronium and hydroxide ions, pure water is neither acidic nor basic; it is termed *neutral*.

25:11 The Ion Product of Water

In neutral water, $[H_3O^+]$ and $[OH^-]$ both have a value of 10^{-7}. Their product $[H_3O^+] \times [OH^-]$ is equal to $10^{-7} \times 10^{-7}$ or 10^{-14}.

It can be shown experimentally that in all water solutions the product of the concentrations of the hydronium and hydroxide ions is 10^{-14}. This value is an important constant, termed the *ion product of water constant*.

In acid solutions, the hydronium ion concentration is larger than that of the hydroxide ion. In alkaline solutions the reverse is true. Nevertheless, in all cases

$$[H_3O^+][OH^-] = 10^{-14}$$

25:12 The pH

The *pH scale* is used to simplify further the way of expressing the hydronium ion concentration. On this scale, a liquid would be described as having a pH of 7 when the concentration of the hydronium ion is 10^{-7}. The pH represents the *negative power* of the hydronium ion concentration of water, or of any aqueous medium.* In pure

---

*Recall that x^5 has a power of 5. The term power is used here in the same sense. The power is an index.

and neutral water, the pH is 7 and the pOH, similarly defined, is also 7.

Suppose a solute is introduced which increases the number of hydronium ions to a value 10 times as great as in neutral water; this means that the number of hydroxide ions declines automatically to one-tenth the value in neutral water.

Ten times as great as 10^{-7} is
$$10^{-7} \times 10^{1}$$
$$= 10^{-7+1}$$
$$= 10^{-6}$$

Therefore, in this solution $[H_3O^+] = 10^{-6}$ and pH = 6.

Also $[OH^-] = 10^{-8}$ and pOH = 8.

Note that the product of $[H_3O^+]$ and $[OH^-]$ equals 10^{-14} in both solutions. The sum of pH and pOH is 14 in both cases.

The solution whose pH is 6 contains 10 times as many hydronium ions per liter as one of pH 7. Such a solution, which contains more hydronium ions than neutral water, is called an acidic solution. *Acidic solutions have a pH smaller than 7.*

By contrast, suppose that a solute that is added to water causes the hydronium ions to become one-tenth of their former number in neutral water. This results in a tenfold increase in the number of hydroxide ions over their number in neutral water. In order to describe this solution, we may write that:

$$[H_3O^+] = 1/10 \text{ of } 10^{-7}$$
$$\text{or } 10^{-7} \times 10^{-1}$$
$$= 10^{-1-7}$$
$$= 10^{-8}$$
$$\text{While } [OH^-] = 10^{1} \times 10^{-7}$$
$$= 10^{-6}$$
$$\text{Again } [H_3O^+][OH^-] = 10^{-14}$$

According to the definitions of these terms, the pH of this solution is 8 and the pOH is 6.

Such a solution containing fewer hydronium ions and more hydroxide ions than neutral water is called an alkaline solution. *Alkaline solutions have a pH greater than 7.*

25:13   The Measurement of pH

The pH of a solution may be determined by using dyes that change color with a change in pH. Such dyes have a definite color at a definite pH. The dyes may be placed in solution or on strips of paper similar to litmus papers. A solution of dyes used for this purpose is called a Universal Indicator, and the strips of paper are called pH papers.

The fundamental method for measuring the pH of a solution is to measure the voltage between that solution and a standard one, by means of a suitable electrical circuit. The instrument which is employed for this purpose is called a pH meter. The other methods mentioned before are calibrated by reference to the values found by the pH meter.

QUESTIONS

1. List the main general properties of acids and of bases.

2. What is the Arrhenius theory of acids and bases? Why is it called "the water theory of acids and bases"?

3. Why is the Arrhenius theory not satisfactory for acids?

4. What is the Bronsted–Lowry, or proton, theory of acids and bases?

5. Show by equations how the Arrhenius and the Bronsted–Lowry theories would represent the ionization of HCi in water.

6. Define the term *amphoteric*. Give an example.

7. Describe clearly how covalent bonds are formed when ammonia reacts with water, when hydrogen chloride reacts with ammonia, and when hydrogen chloride reacts with water.

8. What is the Lewis theory of acids and bases?

9. In what ways is the Bronsted–Lowry theory superior to the Arrhenius theory?

10. Why is the Lewis theory more general than either the Bronsted–Lowry or Arrhenius theories?

11. Define the terms *neutralization, acidimetry, alkalimetry, titration, indicator*, and *end point*.

12. Describe clearly how a solution of hydrogen chloride could be titrated with a solution of sodium hydroxide.

13. What is the purpose of titration?

14. Define *molarity*. What are the units of molarity?

15. (a) What is the molarity of a hydrochloric acid solution containing 10 g HCl per liter?
    (b) What would be its molarity if it contained 10 g HCl per 100 ml?

16. Find the molarity of a sulfuric acid solution containing 9.8 g H_2SO_4 per 500 ml.

17. What weight of each of the following would be necessary to prepare one liter of a 0.1 M solution of: (a) HCl; (b) HBr; (c) H_2SO_4; (d) H_3PO_4; (e) NaOH; (f)$Ca(OH)_2$?

18. Find the molarity of the following solutions: (a) 10 g of HCl in 1 l; (b) 100 g of H_2SO_4 in 500 ml; (c) 80 g of NaOH in 2 l; (d) 30 g of $Ca(OH)_2$ in 10 l?

19. Calculate the molarity of a HCl solution if a volume of 10 ml of it is neutralized by 25 ml of 1.0 M NaOH.

20. Find the grams of NaOH per liter of solution, if 15 ml of the solution are neutralized by 8 ml of a 0.1 M HCl solution.

21. What would be the molarity of a solution prepared by mixing 400 ml of 0.5 M HCl with 100 ml of 0.75 M H_2SO_4? What would be the concentration of H_3O^+ ions in this mixture?

22. Give an equation to show the dissociation of water.

23. What is the concentration of hydronium ions in pure water?

24. Why is pure water neither acidic nor basic?

25. What is meant by the term "the ion product of water constant"?

26. Define *pH*.

27. Explain why a neutral solution is said to have a pH of seven.

28. Explain how the pH scale expresses the acidity or alkalinity of a solution.

29. What is a "Universal Indicator solution"?

30. What mass of hydronium ion would be found in 3 l of a completely dissociated 0.1 M solution of hydrochloric acid?

26

Chemical Kinetics and Reaction Rates

Chemical kinetics deal with the details of how chemical reactions take place. The subject tries to answer such questions as "What actually takes place between the molecules, ions or atoms of the reactants? How do they collide? With what energy do they collide? Do they form products directly? Do they form intermediate substances which may then change into products? How is the reaction affected by temperature, light, surface, catalysis, concentration, and other effects?" These are important questions which need to be answered for a better control over chemical change.

26:1 Heat of Reaction and Heat Content

Because of its structure and its physical state, every substance has a characteristic internal energy known as the *heat content*. Each mole of a substance has a characteristic heat content just as it has a characteristic mass. As reactants change to products in a chemical change, heat is evolved or absorbed because the heat contents of these respective substances are different. This heat exchange which accompanies a chemical reaction is termed the *heat of reaction*, and is measured experimentally. Heat is released during an exothermic change and absorbed during an endothermic reaction.

To illustrate the ideas of the heat content and the heat of reaction, consider the synthesis of water represented by

$$2H_2 + O_2 \rightarrow 2H_2O + 136.64 \text{ kcal}$$

For one mole of water, the thermochemical equation would be

$$H_{2(g)} + \tfrac{1}{2}O_{2(g)} \rightarrow H_2O_{(l)} + 68.32 \text{ kcal}$$

The equation tells us that (a) the product water has a heat content lower by 68.32 kcal/mole than the elements composing it and (b) the heat of reaction is 68.32 kcal in this case.

If one mole of water is decomposed to produce hydrogen and oxygen, this much energy must be supplied to the reaction. In the electrolysis of water, an endothermic reaction, it is supplied as electric energy. The equation is

$$H_2O_{(l)} + 68.32 \text{ kcal} \rightarrow H_{2(g)} + \tfrac{1}{2}O_{2(g)}$$

Here the products, 1 mole of hydrogen plus ½ mole of oxygen, have a heat content higher by 68.32 kcal than the original mole of water. The two reactions may be shown by a reversible equation:

$$H_{2(g)} + \tfrac{1}{2}O_{2(g)} \rightleftharpoons H_2O_{(l)} + 68.32 \text{ kcal}$$

26:2 The Change in Heat Content

Chemists symbolize the heat content of a substance by the letter H. The *change in heat content* during a reaction, the heat of reaction, is the difference between the heat content of the products and the heat content of the reactants. The heat of reaction then becomes $\triangle H$, the Greek letter $\triangle$ (delta) signifying "change in".

$$\triangle H = \dfrac{\text{heat content}}{\text{of products}} - \dfrac{\text{heat content}}{\text{of reactants}}$$

In this notation, the $\triangle H$ for an exothermic reaction has a negative sign. Thus, in the synthesis of water,

$$\triangle H = -68.32 \text{ kcal/mole}$$

and the thermochemical equation

$$H_{2(g)} + \tfrac{1}{2}O_{2(g)} \rightarrow H_2O_{(l)} \quad \triangle H = -68.32 \text{ kcal}$$

has the same meaning as

$$H_{2(g)} + \tfrac{1}{2}O_{2(g)} \rightarrow H_2O_{(l)} + 68.32 \text{ kcal}$$

According to this sign convention the heat of reaction is said to be negative when the heat content of the system is decreasing (exothermic reaction). It is said to be positive when the heat content of the system is increasing (endothermic reaction).

26:3   Heat of Formation and Heat of Combustion

The *heat of formation* of a compound refers to the heat exchange during the synthesis of one mole of that compound from its elements in a specified state. Generally, such reactions are exothermic, and thus are written with a negative sign. The heat of formation of water is −68.32 kcal per mole.

Fuels, whether for the furnace, automobile, or rocket, are energy-rich substances and the products of their combustion are energy-poor substances. In these combustion reactions the energy yield may be very high and the products of the chemical action may be of little interest compared to the quantity of heat energy evolved.

The combustion of 1 mole of pure carbon (graphite) yields 94.05 kcal of heat energy:

$$C_{(s)} + O_{2(g)} \rightarrow CO_{2(g)} \qquad \triangle H = -94.05 \text{ kcal}$$

The heat of reaction evolved by the complete combustion of 1 mole of a substance is called *the heat of combustion* of the substance.

Exothermic and Endothermic Reactions explained in terms of heat content

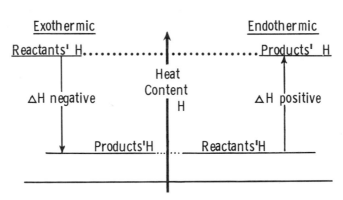

Example : Hydrogen + Oxygen ⇌ Water

Heat Content :   Higher ⇌ Lower

Reaction :

$$\xrightarrow{\text{Exothermic}}$$

$$\xleftarrow{\text{Endothermic}}$$

Thermochemical Equations:

$$2\,H_{2\,(g)} + O_{2\,(g)} \longrightarrow 2\,H_2O_{\,(l)}, \quad \triangle H = -136.6 \text{ k cal}$$

$$2\,H_2O_{\,(l)} \longrightarrow 2\,H_{2\,(g)} + O_{2\,(g)}, \quad \triangle H = +136.6 \text{ k cal}$$

Different pathways for a chemical reaction show the same energy change :

Illustrated by 2 pathways for $C + O_2 \rightarrow CO_2$, $\Delta H = -94.0$ k cal

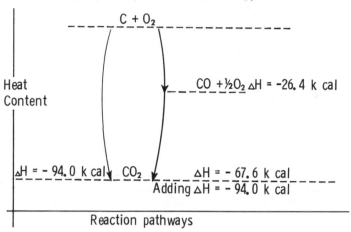

Reaction pathways

26:4   The Conservation of Energy in Chemical Change

The heat absorbed in decomposing a compound is equal to the heat evolved in its formation under the same conditions. At constant pressure the total heat of reaction of a system is the same regardless of the intermediate steps involved.

This is in accord with the law of conservation of energy. Let us apply these principles to the thermochemical equation for the combustion of carbon monoxide:

$$C_{(s)} + \tfrac{1}{2}O_{2(g)} \rightarrow CO_{(g)} \quad \triangle H = -26.41 \text{ kcal}$$
$$CO_{(g)} + \tfrac{1}{2}O_{2(g)} \rightarrow CO_{2(g)} \quad \triangle H = -67.64 \text{ kcal}$$

Adding
$$C_{(s)} + O_{2(g)} \rightarrow CO_{2(g)} \quad \triangle H = -94.05 \text{ kcal}$$

If carbon were burned so as to combine completely with oxygen to form carbon dioxide in one direct step, the heat evolved would also be 94.05 kcal/mole.

$$C + O_2 \rightarrow CO_2 \quad \triangle H = -94.05 \text{ kcal}$$

The above illustrates that thermochemical equations may be combined by addition. They may also be combined by subtraction, in which case, their heat change is reversed. Their coefficients may be multiplied or divided. By such combinations, chemists are able to calculate heat effects for chemical operations.

26:5   The Activation Energy

When hydrogen and oxygen are mixed at room temperature, why do they not combine spontaneously to form water?

Hydrogen and oxygen gases exist as diatomic molecules. The bonds of these molecules must be broken before the new bonds of the molecules of product can form. Bond breaking requires energy and thus an initial energy input is needed to "activate" the molecules of the reactants. Once the reaction begins, the energy released is enough to activate other molecules. The energy needed to activate the reactants is the *activation energy* of this reaction. In this case the energy may be supplied by an electric spark. Otherwise, a flash of light, or a flame from a burner may supply the activation energy.

The Role of the Activation Energy in a chemical reaction

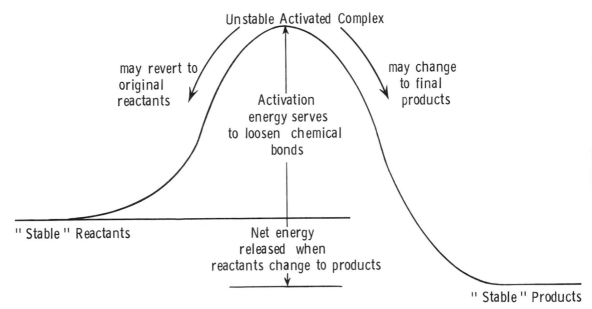

Fig. 26.1   *The role of the activation energy in a chemical reaction*

Fig. 26.1 shows graphically the course of a reaction and the part played by the activation energy.

26:6   Molecular Collisions in Gas Reactions

Consider what happens in a reaction in which reactants and products are all gaseous.

The formation of hydrogen iodide from hydrogen and iodine is such a gaseous reaction:

$$H_{2(g)} + I_{2(g)} \rightleftharpoons 2HI_{(g)}$$

For hydrogen to react with iodine vapor, their molecules must collide. If they do so with enough energy to disrupt their bonds, new bonds leading to the formation of the new molecules of the product may form.

The minimum energy required for this is termed the activation energy of the $H_2 + I_2$

reaction. It is not surprising that the rate of the reaction depends on the number of molecules travelling at such high speeds that their collisions can furnish the activation energy. This is discussed more fully in sec. 26:11.

26:7   The Activated Complex

When molecules with enough activation energy collide, their present bonds break and new ones form. For a brief instant of time a transition state with weak bonds may exist, and this is termed the *activated complex*.

The activated complex may then change in one of two ways:

1. It may form new bonds and thus new product molecules.

2. It may change back to the original reactants by reforming the original bonds.

Let us now return to the $H_2 + I_2$ reaction.

Reactants   Activated Complex   Products

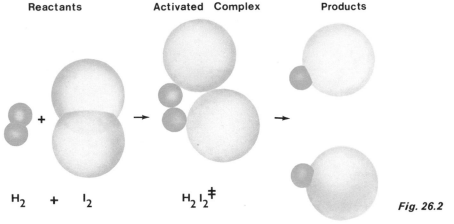

H$_2$ +   I$_2$ H$_2$I$_2$‡

2 H I

Fig. 26.2   *The activated complex*

In the pathway for this reaction, the two reactant molecules are believed to form an activated complex having the intermediate configuration H$_2$I$_2$$\ddagger$ shown in Fig. 26.2 (The symbol $\ddagger$ is commonly used to designate the activated complex.)

Starting with hydrogen and iodine, the bonds of their molecules must be weakened by collision to form the activated complex H$_2$I$_2$$\ddagger$. The activation energy absorbed for this is 43.0 kcal/mole. If the complex then goes on to separate into 2 molecules of HI, 45.5 kcal of energy are evolved. As a result, the net heat evolved is 2.5 kcal and the reaction is slightly exothermic:

$$H_{2(g)} + I_{2(g)} \rightarrow 2HI_{(g)} + 2.5 \text{ kcal}$$

The reverse reaction goes back along the same reaction pathway forming the same activated complex. Now the bonds between hydrogen and iodine atoms in the molecules of HI need to be weakened by collision, and this requires 45.5 kcal/mole. If the complex then decomposes into molecules of H$_2$ and I$_2$, only 43.0 kcal/mole is liberated. As a result, the net energy change is the absorption of 2.5 kcal/mole:

$$2HI_{(g)} + 2.5 \text{ kcal} \rightarrow H_{2(g)} + I_{2(g)}$$

The energy profile for this reversible reaction is shown in Fig. 26.3.

26:8   Factors Affecting the Speed of a Reaction

The speeds of reactions differ greatly. For example, the explosion of dynamite is a chemical reaction that happens at great speed. Other reactions, however, are extremely slow. The question whether the speed of a reaction could be controlled is often important in industry; it might be the deciding factor that determines whether a certain chemical reaction may be used economically or not.

The speed of a chemical reaction may be defined as the number of moles reacting or produced per unit time per unit volume. Five important factors influence the rate of a reaction: (a) the nature of the reactants; (b) the temperature; (c) the amount of exposed surface of the reactants. (d) catalysis; (e) the concentration of the reactants. In some reactions, light and pressure are important deciding factors.

26:9   The Nature of the Reactants

Some substances are extremely reactive and others are less so; the difference is often ascribed

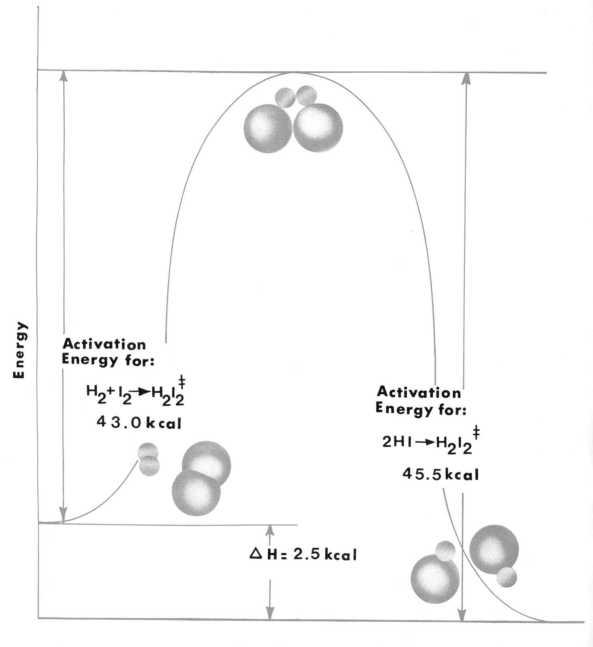

Fig. 26.3   *The energy profile of the hydrogen-iodine reaction*

to the very nature of the material. No doubt as knowledge about the structure of matter improves, better explanations will be offered for differences in reaction rates. Sodium is a very reactive metal, while silver is inert; hydrochloric acid ionizes to a large extent, while acetic acid ionizes only to a slight extent; oxygen is a reactive gas, while nitrogen is not.

26:10   The Effect of Temperature on Reaction Rates

Reactions are always faster at high temperatures and slower at low temperatures. An application of this principle is a refrigerator, which lowers temperatures and thereby slows down the chemical reactions that spoil foods. For most reactions the speed approximately doubles with a rise of 10°C.

In order to react chemically, molecules must have at least enough energy to decompose or to rearrange themselves when they collide. Such molecules are *activated* (sec. 26:5) and the energy responsible for this condition is called the *energy of activation*. At any temperature only a certain fraction of all the molecules have energies equal to the energy of activation. When the temperature is raised about 10°C, the number of molecules in this class is doubled, and the rate of reaction is doubled also.

26:11   The Distribution of Energy Among Molecules

To explain the effect of temperature on the rate of reaction, it must be understood that the molecules of a given system do not all have exactly the same energy. Their average kinetic energy is determined by the temperature; but some molecules have energies greater than the average, while others have less. The reason for this uneven distribution of energy is molecular collision, for as the molecules collide some are speeded up and others are slowed down. The kinetic energy of some molecules increases, while that of others dimin-

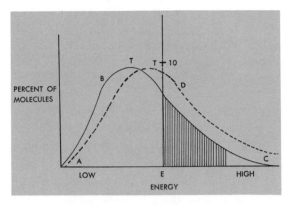

Fig. 26.4   *Energy distribution curve*

ishes, even though the average remains the same at any particular temperature.

The energy distribution among the molecules may be illustrated by a graph (Fig. 26.4). The vertical axis of the graph refers to the percentage of the molecules, while the horizontal axis refers to the energy per mole.

Thus the point A refers to a low value of the energy possessed by a small percentage of the molecules; point C refers to a high value of the energy also possessed by a small percentage of the molecules; and point B refers to the average energy possessed by the largest percentage of the molecules. The graph line ABC describes the distribution of the energy at a temperature T.

Suppose that for a certain reaction, the energy of activation is E. The number of molecules having at least this amount of energy is shown by the area under the curve to the right of E.

If the temperature is raised ten degrees, all the molecules will have a higher kinetic energy. A new graph along the dotted line shows the distribution of energy at the higher temperature.

The average increase in the kinetic energy of the molecules has been relatively small. Thus, if the temperature is about 300°K, then a ten-degree rise is only about 3 per cent increase in the absolute temperature which is not enough to explain the doubling of the rate of reaction, an increase of 100 per cent. An examination of the area under the curve beyond the point E shows that the area has doubled. In other words, the number of molecules having the energy of activation has become twice as great.

26:12   The Amount of Exposed Surface of the Reactants

Chemical reaction occurs at the surfaces of the reacting substances. For example, when zinc is placed in dilute hydrochloric acid, the acid comes in contact with the zinc at the surface of the metal, and that is where reaction occurs. By reducing the size of the pieces of zinc, the exposed surface is increased. Any increase in surface area increases the rate of reaction (Fig. 26.5).

26:13   Catalysts

Catalysts are substances that affect the rate of reaction. Generally, they speed up certain chemical changes, although some are known to slow them down. The catalyst itself is not altered by the reaction and may be recovered afterwards weighing as much as it did originally.

Of all the factors, perhaps the action of a catalyst is the most dramatic. This may be seen in the laboratory preparation of oxygen by heating potassium chlorate. In the presence of the catalyst, manganese dioxide, only moderate heat is needed to decompose potassium chlor-

ate. In the absence of the catalyst, potassium chlorate must be heated to a much higher temperature and for a much longer period of time in order to obtain similar results.

Catalysts are used in industry in the making of ammonia, nitric acid, sulfuric acid, rubber, plastics, textiles, and many other substances. Nature uses catalysts for all the chemical reactions that occur in living organisms. Such catalysts are called *enzymes* and are produced chemically by the body, being distributed by the bloodstream to the points where they function.

To explain how catalysts work, it is supposed that reactant molecules collect on the surface of the catalyst where it is easier for other molecules to collide with them or react with them. Collection of one substance on the surface of another is termed *adsorption*. Some catalysts have the ability to adsorb certain reactants, and this may partly account for their effectiveness.

Some catalysts form unstable compounds or ions with the reactants. Such are termed *intermediate products* since they decompose to form the final products of the reaction. When the final product is formed, the catalyst is restored to its original state. The catalyst may now repeat its performance by combining with another molecule of reactant, and so on. This would explain why the catalyst does not become depleted or altered.

It may happen that the catalyst has the ability to activate the molecules of reactants adsorbed

Fig. 26.5 *Increased surface with subdivision*

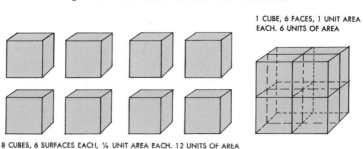

1 CUBE, 6 FACES, 1 UNIT AREA EACH. 6 UNITS OF AREA

8 CUBES, 6 SURFACES EACH, ¼ UNIT AREA EACH. 12 UNITS OF AREA

on its surface. They might become strained or their bonds might be weakened. This would render the molecule unstable, or activated. Another possible explanation of how a catalyst works is that it provides another pathway along which the reaction can proceed. This alternate pathway might require a lower activation energy (Fig. 26.6).

Although the catalysts may speed up chemical reactions, there are two important limitations on their behavior. First, they cannot cause a reaction; they can only speed up reactions that proceed more slowly without them. Second, the catalyst speeds up the establishment of equilibrium (sec. 26:15) by accelerating the forward and reverse reactions to the same extent. It does not influence the position of the equilibrium by producing any more of a desired product than would have been formed without the catalyst.

26:14 The Effect of Concentration

A splint that only glows in air bursts into flame when put into pure oxygen. The air is only about 20 per cent oxygen, so that only one-fifth of all the molecules coming in contact with the splint can react with it to cause combustion. The result is a feeble glow. In pure oxygen, the oxygen molecules are five times as numerous as in air. Therefore the reaction is more rapid, and the splint bursts into flame.

Careful experiment shows that when two substances react, the speed of the reaction is proportional to the relative number of the reacting molecules or ions.

The Law of Mass Action

The conclusion just reached is named the *Law of Mass Action*. Suppose that A and B are the reactants of a chemical change:

Fig. 26.6 *How a catalyst might work in certain reactions*

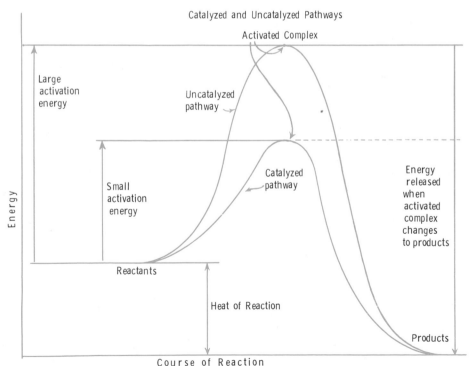

Catalyzed and Uncatalyzed Pathways

Activated Complex

Large activation energy

Uncatalyzed pathway

Small activation energy

Catalyzed pathway

Energy released when activated complex changes to products

Energy

Reactants

Heat of Reaction

Products

Course of Reaction

A + B → Products

When the concentration of A and B are each one mole per liter, there is a certain number of collisions between their particles and the velocity of the reaction is k_1 moles per liter per second. This may be represented by

$$\overrightarrow{V} = k_1$$

If, now, the concentration of A is made two moles per liter, there will be twice as many collisions between particles of A with particles of B since the particles of A are twice as many. Therefore, the velocity of the reaction becomes twice as great as it was formerly. Now it is

$$k_1 \times 2.$$

Similarly if the concentration of B is made three moles per liter, the collisions between particles of B with those of A become three times as numerous and the rate of the reaction also becomes three times as great.

Therefore, when the concentration of A is two moles per liter, and that of B is 3 moles per liter, the rate is 6 times as great as when the concentration of either was only one mole per liter.

Generally, if the concentration of A is represented by [A] and that of B by [B], then the rate of reaction would be expressed as follows:

$$\overrightarrow{V} = k_1[A][B].$$

This is the mathematical expression of the law of mass action.

For a reaction in a solution, the rate depends on the molar concentration of the reactants. For gas reactions, the rate depends on the pressures of the reacting gases, since pressure depends on the number of molecules present.

26:15   Reversible Reactions

In many chemical changes, the products formed react among themselves to form the original materials. Such are called *reversible reactions*.

To represent these, two arrows pointing in opposite directions are used; that is, from the reactants to the products and from the products back to the reactants. To show this, suppose A and B represent reactants that form products C and D. Then, the reversible reaction would be:

$$A + B \rightleftharpoons C + D$$

When A and B are first mixed, their concentration is relatively high and, therefore, the number of collisions between their molecules is large. As a result, the reaction between A and B (the "forward reaction") will be rapid. Gradually, A and B are used up, and the reaction between them slows down. Meanwhile, products C and D have been forming in ever increasing amounts as a result of the reaction between A and B. The "reverse reaction" between C and D starts, slowly at first and more rapidly as more of C and D accumulate. Eventually the forward and the reverse reactions will be going on at equal rates. Such a condition is called *chemical equilibrium*.

Law of Chemical Equilibrium

According to the law of mass action, the rate of the reaction between A and B is given by

$$\overrightarrow{V} = k_1[A][B]$$

and that between C and D is given by

$$\overleftarrow{V} = k_2[C][D]$$

As stated above, at chemical equilibrium the rates of the forward and the reverse reactions are equal,

$$\overrightarrow{V} = \overleftarrow{V}$$

therefore, $k_1[A][B] = k_2[C][D]$

or $\dfrac{[C][D]}{[A][B]} = \dfrac{k_1}{k_2} = K$ (since k_2 and k_1 are constants).

This is the mathematical expression of the *Law of Chemical Equilibrium*. In its simplest form, the law states that *when a reversible reaction reaches equilibrium, the products and the reactants bear a constant ratio to one another.* That constant ratio is called the *Equilibrium Constant, K.*

When reactions are more complex than the above illustrations, the mathematical expression of the law of mass action and the law of chemical equilibrium become more complex too. The ideas employed in more complex cases are extensions of those discussed in the present case.

26:16   Principle of Le Chatelier

Every reversible reaction reaches its own specific equilibrium. This state depends on the pressure and temperature. Once these are given, the concentrations of the reactants and products will be in a definite ratio. It is even possible to calculate the amounts of reactants and products at the equilibrium.

To obtain an idea of how to predict what occurs in a system in equilibrium, imagine a reversible reaction such as $A + B \rightleftharpoons C$ + heat, where A and B are reactants. If more A is added, collisions between molecules of A and B increase, and chances of a reaction between them improve; and the amount of C increases. Similarly, if some A is removed, collisions between molecules of A and B become fewer, and the rate of the forward reaction $A + B \rightarrow C$ is diminished. However, the reverse reaction $C \rightarrow A + B$ will go on at the same rate as before, and as a result there will be less C at the new equilibrium.

To summarize, *if a system in chemical equilibrium is subjected to a change or stress, the reaction that relieves the stress will be favored.* This is called the *Principle of Le Chatelier.* If this principle is applied to the example $A + B \rightleftharpoons C$ + heat, the following events may be predicted:

1. When the temperature of the system at equilibrium is raised, the added heat is used to decompose C. Less C will be present in the new equilibrium at the higher temperature.

2. When the temperature is lowered, less heat is present in the system. This causes the decomposition reaction of C to be slowed down since heat is required for this as seen by the equation. Thus less of A and B would be present at the new equilibrium.

3. If A and B are gases, their combination into product C is a reaction in which the number of gas molecules is diminished. Upon subjecting the mixture to higher pressure, the number of molecules of A and B per unit volume will be greater. Therefore, the collisions between them will increase and the chance of chemical reaction will be better, which will cause more of C to form through reaction of A with B. The removal of some of A and B will mean a reduction of the pressure. The stress to which the system was subjected has been partly removed.

26:17   Predicting Results

A good illustration of the ideas about equilibrium is provided by an important reaction, the exothermic formation of ammonia from hydrogen and nitrogen in which four gas molecules change into two:

$$3H_2 + N_2 \rightleftharpoons 2NH_3 + \text{heat}$$

The following results may be predicted for this reaction.

1. An increase in pressure will favor the production of ammonia.

2. An increase in temperature will favor the breakdown of ammonia.

3. The removal of ammonia will favor the production of more from the union of hydrogen and nitrogen.

In practice, all of these predictions are confirmed (Chapter 33).

Another illustration of the effect of concentration changes on equilibrium is demonstrated by the following reaction:

$$FeCl_3 + 3KCNS \rightleftharpoons$$
Iron + potassium
(III)   thiocyanate
chloride (colorless)

$$Fe(CNS)_3 + 3KCl$$
Iron + potassium
(III)   chloride
thiocyanate
(red)

If more of either of the reactants is added to this equilibrium, the mixture becomes darker red because the equilibrium shifts to the right. If potassium chloride is added, the red color fades because the reaction is reversed.

26:18   "Irreversible" Reactions

Most reactions are reversible to some extent. If, however, one or more of the products are removed, the reverse reaction cannot take place. When this occurs, the forward reaction is said to go to completion. The reaction is termed *irreversible* for practical purposes. No reaction is completely irreversible.

The three most common examples of removal of a product are by the escape of gas, the precipitation of an insoluble product, and the formation of a non-ionized (or poorly ionized) compound.

When sodium chloride, NaCl, and silver nitrate, $AgNO_3$, are reacted in solution, the reaction goes to completion because of the formation of the almost insoluble silver chloride:

$$Na^+_{(aq)} + Cl^-_{(aq)} + Ag^+_{(aq)} + NO_{3(aq)}^- \rightarrow$$
$$AgCl\downarrow_{(s)} + Na^+_{(aq)} + NO_{3(aq)}^-$$

or as a net ionic equation:

$$Cl^-_{(aq)} + Ag^+_{(aq)} \rightarrow AgCl\downarrow_{(s)}$$

When zinc is treated with hydrochloric acid, hydrogen gas is liberated. This causes the reaction to go to completion, since the hydrogen is collected *outside* the reaction flask:

$$Zn_{(s)} + 2HCl_{(aq)} \rightarrow ZnCl_{2(aq)} + H_2\uparrow_{(g)}$$

or as a net ionic equation:

$$Zn_{(s)} + 2H_3O^+_{(aq)} \rightarrow Zn^{2+}_{(aq)} +$$
$$2H_2O_{(l)} + H_2\uparrow_{(g)}$$

When hydrochloric acid neutralizes sodium hydroxide, water forms. Since the ionization of water is exceedingly small, the removal of the hydronium and hydroxide ions is complete, and the reaction is termed irreversible:

$$H_3O^+ + OH^- \rightarrow 2H_2O$$

26:19   Spontaneous and Forced Reactions — The Free Energy

Chemical reactions involve energy. Exothermic reactions release heat, and endothermic reactions require heat, as was discussed earlier. Similarly, some chemical reactions can do work as they proceed while others require that work be done upon them to make them go.

A familiar reaction which performs work as it proceeds is that which takes place in a voltaic cell or battery delivering electricity which can be put to many uses. An electrolytic cell is an illustration of a system where electrical work from the outside causes electrolysis, a chemical reaction, to proceed in the cell.

When a chemical reaction does work, the maximum amount of work performed at constant temperature and pressure can be measured, and is called the *free energy of the reaction*. This is an appropriate name because the system performs this work freely and spontaneously, and it is up to us to take advantage of it, as we do in placing an appliance in the circuit of a voltaic cell.

Work is defined as the product of force and distance. Therefore in a system which does work, there must be some unbalanced or unchecked force, and this is the cause of the work done. An example of an unbalanced force would be the greater tendency for one electrode of a cell to attract electrons than for the other electrode to do so. This greater attraction causes the electrons to move in one direction, thereby giving them kinetic energy which can operate an appliance. When the force is spent, the system is in equilibrium and no more work can be done. A system in equilibrium has no capacity for giving free energy to any appliance or to the surroundings. An example is a "dead" battery. The "dead" battery may, however, be recharged by applying an external voltage to it. This, in effect, is doing work on the battery to force the necessary chemical reaction to take place by electrolysis.

Chemical systems may therefore be classified as:

1. Those in which reactions go spontaneously and are able to give or lose free energy to the outside. Example: the discharging of a battery.

2. Those in chemical equilibrium, which are unable to give free energy to the outside. Example: the dead battery.

3. Those in which reactions are forced to take place by doing work upon them, or giving them free energy from the outside. Example: recharging a battery.

The idea of the free energy is a most useful one in biology. Many chemical reactions go on in living organisms, and it appears as if their objective is to place stores of free energy at the disposal of the animal or plant.

Finally, even if a chemical reaction can give free energy, it might not go automatically if the reactants are not activated. For this, *the energy of activation* needs to be supplied. The materials in the head of a match burn spontaneously, once the energy of activation is supplied by friction.

QUESTIONS

1. Define *speed of reaction.*

2. List the factors that affect the speed of a reaction.

3. Explain carefully what is meant by *energy of activation.*

4. Why does a rise of 10°C usually double the speed of a reaction? Draw a graph to make your explanation clear.

5. Give an example of the effect of surface on the rate of reaction.

6. What is meant by *adsorption*?

7. Describe three ways by which catalysts may effect the speed of a reaction.

8. What are two important limitations on the behavior of catalysts in chemical reactions?

9. Explain why a glowing splint bursts into flame in oxygen but not in air.

10. State the law of mass action.

11. What is a reversible reaction?

12. Explain what is meant by chemical equilibrium?

13. (a) State the principle of Le Chatelier.
    (b) Explain this principle by making clear what would happen in an exothermic reaction, $A + B \rightleftharpoons C + heat$, where equilibrium has been established (i) if the temperature is raised, and (ii) if the temperature is lowered.

14. In the reaction $3H_2 + N_2 \rightleftharpoons 2NH_3 + heat$, describe three ways by which the equilibrium could be shifted.

15. In the reaction $FeCl_3 + 3KCNS \rightleftharpoons Fe(CNS)_3 + 3KCl$, how could the equilibrium be shifted to form more $Fe(CNS)_3$? How could it be shifted to form less?

16. What are the three types of irreversible reactions? Give an example of each type.

27 Colloidal State

27:1 Occurrence

If sugar or salt is stirred in water, the crystals dissolve into molecules or ions. The resulting homogeneous mixture is called a *true solution*. Yet, if fine sand is stirred in water, the crystals do not dissolve and, after stirring, the particles settle. Such a mixture is called a *suspension*.

When starch is stirred in boiling water, a mixture is obtained in which the individual particles of starch are larger than the molecules or ions of the true solution, but not as large as the crystals of a suspension. Such mixtures are called *colloidal dispersions*. The finely divided material, illustrated by the starch, is said to be *dispersed*, rather than dissolved, and is called the *dispersed phase*, rather than solute. The liquid in which the material is dispersed is called the *dispersion medium*, instead of the solvent.

The colloidal state is not limited to solids dispersed in liquids. There are eight combinations of dispersed phase and dispersion medium, which are illustrated by Table 27.1.

27:2 The Particle Size in the Colloidal State

The unit of measurement in describing atoms, molecules, and ions is the *Angstrom unit* (Å), which is 10^{-8} cm. Many atoms and ions are of the order of 1Å to 5Å in diameter. Molecules are larger, depending on their composition.

Colloidal particles have dimensions that begin at about 10 Å and may range up to approximately 2000 Å in diameter in at least one dimension.

TABLE 27.1

Types of Colloidal Dispersions

Colloidal System	Example
1. Gas dispersed in a liquid	Foam on top of beer, or suds in a soapy mixture
2. Gas in a solid	Pastry, foam rubber
3. Liquid in a gas	Fog, cloud and mist
4. Liquid in liquid (Emulsions)	Milk and cream contain butterfat dispersed in water
5. Liquid in a solid	Butter, clay
6. Solid in gas	Smoke and dust
7. Solid in liquid	Glue and paint
8. Solid in solid	Porcelain, enamels

27:3 A Method of Study of the Colloidal State

Colloidal particles are too small to be seen with even the most powerful optical microscopes, whose limit of magnification is set by the nature of light. The shortest wave-length of light that the human eye can detect is 4000 Å or 4×10^{-5} cm. Although this is very small, it is still too large to permit a colloid particle to be seen. Therefore, an electron microscope must be used in the study of these tiny particles. The electron microscope uses a beam of electrons instead of light. Magnifying is done by magnetic fields instead of glass lenses. Magnification of 200,000 times may be obtained, one hundred times as great as the magnification of the most powerful optical microscope. It has been estimated that

225

if a dime were magnified to the same extent as an object in the electron microscope, its diameter would be greater than the height of the tallest skyscraper building.

The electron microscope has transformed the study of colloidal particles from a collection of vague generalizations into a precise science. It has also given a great impetus to all branches of biology and medicine, since most biological substances are colloidal in nature.

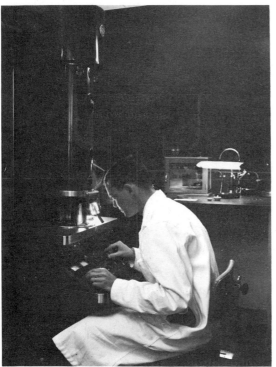

Courtesy Shawinigan Chemicals Limited

Fig. 27.1 *The electron microscope*
The experimenter is studying colloidal particles.

When biological matter, which is mostly colloidal, is studied with the electron microscope, a cast of the surface is made by spraying silver atoms on the surface by means of a special device. This cast is then examined and is found to contain the fine detail of the given material. This is done because such material

could not be introduced into the high vacuum of the electron microscope.

27:4   The Specific Surface of Colloid Particles

The surface exposed per unit mass is called the specific surface of a material. Finely subdivided matter has a high specific surface which is important for several reasons.

1. Surfaces tend to concentrate substances upon themselves if these substances can reduce surface tension. This is called adsorption.

2. The adsorption of ions on the surfaces of colloidal particles gives the colloidal state its electrical properties.

3. Chemical reactions take place at the surface between the reacting substances.

4. The adsorption of reactants on surfaces often speeds up chemical reaction, and this is an important mechanism by which some catalysts work.

27:5   Properties of Colloidal Systems

The Tyndall Beam

When a beam of sunshine enters a darkened room through a small opening in a curtain, many flashing points may be seen in the sunbeam. These flashes of light are reflections from the particles of dust which are themselves too small to be seen even with a microscope. They become visible, however, as sources of reflected light against a darkened background.

The English physicist Tyndall showed that a beam of light becomes visible in like manner in a liquid containing colloidal particles. Ordinarily, the liquid is clear since the colloidal parts are too small to be seen. Upon shining an intense beam of light through the liquid, the light is reflected by the colloidal particles, which thus become sources of reflected light and cause the beam to be seen (Fig. 27.2).

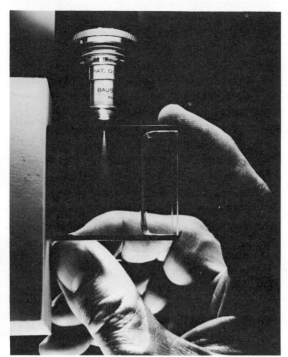

Courtesy Atlas Chemical Industries

Fig. 27.2   *The Tyndall effect*

Brownian Movement

If microscopic particles are examined in water or in smoke, they are found to move in a curious zigzag motion, which became known as Brownian movement after its discoverer Robert Brown. Much later, the motion was explained as the result of molecules of the liquid or gas colliding with the observed particles. Thus, Brownian movement is a striking proof of the idea that molecules have kinetic energy which they can transfer to other particles upon collision. When the latter particles become visible under a microscope, it is possible to calculate the kinetic energy of the invisible molecules.

Brownian movement is a kinetic phenomenon of interest in studies of the kinetic molecular theory. It was discovered in studies with pollen grains and colloidal dispersions.

Filtration and Dialysis

Colloidal particles can pass through filter paper but suspended or precipitated matter cannot. In this way suspended material may be removed from a colloidal dispersion.

If, instead of filter paper, parchment paper is used, the colloidal particles are prevented from passing through, while molecules and ions are not. By taking advantage of this fact, colloidal matter may be separated from molecular and ionic solutes. This process is called *dialysis*.

Electrical Properties

Colloidal particles carry an electrical charge as proven by the fact that they migrate to one of a pair of electrodes immersed in a colloidal dispersion. *Electrophoresis* is the name given to this phenomenon. The presence of the same electrical charge on all the particles acts as a stabilizing factor of the colloidal system. Conversely the removal of such charges causes the colloid to coagulate.

The Cottrell Precipitator, a device for precipitating undesirable smoke and fumes, works on this principle. The particles of smoke carry

Fig. 27.3   *Cottrell precipitator*

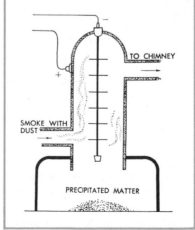

an electrical charge, and the removal of this charge precipitates the particles and removes the smoke (Fig. 27.3).

Fig. 27.4 *The "smog chamber" used in research on air pollution*
Photo shows the metallic lining and the central metallic electrode for precipitation of polluting matter.

Courtesy Phillips Petroleum Company

QUESTIONS

1. Distinguish between a *true solution*, a *suspension*, and a *colloidal dispersion*.

2. Define the terms *dispersed phase* and *dispersion medium*.

3. List the eight types of colloidal systems and give an example of each.

4. What is an Angstrom unit?

5. Express the following in Angstrom units: 1 cm; 0.001 cm; 1/10 cm; 1/1,000,000 cm.

6. What are the dimensions of colloidal particles?

7. Why are colloidal particles invisible by ordinary light, even when a microscope is used?

8. Explain clearly the method used to permit the visual examination of colloidal particles.

9. Explain why colloids have such a great surface area.

10. What is meant by the terms *specific surface, adsorption*?

11. What is the importance of a great specific surface?

12. Describe and explain the Tyndall beam.

13. How could an apparently clear colloidal dispersion be distinguished from a true solution?

14. What is the Brownian movement?

15. (a) Describe the process of dialysis.
    (b) How is this process applied?

16. (a) What evidence is there that colloidal particles are electrically charged?
    (b) How is the electrical charge related to the stability of a colloidal system?

CHAPTER 28

The Halogens

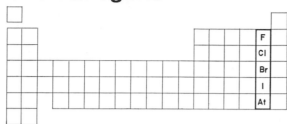

28:1 The Halogen Elements

The five elements fluorine, chlorine, bromine, iodine, and astatine of group VII in the periodic table are called the *halogens*. The word halogen means *salt former*, and these five elements occur in nature as salts rather than as free elements.

The halogens have many common characteristics, because in the outermost shell they each have seven electrons which fill the *s* and two of the *p* orbitals. The last *p* orbital contains only one electron. In chemical combinations the halogens normally gain one electron in this half-filled *p* orbital. Even when they share

electrons in covalent bonds, they are usually the more electronegative of the pair of atoms bonded and, for these reasons, are said to be strong oxidizing agents. Electronegativity among the halogens decreases with increase in atomic size; consequently fluorine is the most electronegative. The smaller, lighter halogens are able to replace the larger, heavier ones from their compounds.

The distribution of electrons in the atoms of these elements is given in Table 28.1.

The atoms of these elements have seven electrons in their outer shell. Two of these are *s* electrons and five are *p* electrons.

TABLE 28.1

Electron Configurations of the Elements of Group VII

		Energy Levels																
		n = 1	2		3			4				5			6			
Element	Atomic Number	Sublevels and Orbitals																
		1s	2s	2p	3s	3p	3d	4s	4p	4d	4f	5s	5p	5d	6s	6p		
Fluorine	9	2	2	5														
Chlorine	17	2	2	6	2	5												
Bromine	35	2	2	6	2	6	10	2	5									
Iodine	53	2	2	6	2	6	10	2	6	10		2	5					
Astatine	85	2	2	6	2	6	10	2	6	10	14	2	6	10	2	5		

28:2   Chlorine

(a) *Discovery and Occurrence*

The story of chlorine began in the year 1774, when a Swedish pharmacist by the name of Scheele discovered that the mineral called pyrolusite (crude manganese dioxide) gave off a greenish-yellow gas on exposure to hydrochloric acid. He found that this gas stung his nose and throat and nearly blinded him. He also noted that it had an acid taste in water and that it bleached flowers and attacked metals. In 1810, Sir Humphry Davy showed, by failing to decompose it, that the gas was an element. He called it chlorine from the Greek words meaning *greenish-yellow*.

Chlorine is not found free in nature because it is a very active element. Its most important compound is sodium chloride, which is found in sea water and in salt deposits in the earth. Other chlorides, such as those of potassium, calcium, and magnesium, are also present in these salt deposits which were formed by the evaporation of inland seas many centuries ago. This process may be seen taking place today in such areas as the Dead Sea and the Great Salt Lake.

(b) *Preparation*

A common method of preparing chlorine is to cause removal of one electron from chloride ions. This may be done by treating hydrochloric acid with manganese dioxide.

In this reaction, manganese dioxide removes the electron from the chloride ions. The manganese dioxide is thus an oxidizing agent while the chloride ion is a reducing agent. The reaction is as follows:

$$MnO_2 + 4HCl \rightarrow MnCl_2 + Cl_2\uparrow + 2H_2O$$

Half-reaction of reducing agent:
$$2Cl^- - 2e \rightarrow 2Cl^0$$
$$2Cl^0 \rightarrow Cl_2 \uparrow$$

Half-reaction of oxidizing agent:
$$MnO_2 + 4H_3O^+ + 2e \rightarrow Mn^{2+} + 6H_2O$$

The chlorine is collected by the upward displacement of air because it is heavier than air and is moderately soluble in water. The apparatus used is illustrated in Fig. 28.1. When the bottles are full may be determined by the greenish-yellow color of the gas.

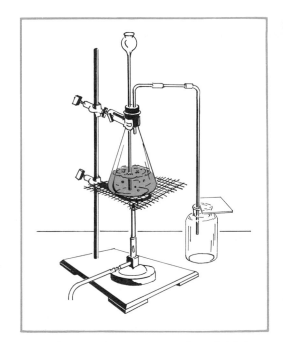

Fig. 28.1   *Laboratory preparation of chlorine*

An alternate source of chloride ions is sodium chloride, which when treated with MnO_2 and sulfuric acid, produces chlorine.

$$2NaCl + MnO_2 + 2H_2SO_4 \rightarrow$$
$$Na_2SO_4 + MnSO_4 + Cl_2\uparrow + 2H_2O$$

Note that the ionic equations for this reaction are exactly the same as those in the previous reaction, because the same ions are involved.

(c) *Commercial Preparation*

Chlorine, hydrogen, and sodium hydroxide are all produced when brine is electrolyzed. The process is carried out industrially in specially designed cells such as the one shown in Fig. 28.2.

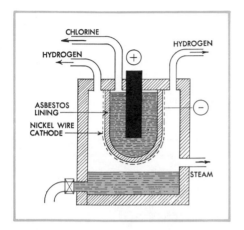

Fig. 28.2 *Electrolysis of brine in the Nelson cell*

Sodium hydroxide drips through the cathode and collects at the bottom of the cell. Chlorine is discharged at the anode, and hydrogen gas is discharged at the cathode. The reason for the discharge of hydrogen gas instead of metallic sodium is the fact that less energy is required to convert hydronium ions to hydrogen atoms and molecules than to convert sodium ions to sodium atoms. Sodium hydroxide collects in the solution as electrolysis proceeds:

$$2NaCl + 2H_2O \rightarrow Cl_2\uparrow + H_2\uparrow + 2NaOH$$

To prevent the chlorine from reacting with the sodium hydroxide in these cells, the anode is usually covered with an asbestos diaphragm.

Chlorine can also be prepared commercially along with metallic sodium by the electrolysis of fused sodium chloride (Chapter 44).

(d) *Physical Properties*

Some physical properties of the elements are given in Table 28.2.

TABLE 28.2

Physical Properties of
Fluorine, Chlorine, Bromine, and Iodine

Element	Melting Point (°C)	Boiling Point (°C)	Color and State at Ordinary Conditions
Fluorine	−223	−187	pale yellow gas
Chlorine	−102	−35	greenish-yellow gas
Bromine	−7.2	59	deep red liquid
Iodine	113.5	184	steel-gray solid

Chlorine is 2½ times as heavy as air. It is moderately soluble; one volume of water dissolves about two volumes of the gas at 20°C and 760 mm pressure. Chlorine has a penetrating odor, and it causes pain when inhaled. Alcohol or ammonia fumes help to ease the irritation. It forms a golden colored liquid at about −35°C and 760 mm. It is transported as a liquid in steel cylinders.

(e) *Chemical Properties*

With seven electrons in its outer shell, chlorine can assume several positive oxidation numbers as well as one negative oxidation number as Table 28.3 shows.

In accordance with its electronic structure, the following are some chemical properties of chlorine.

1. Chlorine reacts with most metals to form chlorides. The presence of a trace of moisture speeds up the reaction between chlorine and the less reactive metals. Some examples are:

$$2Fe + 3Cl_2 \rightarrow 2FeCl_3$$
$$Cu + Cl_2 \rightarrow CuCl_2$$

A thrilling example of the marvels of chemical change is the reaction that occurs when sodium is brought into contact with

TABLE 28.3

Main Oxidation Numbers of Chlorine

Oxidation Numbers	Examples
1 −	NaCl, sodium chloride
	HCl, hydrogen chloride
0	Cl_2, molecular chlorine
1 +	NaClO, sodium hypochlorite
	HClO, hypochlorous acid
3 +	$NaClO_2$, sodium chlorite
	$HClO_2$, chlorous acid
5 +	$NaClO_3$, sodium chlorate
	$HClO_3$, chloric acid
7 +	$NaClO_4$, sodium perchlorate
	$HClO_4$, perchloric acid

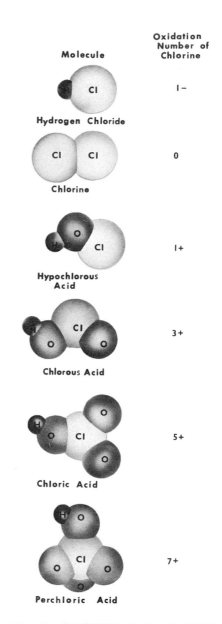

Molecule	Oxidation Number of Chlorine
Hydrogen Chloride	1 −
Chlorine	0
Hypochlorous Acid	1 +
Chlorous Acid	3 +
Chloric Acid	5 +
Perchloric Acid	7 +

chlorine. Sodium is a highly reactive metal, combining with water to form hydrogen gas and sodium hydroxide. It burns the skin when touched because of the heat liberated in its reaction with the moisture on the hand. Chlorine is also a highly reactive and toxic substance. Yet, when both are brought together the resultant chemical change transforms these two substances into common salt:

$$2Na + Cl_2 \rightarrow 2Na^+Cl^-$$

2. Chlorine reacts with hydrogen; a mixture of chlorine and hydrogen reacts vigorously when ignited or exposed to a strong light source:

$$H_2 + Cl_2 \rightarrow 2HCl$$

If a hydrogen generator is set up and allowed to run until all the air is expelled, the hydrogen may be ignited safely at the end of the delivery tube. If lowered into a jar of chlorine, this jet of burning hydrogen continues to burn, forming hydrogen chloride.

3. Chlorine combines with the hydrogen of

certain compounds. If turpentine, for example, is poured on a piece of filter paper, and the paper is thrust quickly into a jar of chlorine, a flash of yellow flames flares up and a large amount of black smoke is formed:

$$C_{10}H_{16} + 8Cl_2 \rightarrow 16HCl + 10C$$

A lighted candle burns in a jar of chlorine with a very smoky flame forming similar products.

4. Chlorine combines with most of the non-metals, except fluorine. It forms compounds with oxygen and nitrogen only indirectly. It combines with phosphorus to form phosphorus trichloride.

$$P_4 + 6Cl_2 \rightarrow 4PCl_3$$

5. Chlorine "adds" to many compounds; for example:

$$2FeCl_2 + Cl_2 \rightarrow 2FeCl_3$$
$$2CuCl + Cl_2 \rightarrow 2CuCl_2$$

6. Chlorine is a bleaching agent. When chlorine is dissolved in water, hydrochloric and hypochlorous acids are formed; the hypochlorous acid formed is unstable and decomposes yielding atomic oxygen:

$$Cl_2 + H_2O \rightarrow HCl + HClO$$
$$HClO \rightarrow HCl + (O)$$

The atomic oxygen has the ability to combine with the colored matter in many substances. After such treatment, the substances are whiter in appearance and are said to have been bleached.

7. Chlorine is poisonous. Even in small quantities chlorine attacks the moist membranes of the respiratory system. One part of chlorine in 30,000 parts of air is a lethal mixture.

(f) *Uses*

1. In industry, chlorine is used for bleaching cotton and wood pulp, but not for bleaching wool or natural silk as it hardens and destroys these materials. If chlorine is passed over calcium hydroxide (slaked lime), a compound known as *chloride of lime* is formed:

$$Ca(OH)_2 + Cl_2 \rightarrow CaOCl_2 + H_2O$$

Then, the $CaOCl_2$ reacts with an acid to cause bleaching action:

$$CaOCl_2 + H_2CO_3 \rightarrow CaCO_3 + HCl + HClO$$
(from air)

The hypochlorous acid formed is the actual cause of the bleaching action.

Laundry bleach or Javel water is made by adding chlorine to cold sodium hydroxide solution:

$$2NaOH + Cl_2 \rightarrow NaClO + NaCl + H_2O$$
Sodium hypochlorite

Dilute sodium hypochlorite is also a bleaching agent.

2. Chlorine is a good disinfectant, since it destroys bacteria. It is used to purify drinking water and water in swimming pools. In communities where it has been added to the water supply, typhoid fever and dysentery have been practically eliminated. Only about three pounds of chlorine are needed to disinfect a million gallons of water.

3. Chlorine is used to make many useful materials such as carbon tetrachloride, CCl_4, a good solvent; chloroform, $CHCl_3$, a solvent; and hydrochloric acid, HCl.

Thus chlorine can cause great discomfort or even death, as well as contribute to the comfort and health of man.

28:3 Fluorine

(a) *Preparation*

Fluorine is so strongly electronegative that no known chemical substance can remove an electron from the fluoride ion. Fluorine was first prepared by electrolyzing potassium hydrogen fluoride, KHF_2, dissolved in liquid hydrogen fluoride. Fluorine is now prepared by the electrolysis of a solution of potassium fluoride and hydrogen fluoride in a stainless steel or copper cell. A fluoride coating forms on these metals and protects them during the process. A graphite anode is used.

(b) Properties

Fluorine is the most active nonmetallic element because of its strong electronegativity. It unites explosively with hydrogen even in the dark, $H_2 + F_2 \rightarrow 2HF$, and it forms compounds with practically all elements.

Courtesy Argonne National Laboratory

Fig. 28.3 *Xenon tetrafluoride crystals*
The formation of compounds with xenon had been thought impossible until recently.

Fluorine has the distinction of being the first element to form a binary compound with xenon, one of the noble gases. Scientists have assumed for years that the "inert gases" with a complete outer shell of electrons would not form compounds. Recently it was shown that when fluorine and xenon are reacted at 400°C, stable crystals of xenon tetrafluoride result:

$$2F_2 + Xe \rightarrow XeF_4$$

Shortly before XeF_4 was prepared, another compound, xenon hexafluoroplatinate had been synthesized.

28:4 Bromine

(a) Occurrence and Preparation

Sodium bromide and magnesium bromide are widely distributed in nature. For many years bromine was obtained from these compounds, which are found in small amounts in salt deposits. Now most bromine is prepared from sea water.

The element was discovered in 1826 by the French chemist Balard who obtained it by treating the liquid from a natural salt well with chlorine. Even today the commercial production of bromine depends upon the ability of chlorine to displace bromine from its salts. This happens because the chlorine has a smaller atomic radius and, consequently, is more electronegative than bromine:

$$2Br^- + Cl_2 \rightarrow 2Cl^- + Br_2\uparrow$$

Sea water or water from salt wells is acidified, and chlorine is added. The bromine is removed by blowing air through the solution, which carries off the bromine as part of the gaseous mixture. In the laboratory, bromine is made by heating a mixture of manganese dioxide, sulfuric acid, and sodium bromide in a retort.

$$2NaBr + MnO_2 + 2H_2SO_4 \rightarrow$$
$$Na_2SO_4 + MnSO_4 + 2H_2O + Br_2\uparrow$$

(b) Properties

Bromine and mercury are the only two elements that are liquids at room temperature and pressure. The dark red bromine is about three times as dense as water. It is moderately soluble in carbon tetrachloride, in carbon disulfide, and in bromide salt solutions. Bromine vaporizes readily, and its vapors are irritating and poisonous; burns produced by it are difficult to heal.

Since bromine is not as electronegative as chlorine, it is also not as active. It unites with hydrogen slowly. It combines with some of the metals to form bromides.

28:5 Iodine

(a) Occurrence and Preparation

The French chemist Courtois discovered iodine in 1811 when he noticed purple vapor arising from some ashes of seaweed. Most of the iodine produced today comes from oil-well brine. The brine is treated with chlorine, and the iodides present in the brine yield free iodine:

$$2NaI + Cl_2 \rightarrow I_2 + 2NaCl$$

In the laboratory, iodine is produced by treating an iodide salt with manganese dioxide and sulfuric acid:

$$2NaI + MnO_2 + 2H_2SO_4 \rightarrow Na_2SO_4 + MnSO_4 + 2H_2O + I_2$$

The chemical reaction is similar to the preparation of bromine. An electron is removed from the iodide ion by the electron-gaining manganese dioxide.

Bromine also may be used to displace iodine. Since the atom of bromine is smaller than that of iodine, it is more electronegative, and is able to remove an electron from the iodide ion:

$$2NaI + Br_2 \rightarrow 2NaBr + I_2$$

(b) Properties

Iodine, a steel-gray crystalline solid, sublimes to form a violet-colored vapor which, like chlorine, is irritating.

Iodine is not very soluble in water, but it is soluble in iodide solutions. Iodine forms a dark brown solution in alcohol and a purple solution in carbon disulfide and carbon tetrachloride. Iodine turns starch blue; this property is used as a test both for iodine and for starch.

Iodine is less active chemically than chlorine or bromine. It forms iodides with some metals and unites spontaneously with phosphorus.

(c) Uses

Iodine is used to make iodides. Tincture of iodine, consisting of iodine and alcohol, is a well-known antiseptic.

QUESTIONS

1. What is the meaning of the term *halogen*?
2. List the halogens in decreasing order of chemical activity.
3. Why is fluorine more active than chlorine?
4. Describe how chlorine was discovered.
5. Is chlorine found free in nature? Explain your answer.
6. Account for the active nature of chlorine.
7. What compounds of chlorine are commonly found in nature?
8. (a) Describe, with the aid of a labelled diagram, the laboratory preparation of chlorine from manganese dioxide and hydrochloric acid. Write the equation for the reaction.
   (b) Show how this reaction is an oxidation-reduction type.
9. Write the equations to show how chlorine may be prepared by heating sulfuric acid, sodium chloride, and manganese dioxide together.
10. Write the equation for the reaction of chlorine with water.

11. Balance the following:
$$KMnO_4 + HCl \rightarrow KCl + MnCl_2 + Cl_2\uparrow + H_2O$$
$$PbO_2 + HCl \rightarrow PbCl_2 + Cl_2\uparrow + H_2O.$$

12. Give the equation representing the electrolysis of fused sodium chloride.

13. What are the products of the electrolysis of brine?

14. State five physical properties of chlorine.

15. Faraday liquefied chlorine in 1823. Why was it the first gas to be liquefied?

16. Write the equations for the combination of chlorine with: (a) iron; (b) zinc; (c) aluminum; (d) sodium.

17. Why should precautions be taken when working with chlorine?

18. How could one safely show that hydrogen and chlorine have a strong chemical affinity?

19. Write the equation to show the reactions between chlorine and each of the following: (a) carbon monoxide; (b) iron (II) chloride; (c) copper (I) chloride. Name the products in each case.

20. What is bleaching powder? Laundry bleach?

21. Why is chlorine used in making water safe?

22. Give three uses of chlorine other than those mentioned above.

23. How much MnO_2 would be required to release 10 liters of chlorine from sufficient HCl, if the chlorine is measured at 20°C and 780 mm pressure?

24. (a) How is fluorine prepared commercially?
    (b) List four physical and four chemical properties of fluorine.

25. (a) How is bromine prepared commercially?
    (b) How may it be prepared in the laboratory?
    (c) List four physical and three chemical properties of bromine.

26. (a) How is iodine produced commercially?
    (b) How may it be prepared in the laboratory?
    (c) List four physical and two chemical properties of iodine.
    (d) What are some uses of iodine?
    (e) Describe the test for starch or for iodine.

27. What volume of chlorine could be obtained from 20 g of sodium chloride by electrolysis, if the chlorine is measured at −10°C and 733 mm pressure?

28. What weight of hydrogen chloride could be made from 10 l of chlorine, if the chlorine is measured at 25°C and 765 mm pressure?

29. What is the simplest formula of a compound which contains 79.7% chlorine and 20.3% aluminum?

30. If 8 ml of chlorine and 3 ml of hydrogen are mixed in the dark and then exposed to light, what gases would result and what would be their volumes?

31. How much bromine and iodine respectively could be obtained from 20 g of sodium bromide and 20 g of sodium iodide?

CHAPTER

29 Compounds of the Halogens

29:1 Compounds of Chlorine

(a) Sodium Chloride

Anyone who thinks of salt usually visualizes sodium chloride, NaCl. This compound of chlorine is one of the most useful and most abundant compounds utilized by man. In ancient Rome salt was so important that soldiers received a special pay called *salarium* for the purchase of this commodity. The word "salary" was derived from *salarium*; and the expression "He is not worth his salt" is common today.

Sodium chloride is found in sea water, salt lakes, and deposits formed by the evaporation of inland seas many thousands of years ago. Sea water contains on the average about 3 per cent salt, while the Dead Sea and Great Salt Lake contain about 20 per cent. Canadian de-

Fig. 29.1 Interior of a salt mine near Windsor, Ontario

Courtesy The Canadian Salt Company Limited

posits of rock salt, or halite, are found at Windsor, Ontario, Unity, Saskatchewan, and Malagash, Nova Scotia. An area of about 100,000 square miles under Texas, Oklahoma, and Kansas is occupied by a deposit of salt about 300 to 600 feet in thickness. In Europe a famous deposit of salt is located at Stassfurt, Germany.

In some cases, where a deposit of salt is easily accessible, salt is mined by excavation. Usually, however, a well is drilled down to the deposit of salt. The well consists of two pipes, one inside the other. Water, which is forced down the outside pipe at high pressure, dissolves the salt; and the brine (salt solution) is forced up the inner pipe. The brine is placed in tanks where insoluble substances settle out and where it may be treated chemically to remove other impurities. It is then filtered and evaporated under vacuum. When salt crystallizes from the solution, it is dried, screened, and packaged.

It is too costly to separate salt from any solution by artificial evaporation if the solution contains less than 17 per cent salt. In hot countries where rock salt is not available, sea water is run into shallow basins and the heat of the sun evaporates the water.

Sodium chloride crystallizes into cubic crystals which melt at 800°C. These crystals usually contain some water mechanically enclosed in tiny droplets inside the crystal lattice. When rock salt is heated, or when a salt solution is evaporated, the crystals fly apart with a crackling sound caused by the changing of this water to steam.

Sodium chloride is quite soluble in water; 35.7 g dissolve in 100 g of water at 0°C, and 39.8 g at 100°C. This is unusual, because most

238   BASIC MODERN CHEMISTRY

solids are much more soluble in hot water than in cold.

Pure sodium chloride is non-hygroscopic and does not cake unless the humidity is very high. Salt usually hardens because of impurities in it, such as calcium or magnesium chloride, which absorb moisture. "Free-running" salt is prepared by precipitating the calcium and magnesium from the original salt solution before evaporation.

Very pure sodium chloride may be obtained by adding hydrochloric acid to a saturated solution of the salt. The excess of chloride ion from the salt and the acid decreases the solubility of the salt so that it precipitates.

Physiological saline is the name of a salt solution, 0.9 per cent NaCl by weight, used frequently in medicine. The special property of this solution is that it has the same osmotic pressure as the cells, tissue, and blood of the human body. Solutions of the same osmotic pressure are called *isotonic*.

To prevent water entering or leaving the tissues, adjoining solutions have to be of equal osmotic pressure. This is the chief reason for the use of isotonic solutions for drops applied to the eyes, nose, and ears, and for injection of drugs.

An adult needs about one teaspoon of salt per day. From this, gastric cells produce the hydrochloric acid essential for digestion. Perspiration contains salt; in hot weather a greater-than-normal intake of salt is necessary to maintain physical well being.

Salt is used for curing fish, meat, and hides. It is a raw material in the industrial manufacture of sodium hydroxide, sodium carbonate and bicarbonate, hydrochloric acid, sodium metal, chlorine, soap, glass, and enamel. In fact, sodium chloride is the ultimate source of practically all compounds containing sodium or chlorine.

Salt melts ice even in freezing weather because of its great attraction for water. It forms bonds with the water molecules in the ice crystal causing the ice to melt. A solution may thus be obtained with a freezing point as low as $-22°C$. Salt has been used for a long time on streets, walks, and railway tracks to remove ice. Freezing mixtures are made with it for cold storage plants and in the manufacture of artificial ice and the making of ice cream.

(b) *Calcium Chloride*

Calcium chloride, $CaCl_2$, is a soluble, white salt that crystallizes from water as a hexahydrate, $CaCl_2 \cdot 6H_2O$. When heated, part of the water is lost and the monohydrate, $CaCl_2 \cdot H_2O$, results. At a high temperature anhydrous $CaCl_2$ is obtained.

The monohydrate, often used on roads to melt ice, may also be used to keep dusty roads moist in the summer time. A saturated solution of calcium chloride will not freeze until a temperature of $-50°C$ has been reached. Because of this property, it is sometimes used as the brine in cold storage plants.

Calcium chloride is obtained mainly as a by-product from the Solvay process (Chapter 44), which produces calcium chloride in such large amounts that it is relatively cheap.

(c) *Hydrogen Chloride*

Pure gaseous hydrogen chloride was first prepared in 1772 by Priestley, who called it "marine-acid gas" because it was made from sea salt.*

PREPARATION

The following are some of the methods for preparing hydrogen chloride gas.

1. Hydrogen chloride can be prepared by heating sodium chloride with concentrated sulfuric acid. The apparatus used is the same as in Fig. 28.1.

*Originally, the water solution of this gas was called muriatic acid, probably because of the term "marine-acid gas". The present name is hydrochloric acid.

$$NaCl + H_2SO_4 \rightarrow NaHSO_4 + HCl\uparrow$$

The gas must be collected by the upward displacement of air because it is very soluble in water and it is heavier than air. When the bottles are full may be determined by the use of moist, blue litmus paper, which turns red on contact with the gas, owing to the formation of hydrochloric acid. $NaHSO_4$, which is called sodium hydrogen sulfate, sodium bisulfate, or sodium acid sulfate, is an example of an acid salt.

The action of sulfuric acid on salt illustrates a general method of making acids; namely, by treating a salt of the required acid with sulfuric acid. Another example is the preparation of nitric acid by treating sodium nitrate with sulfuric acid (Chapter 33). Sulfuric acid is used for a number of reasons: it has the highest boiling point of most of the common acids; it supplies the hydrogen needed for the double decomposition reaction which produces the derived acid; it absorbs water, and this dries the acid evolved; and it is relatively inexpensive.

2. Hydrogen chloride is prepared industrially by the same method as outlined above. In this case, the use of large amounts of sodium chloride and the high temperature cause the following reaction:

$$2NaCl + H_2SO_4 \rightarrow Na_2SO_4 + 2HCl\uparrow$$

Na_2SO_4, sodium sulfate, is a normal salt which is also known as salt cake.

3. Hydrogen chloride can be made by the direct union of hydrogen and chlorine:

$$H_2 + Cl_2 \rightarrow 2HCl$$

The gas obtained by burning hydrogen in chlorine is very pure; impurities in hydrogen chloride prepared with sulfuric acid usually cause a yellowish tinge to the gas.

PHYSICAL PROPERTIES

Pure hydrogen chloride is a colorless gas with a sharp, irritating odor. It is heavier than air. It is extremely soluble in water; approximately 500 liters of the gas dissolve in one liter of water at STP. A saturated solution contains about 39 per cent of the gas, but the laboratory acid has about 37 per cent. Because of its great affinity for water, the gas fumes in moist air, owing to the formation of a mist of hydrochloric acid.

The gas cannot be boiled out of its solution entirely because a constant boiling mixture* is formed which boils at 110°C. This solution contains about 20 per cent of HCl by weight.

The large solubility of hydrogen chloride in water may be demonstrated with a "fountain experiment". The apparatus is assembled as shown in Fig. 29.2 and the flask is filled with dry hydrogen chloride. A little water is placed in the medicine dropper. When the bulb of the dropper is squeezed, the ejected water dissolves some of the hydrogen chloride, thus lowering the pressure. This causes the air to push water up through the jet in fountain-like fashion.

CHEMICAL PROPERTIES OF HYDROGEN CHLORIDE AND ITS WATER SOLUTION

On the one hand, anhydrous hydrogen chloride is a stable gas, is a poor conductor of electricity, and does not even attack metals at low temperature; on the other hand, when it comes in contact with water, it acts as proton donor and forms hydrochloric acid (Chapter 25).

(d) Hydrochloric Acid

Hydrochloric acid is the most important manufactured halogen compound. It has been known for a very long time: the alchemists prepared it

---

*A constant boiling mixture is one whose vapor has the same composition as the liquid solution. Therefore, no change in composition occurs as boiling proceeds, and the boiling temperature remains constant.

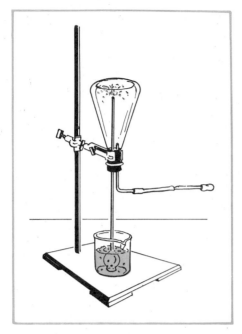

Fig. 29.2 *The hydrogen chloride fountain*

by the reaction of sulfuric acid on salt.

Hydrochloric acid is a typical strong acid. It readily displaces weaker acids from their salts. It reacts with the metals above hydrogen in the Electromotive Series to form hydrogen:

$$Zn + 2HCl \rightarrow ZnCl_2 + H_2\uparrow$$

It neutralizes bases:

$$NaOH + HCl \rightarrow NaCl + H_2O$$

Like other acids it affects indicators:

$$HCl + Ind^- \rightarrow HInd + Cl^-$$

where HInd and Ind$^-$ are the different forms of the indicator which are differently colored.

USES

Hydrochloric acid is used as a laboratory reagent for testing and analysis.

In forming gelatine and glue from the tendons of animals, a small amount of hydrochloric acid is added to the water in which the tendons are heated. Glucose is made from starch in a similar manner. In these processes the acid acts as a catalyst.

Hydrochloric acid is used to remove oxides from metals, a procedure that must be done before one metal is plated with another. The process is called "pickling". A cheaper substitute for pickling is sulfuric acid, but hydrochloric acid is preferred because it forms soluble chlorides whereas sulfuric acid forms insoluble sulfates.

A chloride is a salt formed by replacing the hydrogen of hydrochloric acid with a metal or metallic radical. Examples are zinc chloride ($ZnCl_2$) and ammonium chloride (NH_4Cl). All common chlorides are soluble excepting silver chloride ($AgCl$), mercury (I) chloride (Hg_2Cl_2), and lead chloride ($PbCl_2$). The latter is slightly soluble in cold water but much more soluble in hot.

(e) Test for Chlorides

To test for the chloride ion, a solution of silver nitrate is added to the solution to be tested. The resultant double decomposition precipitates insoluble white silver chloride:

$$AgNO_3 + Cl^- \rightarrow AgCl\downarrow + NO_3^-$$

The precipitate is divided into three portions: the first is kept for comparison; to the second is added a little nitric acid; and to the third is added some concentrated ammonium hydroxide. Silver chloride is insoluble in the nitric acid but dissolves in the ammonium hydroxide. The test with nitric acid and ammonium hydroxide is necessary because white silver salts other than the chloride are insoluble in water, but are soluble in nitric acid.

It will be noted that silver chloride darkens on exposure to light, for light slowly reduces the salt to metallic silver. This reaction is the basis of photography (Chapter 46).

(f) Chlorates

Potassium chlorate is a common laboratory

chemical. It may be prepared by adding chlorine to a warm saturated solution of potassium hydroxide. Potassium hypochlorite is produced, which changes to potassium chlorate and potassium chloride as soon as it is formed:

$$3Cl_2 + 6KOH \rightarrow 3KCl + 3KClO + 3H_2O$$
$$3KClO \rightarrow 2KCl + KClO_3$$

The electrolysis of a warm potassium chloride solution produces the same results:

$$2KCl + 2HOH \rightarrow 2KOH + H_2\uparrow + Cl_2\uparrow$$
$$Cl_2 + 2KOH \rightarrow KCl + KClO + H_2O$$
$$3KClO \rightarrow 2KCl + KClO_3$$

Potassium chlorate is a vigorous oxidizing agent. This is consistent with the high oxidation number $(5+)$ of chlorine in the chlorate ion. It produces an explosive mixture with many oxidizable materials, such as sulfur and carbon.

29:2 Compounds of Fluorine

Small amounts of fluoride salts are sometimes added to drinking water to make tooth enamel less prone to decay. Fluorinated hydrocarbons called "Freons" are used as refrigerating media. They are used as a propellent in some spray cans because they are odorless, non-flammable, and non-toxic. Cryolite, $AlF_3 \cdot 3NaF$, a mineral, is used as a solvent for aluminum oxide in the production of aluminum. Fluorspar, CaF_2, is the most important source of fluorine and its compounds.

Hydrogren fluoride is formed by treating fluorspar with sulfuric acid:

$$CaF_2 + H_2SO_4 \rightarrow CaSO_4 + 2HF\uparrow$$

This useful compound is a colorless gas which fumes in moist air, as it combines with water vapor forming a mist of hydrofluoric acid. The acid is very poisonous and corrosive.

Hydrogen fluoride shows hydrogen bonding (Chapter 21). This is deduced from the fact that it boils at a higher temperature than hydrogen chloride. Also, the hydrogen fluoride molecule is highly polar, due to the electronegativity of the fluorine, and forms associated molecules as follows:

Hydrogen fluoride is probably more complex than the formula HF would suggest. There is some evidence for the existence of molecules of H_2F_2, H_3F_3, and even H_6F_6.

Because of the hydrogen bonding, hydrofluoric acid does not ionize greatly:

$$H_2O + H_2F_2 \rightleftharpoons H_3O^+ + HF_2^-$$

It is not as strong as hydrochloric acid. It reacts with most substances, including glass, and therefore must be kept in wax or plastic containers.

To etch glass, the glass is first coated with wax. The design is scratched through the wax and the glass is exposed to hydrogen fluoride gas, or hydrofluoric acid. The hydrogen fluoride attacks the glass where it is exposed, but not where it is covered with wax. The design is thus etched out.

Hydrofluoric acid is used as a catalyst in making high octane gasoline and to make synthetic cryolite.

29:3 Compounds of Bromine

Pure hydrogen bromide is prepared by the action of phosphorus tribromide on water.

$$PBr_3 + 3H_2O \rightarrow H_3PO_3 + 3HBr\uparrow$$

Sulfuric acid cannot be used for this reaction, because the sulfate ion has the ability to remove electrons from the bromide ion, liberating free bromine:

$$\begin{array}{cccc} 6+ & 1- & 0 & 4+ \\ H_2SO_4 + & 2HBr \rightarrow Br_2 + & SO_2 + 2H_2O \\ \uparrow & \downarrow & & \\ 2e & = 2 \times 1e & & \end{array}$$

The water solution of hydrogen bromide is a strong acid, called hydrobromic acid.

Sodium and potassium bromide are used in medicine as sedatives, and silver bromide is an ingredient in photographic film. Ethylene dibromide, $C_2H_4Br_2$, is mixed with lead tetra-ethyl, $Pb(C_2H_5)_4$, in gasoline to prevent the deposit of undesirable lead oxides in the cylinders of a car.

Test for Soluble Bromides

Bromine is very soluble in carbon tetrachloride, forming an orange-red solution. Chlorine displaces bromine from its salts. These two facts form the basis of the test for a soluble bromide.

In the test a mixture of chlorine water and carbon tetrachloride is stirred into the solution to be tested:

$$Cl_2 + 2Br^- \rightarrow Br_2 + 2Cl^-$$

The bromine, being more soluble in the carbon tetrachloride than in the water, dissolves in the carbon tetrachloride to form an orange-red solution. This solution separates in a layer below the aqueous solution, because water and carbon tetrachloride are not miscible and the carbon tetrachloride has the greater density.

29:4   Compounds of Iodine

Hydrogen iodide is made by treating phosphorous tri-iodide with water.

$$PI_3 + 3H_2O \rightarrow H_3PO_3 + 3HI$$

A small amount of iodine (about 0.005 g) is necessary in the human body. The thyroid gland requires the iodine to make thyroxin, one of the regulations of metabolism. If iodine is lacking, the gland enlarges in an effort to make more thyroxin, and a goitre results. Most foods contain no iodine; so, to supply the dietary deficiency, about 0.025 per cent sodium or potassium iodide may be added to salt. The product is known as iodized salt.

Di-iodine pentoxide, I_2O_5, is used to detect and measure the amount of carbon monoxide in the air. It is reduced to free iodine by the monoxide.

$$5CO + I_2O_5 \rightarrow 5CO_2 + I_2$$

Test for Soluble Iodides

As in the bromide test, a mixture of chlorine water and carbon tetrachloride are added to the solution to be tested. The chlorine displaces the iodine:

$$Cl_2 + 2I^- \rightarrow I_2 + 2Cl^-$$

A purple color in the carbon tetrachloride layer indicates the presence of an iodide.

QUESTIONS

1. Write a note on the occurrence of sodium chloride.

2. Define the term *salt*.

3. What fundamental processes are involved in producing table salt from brine?

4. Why does freezing brine make it more concentrated?

5. Why does salt cake in moist weather?

6. (a) How is "free running" salt made?
   (b) How is pure salt made?

7. (a) Is NaCl a molecular formula? Explain your answer.
   (b) What is the physiological importance of salt?
   (c) List several uses of salt.

8. How does salt melt ice?

9. (a) How is calcium chloride obtained?
   (b) What are the principal uses of this substance?

10. Outline the history of hydrochloric acid.

11. Sketch and label the apparatus used to prepare hydrogen chloride in the laboratory. Describe the preparation.

12. Give four reasons for using sulfuric acid in the preparation of hydrogen chloride.

13. How is hydrochloric acid prepared commercially?

14. (a) List the physical properties of hydrogen chloride.
    (b) List the chemical properties of hydrogen chloride and its water solution.

15. (a) Why is hydrochloric acid termed a typical strong acid?
    (b) Write a paragraph on the uses of hydrochloric acid.

16. In terms of electronegativity, how can one explain that NaCl is ionic and CCl_4 is covalent?

17. What chlorides are insoluble?

18. Outline the test for the chloride ion.

19. Why must the precipitate formed in the test for the chloride ion be tested with nitric acid and ammonium hydroxide?

20. (a) Outline the production of potassium chlorate.
    (b) Give some uses of the compound.

21. Write the equations to illustrate the following:
    (a) The laboratory preparation of hydrogen chloride; (b) the burning of hydrogen in chlorine; (c) the oxidation of hydrogen chloride to chlorine; (d) the addition of hydrogen chloride to water; (e) the addition of ammonia to hydrogen chloride; (f) the reaction between zinc and hydrochloric acid; (g) the reaction between sodium hydroxide and hydrochloric acid; (h) the test for a chloride; (i) the addition of ammonium hydroxide to silver chloride; (j) the addition of excess chlorine to a saturated solution of potassium hydroxide; (k) the electrolysis of a warm solution of potassium chloride.

22. Show electronically how the production of $KClO_3$ is an oxidation-reduction reaction.

23. What are some uses of sodium fluoride?

24. What is "Freon" and for what is it used?

25. (a) Write the equation for the preparation of hydrogen fluoride.
    (b) What are some uses of this substance?
    (c) Why does some hydrogen fluoride exist as H_6F_6 molecules?

26. How may pure hydrogen bromide be made?

27. Why do sulfuric acid and a bromide not yield pure hydrogen bromide?

28. List four compounds of bromine and give a use for each.

29. Describe the test for a bromide salt.

30. Give the equation for the laboratory production of hydrogen iodide.

31. Explain why iodized salt should be used in the diet.

32. Balance this equation: $I_2O_5 + CO \rightarrow CO_2 + I_2$. What is a practical use of this reaction?

33. How much sulfuric acid is needed to combine with 10 g of sodium chloride to form sodium hydrogen sulfate and hydrogen chloride?

34. Find the weight of chlorine required (a) to displace 5 g of bromine from potassium bromide, and (b) to replace 5 g of iodine from potassium iodide.

30 Sulfur

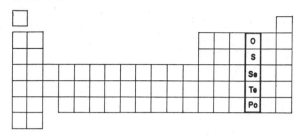

30:1 The Sulfur Family

The elements of group VI of the periodic table are oxygen (O), sulfur (S), selenium (Se), tellurium (Te), and polonium (Po). The distribution of electrons in the atoms of these elements is given in Table 30.1.

The atoms of these elements all have 6 electrons in their outer shell. Two of these are *s* electrons and four are *p* electrons.

The presence of six electrons in the *s* and *p* orbitals helps explain the combining capacity and the oxidation numbers of these elements.

Oxygen was discussed in Chapter 13. Selenium and tellurium are rare, and polonium is exceedingly rare. In their physical and chemical properties, selenium and tellurium resemble sulfur. A peculiar feature of selenium atoms is that they lose their outer electrons when exposed to light.

Selenium is useful for making photoelectric cells, which pass an electric current when light shines on them. Polonium, discovered by Marie

TABLE 30.1

Electron Configuration of the Elements of Group VI

Element	Atomic Number	Energy Levels																
		n = 1	2		3			4				5			6			
		Sublevels and Orbitals and their Electrons																
		1s	2s	2p	3s	3p	3d	4s	4p	4d	4f	5s	5p	5d	6s	6p		
Oxygen	8	2	2	4														
Sulfur	16	2	2	6	2	4												
Selenium	34	2	2	6	2	6	10	2	4									
Tellurium	52	2	2	6	2	6	10	2	6	10		2	4					
Polonium	84	2	2	6	2	6	10	2	6	10	14	2	6	10	2	4		

Curie, is of interest as a highly radioactive element.

30:2   Occurrence

As long ago as 1000 B.C., the yellow, brittle, lustrous, solid element sulfur was burned and used as a fumigant. In the free state it was used as a medicine. Early myths considered sulfur to be an essential part of all matter that could be burned; that is, it was the element of fire. It was, in fact, called brimstone (fire-stone).

Sulfur is one of the most abundant elements, making up about 0.1 per cent of the earth's crust. It occurs in the free state in Sicily, Japan, Spain, Iceland, Mexico, and the United States. It is found much more widely distributed in the compound form as sulfates in gypsum ($CaSO_4 \cdot 2H_2O$) and barite ($BaSO_4$), and as sulfides in galena (PbS), cinnabar (HgS), zinc blende (ZnS), and iron pyrites (FeS_2). Many ores, such as those of silver and copper, contain sulfides. Sulfur is also present in some proteins.

30:3   Production

Most of the world's supply of sulfur was once obtained from Sicily, where a mineral containing sulfur is placed in iron retorts and heated. As the sulfur boils, the vapors come off and the impurities are left behind. The vapor is condensed in large brick chambers, first as a fine powder which forms a floral pattern like frost on a window pane. For this reason, sublimed (or distilled) sulfur in fine powdered form is called *flowers of sulfur*. As the temperature of the chambers becomes higher, flowers of sulfur melt, and the liquid is run into cylindrical moulds where it hardens. This form of sulfur is called *roll sulfur*.

In 1865, oil prospectors discovered huge deposits of elemental sulfur in Louisiana and Texas. The sulfur lies about 500 feet below the surface. Usually this would present no difficulty, but the presence of much quicksand and water made conventional mining methods impossible, and for several years these deposits remained unused.

In Philadelphia, a young druggist named Herman Frasch heard about these deposits. He was fascinated with chemical engineering, and after selling his store he tackled the problem of mining the sulfur from the Louisiana deposits.

30:4   The Frasch Process

Frasch's plan was to sink a well, like an oil well, to the sulfur deposits. Inside the casing he proposed to place two concentric pipes (see Fig. 30.1). Through the outer pipe, water at about 170°C was to be pumped. This would pass to the sulfur deposit through perforations in the bottom of the pipe and would melt the sulfur (m.p. about 114.5°C). Compressed air at about 500 pounds per square inch would be sent down the inner pipe. Frasch reasoned that melted sulfur, air, and water would then be forced up the centre pipe.

Fig. 30.1   *The Frasch process for obtaining sulfur*

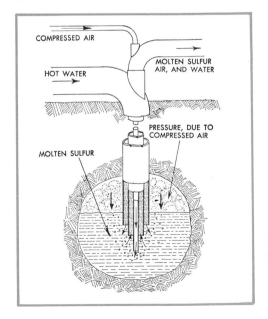

COMPRESSED AIR

MOLTEN SULFUR AIR, AND WATER

HOT WATER

PRESSURE, DUE TO COMPRESSED AIR

MOLTEN SULFUR

Frasch had great difficulty in finding backers for his scheme. One prominent individual stated that he would swallow every ounce of sulfur that Frasch could obtain by his process. Eventually, however, Frasch succeeded in obtaining the necessary capital and the first well was sunk. It was with great trepidation that the pumps were started, but the method was so successful that 40 barrels were filled with sulfur within 15 minutes. A new industry came into existence. A single Frasch well can produce about 400 tons of pure sulfur daily.

At present, only about 40 per cent of the world's sulfur comes from native deposits. The remainder is obtained from sulfide ores, natural gas, and industrial gases.

30:5   Physical Properties

Sulfur is an allotropic element; that is, it exists in several crystalline and amorphous forms. It is a pale yellow, soft, brittle solid if crystalline, but is plastic or pliable in the amorphous form. All forms are practically insoluble in water.

The familiar rhombic crystal type of sulfur is odorless and tasteless and very soluble in carbon disulfide (CS_2). Rhombic crystals may be made by dissolving sulfur in carbon disulfide and allowing the liquid to evaporate. This form of sulfur is made up of ring-shaped molecules consisting of eight atoms each.

When rhombic sulfur is maintained at a temperature between 95.5°C and 114.5°C for some time, it slowly changes to monoclinic or prismatic crystals (see Fig. 30.2). The *transition point* is the temperature at which an allotropic element changes its crystalline form. At 95.5°C, a transition point for sulfur, the element changes from rhombic to monoclinic form.

Monoclinic crystals may be made by melting sulfur and pouring it into a filter paper folded for filtering. When the sulfur is partly solidified and the paper is opened out, the monoclinic crystals may be seen. This form of sulfur is darker than the rhombic form. It melts at 119°C. If allowed to stand for several days, it will revert to the rhombic form; it is stable only above 95.5°C. Monoclinic crystals consist of an eight-membered ring molecule.

When heated rapidly, sulfur melts at 114.5°C to form a straw-colored liquid. If heated slowly, a large part of the sulfur would change to the monoclinic form that melts at 119°C. In the

Fig. 30.2   *Crystalline forms of sulfur*

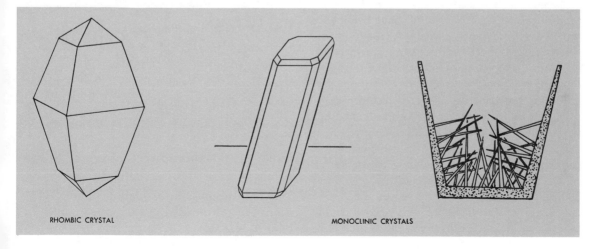

RHOMBIC CRYSTAL

MONOCLINIC CRYSTALS

Fig. 30.3 *Two representations of the S$_8$ molecule*

molten condition, it consists of ring-shaped S$_8$ molecules, as it did in the crystalline form. Its fluidity results from the sulfur rings being able to roll over one another easily. As the temperature is raised, the S$_8$ molecules begin to break up, and open chains of sulfur atoms form. As the ring molecule opens, the two atoms that are separated have an unshared electron each. These atoms form bonds with atoms from other ring molecules, and long chains may result.

These chain-like molecules form a dark brown substance that is viscous, owing to the length of the molecules. At a temperature of around 200°C, the sulfur can hardly be poured. Above 200°C the sulfur becomes less viscous as the long molecules begin to break up. Sulfur boils

at 445°C, forming a yellow vapor, which consists of S$_8$ molecules.

When sulfur at the boiling point is poured into cold water, it solidifies to form an amber-colored plastic mass which may be stretched like rubber; it is called plastic or amorphous sulfur. The plastic property results from the sudden cooling which did not allow ring molecules to re-form. This form of sulfur is insoluble in carbon disulfide. Upon standing for a few days, it slowly changes to rhombic crystals because the chains re-form S$_8$ molecules.

TABLE 30.2	
Main Oxidation Numbers of Sulfur	
Oxidation Numbers	Examples
2 −	H$_2$S, hydrogen sulfide Na$_2$S, sulfide salts S^{2-} sulfide ion
0	S^0, S$_8$, atomic and molecular sulfur
4 +	SO$_2$, sulfur dioxide H$_2$SO$_3$, sulfurous acid Na$_2$SO$_3$, sulfite salts NaHSO$_3$, hydrogen sulfite salts SO$_3^{2-}$, HSO$_3^-$, sulfite and hydrogen sulfite ions
6 +	SO$_3$, sulfur trioxide H$_2$SO$_4$, sulfuric acid Na$_2$SO$_4$, sulfate salts NaHSO$_4$, hydrogen sulfate salts SO$_4^{2-}$, HSO$_4^-$, sulfate and hydrogen sulfate ions

30:6   The Oxidation Numbers of Sulfur

With six electrons in the outer shell, sulfur commonly shows an oxidation number of 2$^-$ and several positive oxidation numbers as shown in Table 30.2

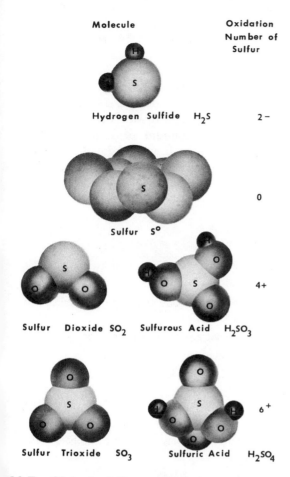

Molecule		Oxidation Number of Sulfur
Hydrogen Sulfide	H_2S	2−
Sulfur	S^o	0
Sulfur Dioxide SO_2	Sulfurous Acid H_2SO_3	4+
Sulfur Trioxide SO_3	Sulfuric Acid H_2SO_4	6+

30:7 Chemical Properties

1. Sulfur unites with many metals. If these metals are finely divided, the reaction may be very vigorous, resulting in combustion:

$$Fe + S \rightarrow FeS$$
$$2Cu + S \rightarrow Cu_2S$$
$$Zn + S \rightarrow ZnS$$

2. It combines with hydrogen slowly at high temperature to form hydrogen sulfide. The reaction is rapid if hydrogen is bubbled through boiling sulfur:

$$H_2 + S \rightarrow H_2S$$

3. Sulfur combines with some non-metals as does oxygen. A highly heated mixture of

coke and sulfur forms carbon disulfide, CS_2. This is a colorless liquid with a bad odor. It vaporizes easily, and the vapors are poisonous and highly inflammable. Its principal use is as a solvent for waxes and gums.

Sulfur burns with a pale blue flame in air or oxygen to form sulfur dioxide:

$$S + O_2 \rightarrow SO_2$$

Here the oxidation number of the sulfur is 4+. Sulfur trioxide, SO_3 (oxidation number 6+), may be formed by special procedures, as will be seen in the next chapter.

30:8 Uses

The vulcanization of rubber was discovered by Charles Goodyear in 1839 while experimenting with rubber mixtures; he accidentally dropped some rubber and sulfur on a hot stove. Without sulfur, rubber is brittle in winter and sticky in summer. Vulcanization converts the sticky mass of raw rubber into the tough, yet elastic, familiar substance in use today. Rubber tires for cars, trucks, and airplanes are made by vulcanization.

When sulfur is boiled with calcium hydroxide, a dark brown liquid called "Bordeaux mixture" is formed. This is used as a spray to kill fungus growths and insects on trees and plants. Very finely divided sulfur known as colloidal or wettable sulfur may also be used for this purpose.

Sulfa drugs and certain ointments contain sulfur; mites that cause scabies, or itch, are controlled with such ointments.

Much sulfur is used in the manufacture of calcium hydrogen sulfite, $Ca(HSO_3)_2$, which is an important chemical to the pulp and paper industry (Chapter 31).

The modern "strike-anywhere" match contains potassium chlorate and phosphorus sulfide (P_4S_3) bound together on the tip with glue. The end of the match stick is paraffin-coated so that it will ignite more easily. When the match head is struck, heat of friction ignites the phosphorus sulfide, and the potassium chlorate supplies the needed oxygen. To prevent a glowing tip after the match is extinguished (which might cause a fire), before the match head is applied, the matchstick is dipped into a solution of sodium sulfate or ammonium phosphate.

The tip of the safety match is made of antimony sulfide (Sb_2S_3) and potassium chlorate. This mixture has a higher ignition temperature than the phosphorus sulfide–potassium chlorate mixture used in the ordinary match. A mixture of non-poisonous red phosphorus, an abrasive, and a glue is applied to the match box. A high temperature results when the match head is rubbed on this mixture at the point of contact, igniting the red phosphorus. The flame, however, is so small that it will not ignite the box.

The greatest amount of sulfur is used in making sulfuric acid, one of the most valuable of all industrial chemicals, and one of the topics of the next chapter.

QUESTIONS

1. Write a paragraph on the occurrence of sulfur.

2. What is *flowers of sulfur* and why is it so called?

3. Draw a diagram and explain fully the Frasch method of mining sulfur.

4. List the allotropic forms of sulfur.

5. Explain how two crystalline forms of sulfur may be made and give the physical properties of each. Draw a diagram of each type of crystal.

6. How may amorphous sulfur be prepared? What are its chief properties?

7. (a) Describe the changes in sulfur as it is heated to its boiling point.
   (b) Account for these changes.

8. Define transition point and apply this term to sulfur.

9. (a) In what ways are sulfur and oxygen similar?
   (b) Account for this similarity.

10. Give formulas of compounds to show where sulfur has oxidation numbers of $2-$, $4+$, and $6+$.

11. Draw an electronic diagram to show the structure of H_2S.

12. List three chemical properties of sulfur.

13. What is vulcanization and how was it discovered?

14. Of what use is sulfur in medicine?

15. What is "Bordeaux mixture" and for what is it used?

16. How is sulfur used in paper making?

17. (a) Describe the structure of the modern match.
    (b) What is after-glow? How is it prevented?
    (c) How does a safety-match work?

18. What is the most important compound of sulfur?

19. What weight of elemental sulfur would be obtained from 110 g of gypsum, $CaSO_4 \cdot 2H_2O$?

20. Calculate the simplest formula of a compound that contains 23.1 per cent magnesium, 30.7 per cent sulfur, and 46.2 per cent oxygen.

21. How many tons of PbS would be required to yield 10 tons of sulfur?

CHAPTER

31 Compounds of Sulfur

31:1 Sulfur Dioxide

Sulfur dioxide, SO_2, is usually present in gases from volcanoes and in water from certain sulfur springs. Coal contains sulfur in the combined form, and this produces sulfur dioxide when the coal is burned. City air may contain small amounts of this gas.

Preparation

LABORATORY

Salts containing the SO_3^{2-} group are called sulfites. They are derivatives of sulfurous acid, H_2SO_3, a weak acid. If any of these salts are treated with strong acid, sulfurous acid is formed, which breaks down to form water and sulfur dioxide. Gentle heat is needed to make the reaction go to completion. Sodium sulfite is usually treated with sulfuric or hydrochloric acid:

$$Na_2SO_3 + H_2SO_4 \rightarrow Na_2SO_4 + H_2O + SO_2\uparrow$$

Sulfur dioxide is collected by the upward displacement of air because, like hydrogen chloride, it is heavier than air and very soluble in water. When the bottles are filled may be determined by the use of moist blue litmus paper, which, because of the formation of sulfurous acid, turns red on contact with the gas:

$$H_2O + SO_2 \rightleftharpoons H_2SO_3$$

INDUSTRIAL

About 90 per cent of the sulfur used industrially is burned to produce sulfur dioxide. The gas is also produced by the roasting of metallic sulfides and the heating of iron pyrites, FeS_2, in air:

$$4FeS_2 + 11O_2 \rightarrow 2Fe_2O_3 + 8SO_2\uparrow$$

Zinc blend is another example:

$$2ZnS + 3O_2 \rightarrow 2ZnO + 2SO_2\uparrow$$

Physical and Chemical Properties

Sulfur dioxide is a colorless gas with a strong, choking odor like that of burning matches. It is heavier than air and is very soluble in water because it reacts with water. It can be liquefied at $20°C$ with a pressure of three atmospheres (45 pounds per square inch).

Sulfur dioxide is a stable compound. It does not burn or support combustion. A catalyst, like platinum or vanadium pentoxide, causes sulfur dioxide to combine with oxygen to form sulfur trioxide, SO_3. In this reaction, the oxidation number of sulfur is raised from $4+$ to $6+$, as the sulfur atom now shares its electrons with a third oxygen atom:

$$\overset{4+}{2SO_2} + O_2 \rightarrow \overset{6+}{2SO_3}$$

Thus, in this reaction sulfur dioxide acts as electron donor.

Sulfur dioxide may also act as electron acceptor or oxidizing agent as in its reaction with hydrogen sulfide:

$$\overset{4+}{SO_2} + \overset{2-}{2H_2S} \rightarrow 2H_2O + \overset{0}{3S}\downarrow$$
$$\uparrow \qquad\qquad \downarrow$$
$$4e \quad = 2 \times 2e$$

This reaction accounts for some of the sulfur deposits found in volcanic and hot spring areas.

Sulfur dioxide combines readily with water to form the weak, unstable sulfurous acid, H_2SO_3, as already mentioned.

Sulfurous acid is a good bleaching agent because of its reducing properties:

$H_2SO_3 + dye \rightarrow H_2SO_4 + $ colorless compound

However, the bleaching is not as lasting as that by chlorine because oxygen of the air may combine with the reduction products, re-creating a color.

A similar reaction takes place to some extent if sulfurous acid is exposed to air:

$$2H_2SO_3 + O_2 \rightarrow 2H_2SO_4$$

It is used for bleaching straw, silk, feathers, dried fruits, molasses, and canned corn. Sulfurous acid may also be used as a food preservative, but, since the acid is somewhat undesirable, its use must be indicated on the food label.

Sulfurous acid, like any other acid, neutralizes bases, and when it does so, sulfites are formed:

$$2NaOH + H_2SO_3 \rightarrow Na_2SO_3 + 2H_2O$$
$$Ca(OH)_2 + H_2SO_3 \rightarrow CaSO_3 + 2H_2O$$

Chemical Test for a Sulfite

Sulfite salts, sulfurous acid, and sulfur dioxide all produce a marked color change with potassium permanganate solution, and this is the basis of the chemical test for these compounds. The reaction is an electronic exchange in which the sulfur compounds transfer electrons to the permanganate ion. The latter ion gives a purple color to its solution. When it gains electrons it changes to the colorless manganese (II) (Mn^{2+}) ion. This color change identifies sulfite salts, sulfur dioxide, and sulfurous acid. The equation representing the reaction is:

$$\overset{7+}{2KMnO_4} + \overset{4-}{5H_2SO_3} \rightarrow$$
$$\underset{2 \times 5e\ =\ 5\ \times\ 2e}{\uparrow \qquad \downarrow}$$

$$\overset{6+}{K_2SO_4} + \overset{2+}{2MnSO_4} + \overset{6+}{2H_2SO_4} + 3H_2O$$

When carrying out this test, hydrochloric acid is added to the unknown salt, and the mixture is warmed in a flask or test tube. Any evolved gas is passed through potassium permanganate solution. If the solution is decolorised, the original material contained a sulfite.

$$SO_3^{2-} + 2H_3O^+ \rightarrow 3H_2O + SO_2\uparrow$$
$$SO_2 + H_2O \rightarrow H_2SO_3$$

Uses

The most common use of sulfur dioxide is for making sulfuric acid. It is used to some extent as a refrigerant in mechanical refrigerators. While it absorbs less heat in evaporating than do some gases, such as ammonia, it liquefies so easily that it is a convenient gas to use. The use of sulfur dioxide in the bleaching and preservation of food has already been discussed.

Sulfite pulp, a very important material for making high quality paper, consists of a long fibre of cellulose, which gives paper high tensile strength. Wood in its natural state consists principally of cellulose fibres and a glue-like substance called lignin. To convert the wood into sulfite pulp, the wood is first chopped into tiny chips. Then the chips are placed in a heated calcium hydrogen sulfite solution, which is made by bubbling sulfur dioxide through a suspension of calcium hydroxide. The lignin dissolves in the solution leaving free cellulose fibres.

Sulfur dioxide is used in making sulfites which are, in turn, important for producing small amounts of sulfur dioxide, as, for instance, in the laboratory. Cotton is normally bleached by means of chlorine, but if any chlorine remains on the cloth, the cloth will be slowly destroyed. The chlorine is usually removed by passing the cloth through a sulfite solution. When used in this way, the sulfite is called an *antichlor*:

$$Na_2SO_3 + Cl_2 + H_2O \rightarrow Na_2SO_4 + 2HCl\uparrow$$

31:2   Hydrogen Sulfide

Hydrogen sulfide is frequently found in volcanic gas, sulfur springs, coal gas, and gases formed during the decay of organic matter containing sulfur.

Preparation

Hydrogen sulfide is prepared both in the laboratory and commercially by the action of hydrochloric acid on a sulfide. Iron (II) sulfide is commonly used for this purpose:

$$FeS + 2HCl \rightarrow FeCl_2 + H_2S\uparrow$$

In the laboratory, hydrogen sulfide is prepared in the same type of apparatus as is used for the production of sulfur dioxide. The gas is collected by the upward displacement of air because it is fairly soluble in water and is heavier than air. When the bottles are full can be determined by the use of filter paper moistened with a solution of lead acetate. The paper turns black on contact with the gas owing to the formation of lead sulfide.

$$Pb(CH_3COO)_2 + H_2S \rightarrow PbS\downarrow + 2CH_3COOH$$

Physical Properties

Hydrogen sulfide is colorless, slightly heavier than air, and fairly soluble in water because it acts as a proton donor to the water. One volume of water dissolves three volumes of the gas. The gas may be easily liquefied, and it may be purchased in this form in steel cylinders. The most characteristic property of this compound is its objectionable odor, resembling that of rotten eggs.

The absence of hydrogen bonding causes H_2S to have a boiling point of $-60°C$. Water has a boiling point of $100°C$ due to hydrogen bonding.

Chemical Properties

A water solution of hydrogen sulfide is called hydrosulfuric acid:

$$H_2S + H_2O \underset{-H_2O}{\overset{+H_2O}{\rightleftharpoons}} H_3O^+ + HS^- \rightleftharpoons 2H_3O^+ + S^{2-}$$

H_2S is a weak acid because the electronegativity difference between hydrogen and sulfur is not great (H is 2.1 and S is 2.5). The bond is largely covalent.

Hydrogen sulfide reacts with many salts to produce colored sulfides. Several examples of the reaction of hydrogen sulfide with metallic ions are given in Table 31.1.

The sulfides of the alkali metals are soluble. Paint often changes color because of the reaction of a metallic pigment with hydrogen sulfide. Lithopone, a white pigment consisting of barium sulfate ($BaSO_4$), is often used in white paint because it does not darken with hydrogen sulfide.

Since sulfur has its lowest possible oxidation number of $2-$ in hydrogen sulfide, this compound is a good reducing agent, usually producing free sulfur upon oxidation:

$$2H_2S + SO_2 \rightarrow 2H_2O + 3S\downarrow$$

Hydrogen sulfide does not support combustion; it burns in air producing sulfur dioxide:

$$2H_2S + 3O_2 \rightarrow 2H_2O + 2SO_2\uparrow$$

If the supply of oxygen is deficient, a deposit of sulfur may form:

$$2H_2S + O_2 \rightarrow 2H_2O + 2S\downarrow$$

The latter reaction occurs slowly if hydrogen sulfide is mixed with air, or if it is in a water solution containing some dissolved air. If traces of hydrogen sulfide are present in air, finely divided sulfur forms and causes some metals to tarnish by forming a sulfide. This is notable with silver and copper:

$$2Ag + S \rightarrow Ag_2S \text{ (black)}$$

Recently, a process has been perfected in which silver articles can be coated with silicone, which prevents tarnishing for a long time.

TABLE 31.1

Reactions of H₂S with Metallic Ions

Pb(CH₃COO)₂ lead acetate	$+ H_2S \rightarrow$	PbS $\downarrow + 2CH_3COOH$ Lead sulfide (black)
$CuSO_4$	$+ H_2S \rightarrow$	CuS $\downarrow + H_2SO_4$ Copper sulfide (black)
$Cd(NO_3)_2$	$+ H_2S \rightarrow$	CdS $\downarrow + 2HNO_3$ Cadmium sulfide (yellow)
$ZnSO_4$	$+ H_2S \rightarrow$	ZnS $\downarrow + H_2SO_4$ Zinc sulfide (white)
$2AsCl_3$	$+ 3H_2S \rightarrow$	As₂S₃ $\downarrow + 6HCl$ Arsenic sulfide (orange-yellow)
$2SbCl_3$	$+ 3H_2S \rightarrow$	Sb₂S₃ $\downarrow + 6HCl$ Antimony sulfide (reddish orange)

Hydrogen sulfide is poisonous. In small amounts it inflames the throat and produces headache, nausea, and dizziness. Large quantities may cause death. It is especially dangerous because it has an anaesthetic effect on the olfactory lobes, and even a person in a dangerous concentration of the gas accustoms himself to it after a short exposure.

Test for a Sulfide

To test for a sulfide, a little hydrochloric acid is added to the unknown in a test tube and the mixture is warmed. The gas evolved is allowed to come in contact with filter paper moistened with lead acetate solution. A black precipitate or color shows the presence of a sulfide.

Uses

This gas is used in the analysis of ores and metals. It is possible to separate groups of metals from one another because their sulfides have different solubilities in acid and base solutions. Often the color of a sulfide indicates the presence of a certain metal.

31:3   Sulfuric Acid

Sulfuric acid is one of the most important compounds of chemistry. It is difficult to name one modern manufactured article that does not make use of this acid directly or indirectly at some stage. The standard of living or industrial activity of any country can be judged by the per capita consumption of sulfuric acid.

Sulfuric acid is manufactured by two methods; these are the newer Contact Process and the old Lead Chamber Process.

The Contact Process

a. Sulfur is burned in dry air and sulfur dioxide is formed:

$$2SO_2 + O_2 \rightarrow 2SO_3\uparrow$$

Vanadium pentoxide or platinized silica gel are now used as the catalyst instead of the platinum metal used formerly. These are less expensive and more resistant to any impurities still present in the mixture of reacting gases. Such impurities are trace amounts of arsenic, antimony, selenium, and chlorine.

The temperature must be about 450°C. Above this temperature, some of the sulfur trioxide is decomposed, while below this temperature some of the sulfur dioxide remains unchanged.

Courtesy Canadian Industries Limited

Fig. 31.1 *A view of a modern contact plant*

$$S + O_2 \rightarrow SO_2\uparrow$$

b. The sulfur dioxide and excess air are passed through a hot gas filter where most impurities are removed. The gases then pass into the main reactor, called the Contact Tower. This tower contains perforated shelves supporting a catalyst.

c. When the gases come in contact with the catalyst, the union of sulfur dioxide and oxygen produces sulfur trioxide.

d. The sulfur trioxide is cooled and then passed to the absorption towers. Concentrated sulfuric acid is pumped into the top of the towers, and as this liquid descends the tower, it absorbs the sulfur trioxide gas to form "fuming sulfuric acid" or oleum:

$$SO_3 + H_2SO_4 \rightarrow H_2SO_4.SO_3 \text{ (oleum)}$$

Concentrated sulfuric acid needs to be used in the absorption towers because pure water tends to form a fine mist which is difficult to

Fig. 31.2 *The contact process for making sulfuric acid*

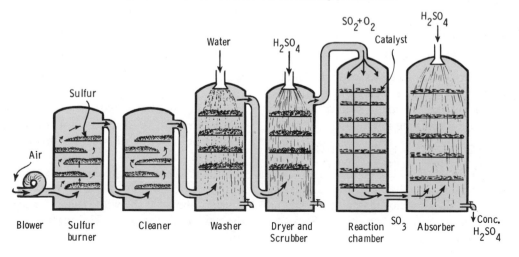

			Water	H_2SO_4		$SO_2 + O_2$ Catalyst	H_2SO_4
Air	Sulfur						↓ Conc. H_2SO_4
Blower	Sulfur burner	Cleaner	Washer	Dryer and Scrubber	Reaction chamber	SO_3 Absorber	

precipitate. Thus, concentrated acid needs to be used to manufacture more sulfuric acid.

Fuming sulfuric acid, called oleum, is the product obtained from the absorption towers. It fumes in air because some of the sulfur trioxide dissolved in it escapes into the air where it reacts with the water vapor:

$$SO_3 + H_2O \rightarrow H_2SO_4$$

The oleum is finally diluted to the desired concentration:

$$H_2SO_4.SO_3 + H_2O \rightarrow 2H_2SO_4$$

Pure H_2SO_4 is properly called hydrogen sulfate.

Physical Properties

Sulfuric acid is a colorless, odorless, syrupy, heavy liquid with a density of 1.84 g/ml. It has long been called oil of vitriol because of its appearance. It boils at 338°C. A great deal of heat is liberated when sulfuric acid is diluted with water, due to the donation of protons to the water molecules, as well as the hydration of the sulfate ion. For this reason, the acid must be added to the water, so that the heavy acid sinks through the water and the heat is evenly dispersed. If the water is added to the acid, the first few drops of water are changed to steam, which will splatter acid from its container.

Chemical Properties

DILUTE SULFURIC ACID

When sulfuric acid is added to water, it donates protons to the water molecules in two steps, first producing the hydrogen sulfate ion, and second giving the sulfate ion:

$$H_2SO_4 + H_2O \rightarrow HSO_4^- + H_3O^+$$
$$HSO_4^- + H_2O \rightarrow SO_4^{2-} + H_3O^+$$

Dilute solutions of the acid are completely ionized. The dilute acid reacts with metals above hydrogen in the Electromotive Series to yield hydrogen:

$$Zn + H_2SO_4 \rightarrow ZnSO_4 + H_2\uparrow$$

Dilute sulfuric acid neutralizes bases:

$$2NaOH + H_2SO_4 \rightarrow Na_2SO_4 + 2H_2O$$

It reacts with metallic oxides:

$$CuO + H_2SO_4 \rightarrow CuSO_4 + H_2O$$

Because sulfuric acid has such a high boiling point, it liberates other acids from their salts.

Examples:

$$FeS \quad + H_2SO_4 \rightarrow FeSO_4 \quad + H_2S\uparrow$$
$$2NaCl \quad + H_2SO_4 \rightarrow Na_2SO_4 + 2HCl\uparrow$$
$$Na_2SO_3 + H_2SO_4 \rightarrow Na_2SO_4 + H_2SO_3$$

then $H_2SO_3 \rightarrow H_2O + SO_2\uparrow$
$$2NaNO_3 + H_2SO_4 \rightarrow Na_2SO_4 + 2HNO_3\uparrow$$

CONCENTRATED SULFURIC ACID

Pure hydrogen sulfate or concentrated sulfuric acid is a good oxidizing agent. This is due to the high oxidation number of 6+ of sulfur in the sulfate ion. In this condition, the sulfur atom is apt to gain electrons, and as a result hot concentrated H_2SO_4 reacts even with copper, a metal below hydrogen in the Electromotive Series. It should be noted that no hydrogen is produced in this reaction. Instead, sulfur changes in its oxidation state from 6+ to 4+, resulting in the formation of sulfur dioxide gas.

$$\begin{array}{cccc} 0 & 6+ & 2+ & 4+ \\ Cu + & 2H_2SO_4 \rightarrow & CuSO_4 + & SO_2 + 2H_2O \\ \downarrow & & & \uparrow \\ 2e & & & 2e \end{array}$$

When metals above hydrogen in the Electromotive Series react with hot concentrated H_2SO_4 both sulfur dioxide and hydrogen are produced.

At 450°C and atmospheric pressure, sulfuric acid decomposes into sulfur trioxide and water. This accounts for the white fumes formed when the acid is evaporated. The reaction is reversible:

$$H_2SO_4 \rightleftharpoons H_2O + SO_3\uparrow$$

Sulfuric acid is a strong dehydrating agent; gases may be dried by passing them through it. When the concentrated acid comes in contact with carbohydrates, it decomposes them so that the hydrogen and oxygen present in the carbohydrates are removed as water, and a black residue of carbon remains:

$$\overset{H_2SO_4}{(C_6H_{10}O_5)_n \rightarrow n(5H_2O + 6C)}$$
cellulose

$$\overset{H_2SO_4}{C_{12}H_{22}O_{11} \rightarrow 11H_2O + 12C\downarrow}$$
sucrose

Proteins are also charred by the concentrated acid.

Test for a Sulfate

A few drops of barium chloride reagent is added to the solution being tested. If a white precipitate forms, the presence of a sulfate is indicated:

$$BaCl_2 + H_2SO_4 \rightarrow BaSO_4\downarrow + 2HCl$$

It is necessary to test the solubility of the precipitate in hydrochloric acid because certain other materials, such as carbonates, may give a white precipitate with the barium chloride. Such precipitates dissolve in hydrochloric acid.

Uses of Sulfuric Acid

About one-quarter of the sulfuric acid made is used to produce fertilizer. Phosphorus is an essential element for plant growth, but it is easily depleted from the soil. Rock phosphate, $Ca_3(PO_4)_2$, is a plentiful mineral, but it is insoluble. However, when treated with sulfuric acid, it changes to calcium dihydrogen phos-

phate, which is soluble and useful to plants. The product is called superphosphate and is used as fertilizer.

$$Ca_3(PO_4)_2 + H_2SO_4 \rightarrow$$
$$2CaSO_4 + Ca(H_2PO_4)_2$$
superphosphate

Petroleum products contain many compounds that are dark in color or turn dark on exposure to air. These compounds, together with waxes and gums, are removed by treating the oil product with sulfuric acid.

The dehydrating action of sulfuric acid makes it a necessity in the nitration of glycerol, cotton, toluene, and other compounds from which explosives are made. Sulfuric acid is also used to make cellulose film and rayon.

The acid is often used to clean or "pickle" metals before they are plated with another metal. Of the hundreds of other processes using sulfuric acid, a few are the making of sulfate salts, paper, leather, dyes, drugs, paints, and other acids. The acid is used as the electrolyte in lead storage batteries.

31:4 Some Sulfates

In the seventeenth century a Bavarian, Johann Glauber, cured himself of a fever by drinking the water from a certain well. He tested the water and discovered sodium sulfate, Na_2SO_4. $10H_2O$, although he did not know its composition. This compound has since been known as Glauber's salt, and it has been used as a laxative for more than 300 years. It is sometimes called *salt cake*. About the same time that Glauber discovered his salt, an English physician extracted magnesium sulfate, $MgSO_4.7H_2O$, from the waters of some springs near Epsom, England. He wrote a book on the medicinal uses of this salt. Even today many patent medicines and bottled mineral waters contain one or both of these salts.

QUESTIONS

1. Where does sulfur dioxide occur naturally?

2. (a) List three methods of preparing sulfur dioxide.
   (b) Describe the laboratory method in detail giving the equation.

3. Give five physical properties of sulfur dioxide.

4. (a) How may sulfur dioxide act as both an oxidizing agent and as a reducing agent?
   (b) List three other chemical properties of the gas.

5. Explain the bleaching action of sulfur dioxide.

6. List the properties of sulfurous acid.

7. (a) How may sulfites be prepared?
   (b) Describe the chemical test for a sulfite.

8. Name as many uses of sulfur dioxide as you can.

9. Show electronically how hydrogen and sulfur combine chemically.

10. (a) Describe the laboratory method of preparing hydrogen sulfide. Give the equation.
    (b) What is the chemical test for hydrogen sulfide?
    (c) List the physical properties of hydrogen sulfide.

11. Give equations to show the burning of hydrogen sulfide in ample and in deficient air.

12. Explain the tarnishing of silver. Give equations to illustrate your answer.

13. Why is hydrogen sulfide a dangerous poison?

14. (a) What is hydrosulfuric acid?
    (b) Why is this a weak acid?

15. Give the equations for the preparation of and the color of the following sulfides: PbS, CuS, ZnS, As_2S_3, Sb_2S_3.

16. What is the chemical test for a sulfide?

17. Of what use is hydrogen sulfide?

18. Why is sulfuric acid so important to man?

19. Describe the contact process of manufacturing sulfuric acid in detail giving the equations and a sketch of the apparatus.

20. (a) Give the physical properties of sulfuric acid.
    (b) Explain how it should be diluted.

21. List the chemical properties of dilute sulfuric acid and illustrate each with an equation when possible.

22. Give the chemical properties of concentrated sulfuric acid. Account for its strong oxidizing properties.

23. What is the test for a sulfate?

24. What is superphosphate?

25. Give as many uses of sulfuric acid as you can.

26. What is Glauber's salt? Epsom salt?

27. Find the number of moles of sodium sulfite required to yield 10 l of sulfur dioxide measured at $-100°C$ and 743 mm pressure.

28. How many grams of sulfur would be required to make 500 ml of a 0.5 M solution of sulfurous acid?

29. Find the molarity of a sulfuric acid solution, if 10 ml of it are neutralized by 7 ml of a 0.2 molar solution of sodium hydroxide.

30. Calculate the volume of hydrogen sulfide obtained by the reaction of 10 g of iron sulfide with sulfuric acid. The hydrogen sulfide is measured at 15°C and 788 mm pressure.

31. It is desired to manufacture 100 lbs of cadmium sulfide for a pigment. What weight of cadmium nitrate would be required?

32. How much sulfur is required to make 50 lbs of hydrogen sulfate?

33. Find the relative rates of diffusion of hydrogen sulfide and sulfur dioxide.

34. Suppose that a farmer wishes to place 10 lbs of available phosphorus on each acre of his field. Find the weight of superphosphate per acre required.

32 Nitrogen and Phosphorus

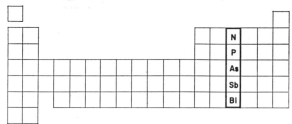

32:1 From Non-metal to Metal

Group V of the periodic table consists of nitrogen, phosphorus, arsenic, antimony, and bismuth. Nitrogen and phosphorus are non-metals, while bismuth is a metal, forming the cation of salts, as in $BiCl_3$. Arsenic and antimony show both metallic and non-metallic characteristics.

Group V illustrates very well that increase in atomic size causes differences in electronegativity. The electronegativity of nitrogen is 3.0, while that of bismuth is about 2.0. The relatively high electronegativity of nitrogen causes it to behave as a non-metal, while the relatively low electronegativity of bismuth causes it to behave as a metal. The intermediate elements have properties between these extremes.

The cause of the metallic nature shown by the elements of large atomic size is the easy removal of the outer electrons. As the distance between the electrons and the nucleus increases, the force keeping these outer electrons within the atom diminishes, and the element behaves as a metal.

The distribution of electrons in the atoms of these elements is given in the Table 32.1.

TABLE 32.1

Electron Configuration of the Elements of Group V

		Energy Levels				
		n = 1	2	3	4	5	6
Element	Atomic Number	Sublevels and Orbitals and Their Electrons					
		1s	2s 2p	3s 3p 3d	4s 4p 4d 4f	5s 5p 5d	6s 6p
Nitrogen	7	2	2 3				
Phosphorus	15	2	2 6	2 3			
Arsenic	33	2	2 6	2 6 10	2 3		
Antimony	51	2	2 6	2 6 10	2 6 10	2 3	
Bismuth	83	2	2 6	2 6 10	2 6 10 14	2 6 10	2 3

Each of these elements has five electrons in its outer shell. Two of these electrons fill the *s* orbital and the other three electrons fill the three *p* orbitals singly.

This electronic pattern gives to the atoms their covalence of 3 shown in NH_3, PH_3, AsH_3 and SbH_3. Because of its large size, the bismuth atom has lost the power to share electrons with hydrogen and, therefore, it does not form a stable hydrogen compound.

32:2 Nitrogen

The analysis of air shows that nitrogen makes up about four-fifths of the atmosphere. While nitrogen is inert, oxygen, the other important gas in air, is highly reactive. Nitrogen was so named because it was found in "nitre", or potassium nitrate. The nitrogen in the air dilutes the oxygen to the point where combustion, respiration, and oxidation of metals are reasonably slow. In an atmosphere of pure oxygen, life as we know it would cease to exist because these processes would be so much faster than at present.

Nitrogen in the combined state is found in certain salts, the most important of which are ammonium chloride and sodium nitrate, the latter known as saltpetre. The world's largest deposit of this salt is found in Chile; smaller accumulations are found in many other countries. At one time, these deposits were of great economic importance because nitrogen compounds could not be made synthetically, as they are today. The production of compounds from atmospheric nitrogen is called *nitrogen fixation*.

Proteins are complex compounds containing mainly carbon, hydrogen, oxygen, and nitrogen They are essential constituents of all living matter. Nitrogen compounds must be present in animal diets and plant fertilizers, since new tissues for growth, repair, and maintenance of both plants and animals require proteins.

The Nitrogen Cycle

The nitrogen of the air cannot, unfortunately, be used directly by the majority of plants and animals. Only certain bacteria are able to convert free nitrogen into valuable compounds. They are called the nitrogen fixing bacteria.*

These bacteria change nitrogen compounds to plant proteins, which are eaten by animals to become animal protein. Finally, the nitrogen is

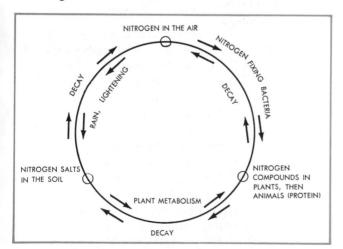

Fig. 32.1 *The nitrogen cycle*

*The nitrogen fixing bacteria are found at the roots of plants called legumes, such as clover, peas, beans, and alfalfa. Little swellings, called nodules, on the roots of these plants are filled with the nitrogen fixing bacteria.

excreted as animal waste. This is decomposed by other bacteria, thus liberating the nitrogen back into the air and completing the cycle.

The passing of nitrogen from one form to another in the course of natural events may be traced by means of Fig. 32.1.

Preparation

ATMOSPHERIC NITROGEN

This may be prepared by the removal of atmospheric oxygen or by the distillation of liquid air. The nitrogen obtained by these methods is not pure, but since the impurities are not active chemically, the properties of nitrogen may be observed.

CHEMICAL NITROGEN

Although pure nitrogen may be prepared by heating ammonium nitrite, this method is rather dangerous because ammonium nitrite may explode when heated.

$$NH_4NO_2 \rightarrow N_2\uparrow + 2H_2O$$

If, instead, ammonium chloride and sodium nitrite are mixed and heated, the method is safe because the ammonium nitrite decomposes as fast as it is formed.

$$NH_4Cl + NaNO_2 \rightarrow NH_4NO_2 + NaCl$$

The apparatus used is similar to that used for the preparation of oxygen.

Physical Properties

Nitrogen is a colorless, odorless, and tasteless gas. It is slightly soluble in water because it does not interact with the water, is less dense than air, and it boils at $-196°C$ and freezes at $-210°C$.

Chemical Properties

Nitrogen shows a large variety of oxidation numbers ranging from $3-$ to $5+$ as shown in Table 32.2.

At high temperatures, nitrogen combines with some metals, such as magnesium, aluminum, calcium, and iron, to form nitrides. One example is

$$3Mg + N_2 \rightarrow Mg_3N_2$$

The oxidation number of nitrogen in these compounds is $3-$, because nitrogen is more electronegative than the metals. On the whole, however, the nitrogen molecule is inert because of the bonding provided by six shared electrons forming a triple bond. Nitrogen combines with oxygen only when large amounts of energy are supplied to the gases. In a flash of lightning, the electrical energy supplied by the lightning causes some nitrogen and oxygen to combine to form nitric oxide, NO, and nitrogen dioxide, NO_2:

$$N_2 + O_2 \rightarrow 2NO$$
$$2NO + O_2 \rightarrow 2NO_2$$

TABLE 32.2

Main Oxidation Numbers of Nitrogen

Oxidation Numbers	Examples
$3-$	NH_3 ammonia, NH_4^+ ammonium ion
0	N_2 molecular nitrogen
$1+$	N_2O nitrous oxide
$2+$	NO nitric oxide
$3+$	N_2O_3 dinitrogen trioxide
	HNO_2 nitrous acid
	$NaNO_2$ sodium nitrite
	NO_2^- nitrite ion
$4+$	NO_2 nitrogen dioxide
	N_2O_4 dinitrogen tetroxide
$5+$	N_2O_5 dinitrogen pentoxide
	HNO_3 nitric acid
	$NaNO_3$ sodium nitrate
	NO_3^- nitrate ion

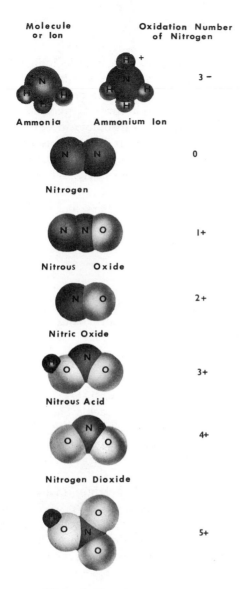

Molecule or Ion	Oxidation Number of Nitrogen
Ammonia Ammonium Ion	3 −
Nitrogen	0
Nitrous Oxide	1+
Nitric Oxide	2+
Nitrous Acid	3+
Nitrogen Dioxide	4+
Nitric Acid	5+

Nitrogen also combines with hydrogen to form ammonia:

$$N_2 + 3H_2 \rightarrow 2NH_3$$

Nitrogen is used in incandescent light bulbs to conduct heat from the filament, and in high temperature mercury thermometers to prevent the mercury from boiling.

32:3 Phosphorus

Phosphorus is so active that it is never found free in nature. It is named from a Greek word meaning "light-giver", because when exposed to air it glows in the dark as a result of slow oxidation. It occurs mainly in a mineral called rock phosphate, which contains calcium phosphate, $Ca_3(PO_4)_2$. This mineral is thought to have been formed from bones of prehistoric animals because bones and teeth contain calcium phosphate. It is found also in living cells, seeds, and eggs.

To Prepare Phosphorus

A mixture of calcium phosphate, sand, and coke is heated in an electric furnace:

$$2Ca_3(PO_4)_2 + 6SiO_2 \rightarrow P_4O_{10} + 6CaSiO_3$$
$$P_4O_{10} + 10C \rightarrow P_4\uparrow + 10CO\uparrow$$

The phosphorus leaves the furnace as a vapor, which is condensed under water. The carbon monoxide is burned as waste. Calcium silicate, the molten slag, is drawn off from the bottom of the furnace.

Allotropic Forms

There are two important allotropic forms of phosphorus: white and red.

WHITE PHOSPHORUS

White phosphorus results when the vapors of phosphorus condense. In this allotropic form, each phosphorus atom is attached to three others to produce molecules of P_4. White phosphorus is a waxy, soft, translucent solid and is

Fig. 32.2 *Pyramid-like structure of P_4*

Structure of P_4

about twice as dense as water. This form of phosphorus usually takes on a lemon-yellow color due to partial conversion to the red allotropic form. It is insoluble in water, in which it is stored; but it dissolves in carbon disulfide. Its melting point, 44°C, must be determined by heating the solid under water for otherwise it would burst into flame before melting. Its kindling temperature when exposed to air is 35°C; because of its low kindling temperature, it cannot be picked up safely with the fingers.

Phosphorus unites with oxygen to form white fumes of phosphoric oxide, P_4O_{10}. The flame is dazzlingly brilliant if pure oxygen is used.

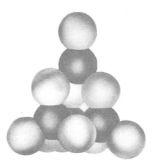

Structure of P_4O_{10}

White phosphorus is very poisonous, causing deterioration of the bones of workers who come in contact with it. This was a major health hazard when white phosphorus was used in matches; fortunately, the safe red form of phosphorus may be used instead, and the white variety is now prohibited by law.

RED PHOSPHORUS

If white phosphorus is heated to 250°C in the absence of air and with a little iodine as a catalyst, the P_4 molecules combine to form much larger molecules. The product is a red powder, an allotropic form of phosphorus.

Red phosphorus is insoluble in both water and carbon disulfide. It is not poisonous, if pure. Its kindling temperature is about 250°C so that it can be handled safely. When ignited, it forms the same product as white phosphorus. If red phosphorus is sublimed at 290°C out of contact with air, the condensed vapors form white phosphorus.

Uses

Most of the phosphorus produced is used to make phosphoric acid, H_3PO_4, and phosphorous acid, H_3PO_3. Phosphoric oxide, formed by burning phosphorus, is the anhydride of phosphoric acid:

$$P_4O_{10} + 6H_2O \rightarrow 4H_3PO_4$$

Diphosphorus trioxide, P_2O_3, is the anhydride of phosphorous acid. Salts of these acids are used in medicine, washing powders, and baking powder. Sodium hexametaphosphate, $(NaPO_3)_6$, softens water without forming a precipitate.

Phosphorus is used in certain tin and bronze alloys to make them corrosion resistant in salt water. Red phosphorus is used in making matches. Superphosphate fertilizer (Chapter 31) is often enriched with phosphoric acid.

QUESTIONS

1. Relate the metallic and nonmetallic character of the elements in group V to atomic size and electronegativity.

2. Why does bismuth not form a stable compound with hydrogen?

3. Why is so much nitrogen found free in nature?

4. Where is nitrogen found in the combined state?

5. What is meant by nitrogen fixation?

6. Why are nitrogen compounds so important in the soil?

7. Outline the nitrogen cycle.

8. (a) What are legumes?
   (b) Explain the importance of these plants.

9. What is the difference between atmospheric and chemical nitrogen?

10. Describe, with the aid of a labelled diagram, how chemical nitrogen may be prepared in the laboratory.

11. Complete these equations: (a) $P_4 + O_2 \rightarrow$ (b) $P_4O_{10} + H_2O \rightarrow$ (c) $NH_4Cl + NaNO_2$ + heat $\rightarrow$ (d) NH_4NO_2 + heat $\rightarrow$.

12. Why is nitrogen not very soluble?

13. List six physical properties of nitrogen.

14. What explanation might be offered for the inert nature of nitrogen?

15. Give equations to show the reaction of magnesium, aluminum, and calcium with nitrogen.

16. What are three important chemical properties of nitrogen?

17. Outline the uses of nitrogen.

18. How does phosphorus occur in nature?

19. Describe how elemental phosphorus is made.

20. Describe the atomic arrangement of white phosphorus.

21. List the physical properties of white phosphorus.

22. List the chemical properties of white phosphorus.

23. How may red phosphorus be prepared?

24. List the properties of red phosphorus.

25. What are the differences between red and white phosphorus?

26. Name four uses of phosphorus or its compounds.

27. (a) A compound contains 43.8 per cent nitrogen, 50 per cent oxygen and 6.2 per cent hydrogen. Find its simplest formula.
    (b) If the molecular mass of this compound is 64 amu, find its true formula.

28. (a) Find the simplest formula of a compound containing 43.7 per cent phosphorus and 56.3 per cent oxygen.
    (b) Find the molecular formula if the molecular mass is 284 amu.

29. How much carbon is needed to produce 100 g of phosphorus from calcium phosphate?

30. How many molecules are there in 1 l of ammonia measured at 20°C and 770 mm pressure?

33 Compounds of Nitrogen

33:1 Ammonia

Occurrence

Ammonia is formed whenever organic matter containing nitrogen is decomposed. For this reason, the air, the soil, and some natural waters contain small amounts of it. The ammonia in the soil may produce compounds that plants can use.

Laboratory Preparation

In the laboratory ammonia is prepared by heating any ammonium salt with any non-volatile base. Usually ammonium chloride and calcium oxide are used along with a few drops of water. The following reactions occur:

$$CaO + H_2O \rightarrow Ca(OH)_2$$

With the application of heat, ammonia is evolved:

$$2NH_4Cl + Ca(OH)_2 \rightarrow CaCl_2 + 2H_2O + 2NH_3\uparrow$$

The ammonia is collected by downward displacement of air because it is lighter than air and very soluble in water. A perfectly dry bottle should be used because one volume of water dissolves about 1300 volumes of ammonia and even a drop of water in a bottle dissolves about 60 ml of the gas.

When the bottles are full may be determined by the use of moist red litmus paper held at the mouth of the collection bottle. The red litmus turns blue on contact with the gas, owing to the formation of the base, ammonium hydroxide:

$$NH_3 + H_2O \rightarrow NH_4OH \rightarrow NH_4^+ + OH^-$$

The preparation of ammonia is a good example of the displacement of a weak base by a stronger one. The strong base $Ca(OH)_2$ is more

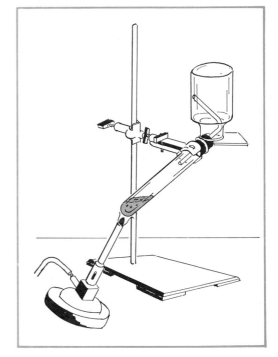

Fig. 33.1 Laboratory preparation of ammonia

highly ionized than the weaker NH_4OH. The latter forms and then decomposes to NH_3, a gas, and H_2O. The equation showing the different stages of this reaction is:

$$NH_4^+ + OH^- \rightleftharpoons NH_4OH \rightleftharpoons NH_3\uparrow + H_2O$$

This reaction is generally reversible. In the preparation of ammonia gas, it proceeds to completion because the ammonia is removed.

The Haber Process for Preparing Ammonia: A Study in Equilibrium

This process consists of the direct combination of nitrogen and hydrogen and is the most important of all methods of nitrogen fixation; that is, the formation of useful compounds from the free nitrogen of the air. The reaction is as follows:

$$N_2 + 3H_2 \rightleftharpoons 2NH_3 + heat$$
$$1 \text{ vol.} + 3 \text{ vol.} \rightarrow 2 \text{ vol.}$$

The success of this synthesis depends on the use of the Principle of Le Chatelier (Chapter 26). From this principle, the best conditions of pressure and temperature for the highest yield of ammonia can be deduced. The best conditions are necessary because a mixture of nitrogen and hydrogen forms so little ammonia under ordinary conditions that the reaction is of no practical value.

Notice that in the above reaction four molecules of gas (three of hydrogen and one of nitrogen), form two molecules of ammonia. The application of pressure to the mixture of the larger number of molecules of nitrogen and hydrogen is a stress which is relieved by the formation of the lesser number of molecules of ammonia. Pressures as high as 1000 atmospheres have been used, causing a marked increase in the yield of ammonia.

Since the reaction is exothermic, a higher yield of ammonia would be obtained if the reaction were carried out at a lower temperature, but unfortunately, the reaction is too slow at low temperatures; therefore, a "happy medium" is chosen. In actual practice, the reaction is carried out at about 400°C. At this temperature the yield might not be as high as might be wished, but the rate of the reaction is faster than at a lower temperature.

A successful catalyst for the production of ammonia consists of porous iron containing small quantities of potassium and aluminum oxides. Remember that the use of a catalyst only affects the speed of the forward and reverse reactions to the same degree; a catalyst does not shift an equilibrium, but it does cause an equilibrium to be reached much sooner.

To keep the reaction producing more ammonia, the gas formed must be removed quick-

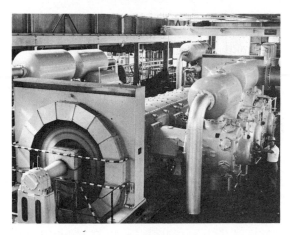

Fig. 33.2 *The large compressors used in the Haber process for producing ammonia*

ly. This is done by cooling the gases after passing them over the catalyst. The ammonia formed is condensed to a liquid. The unchanged gas is then mixed with more hydrogen and nitrogen in the correct ratio and recirculated.

Other Sources of Ammonia

1. The destructive distillation of coal (Chapter 34) is one industrial source of ammonia. The main products from this process are coke and coal gas. By-products are ammonia, benzene, toluene, and coal tar.

2. In the *cyanamide process*, calcium carbide is made by heating calcium oxide and coke in an electric furnace. Much heat is required because this reaction is endothermic:

$$CaO + 3C + heat \rightarrow CaC_2 + CO\uparrow$$

The calcium carbide is now heated with nitrogen to form calcium cyanamide:

$$CaC_2 + N_2 \rightarrow CaCN_2 + C + heat$$

As this reaction is exothermic it proceeds by itself once it is started.

The calcium cyanamide is next treated with steam under pressure to produce ammonia gas:

$$CaCN_2 + 3H_2O \rightarrow CaCO_3 + 2NH_3\uparrow$$

A similar reaction takes place slowly if calcium cyanamide is added to the soil. Calcium cyanamide is often used in fertilizers. It is at present produced at Welland, Ontario, where large amounts of electricity are available for the furnaces.

Chemical Properties

In the ammonia molecule the nitrogen atom has formed three covalent bonds with hydrogen, and there are still two unshared electrons. The chemical properties of ammonia depend on this pair of unshared electrons.

1. BOND FORMATION

Ammonia donates its pair of unshared electrons to form a covalent bond (Chapter 19) in the ammonium ion and in complex ions.

Examples

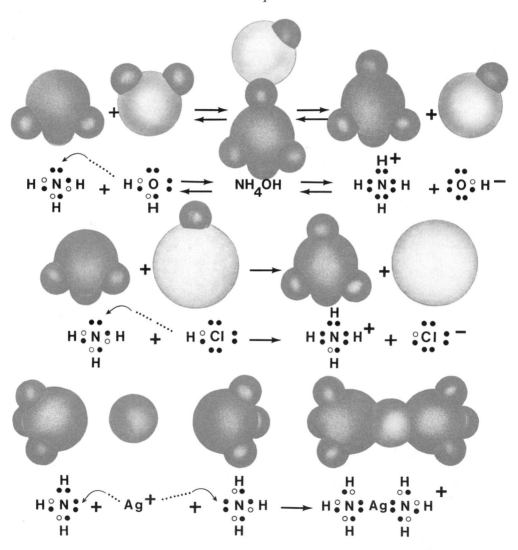

2. OXIDATION OF AMMONIA

In ammonia, the oxidation number of the nitrogen is $3-$; therefore ammonia can act as a reducing agent. When it gives up electrons, it may be changed to free nitrogen, N_2, nitric oxide, NO, or even nitric acid, HNO_3. In these substances the oxidation numbers of ammonia are 0, 2+, and 5+ respectively.

Examples

(i) *Oxidation change from 3— to 0*

Ammonia burns in pure oxygen with a yellow flame to produce free nitrogen and water:

$$\overset{3-}{4NH_3} + \overset{0}{3O_2} \rightarrow \overset{0}{2N_2}\uparrow + \overset{2-}{6H_2O}$$

$$4 \times 3e = 3 \times 2 \times 2e$$

Copper oxide reacts with ammonia to liberate nitrogen:

$$\overset{2+}{3CuO} + \overset{3-}{2NH_3} \rightarrow \overset{0}{3Cu} + \overset{0}{N_2}\uparrow + 3H_2O$$

$$3 \times 2e = 2 \times 3e$$

(ii) *Oxidation change from 3— to 2+*

Oxygen reacts with ammonia to form nitric oxide in the presence of hot platinum which acts as a catalyst:

$$\overset{3-}{4NH_3} + \overset{0}{5O_2} \rightarrow \overset{2+}{4NO} + \overset{2-}{6H_2O}$$

$$4 \times 5e = 5 \times 2 \times 2e$$

Physical Properties

Ammonia gas is colorless and has a characteristic sharp, irritating odor that is poisonous only when concentrated. It is lighter than air, freezes at $-77.7°C$, and boils at $-33.3°C$. Its heat of vaporization is 327 cal/g which is higher than that of any other liquid except water. This property makes it a very good refrigerant.

One volume of water dissolves 1300 volumes of ammonia at STP. The high solubility of ammonia in water is due to the interaction of the ammonia with the water (Chapter 25). This solubility can be shown with the ammonia fountain, which is similar to that used for the hydrogen chloride fountain (Fig. 29.2).

Compared to phosphine, PH_3, and arsine, AsH_3, ammonia has a high boiling point, melting point, heat of vaporization, and heat of fusion. This is caused by hydrogen bonding between the hydrogen in one molecule and the nitrogen in other molecules of ammonia.

Uses

Ammonia is used as a refrigerant, a fertilizer, and, in solution, as a water softener and cleanser. In the chemical industry, it is a valuable raw material in the production of nitric acid by the Ostwald process (33:4), of sodium carbonate by the Solvay process (Chapter 44), and of ammonium salts. The latter are made by adding ammonia to an acid solution. In each case, ammonium hydroxide neutralises an acid. These salts have important uses.

Thus ammonia is dissolved in sulfuric acid or phosphoric acid to form ammonium sulfate or phosphate, valuable ingredients of fertilizers:

$$2NH_4OH + H_2SO_4 \rightarrow (NH_4)_2SO_4 + 2H_2O$$
$$3NH_4OH + H_3PO_4 \rightarrow (NH_4)_3PO_4 + 3H_2O$$

33:2 Ammonium Salts

These are all soluble and are strong electrolytes, even though ammonium hydroxide is a weak electrolyte. They decompose when heated, many of them yielding ammonia and an acid. For example, ammonium chloride when heated reacts to form ammonia and hydrogen chloride:

$$NH_4Cl \rightarrow NH_3\uparrow + HCl\uparrow$$

When two metal surfaces are to be joined by soldering, it is necessary for the surfaces to be clean. They are often covered with metallic oxides which must be removed before the solder will adhere. Ammonium chloride acts as a good cleaning agent because the ammonia formed upon heating reduces the metallic oxides, which are dissolved by the hydrogen chloride.

Ammonium chloride is also used as one of the electrolytes of dry cells.

Ammonium nitrate, NH_4NO_3, is used in fertilizer and in making explosives. It is a dangerous salt because it may explode when heated.

Ammonium carbonate is an unstable salt which, when mixed with alcohol, forms "spirits of ammonia" to which, in turn, perfume may be added to make smelling salts:

$$(NH_4)_2CO_3 \rightarrow CO_2\uparrow + H_2O + 2NH_3\uparrow$$

Test for Ammonium Salt

Any ammonium salt heated with a non-volatile base, such as calcium oxide or sodium hydroxide, yields ammonia. The gas may be detected by odor, but a more reliable method of detection is to use moist red litmus paper, which may be placed on the convex side of a watch glass and held over a beaker containing the heated mixture. If the litmus turns blue, the presence of the ammonium ion is proved.

33:3   Oxides of Nitrogen

Introduction

Five examples of oxides of nitrogen are given in Table 33.1. The first three gases on the list

TABLE 33.1		
Oxides of Nitrogen		
Name of Gas	Formula	Oxidation Numbers of N
Nitrous oxide	N_2O	1+
Nitric oxide	NO	2+
Nitrogen dioxide	NO_2	4+
Dinitrogen trioxide	N_2O_3	3+
Dinitrogen pentoxide	N_2O_5	5+

may be prepared quite easily. While the last two can also be prepared, they are of little value. Nitrogen does not combine directly with oxygen except at very high temperatures or by the addition of large amounts of energy. For laboratory purposes, the oxides of nitrogen are prepared by the decomposition of nitrogen compounds.

Nitrous oxide

If ammonium nitrate is heated, a colorless gas with a slightly sweetish odor is evolved. Nitrous oxide may be prepared in the laboratory by gently heating ammonium nitrate in an apparatus such as the one used to prepare oxygen. Ammonium nitrate may explode if strongly heated. Since the gas is only moderately soluble, it may be collected over water:

$$NH_4NO_3 \rightarrow 2H_2O + N_2O\uparrow$$

Nitrous oxide causes a glowing splint to burst into flame because it readily decomposes into nitrogen and oxygen:

$$2N_2O \rightarrow 2N_2\uparrow + O_2\uparrow$$

The resultant gas contains two parts of nitrogen to one part of oxygen by volume, while air contains only one-fifth oxygen. Phosphorus and sulfur burn in nitrous oxide as they do in oxygen.

Nitrous oxide may be distinguished from oxygen because the latter forms brown nitrogen dioxide, NO_2, with nitric oxide, NO, according to the equation

$$O_2 + 2NO \rightarrow 2NO_2\uparrow \text{ (brown)}$$

Nitrous oxide, on the other hand, fails to react with nitric oxide.

Sir Humphrey Davy discovered that nitrous oxide when inhaled produced a peculiar intoxication; hence, the gas was called "laughing gas", and people used to meet together for the sole purpose of enjoying its effects. It was soon noticed that persons under the influence of nitrous oxide became insensible to pain. As a result of this observation, the gas came into use as an anaesthetic, and it is still used, mixed with oxygen, in both dentistry and surgery.

Nitric oxide

Nitric oxide may be prepared by the action of dilute nitric acid on copper:

$$\overset{0}{3Cu} + \overset{5+}{8}\overset{2+}{HNO_3} \rightarrow 3Cu(NO_3)_2 + 4H_2O + \overset{2+}{2NO}\uparrow$$

$$3 \times 2e \qquad = \qquad 2 \times 3e$$

A gas-generating apparatus such as the one used in preparing hydrogen may be employed, and the gas is collected over water, as it is only slightly soluble. The gas is colorless, but it turns brown on contact with air at ordinary temperatures because of the formation of nitrogen dioxide.

$$\overset{2+}{2NO} + O_2 \rightarrow \overset{4+}{2NO_2}$$

Nitric oxide is prepared industrially by passing ammonia mixed with air over finely divided platinum at about 700°C:

$$\overset{3-}{4NH_3} + \overset{0}{5O_2} \rightarrow 6H_2O + \overset{2+2-}{4NO}$$

$$4 \times 5e = 5 \times 2 \times 2e$$

The nitric oxide is then converted to nitric acid. Small amounts of nitric oxide are produced by engine sparks and combustion:

$$N_2 + O_2 \rightarrow 2NO$$

When nitric oxide comes into contact with air and water, nitric acid is formed. In a largely industrialized area, a considerable amount of nitric oxide may accumulate in the air. If fog should settle over the area, a smog containing nitric acid could develop and be a serious health problem.

Nitrogen dioxide

This gas is prepared by treating copper or other metals with concentrated nitric acid:

$$\overset{0}{Cu} + \overset{5+}{4}\overset{2+}{HNO_3} \rightarrow Cu(NO_3)_2 + 2H_2O + \overset{4+}{2NO_2}\uparrow$$

$$2e \qquad = \qquad 2 \times 1e$$

It is also produced when a nitrate of a heavy metal is heated:

$$\overset{5+}{2Pb(NO_3)_2} \rightarrow 2PbO + \overset{0}{O_2}\uparrow + \overset{4+}{4NO_2}\uparrow$$

$$2 \times 2e = 4 \times 1e$$

Nitrogen dioxide is formed when nitric oxide is exposed to air:

$$2NO + O_2 \rightarrow 2NO_2\uparrow \text{ (brown)}$$

From molecular mass determinations, it has been shown that nitrogen dioxide at room temperature is actually about 80 per cent dinitrogen tetroxide:

$$2NO_2 \rightleftharpoons N_2O_4 \text{ (colorless)}$$

If the temperature is lowered, the color becomes lighter since more of the tetroxide is formed. If the temperature is raised, the color darkens because more of the dioxide is formed.

Nitrogen dioxide unites with water to form nitric and nitrous acid.

$$\overset{4+}{2NO_2} + H_2O \rightarrow \overset{5+}{HNO_3} + \overset{3+}{HNO_2}$$

$$1e \quad = \quad 1e$$

33:4 Nitric Acid

Preparation

THE LABORATORY METHOD

In the laboratory, nitric acid is prepared by heating sodium nitrate with concentrated sulfuric acid:

$$2NaNO_3 + H_2SO_4 \rightarrow Na_2SO_4 + 2HNO_3\uparrow$$

This reaction must be carried out in an all-glass apparatus, because hot nitric acid is a vigorous oxidizing agent which destroys rubber. The heat must be carefully controlled because excessive heat will decompose the nitric acid:

$$4HNO_3 \rightarrow 2H_2O + 4NO_2\uparrow + O_2\uparrow$$

In spite of careful heating, some decomposition may occur causing the acid collected to have some color from the dissolved nitrogen dioxide.

INDUSTRIAL: THE OSTWALD PROCESS

In this process, ammonia is oxidized to nitric oxide over a hot (700°C) platinum catalyst:

$$\overset{3-}{4NH_3} + \overset{2+}{5O_2} \rightarrow 4NO\uparrow + 6H_2O$$
$$4 \times 5e = 5 \times 2 \times 2e$$

The nitric oxide then combines with more oxygen from air to form nitrogen dioxide,

$$2NO + O_2 \rightarrow 2NO_2\uparrow$$

which, in turn, is absorbed in water to form a mixture of nitric acid, nitrous acid, and nitric oxide:

$$NO_2 + H_2O \rightarrow HNO_3 + HNO_2$$
$$3NO_2 + H_2O \rightarrow 2HNO_3 + NO\uparrow$$

The nitric oxide is re-circulated to form more nitric acid, as above. About ten volumes of air are used with one volume of ammonia. This process, perfected shortly before the First World War by the German chemist Ostwald, furnished the nitric acid essential for making explosives during the war.

NATURAL OCCURRENCE

Traces of nitric acid are formed in nature whenever lightning flashes. First some nitrogen and oxygen combine to form nitric oxide.

$$N_2 + O_2 + \text{energy (from lightning)} \rightarrow 2NO\uparrow$$

The nitric oxide reacts with oxygen in air to form nitrogen dioxide,

$$2NO + O_2 \rightarrow 2NO_2\uparrow$$

and finally, the nitrogen dioxide reacts with

water or rain to form a very small amount of nitric and nitrous acid.

$$2NO_2 + H_2O \rightarrow HNO_3 + HNO_2$$

The acids are carried down with the rain and combine with the salts in the soil to form valuable nitrate fertilizers. They also play a part in erosion, attacking and decomposing rock particles.

Physical Properties

Pure nitric acid is a colorless liquid with a sharp, choking odor. It freezes at −42°C and boils at 86°C. It is heavier than water. It is miscible with water in all proportions and forms a constant boiling mixture with it consisting of about 68 per cent HNO_3. Thus, water and nitric acid cannot be completely separated by distillation.

Chemical Properties

In nitric acid the nitrogen has an oxidation number of $5+$. The five outer electrons of the nitrogen atom are shared with oxygen. Oxygen is more electronegative than nitrogen and therefore the electrons are displaced, partially at least, from the nitrogen toward the oxygen atoms.

While a large atom might have so many electrons displaced without too much difficulty, a small atom like nitrogen is placed under considerable strain by such a large electrical charge. This causes nitric acid to be highly unstable and reactive. The majority of reactions of nitric acid result in nitrogen assuming a lower oxidation number by gaining electrons. The easier it is to remove electrons from any particular atom, the larger is the number of electrons gained. Thus nitric acid gains eight electrons from magnesium, a reactive metal, but only three electrons from copper, an unreactive metal, to form ammonia and nitric oxide respectively:

$$\overset{0}{4Mg} + \overset{5+}{9HNO_3} \rightarrow \overset{2+}{4Mg(NO_3)_2} + \overset{3-}{NH_3}\uparrow + 3H_2O$$

$$4 \times 2e \qquad = \qquad 1 \times 8e$$

$$\overset{0}{3Cu} + \overset{5+}{8HNO_3} \rightarrow \overset{2+}{3Cu(NO_3)_2} + \overset{2+}{2NO} + 4H_2O$$

$$3 \times 2e \qquad = \qquad 2 \times 3e$$

If the acid is concentrated, the number of electrons gained is less per nitrate ion. When copper is treated with concentrated nitric acid, nitrogen dioxide, NO_2, is evolved. In this compound nitrogen has an oxidation number of $4+$. Presumably only one electron is gained per ion, causing the change from $5+$ to $4+$:

$$\overset{0}{Cu} + \overset{5+}{4HNO_3} \text{ (conc)} \rightarrow$$

$$2e \qquad =$$

$$\overset{2+}{Cu(NO_3)_2} + \overset{4+}{2NO_2} + 2H_2O$$

$$2 \times 1e$$

The instability of nitric acid is shown by its ease of decomposition:

$$\overset{5+}{4HNO_3} \rightarrow \overset{4+}{4NO_2} + 2H_2O + O_2\uparrow$$

In this reaction, the oxidation number changes from $5+$ to $4+$ showing a gain of one electron. The electron donor is the originally combined oxygen, which loses electrons to become free oxygen.

The reaction may be shown by placing a few drops of the acid in a test tube. The test tube should be held in a nearly horizontal position over a gentle flame. Brown fumes appear as the liquid vaporizes. Bottles of nitric acid turn brown after a time if exposed to light because the same reaction takes place slowly.

So great is the electron-gaining power of nitric acid, that it removes electrons even from such non-metals as carbon and sulfur:

$$\overset{5+}{4HNO_3} + \overset{0}{C} \rightarrow \overset{4+}{4NO_2} + \overset{4+}{CO_2} + H_2O$$

$$4 \times 1e = 1 \times 4e$$

$$\overset{5+}{6HNO_3} + \overset{0}{S} \rightarrow \overset{4+}{6NO_2} + \overset{6+}{H_2SO_4} + 2H_2O$$

$$6 \times 1e = 1 \times 6e$$

A mixture of nitric and hydrochloric acid is called *aqua regia*. This name was coined by the alchemists because this material dissolves the noble metals, gold and platinum, while either acid alone does not.

Nitric acid reacts with many organic compounds to add $-NO_2$ or $-NO_3$ groups to their molecules. This process is known as *nitration*. In this reaction, a molecule of water forms between the nitric acid and the organic substance. Concentrated sulfuric acid is added to absorb the water so formed. From glycerol is thus produced glyceryl trinitrate, nitroglycerine. Similarly, toluene forms trinitro toluene, T.N.T., and cellulose forms gun cotton and cellulose nitrate. Many nitrated compounds are valuable solvents or materials used in the manufacture of dyes and drugs.

Uses

Nitric acid is used to make explosives, dyes, drugs, plastics, and lacquers. It is used in "pickling" brass, in photoengraving, and for separating gold from silver. Nitrates, produced by the action of the acid upon metals, oxides, or hydroxides, are valuable fertilizers and industrial chemicals.

Test for Nitrates

In testing for nitrates a fresh solution of iron (II) sulfate is prepared. A little of this solution is mixed in a test tube with the solution being tested. Concentrated sulfuric acid is next added carefully down the side of the test tube. The heavy acid forms a layer at the bottom of the test tube. At the juncture of the two liquids, the sulfuric acid liberates nitric acid from any nitrate that may be present. The nitric acid decomposes to give small amounts of nitric oxide. This nitric oxide unites with the iron (II) sulfate to form a brown substance, iron (II) nitroso sulfate $Fe(NO)SO_4$. A brown ring thus forms at the juncture of the two liquids if nitrate is present.

33:5   Cyanides

Salts containing the CN^- group are called *cyanides*. They are among the most poisonous substances known. Hydrogen cyanide, known as prussic acid, is used in gas chambers for executions. All cyanides yield hydrogen cyanide, HCN, if treated with sulfuric acid:

$$NaCN + H_2SO_4 \rightarrow HCN\uparrow + NaHSO_4$$

Sodium cyanide, NaCN, is used in electroplating. Sodium or potassium cyanide hydrolyzes in moist air to form a little hydrogen cyanide.

$$NaCN + HOH \rightleftharpoons NaOH + HCN\uparrow$$

Great care must be used in handling these compounds. Acids should never be added to cyanides; nor should they be subjected to electrolysis without proper precautions.

QUESTIONS

1. Draw a diagram to show the structure of the ammonia molecule.

2. Why does the ammonium ion have a charge of $1+$?

3. Write a note on the occurrence of ammonia.

4. (a) Describe, with the aid of a labelled diagram, the laboratory preparation and collection of ammonia.
    (b) Write the equations for the reactions involved.
    (c) Why does this reaction go to completion?

5. (a) Why must the bottles in which ammonia is collected be dry?
    (b) How can it be determined when they are full? Explain your answer and give equations.

6. Why does ammonia dissolve in water, while neither nitrogen nor hydrogen is particularly water-soluble?

7. Describe the Haber Process. In your description clearly explain the three conditions needed to form a good yield of ammonia.

8. (a) Why must the ammonia formed in the Haber Process be quickly removed from the reacting gases?
    (b) How is it removed?

9. Explain how the correct mixture of hydrogen and nitrogen for use in the Haber Process is obtained.

10. What is one commercial source of ammonium sulfate?

11. Many fertilizers contain ammonium phosphate. Can you offer an explanation for this?

12. List the physical properties of ammonia.

13. Account for the fact that ammonia has a higher melting point, boiling point, heat of vaporization, and heat of fusion than PH_3 and the other hydrides of group V.

14. Draw a three dimensional diagram to show the arrangement of the atoms in the ammonia molecule. What orbitals are used for bond formation?

15. Summarize the chemical properties of ammonia.

16. How do the chemical properties of ammonia depend on the electronic structure of its molecule?

17. Give three examples of the formation of a covalent bond by ammonia. Write equations to illustrate.

18. (a) What is the oxidation number of nitrogen in ammonia? In nitric oxide?
    (b) Write an equation for the oxidation of ammonia to nitric oxide.

19. What is the test for ammonia?

20. Give five uses of ammonia.

21. What are the common properties of ammonium salts?

22. Why is ammonium chloride needed in soldering?

23. What are smelling salts?

24. Describe the test for the ammonium ion.

25. List the oxides of nitrogen with their formulas. Indicate the oxidation number of the nitrogen in each.

26. Draw a labelled diagram and describe the preparation of nitrous oxide. Write the equation.

27. What are the important properties of nitrous oxide?

28. How may nitrous oxide be distinguished from oxygen?

29. Give equations to show several ways of preparing nitric oxide. Show the oxidation numbers of nitrogen in each case.

30. What are the properties of nitric oxide?

31. (a) How may nitrogen dioxide be prepared? Write the equations and show the oxidation numbers of the nitrogen in each method.
    (b) Why is this gas called dinitrogen tetroxide?

32. Write the equation to show how an electric spark will result in the formation of nitric acid.

33. Describe the Ostwald process. Give the equations.

34. Draw a labelled diagram of, and explain the laboratory preparation of nitric acid. Write the equation. Why should the temperature be kept low?

35. List the physical properties of nitric acid.

36. Explain electronically why nitric acid is unstable and reactive.

37. Why does dilute nitric acid form ammonia with magnesium, but nitric oxide with copper?

38. Explain the reaction of copper with concentrated nitric acid.

39. Give equations to show the reactions of hot nitric acid with carbon and sulfur. Show the oxidation numbers of the nitrogen in each case.

40. Explain electronically why nitric acid decomposes on heating. Give the equation.

41. (a) What is *aqua regia*?
    (b) For what is it used?

42. (a) What is *nitration*?
    (b) What are some uses of this process?

43. Summarize the chemical properties of nitric acid.

44. What are the uses of nitric acid?

45. Describe the test for the nitric acid.

46. (a) Find the mass of hydroxide ions in 100 ml of a 0.1 M solution of ammonium hydroxide.
    (b) Find the mass of hydroxide ions in 500 ml of a 0.1 M solution of calcium hydroxide.

47. Calculate the volume of hydrogen and nitrogen required to produce 600 ml of ammonia by the Haber process.

48. Balance the following equations, showing the method used.
    (a) $KMnO_4 + SnCl_2 + HCl \rightarrow KCl + MnCl_2 + SnCl_4 + H_2O$
    (b) $Zn + HNO_3 \rightarrow Zn(NO_3)_2 + NH_4NO_3 + H_2O$

49. Calculate the mass of nitric acid obtained from one liter of ammonia, if the ammonia is measured at 22°C and 753 mm pressure.

50. How many grams of copper would be required to produce 50 g of copper nitrate?

CHAPTER
34 Carbon

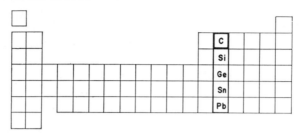

34:1 The Element and its Occurrence

Carbon is present in approximately 1,000,000 known compounds, and new carbon compounds are being synthesized all the time. Many carbon compounds are used daily in various forms by man and are, indeed, essential to his existence. Although forming so many important and varied compounds, it is estimated that carbon constitutes only 0.03 per cent of the earth's crust. It occurs in coal, wood, petroleum, and natural and artificial gas. Vast deposits of metal carbonates are found, mainly those of calcium and magnesium which make up limestone and dolomite.

34:2 Physical and Chemical Properties

All forms of carbon are similar in that they are insoluble in water, acids, bases, and other materials. They are all black or greyish-black solids, except diamond which is colorless when pure. They are odorless and tasteless. The microcrystalline forms of carbon dissolve in some molten metals such as iron. When heated out of contact with air, carbon does not melt; instead it vaporizes. Under great pressure carbon can be melted. Its melting point, although not yet accurately determined, is about 3500°C.

All forms of carbon burn in ample air or oxygen to form carbon dioxide. Carbon monoxide forms if the oxygen or air supply is limited.

Carbon is a good reducing agent and is commonly used to reduce oxide ores to metals:

$$\overset{3+}{Fe_2}O_3 + \overset{0}{3C} \rightarrow \overset{0}{2Fe} + \overset{2+}{3CO}$$

$$\overset{2+}{2Cu}O + \overset{0}{C} \rightarrow \overset{0}{2Cu} + \overset{4+}{CO_2}$$

$$\overset{4+}{CO_2} + \overset{0}{C} \rightarrow \overset{2+}{2CO}$$

Carbon reacts with some elements to form carbides:

$$CaO + 3C \rightarrow CaC_2 + CO$$
$$\text{calcium carbide}$$

$$SiO_2 + 3C \rightarrow SiC + 2CO$$
$$\text{silicon carbide}$$

Some carbides are of great commercial value because of their hardness.

34:3 Allotropic Forms of Carbon

There are two allotropic forms of crystalline carbon — diamond and graphite. All the other forms of free carbon, as found in coal, coke, charcoal, boneblack, and lampblack, are usually called amorphous or non-crystalline forms. There is strong evidence to show that the so-called amorphous forms are in reality microcrystalline, composed of crystals too small to be seen by ordinary optical methods, but whose structure is revealed by X ray analysis.

Although the electronic structure of the carbon atom, which best explains carbon's allotropy, was studied previously (Chapters 19, 22), some of the ideas stated there will be reviewed here.

34:4 Electronic Structure

The atomic number of carbon is six. It is the first element of group IV of the periodic table. Its six electrons are distributed as follows: two are in the first shell, and four are in the second, occupying the $2s$ and $2p$ orbitals, thus:

When the carbon atom joins other atoms, its orbitals hybridize in three ways.

a. The single s and the three p orbitals may hybridize to form four sp^3 orbitals (Chapter 19), thus giving rise to a tetrahedral structure around the carbon atom. This is found in diamond, methane, and the saturated organic compounds.

b. The single s and two of the p orbitals may hybridize to form three sp^2 orbitals, thus giving rise to a planar structure around the carbon atom (Chapter 37). This is found in graphite and in the unsaturated or double-bonded organic compounds.

c. The single s may hybridize with one p to form two sp orbitals (Chapter 35), thus giving rise to linear molecules such as carbon dioxide and acetylene.

34:5 Diamond and Graphite

The carbon atoms in diamond have the tetrahedron geometrical structure. They are held together in a lattice by covalent bonds, which are extremely effective with such small atoms as carbon. As a result, diamond has many striking properties: it is the hardest substance known; it has a higher melting point than any other element; and it is a non-conductor of electricity. These properties exist because the electrons cannot move freely from one atom to another, all outer electrons being in covalent bonds.

In graphite, on the other hand, each atom of carbon is attached to three other atoms by strong covalent bonds in the same plane. The fourth available electrons are paired in long, weaker bonds.

The weakness of the bond between layers of the graphite crystal allows the planes to slide over one another. This gives graphite a soft, greasy, and slippery feeling. Since the electrons in this bond may be moved freely, graphite is a good conductor of electricity.

Occurrence, Production, and Uses of Diamond

The principal diamond-producing regions of the world are South Africa and Brazil. The diamond is weighed in carats (the carat weighs 1/5 of a gram). The largest diamond ever found weighed 3,032 carats (1.37 lbs).

In Africa, diamonds are found in blue-colored earth. This is mixed with water and run over grease-covered trays. The diamonds stick in the grease, while the earth is washed away. The composition of this blue earth indicates that it was originally mineral-bearing volcanic rock. Most likely the diamonds were formed because this rock, when molten, came in contact with some coal deposits, dissolving the carbon of the coal. As the rock cooled, the carbon crystallized under great pressure into diamond. Later, weathering actions caused the disintegration of the rock, leaving the diamond.

Henri Moissan attempted to make small diamonds in 1893. He prepared pure carbon by charring sugar. He dissolved this in molten iron and plunged the mass of iron into cold water. The outer part of the mass solidified and contracted producing great pressure. After cooling, the iron was dissolved in hydrochloric acid, and if any diamonds were recovered, they were too small to be of any practical use.

In 1956 a group of scientists at the General Electric Company discovered a process for making diamonds commercially. The diamonds produced, although too small for gems, are large enough for many practical uses. By 1960 these diamonds were being produced at a price lower or comparable to the cost of the natural product.

The value of the diamond as a gem is largely due to its very high refractive index; that is, the amount of bending that light undergoes in passing through a material. For use as a gem the diamond is shaped so that it has a number of flat surfaces (facets) meeting at angles. The surfaces act as internal reflectors, and light entering the diamond is effectively separated into its colors giving the gem a great brilliance. The flat surfaces are formed by allowing a steel disc coated with oil and diamond dust to rotate against the diamond, which is held in a clamp.

The diamond is essential to modern industry. Many machine parts are fashioned with grinding wheels, which are composed of materials so hard that they themselves can be cut only by diamond. Diamond drills are used in mining for obtaining ore samples. A diamond drill consists of diamonds set into the end of a cylinder. As the drill revolves, it bites into the rock, leaving a solid core of sample material inside the cylinder. The core is examined to determine its mineral content.

Occurrence, Production, and Uses of Graphite

Graphite is found in many parts of the world, but chiefly in Canada, Siberia, and Ceylon. It, too, was probably formed by volcanic heat in contact with coal deposits. The natural form contains grit and many other impurities.

Synthetic graphite is prepared by means of an electric furnace. In the furnace a core of loosely packed carbon is placed between two electrodes and is surrounded by a packing of coal. The heat produced by the passage of electricity between the electrodes forms the graphite from the coal surrounding the carbon core. Air is excluded by covering the coal with a layer of sand (see Fig. 34.1). The graphite produced by this process is very pure and free from grit.

Graphite, a black, shiny, soft solid, leaves a mark when it is drawn across a paper. The name graphite comes from the Greek word meaning "to write". Because it was originally thought to be a form of lead, it is sometimes called plumbago or black lead. The lead of a pencil is a mixture of graphite, clay, and wax heated in a mould. Hard lead contains more clay than does soft lead.

Graphite is an excellent dry lubricant because its crystalline structure allows one layer to slide over another. It is sometimes mixed with oil to form a high-temperature lubricant. Because it

Fig. 34.1 *The manufacture of graphite*
Heat is developed because of the high resistance of the carbon core.

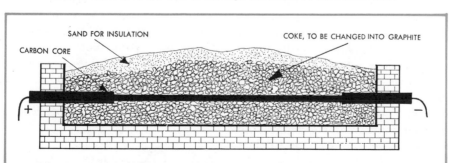

SAND FOR INSULATION

COKE, TO BE CHANGED INTO GRAPHITE

CARBON CORE

is a good conductor of electricity, graphite is often used for electrodes. A non-conductor may be made conductive by coating it with graphite. Graphite is therefore used in electroplating and electrotyping. Graphite crucibles are used for making high-grade steel and other alloys. Certain oil-retaining bearings contain graphite. It is also used as a pigment in black paint and as an ingredient of dry cells.

34:6   Coal

Coal may be regarded as a mixture of carbon plus remains of organic matter. Many millions of years ago the growth of vegetation was much more prolific than it is now. In many places a considerable depth of decaying vegetation was built up, and, where these deposits became permanently flooded for some reason, swamps were formed. Decomposition of the plant matter, aided by bacteria and fungi, caused its transformation first into peat and then into lignite. Gradually the deposits became covered over with silt, sometimes to a great depth. The weight of the silt and water above the deposit caused pressure and heat which gradually changed the lignite into soft bituminous coal. If the soft coal were then subjected to greater pressure or heat, it changed into anthracite, or hard coal. Deposits of peat, lignite, and bituminous and anthracite coal are widespread throughout the world.

Soft coal is often inefficiently burned passing much carbon and many carbon compounds into the air as smoke. Where soft coal is a major fuel, smog (a mixture of smoke, fog, and sometimes dangerous oxides) is often a problem.

Smoke from the combustion of coal can be controlled by down-draft combustion or by smoke precipitators. In a down-draft furnace, air is forced through the burning coal from the top. This results in more complete combustion. Smoke precipitators were discussed in Chapter 27.

Combustion of coal supplies about 40 per cent of the world's energy requirements. The rest comes from natural gas, petroleum, water power, and nuclear energy. The major use of coal is in generating electrical energy, and about one-quarter of the bituminous coal mined is used in making coke for the iron and steel industry.

In 1931, Bergius, a German chemist, patented a process for making gasoline from coal. Powdered coal mixed with heavy oil is heated to about 4000°C at 200 atmospheres of pressure, in contact with hydrogen and a catalyst. The carbon of the coal and the hydrogen combine to form various hydrocarbons. These can be separated by distillation, and one of the products is gasoline.

Another process called the Fisher-Tropsch process uses coal and steam to produce a mixture of carbon monoxide and hydrogen:

$$C + H_2O \rightarrow CO\uparrow + H_2\uparrow$$

These gases are then converted into hydrocarbons with the aid of a catalyst:

$$7CO + 15H_2 \xrightarrow[\text{catalyst}]{\text{iron}} C_7H_{16} + 7H_2O$$

The above processes produce gasoline of good quality, but it is more expensive than the petroleum product. The processes could be used, however, in the event of a petroleum shortage. In fact, Germany made practically all its gasoline and oil by these methods during the Second World War.

Experimental work is going on at the present time to produce industrial gas from coal deposits without mining. The coal is ignited and supplied with air from pipes leading down to the coal:

$$2C + O_2 \rightarrow 2CO\uparrow$$

The resultant gas is then forced up other pipes to the surface. Pure oxygen in place of air is found to be more effective. Low grade or inaccessible coal seams may thus become valuable assets.

34:7   Coke, Charcoal, Lampblack, Carbon Black, and Acetylene Black

Coke, a form of carbon of great industrial importance, is generally obtained by heating soft coal in ovens, thus driving off the volatile constituents of the coal. This process is called *destructive distillation*. The residue of the destructive distillation of coal is coke.

Coke is used mostly to reduce metals, especially iron, from ores. It burns with practically no flame and leaves little residue.

If the process of destructive distillation is applied to wood, charcoal is obtained. It burns with no smoke and leaves little ash. During the first part of the Industrial Revolution, the stately oaks of England practically disappeared to make charcoal for reducing iron ore. Fortunately, it was soon discovered that coke could be used successfully for this purpose.

Powdered charcoal is frequently pressed into briquets. These find a wide use as fuel for use at picnics and for broiling foods.

All forms of amorphous carbon have high adsorptive power. This means they can collect thin layers of molecules of various materials on their surface. This property is mostly due to the large surface the carbon presents because of its porous structure. Thus, poisonous or odorous gases may be removed from air by passing the air through layers of charcoal. Portable gas masks contain charcoal made from coconut shells because such charcoal is more resistant to breakage than is wood charcoal. It thus retains its porous structure and its adsorptive power longer. Charcoal may be used also to decolorize and deodorize liquids. Many indus-

trial solvents and waste substances are adsorbed by charcoal, and in the field of biochemistry charcoal is used to adsorb the antibiotic streptomycin from its mould culture.

Animal or bone charcoal is formed when bones are destructively distilled. This material contains a small percentage of carbon and a great deal of calcium phosphate. It is very effective in decolorizing solutions of crude sugar to form the white variety.

Charcoal may be made more adsorptive by a process known as *activation*. The charcoal is heated for long periods in contact with steam or air-steam mixtures. This increases porosity and removes impurities already adsorbed. One cubic centimeter of activated charcoal may contain 10,000,000 cm^2 of adsorptive surface.

In making wood charcoal, gas is given off from which a dark brown liquid may be condensed. This liquid, called *pyroligneous acid*, yields acetic acid, acetone, and methanol (wood alcohol).

A smoky candle flame produces lampblack. A long wick conducting the melted paraffin too far from the centre of the flame becomes so cool that some of the carbon from the decomposing paraffin is not hot enough to burn. It is driven off into the air as black smoke. Commercial lampblack is made by burning oils in limited air. The smoky flames are directed against a revolving steel drum kept cool with running water. The soot or lampblack is then scraped off the drum.

Carbon black is made in the same way as lampblack except that natural gas is used as the source of carbon. This finely divided form of carbon, which is so important that about 10 per cent of the natural gas produced is used to make it, is used to make printers' ink, carbon paper, typewriter ribbons, phonograph records, black paint, and rubber goods.

Acetylene black is made by incomplete combustion of acetylene. This is a very finely divided material of uniform particle size.

QUESTIONS

1. Give a brief account of the importance of carbon and its compounds.

2. What are the allotropic forms of carbon?

3. (a) Describe the electronic structure of carbon.
   (b) To what orbitals can the carbon atom hybridize?
   (c) What different structures are associated with each type of orbital?

4. Why does carbon have a combining capacity of four?

5. List the properties of diamond and graphite.

6. Explain why diamond and graphite exhibit different properties.

7. List the common physical properties of carbon.

8. Summarize the common chemical properties of carbon.

9. Write the equations for the reduction of Fe_2O_3 and CuO by carbon.

10. In what processes are these reactions used?

11. Account for the formation of diamonds in nature.

12. Describe how artificial diamonds are produced.

13. Why is the diamond valued as a gem?

14. How are diamonds used in industry?

15. How was graphite formed in nature?

16. How is graphite made synthetically?

17. (a) List the principal properties of graphite.
    (b) What are the uses of this material?

18. Account for the formation of coal deposits.

19. Contrast the properties of anthracite and bituminous coal.

20. Describe the operations of a smoke precipitator.

21. Write a paragraph on the importance of coal.

22. Name and describe two processes for making gasoline from coal.

23. Describe how coke is made. Of what importance is this material?

24. Of what importance is wood charcoal?

25. Define *adsorption*.

26. Explain how a gas mask works.

27. For what is bone charcoal used?

28. What is "activated charcoal"?

29. List the main products obtained by destructively distilling coal and wood.

30. How are lampblack and carbon black made? What are the uses of this form of carbon?

31. A gaseous compound contains 92.3 per cent carbon and 7.7 per cent hydrogen. One liter of the gas at STP weighs 1.16 g. Find its molecular formula.

32. Find the volume of carbon dioxide, measured at STP, obtained from burning 5 g of carbon completely.

33. Calculate the weight of silicon carbide that could be obtained from 350 g of silicon dioxide.

34. (a) Find the volume of carbon dioxide measured at 313°C and 710 mm pressure obtained by burning 0.5 g of carbon.

    (b) Find the molarity of the carbonic acid formed by dissolving all of the carbon dioxide in 10 liters of solution.

CHAPTER
35 Carbon Dioxide

35:1 Importance and Occurrence

Carbon dioxide gas is the primary food of the plant kingdom. From it plants build up sugars and starches with the aid of sunlight in a process known as *photosynthesis*. Animals eat the sugars and starches as part of their diet requirement. Yet, in spite of the great importance of carbon dioxide, it constitutes a mere 0.04 per cent of the air; that is, four volumes in 10,000.

The gas is formed whenever fuels containing carbon are burned. Decay and fermentation also produce it. The exhaled breath contains one hundred times as much carbon dioxide as was inhaled, and the respiration of all living things produces the gas. Metallic carbonates and hydrogen carbonates in the earth's crust contain vast amounts of chemically fixed carbon dioxide.

35:2 The Carbon Dioxide Cycle in Nature

As was mentioned above, carbon dioxide is used by plants to synthesize sugars and starches. Green plants absorb carbon dioxide and water. Using light energy and the catalyst chlorophyll, the green coloring matter of plants, the plants convert the carbon dioxide and water to glucose (sugar) and starch. Oxygen is given off to the air in the process:

$$6CO_2 + 6H_2O \rightarrow C_6H_{12}O_6 + 6O_2\uparrow$$
$$\text{glucose}$$

$$nC_6H_{12}O_6 \rightarrow (C_6H_{10}O_5)_n + nH_2O$$
$$\text{starch}$$

From the basic sugar and starch, many plant products are formed, these being the ultimate source of food for all living things. At the same time, a proper carbon dioxide-oxygen level is maintained in the atmosphere. This carbon dioxide-oxygen cycle not only permits life to exist, but also accounts for the formation in past ages of our resources of coal and oil, since these are mostly residues of materials formed by photosynthetic processes (Fig. 35.1).

35:3 Preparation of Carbon Dioxide

a. Carbon dioxide is prepared in the laboratory by treating a carbonate or hydrogen carbonate with an acid:

$$CaCO_3 + 2HCl \rightarrow CaCl_2 + H_2CO_3$$
$$H_2CO_3 \rightarrow H_2O + CO_2\uparrow$$

The gas may be collected by displacement of water from a bottle in a trough, or by upward displacement of air. If the latter method is used, when the bottles are full

Fig. 35.1 *The carbon dioxide cycle in nature*

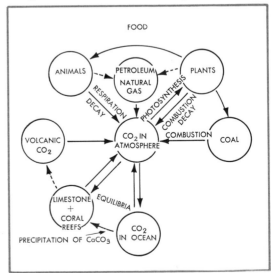

may be determined by the use of a burning splint, which is extinguished in the gas.

b. Commercial carbon dioxide is obtained from the burning of fuels. Thus, with methane, CH_4

$$CH_4 + 2O_2 \rightarrow CO_2\uparrow + 2H_2O$$

c. Fermentation produces carbon dioxide; as an example, yeast added to a glucose solution ferments the sugar to ethanol, an alcohol, and CO_2:

$$C_6H_{12}O_6 \rightarrow 2C_2H_5OH + 2CO_2\uparrow$$

35:4 Electronic Structure

The electronic structure of carbon dioxide will help to explain its properties. In carbon dioxide, the carbon atom is attached to two atoms of oxygen. The three atoms of the molecule lie in a straight line (Fig. 35.2).

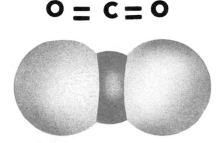

Fig. 35.2 *The carbon dioxide molecule, a linear molecule*

The shape of the molecule is thus different from that of H_2O, SO_2, and H_2S in which the atoms are at angles of 105°, 120°, and 90° respectively.

The linear shape of the molecule causes it to be non-polar since both ends are similar. Therefore, carbon dioxide has a relatively low boiling point and may be liquefied only at great pressure.

In the carbon dioxide molecules, the carbon and the oxygen atoms share four electrons forming double bonds as shown in (2) below.

These electrons do not remain equally distributed but may rearrange themselves as shown in (1) and (3).

1   2   3

$$O \equiv C - O \longleftrightarrow O = C = O \longleftrightarrow O - C \equiv O$$

The double-headed arrow suggests that the electrons in the molecule are continually changing their location between the atoms causing the structure to alter correspondingly. Thus no one structure truly represents the molecule of carbon dioxide.

Molecules that can be represented by different electronic structures are said to display the property of *resonance*. Resonance causes compounds to be more stable and less reactive than would be expected from their atomic make-up. This is true of carbon dioxide, a relatively inert compound.

The Orbitals in Carbon Dioxide

sp HYBRIDIZATION AND THE LINEAR MOLECULE

In the carbon dioxide molecule, the carbon atom is attached to two oxygen atoms, and for this purpose, the carbon atom needs to provide two orbitals. These are obtained by hybridizing one *s* and one *p* of the four outer orbitals of

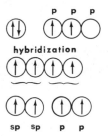

the carbon atom. Thereby two *sp* orbitals are furnished as shown in Fig. 35.3.

Two of these orbitals are used for direct bonding while the two half-filled *p* orbitals are

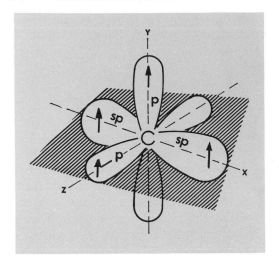

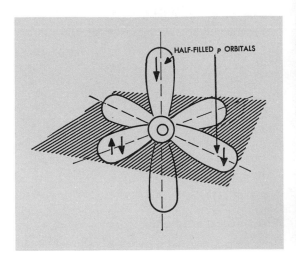

Fig. 35.3   *The carbon atom ready to bond using sp orbitals*
The carbon atom has two sp orbitals formed by hybridizing one s and only one of its p orbitals. The sp orbitals are in a straight line along x and cause the molecule to be linear at this carbon atom. Two half-filled p orbitals pointing along y and z remain at right angles to the line of the molecule. CO_2 and C_2H_2 are examples of molecules formed by sp orbitals.

Fig. 35.4   *The oxygen atom ready to bond to carbon in forming CO_2*
The oxygen atom has its s and one of its p orbitals filled with two electrons. The other two p orbitals are half-filled, with one electron each.

oriented at right angles to the rest of the molecule.

Similarly, the oxygen atom may be represented by (Fig. 35.4).

Each *sp* orbital of carbon overlaps end-to-end with one *p* orbital of oxygen, resulting in a linear molecule (Fig. 35.5).

Fig. 35.5   *The linear carbon dioxide molecule*
The molecule is formed by end to end overlap of carbon's sp orbitals with oxygen's p orbitals.

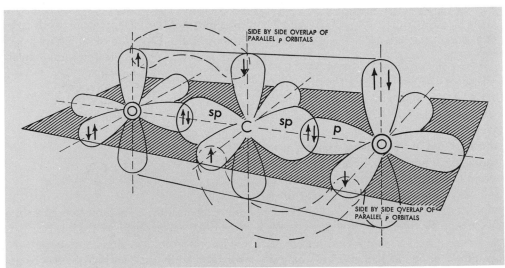

The other two p orbitals of the carbon atom still have one electron each. They orient themselves at right angles to the rest of the molecule. Similarly, the oxygen atoms also have a half-filled p orbital which orients itself at right angles to the line of the molecule. When the p orbitals of the carbon and the oxygen atoms are parallel to each other, there is side-by-side electron cloud overlap between pairs of p orbitals and even between all three parallel p orbitals of the carbon and oxygen atoms.

This is approximately equivalent to the above idea that electrons shuttle from one of the carbon-oxygen bonds in the molecule to the other.

35:5 Physical and Chemical Properties

Carbon dioxide is a colorless, odorless gas about one and one-half times as heavy as air.

At 20°C and high pressure, carbon dioxide condenses to a colorless liquid. If the pressure is removed, evaporation begins. The heat required for evaporation is withdrawn from the liquid, which now becomes so cold that it solidifies to carbon dioxide snow, known as *dry ice*, and is compressed into blocks. This solid sublimes without melting and maintains a temperature of $-78°C$.

At room temperature and pressure, one volume of water dissolves one volume of the gas. At higher pressures or lower temperatures the gas is much more soluble.

Carbon dioxide dissolves in water because it reacts with the water:

$$HOH + CO_2 \rightarrow H_2CO_3 \text{ (carbonic acid)}$$

In solution, carbonic acid donates protons to the water molecule to a slight extent; hence it is a weak acid.

Upon neutralization of carbonic acid with bases, two classes of salts may form depending on the amount of basic solution used.

These are the carbonates and the hydrogen carbonates (bicarbonates):

$$2NaOH + H_2CO_3 \rightarrow Na_2CO_3 + 2H_2O$$
$$NaOH + H_2CO_3 \rightarrow NaHCO_3 + H_2O$$
$$Ca(OH)_2 + H_2CO_3 \rightarrow CaCO_3\downarrow + 2H_2O$$

The last reaction of the three above is used to test for carbon dioxide. If a gas comes in contact with calcium hydroxide solution and a white precipitate forms, the gas is carbon dioxide.

Carbon dioxide does not burn; neither does it support combustion. A burning splint is extinguished in this gas.

35:6 Uses of Carbon Dioxide

(a) Effervescent Beverages

These are made by forcing carbon dioxide under pressure into the beverage. The solution effervesces when pressure is released, because the gas is less soluble under low pressure.

(b) Dry Ice

Carbon dioxide in the solid state is used to refrigerate perishable foods in transit. It is a better refrigerant than ordinary ice because of its low temperature. Also, no liquid is formed as it changes to a gas, and in changing to a gas a given weight of dry ice absorbs three times as much heat as ice does in melting.

(c) Leavening Bread

In order for bread or cake to be light, palatable, and digestible, it must undergo leavening. Carbon dioxide, released by chemical action, is used for this purpose. Baking soda, $NaHCO_3$, is often used with sour milk in home baking because the lactic acid of the milk releases carbon dioxide from the baking soda:

$$H_3O^+ + HCO_3^- \rightarrow H_2O + H_2CO_3 \rightarrow 2H_2O + CO_2\uparrow$$

Baking powders consist of baking soda, plus one of the following: calcium dihydrogen phosphate, $Ca(H_2PO_4)_2$; cream of tartar, $KHC_4H_4O_6$; or sodium aluminum sulfate, $NaAl(SO_4)_2$*.

---

*This compound contains water of hydration, $NaAl(SO_4)_2.12H_2O$. The protons are donated by the water of hydration.

When dry, these substances do not react, but in water they act as proton donors, forming hydronium ions. The latter then react with the hydrogen carbonate ion as shown above to liberate carbon dioxide. Some starch is added to baking powder to absorb moisture and prevent reaction during storage.

(d) Extinguishing Fires

Carbon dioxide is an excellent fire extinguishing material because it does not support combustion and, being heavier than air, it blankets a fire by cutting off the oxygen supply. It is inexpensive, easily liberated in large quantities, non-poisonous, and leaves no residue. It does not damage even fragile materials.

Liquid carbon dioxide for fighting fires is commonly stored in steel cylinders, for use aboard ships and aircraft and in buildings. When a valve is opened, carbon dioxide snow is formed by the rapid evaporation of the liquid. The snow cools the burning material and also cuts off the air supply.

A very common type of fire extinguisher uses a solution of sodium hydrogen carbonate (sodium bicarbonate, or soda) and a bottle of concentrated sulfuric acid with a loose stopper suspended above it (Fig. 35.6). When this is in-

Fig. 35.6   *Soda fire extinguisher*

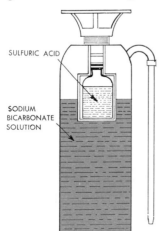

SULFURIC ACID

SODIUM
BICARBONATE
SOLUTION

verted, the acid and soda mix, and the carbon dioxide expels the soda water with great force.

$$2NaHCO_3 + H_2SO_4 \rightarrow Na_2SO_4 + 2H_2O + 2CO_2\uparrow$$

Another type of extinguisher contains carbon dioxide under pressure in a solution of soda. This requires merely the opening of a valve for use.

Oil and electrical fires are often extinguished by foamite. Water alone would cause the oil to float upward to the water surface where it would continue to burn, and it would cause short circuiting of electricity in an electrical fire. Foamite liquid contains a wetting agent, baking soda, and licorice in water. Aluminum sulfate solution is used in place of the sulfuric acid of the ordinary soda-acid extinguisher. Soda and aluminum sulfate solutions react as follows:

$$Al_2(SO_4)_3 + 6NaHCO_3 \rightarrow$$
$$2Al(OH)_3 + 6CO_2\uparrow + 3Na_2SO_4$$

The jelly-like aluminum hydroxide produced by the reaction and the licorice entrap the bubbles of carbon dioxide in a tough foam. This blankets the burning material, effectively cutting off the air supply. The wetting agent allows better mixing of the foam with oil.

"Pyrene" extinguishers contain carbon tetrachloride (CCl_4). Sometimes they are pressurized with carbon dioxide. Pyrene is effective for oil fires, since it is a grease solvent, but an unpleasant gas called phosgene is formed by carbon tetrachloride. The vapors of both carbon tetrachloride and of phosgene are toxic.

(e) Making of Carbonate and Hydrogen Carbonate Salts

Carbon dioxide is used in the Solvay process to manufacture sodium carbonate and hydrogen carbonate (Chapter 44).

(f) Manufacture of Urea

Urea ($(NH_2)_2CO$) is a valuable fertilizer and is used as a raw material in the manufacture of plastics. It is sometimes used in treating wounds and preserving wood. It could also be used to melt ice. Urea is made by uniting ammonia and carbon dioxide:

$$2NH_3 + CO_2 \rightarrow (NH_2)_2CO + H_2O$$

35:7 Test for Carbonate or Hydrogen Carbonate

Acids liberate carbon dioxide from carbonates or hydrogen carbonates. If the resulting gas is passed into a solution of calcium hydroxide, a fine white precipitate of calcium carbonate forms which causes the solution to appear milky:

$$Ca(OH)_2 + CO_2 \rightarrow CaCO_3\downarrow + H_2O$$

If excess carbon dioxide is used, it dissolves the precipitate because soluble calcium hydrogen carbonate is formed:

$$CaCO_3 + H_2O + CO_2 \rightarrow Ca(HCO_3)_2$$

35:8 Carbon Monoxide

The burning of fuels containing carbon in limited air produces carbon monoxide:

$$2C + O_2 \rightarrow 2CO\uparrow$$

This gas may also be formed by the reduction of carbon dioxide by hot carbon:

$$CO_2 + C \rightarrow 2CO\uparrow$$

A typical ingredient of gasoline is octane, C_8H_{18}. It may be burned incompletely in the engine of the car producing some carbon monoxide:

$$C_8H_{18} + 12O_2 \rightarrow CO\uparrow + 9H_2O + 7CO_2\uparrow$$

If enough air is mixed with the gasoline to burn it completely, the mixture burns too slowly in the cylinders and the engine does not function properly.

35:9 Laboratory Preparation

Carbon monoxide may be prepared in the laboratory by dropping formic acid into hot sulfuric acid. The sulfuric acid breaks down the formic acid into water and carbon monoxide:

$$\overset{H_2SO_4}{HCOOH \rightarrow H_2O + CO\uparrow}$$

This reaction occurs because sulfuric acid has a strong affinity for water.

35:10 Electronic Structure and Properties

In the molecule of carbon monoxide, there are enough outer electrons for them to form double and even triple bonds between the carbon and the oxygen, so that the compound has the property of resonance. Therefore, it is quite stable at room temperature. It does not react with water to any marked extent. It bears some resemblance to nitrogen N_2, having the same number of electrons and the same molecular

TABLE 35.1

Comparison of Carbon Monoxide and Nitrogen

	Carbon monoxide	Nitrogen
Formula	CO	N_2
Molecular Mass	12 + 16 = 28 amu	14 + 14 = 28 amu
Electrons	4 + 6 = 10	5 + 5 = 10
Melting Point	−207°C	−209°C
Boiling Point	−190°C	−196°C
Density of Liquid	0.793 g/ml	0.796 g/ml

mass and even the bonds between the atoms are somewhat similar.

Carbon monoxide is a colorless, tasteless gas. It has a slight odor, but this is difficult to detect. It is lighter than air and is slightly soluble. Only at low temperatures and high pressures does it liquefy. It burns with a pale blue flame to form carbon dioxide:

$$2CO + O_2 \rightarrow 2CO_2\uparrow$$

Because it is a good reducing agent, it is frequently used to extract metals from oxide ores; for example:

$$Fe_2O_3 + 3CO \rightarrow 2Fe + 3CO_2\uparrow$$
$$CuO + CO \rightarrow Cu + CO_2\uparrow$$

With suitable catalysts, carbon monoxide combines with hydrogen to form methanol:

$$CO + 2H_2 \rightarrow CH_3OH$$

When carbon monoxide and nickel are heated together, the two combine to form gaseous carbonyls:

$$Ni + 4CO \rightarrow Ni(CO)_4\uparrow$$
(Nickel Carbonyl)

Further heating reverses this reaction, precipitating the nickel in purified form. Nickel is extracted from its ore by this method.

Carbon monoxide is very poisonous. This is because it has about 300 times more attraction for the haemoglobin of the red blood cells than does oxygen. Haemoglobin is the oxygen carrier of the blood, and when carbon monoxide is inhaled, it enters the blood stream where it combines with the haemoglobin displacing the oxygen. The victim collapses from the lack of vital oxygen. First aid treatment requires fresh air and artificial respiration.

Carbon monoxide is not adsorbed by activated charcoal to any extent; the ordinary gas mask is therefore ineffective against this poison. A mixture of MnO_2, CuO, Co_2O_3, and Ag_2O in pellet form, called *hopcalite*, is found to catalyze the oxidation of carbon monoxide to carbon dioxide. A canister containing hopcalite is put in gas masks to be used where carbon monoxide might be encountered.

35:11   Detection of Carbon Monoxide

Canaries were once used in coal mines to detect the presence of carbon monoxide, for they are much more sensitive to this gas than humans; but color-detector tubes are now used for this purpose. One such device contains iodine pentoxide, which reacts with carbon monoxide as follows:

$$5CO + I_2O_5 \rightarrow 5CO_2 + I_2$$

The iodine liberated causes a color change which is proportional to the amount of carbon monoxide present. Comparison of the color with a chart reveals the extent of contamination. In some places, such as motor tunnels, the air is tested at all times by a recording mechanism. When the monoxide content of the air reaches a certain percentage, ventilating fans are automatically started.

35:12   Other Carbon Compounds

Carbides

Many metals form carbides when heated to a high temperature in contact with carbon. Of the carbides, *calcium carbide*, made at Shawinigan Falls, Quebec, is one of the most important. The product is made by heating calcium oxide and coke in an electric furnace:

$$CaO + 3C \rightarrow CaC_2 + CO\uparrow$$

Calcium carbide reacts with water to form acetylene, which is a raw material for many plastics and some varieties of rubber.

Silicon carbide or *carborundum* is made from sand and coke in a similar way:

$$SiO_2 + 3C \rightarrow SiC + 2CO\uparrow$$

The product is blue-black, shiny, and almost as hard as diamond. It is used in abrasive materials.

The cutting edge of some machine tools and masonry drills are made of *tungsten carbide*, W_2C. No other material in use maintains a sharp edge for such a long time. Such tools may be subjected to high temperature without damage, and they are able to cut very hard stone with ease.

Carbon Disulfide

This compound is made by heating sulfur and carbon in an electric furnace:

$$C + 2S \rightarrow CS_2$$

The vapors from the furnace yield the highly inflammable and volatile liquid, carbon disulfide. This material generally has a bad odor. It is a good solvent for sulfur, gums, rubber, fats, and waxes; and it ignites readily so that it should be used with great care and away from any open flame. Its vapors are toxic.

The volatile nature of carbon disulfide may be related to the non-polar nature of its molecule which is linear like the molecule of carbon dioxide. In CS_2, carbon again employs sp orbitals while the sulfur employs its p orbitals as did oxygen in CO_2.

Carbon Tetrachloride

Carbon tetrachloride is a colorless, dense liquid with a pleasant smell. An excellent grease solvent, it is used in dry cleaning. Since the vapors are somewhat poisonous, other less toxic compounds are replacing it as cleaning agents. Carbon tetrachloride is often used in small fire extinguishers as it is non-flammable.

Carbon tetrachloride is a non-polar liquid because of the geometry of its molecule. Since the carbon atom is joined to four other atoms, it employes sp^3 orbitals, and the molecule is tetrahedral (Chapter 19). In such a molecule, whatever polarity that might be present in each carbon-chlorine bond would be cancelled by the other similar bonds since they are distributed symmetrically.

As a non-polar liquid, carbon tetrachloride dissolves other non-polar substances like grease because the molecules of both solvent and solute are easy to separate and, therefore, intermingle readily. On the other hand, since no bonds can form between carbon tetrachloride and water, no energy is available for breaking the hydrogen bonds of the water; hence, carbon tetrachloride and water do not mix. For similar reasons, carbon tetrachloride does not dissolve salts.

QUESTIONS

1. Write a paragraph on the importance of carbon dioxide.

2. List the natural sources of carbon dioxide.

3. Outline the carbon dioxide cycle.

4. Draw a labelled diagram of the apparatus used for the laboratory preparation and collection of carbon dioxide. Write the equations for the preparation of this gas (a) in the laboratory; and (b) by fermentation.

5. (a) What are the three electronic structures that the molecule of carbon dioxide may have?
   (b) How does the shape of this molecule cause the gas to have a relatively low boiling point?
   (c) What is meant by sp orbitals?

6. (a) What is resonance?
   (b) What general effect does resonance have on the properties of a compound?

7. List the physical and chemical properties of carbon dioxide. Why is this gas quite soluble?

8. List six uses of carbon dioxide.

9. Why do carbonated drinks effervesce when the stopper is removed?

10. (a) Explain how dry ice is made.
    (b) Why is this material such a good refrigerant?

11. What are the essential ingredients of baking powder?

12. Why is carbon dioxide an efficient fire extinguishing material?

13. Draw a diagram and explain the operation of the common soda-acid extinguisher.

14. Write notes on (a) foamite; (b) pyrene.

15. What are some of the uses of urea?

16. Describe the test for the carbonate ion.

17. Why does continued passage of carbon dioxide into calcium hydroxide solution dissolve the precipitate?

18. In what ways is carbon monoxide produced?

19. With the aid of a diagram, explain how carbon monoxide may be prepared and collected in the laboratory.

20. How does the electronic structure of carbon monoxide account for its properties?

21. List the physical and chemical properties of carbon monoxide.

22. How is carbon monoxide used in metallurgy? Account for the poisonous properties of this gas.

23. What is hopcalite, and for what is it used?

24. Write a note on the detection of carbon monoxide.

25. (a) Write equations to show the preparation of calcium carbide and silicon carbide.
    (b) What are some of the uses of these materials?

26. What are the properties and uses of tungsten carbide?

27. (a) How is carbon disulfide made?
    (b) List the properties and uses of this substance.

28. Relate the physical properties of carbon disulfide to its molecular structure.

29. List the properties and uses of carbon tetrachloride.

30. (a) Explain how the molecular geometry of carbon tetrachloride accounts for its properties.
    (b) Why is carbon tetrachloride not soluble in water?

31. (a) Find the weight of carbon dioxide that could be obtained from 10 tons of a given limestone containing 20 per cent impurities.
    (b) How much of this limestone would be required to yield one ton of carbon dioxide?

32. How many moles of sulfur dioxide are there in 50 g of the substance?

33. Ethane gas burns as follows:
$$2C_2H_6 + 7O_2 \rightarrow 4CO_2 + 6H_2O$$
(a) Find the weight of oxygen required to burn 12 g of ethane.
(b) Find the volume at STP of carbon dioxide formed by burning the 12 g of ethane.

34. What would the observed volume of CO_2 be in question 33 if it were measured over water at 22°C and 775 mm pressure?

35. If 5 g of calcium carbonate and 5 g of sodium carbonate are each dissolved in excess hydrochloric acid, find which yields more carbon dioxide and how much more.

36 Some General Properties of Organic Compounds

36:1 The Many Carbon Compounds

The carbon compounds and their mixtures provide the tissues of our bodies, the foods we eat, and the textiles we wear. Paper, rubber, plastics, gasoline, oil, dyes, explosives, and almost all medicines are composed of carbon compounds. About one million such compounds have been prepared and studied. Why is carbon able to form so many compounds? Four reasons might be suggested.

a. Carbon atoms can form stable covalent bonds with one another. This permits chains and rings of carbon atoms to form, and these can grow in length and complexity giving rise to a large number and variety of molecules. The stability of the carbon-to-carbon bond is explained by the *intermediate* electronegativity of carbon. It is not as highly electron attracting as the halogens or as poorly electron attracting as the metals. The carbon-to-carbon bond is therefore both non-polar and stable.

b. Having a bonding capacity of four, the carbon atom can use two of its bonding orbitals to attach itself to other carbon atoms in the chain and yet have two more half-filled orbitals to attach other atoms to itself. This allows for the great variety in the compounds formed by carbon.

c. The outer orbitals hybridize in three different ways forming sp^3, sp^2, and sp orbitals which, in turn, produce molecules that are tetrahedral, planar, and linear, respectively.

d. Carbon forms stable covalent bonds with hydrogen, oxygen, and nitrogen. These elements have electronegativity values of about the same order as carbon. The resulting bonds are not highly polar.

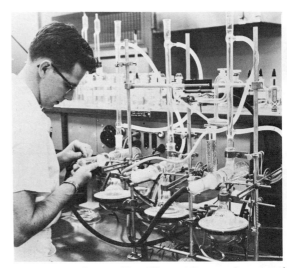

Courtesy Chas. Pfizer and Company, Incorporated

Fig. 36.1 *Organic chemist studying synthesis of new resins for paints*

36:2 Organic Chemistry

Because of the large number, variety, and importance of carbon compounds, they have been grouped together as a field of special interest. Their study is called *organic chemistry*. The name arises from an old belief that such compounds were formed only in plant and animal organisms. The chemistry of living organisms supposedly needed some vital force, since life was such an unusual phenomenon.

Today organic chemistry is the study of the behavior of the compounds formed by carbon with mainly, hydrogen, oxygen, and nitrogen, as well as with other elements to a lesser degree. The study of the chemistry of living processes is called *biochemistry*, a field overlapping biology and chemistry.

36:3   Organic Compounds

Some General Properties

Large numbers of organic compounds could hardly be expected to show exactly the same properties. Yet if allowance for obvious differences is made, it is interesting to see how consistent the properties of organic compounds actually are.

a. They are largely non-polar. The carbon and hydrogen particularly form non-polar bonds because of their almost equal electronegativity (H=2.1 and C=2.5).

b. Organic compounds tend to be insoluble in water. Since they are non-polar they cannot form bonds with water molecules. In view of this, no energy is available to separate the hydrogen bonds of the water; therefore, the organic molecules and the water molecules cannot mix.

   If, however, the organic molecule contains one or more hydroxyl groups, as in the case of ethanol or sucrose, hydrogen bonds may form between them and water molecules. This enables such substances to dissolve in water.

c. Organic compounds tend to be soluble in organic liquids. Since the non-polar organic substances are held together by weak intermolecular forces, their molecules intermingle readily.

d. Their melting and boiling points are low. Only when the molecule contains an OH or NH group, which permits hydrogen bonding, is the compound not so volatile.

e. They are, for the most part, non-electrolytes. As mentioned previously, the bond between hydrogen and carbon is extremely stable and is not likely to be split by ionization for proton donation, that is, to act as an acid. Nor is the hydrogen able to donate a pair of electrons; that is, to function as a base. When, however, the molecule contains a hydroxyl OH group, or an amino NH_2 group, or other similar groups, then acid, base, oxidizing or reducing properties may appear. There are many important organic acids and bases.

Molecular structure and Homologous series

Owing to the ability of the carbon atom to add to itself, organic molecules may become complex. To help visualize the molecule, it is written structurally with bonds connecting atoms and groups. Molecules having similar atoms and differing only by adding more carbon atoms (plus the correct number of hydrogen atoms) are said to make up a *homologous series*.

   A good example is the homologous series of the hydrocarbons, called alkanes, discussed in the next chapter.

Sources

Paper, cotton, sugars, starches, meat, eggs, and proteins are typical of the organic materials obtained from plants and animals. Many liquid and gaseous fuels, such as gasoline and oils, are obtained by the destructive distillation of coal and wood. All of these sources yield mixtures of organic compounds, some of which can be used without further separation. Often, however, pure compounds must be separated from the raw material. With these pure compounds, the organic chemist synthesizes textiles, plastics, rubber, detergents, and a large number of other useful products.

QUESTIONS

1. Write a paragraph on the importance of carbon compounds.
2. Explain clearly why carbon forms so many compounds.
3. Why are carbon-to-carbon bonds quite stable?
4. Why are bonds between carbon and hydrogen, oxygen, or nitrogen not highly polar?
5. Define the terms *organic chemistry* and *biochemistry*.
6. Why are materials like gasoline not soluble in water?
7. Explain why sugar dissolves readily in water.
8. Why are organic compounds usually soluble in organic liquids?
9. Why are the boiling and freezing points of ethane, C_2H_6, lower than those of ethanol, C_2H_5OH?
10. Explain why most organic compounds are non-electrolytes.
11. What general groups of organic compounds are usually electrolytes?
12. Define and give an example of a homologous series.
13. What are the principal sources of organic compounds?

CHAPTER

37 Hydrocarbons and Fuels

37:1 Various Hydrocarbons

Hydrocarbons, the compounds that contain hydrogen and carbon only, are present in natural gas and coal deposits. Some plant hydrocarbons are of great value, rubber latex and turpentine being two examples.

Hydrocarbons that contain only single bonds between the carbon atoms are called *saturated*, while those containing one or more double or triple bonds are said to be *unsaturated*. The saturated hydrocarbons are called *alkanes*.

37:2 Methane

The simplest alkane has the formula of CH_4 and is called methane. Experimental evidence for its formula is its molecular mass of 16 amu and its percentage composition of 75 per cent carbon

and 25 per cent hydrogen. It should be kept in mind that all chemical formulas are based on such experimental evidence.

In methane the carbon atom is attached by four covalent bonds to the hydrogen atoms, building a molecule that is tetrahedral in shape (Chapter 19). Its structure may be represented as in Fig. 37.1.

The molecule is non-polar and therefore has the following properties: (a) it has a low boiling point ($-161.4°C$), evidence of poor intermolecular attraction; (b) it does not dissolve in water because it does not interact with water; (c) it is a non-electrolyte, and (d) it is chemically inert; methane and other hydrocarbons of its class are called *paraffins* (of little affinity) for this reason.

The methane molecule reacts with chlorine at

TABLE 37.1				
Series of Alkane Hydrocarbons				
Name	Formula	Molecular Mass	B.P.	Normal State
Methane	CH_4	16	$-161.4°C$	Gas
Ethane	C_2H_6	30	-88.3	Gas
Propane	C_3H_8	44	-44.5	Gas
Butane	C_4H_{10}	58	-0.6	Gas
Pentane	C_5H_{12}	72	36.2	Liquid
Hexane	C_6H_{14}	86	69.0	Liquid
Heptane	C_7H_{16}	100	98.4	Liquid
Octane	C_8H_{18}	114	124.6	Liquid
Hexadecane	$C_{16}H_{34}$	Melts at 18°C		Solid
Hexacentane	$C_{60}H_{122}$	Melts at 102°C		Solid

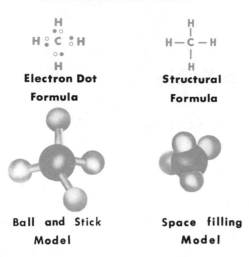

Electron Dot Formula

Structural Formula

Ball and Stick Model

Space filling Model

Fig. 37.1   *Molecular representations of methane*

This is called a *substitution reaction*:

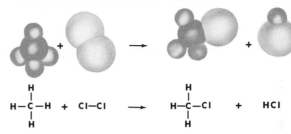

high temperature and pressure by substituting a chlorine atom in place of a hydrogen atom. The organic product is CH_3Cl, called methyl chloride, a refrigerant. More hydrogen atoms in the methane molecule may also be replaced, and the final product formed is CCl_4, carbon tetrachloride.

Fig. 37.2   *Molecular representations of ethane and propane*

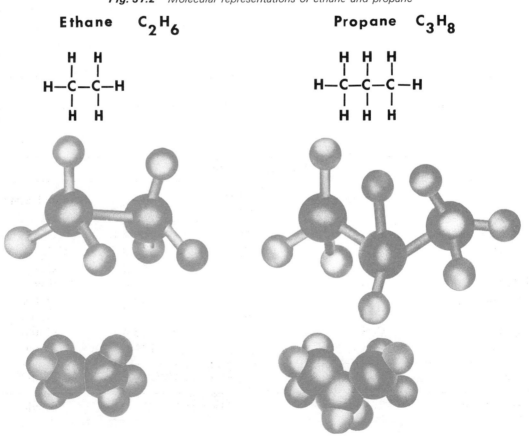

Ethane C_2H_6

Propane C_3H_8

Methane burns to form carbon dioxide and water. This reaction produces much heat:

$$CH_4 + 2O_2 \rightarrow CO_2\uparrow + 2H_2O + Heat$$

37:3 The Alkane Hydrocarbons

All the above physical and chemical properties are characteristic of the alkane hydrocarbons which resemble methane.

Alkane hydrocarbons conform to a general formula C_nH_{2n+2}, where n is the number of carbon atoms in the molecule. Each member of this series differs from methane by one or more CH_2 groups, thus forming a *homologous series*.

37:4 Isomerism

Experiments show that two compounds both having the same molecular formula of C_4H_{10} exist with slightly different physical properties. One has a boiling point of 0.6°C and the other of 12°C, so that there can be no doubt about their difference. The reason for the difference can soon be found by examining the possible structures of such molecules. There are two ways in which the molecule of C_4H_{10} can be drawn: in one the four carbon atoms are in one line or chain; in the second, only three are in one line, and the fourth is attached to the middle carbon:

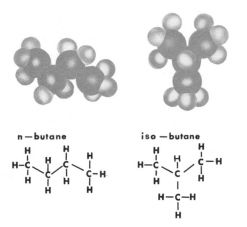

n—butane   iso—butane

Compounds having the same molecular formulas but different structures are called *isomers*, and the phenomenon is called *isomerism*. As the complexity of molecules increases, so does the possibility of isomerism. There are thirty-five known organic compounds with the molecular formula C_9H_{20}! *Nonane*

37:5 Organic Groups or Radicals

To name organic compounds and their isomers, we require a simple way of naming groups of atoms that recur frequently. For example, the CH_3- group occurs three times in the isomer of butane. CH_3- is called the methyl group.

An *organic group* or *radical* may be considered a molecule minus one (or more) hydrogen atoms. They are named accordingly by replacing the *ane* ending by *yl*.

TABLE 37.2			
Alkanes and Alkyl Groups			
Methane	CH_4	Methyl	CH_3-
Ethane	C_2H_6	Ethyl	C_2H_5-
Propane	C_3H_8	Propyl	C_3H_7-
Butane	C_4H_{10}	Butyl	C_4H_9-

The groups are themselves attached to larger molecules and should not be confused with ions. Their general name is the *alkyl group* and they are represented by *R*.

37:6 Physical Properties of the Alkanes

Reference to Table 37.1 shows that the state and boiling point of the hydrocarbons are related to molecular mass and chain length. The first four members of the series are gases at ordinary temperature and pressure. Those from C_5 to C_{20} are liquids, less dense than water, whereas those with more than twenty carbon atoms are wax-like solids. Isomers have slightly different physical properties. In general, the more branched the chain, the lower the boiling point.

Other physical and chemical properties of the entire series resemble those of methane because of the similar electronic structures: they are water insoluble; they dissolve in organic solvents; they are non-electrolytes; they are chemically unreactive, except at high temperature and pressure; they react by substitution of their hydrogen atoms; and they burn readily to liberate much heat and are, therefore, good fuels.

37:7 Natural Gas

Natural gas, largely methane, has, to a great extent, replaced coal gas as an industrial and domestic fuel. This gas is found wherever oil and coal occur, and it issues from the earth when porous rocks, saturated with it, are tapped. Most oil wells produce some natural gas.

Formerly, natural gas was burned as waste at oil wells, but when the value of this material was realized, controls were established, and the wasteful burning of natural gas has greatly diminished.

Natural gas is stripped of its heavy molecules before it is piped to the consumer. Butane and propane, which readily liquefy under pressure, are separated and sold as "Pyrofax", or low pressure gas. It may be stored as liquid in fairly light steel bottles.

The origin of natural gas is likely the same as that of petroleum, the incomplete decomposition of vegetable or animal matter, either with or without bacterial action.

37:8 Petroleum

Crude oil is a mixture of gaseous, liquid, and solid hydrocarbons. Petroleum comes from two Latin words, *petra* meaning rock and *oleum*

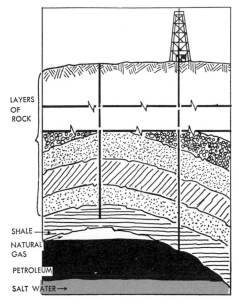

Fig. 37.3 *Typical structure of earth's strata in natural gas fields and oil fields*

meaning oil. This material is well named as can be seen by studying Fig. 37.3.

Likely oil-bearing strata are found by air photography, surface examination of rock, outcroppings, core drillings, and seismographic mapping of the earth's strata. The latter process consists of exploding dynamite in holes in the earth's crust. The reflections of the shock waves from rock layers, on being recorded, allow a geologist to map the substrata.

In drilling an oil well a rotary rig is used. The bit, which is attached to the end of lengths of pipe threaded together, is rotated and bites its way through rock and earth. To keep the drilled hole from caving in and to remove the drillings from the hole, a special type of mud is pumped down the pipe forming the bit stock. This mud ascends between the pipe and the sides of the hole, cementing the sides of the hole and carrying waste material to the surface. Extra lengths of pipe for the bit stock and the machinery for lifting it out of the hole are supported by a derrick (Fig. 37.4).

Courtesy Imperial Oil Limited

Fig. 37.4   *An oil drilling derrick*

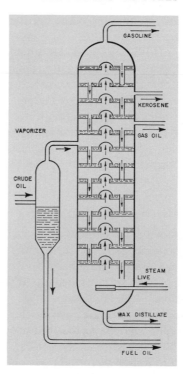

Fig. 37.5   *Bubble tower for the fractional distillation of petroleum*

When a well enters oil strata, gas pressure may be sufficient to force oil to the surface. Such a well is called a gusher. Usually, however, pumps must be used to lift the oil to the surface. The oil is stored in large steel tanks until it is sent to the refinery.

Fractional Distillation

After undesirable impurities, such as sulfur, wax, and clay, are removed, the crude oil is separated into fractions, which consist of mixtures of hydrocarbons having different boiling points. In this process, known as fractional distillation, the oil is heated in a pipe-still consisting of many pipes inside a gas-fired furnace. It is then discharged into the bottom of a fractionating or "bubble" tower where the volatile components form vapors which ascend the tower. The more volatile the vapor, the higher it rises before condensing to a liquid. In this way fractions of the hydrocarbons are sorted

out according to their boiling points (Fig. 37.5).

The heavier fractions with the highest boiling points condense on the lower trays. Several gases, from methane to butane, are collected at the top of the tower. The main products in descending order are naphtha, gasoline, kerosene, heating oil, lubricating oil, waxes, tars, and asphalt.

The residue is petroleum coke, which is used as a fuel and for making electrodes. A 42-gallon barrel of crude oil yields about 21 gallons of gasoline, 16 gallons of fuel oil, 2 gallons of kerosene, 1.5 gallons of lubricating oil, and the remainder consists of other useful products.

Gasoline

Today, gasoline is the most important single product obtained from crude oil. It is a mixture consisting chiefly of hexane C_6H_{14}, heptane

C_7H_{16}, and octane C_8H_{18}. The boiling point of the mixture is about 80°C.

Simple distillation produces only about 5 gallons of gasoline from 42 gallons of crude oil. The yield of gasoline is increased to about 21 gallons per barrel by *catalytic thermal cracking* of heavy molecules. If hydrocarbons of large molecular mass are heated to a high temperature in the absence of air, the molecules disintegrate or "crack" into several smaller fragments.

Example:

$$C_{16}H_{34} \rightarrow C_8H_{18} + C_8H_{16}$$

Molecules with 16 carbon atoms cannot be used as gasoline, but molecules with 8 carbon atoms can. Catalysts have been developed that allow this process to be carried out at fairly low temperatures.

Another method of increasing the yield of gasoline is *polymerization*, the opposite of cracking. In this process, small molecules of similar structure are joined to form larger ones. *Alkylation* is a process of joining saturated and unsaturated hydrocarbons to form larger molecules. About 16 per cent of our gasoline is obtained by cooling and compressing natural gas. The resulting product is *casing head gasoline*. Enriched gasolines with better engine-performance properties are produced by isomerisation of straight chain molecules into branched chains.

GASOLINE AS AN ENGINE FUEL

Any combustible gas can cause an explosion if intimately mixed with air in the right proportions and ignited. The gaseous fuel and oxygen combine almost instantly, and the gases produced by the reaction are greatly expanded by the heat.

However, it has been found in research on the relative merits of the individual hydrocarbons as fuels for internal combustion engines, that those compounds with straight chain molecules tend to explode too rapidly and burn too unevenly upon ignition. Such rapid combustion causes fuel knock in a motor, accompanied by loss of power or damage to the motor.

For maximum power the gas-air mixture should burn quickly in a combustion wave spreading smoothly in all directions from the spark plug. This should occur only when the piston has reached the top of its compression stroke.

In 1921 Thomas Midgely discovered that as little as 3 ml of tetraethyl lead, $(C_2H_5)_4Pb$, added to a gallon of gasoline improved its anti-knock properties greatly. Lead oxide, formed when this compound is used, may foul valves and cylinders unless a little ethylene dibromide, $C_2H_4Br_2$, is added also. The ethylene dibromide forms gaseous lead dibromide and allows the lead to pass out with the exhaust. "Ethyl fluid", an additive that allows higher compression in engines and greater economy of engine operation, is now used in most motor fuels.

OCTANE NUMBERS

The octane number refers to the anti-knock quality of a motor fuel. A branched-chain isomer of octane is an excellent motor fuel, whereas straight-chain heptane is a very poor motor fuel, as mentioned above. By mixing these liquids and using the resultant fuel in a test engine, it is possible to compare the anti-knock qualities of this mixture with those of any other gasoline. The particular mixture of heptane and octane which has the same anti-knock qualities as the gasoline being examined is noted. The percentage of octane in the reference mixture is called the *octane number*, and this number is affixed to the gasoline being compared. A gasoline with an octane rating of 90 ("90 octane") means that this gasoline has the same anti-knock quality as a mixture of 90 per cent octane and 10 per cent heptane. Gasoline quality is supervised by the government, and the octane number of the gasoline sold must be exhibited on the gas pump. Aviation fuels may have an octane rating of 100 or more. These fuels are composed for the most part of carefully selected branched molecules, and their octane number may be increased still more by the addition of "Ethyl fluid".

37:9 Petrochemistry

Natural gas and petroleum are now used in increasing amounts to make organic compounds; included among these are ethanol, glycerol, acetone, ethylene glycol, benzene, and toluene. Such compounds used to be obtained from a variety of sources but are now available directly or indirectly from petroleum. Rubber, plastics, detergents, insecticides, and synthetic fibres, like orlon, dacron and nylon, are synthesized from the above compounds. The industry based on converting petroleum by-products to useful substances is called the *petrochemical industry*.

37:10 Unsaturated Hydrocarbons (The Alkenes and Alkynes)

The unsaturated hydrocarbons are those which contain double or triple bonds between some of the carbon atoms in their molecules. The simplest examples are ethene (or ethylene) C_2H_4 and ethyne (or acetylene) C_2H_2.

Chemical Evidence for Double and Triple Bonds

Why do we believe that double and triple bonds

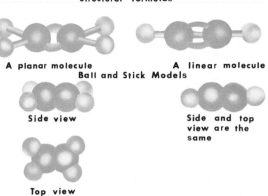

Ethene C_2H_4 Ethyne C_2H_2

H   H
 \   /
  C = C   H—C ≡ C—H
 /   \
H   H

Structural formulas

A planar molecule   A linear molecule
Ball and Stick Models

Side view   Side and top
                           view are the
                           same

Top view

are present in the molecules of these compounds? What chemical evidence can be offered to back up our belief in these structures?

The saturated hydrocarbons react slowly by substituting one of the atoms already present in the molecules by another. The unsaturated hydrocarbons, being more reactive, react by *adding* other atoms to their molecules. This is explained by the "saturating" of the double bond. In this process one of the bonds is left intact between the carbon atoms, while new atoms or groups are added to the open bond. Thus a molecule of ethene adds a molecule of hydrogen to form a molecule of ethane.

Ethene   +   Hydrogen ⟶   Ethane

H   H   H   H
 \   / | |
  C = C   + H_2 ⟶   H—C—C—H
 /   \ | |
H   H   H   H

Similarly, a molecule of acetylene adds two molecules of hydrogen to form a molecule of ethane:

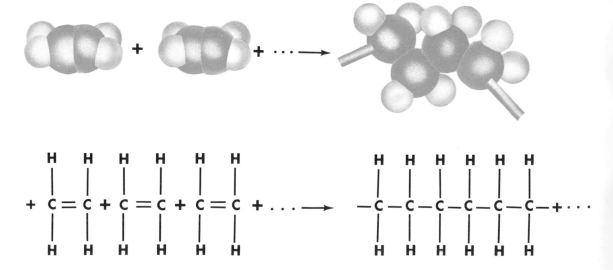

$$H-C\equiv C-H + 2H_2 \rightarrow H-\overset{\displaystyle H}{\underset{\displaystyle H}{C}}-\overset{\displaystyle H}{\underset{\displaystyle H}{C}}-H$$

Ethyne   +   Hydrogen   ⟶   Ethane

Molecules with double bonds are often able to add to each other just as they add other atoms to themselves. Ethene molecules may add to each other and thereby form a large molecule containing as many as 1000 ethene molecules linked together. The resulting product is *polythene* (or polyethylene) which is used in a great assortment of products; for instance, squeeze bottles, ice-cube trays, and large sheets used for insulating buildings under construction.

The formation of polythene from ethene may be represented as follows:

The large molecules formed in this way are called *polymers* (*poly*—many, *mers*—units), and the process of combining many small molecules into larger ones is called *polymerization*. It is through polymerization that plastics, rubber, and textiles are produced synthetically.

Because of its reactivity, ethene is used for the preparation of many synthetic products; for example, at high temperature, ethene reacts with water vapor to form ethanol;

$$\underset{H}{\overset{H}{>}}C=C\underset{H}{\overset{H}{<}} + H-O\underset{H}{\overset{}{\diagdown}} \xrightarrow{H_2SO_4} H-\overset{\displaystyle H}{\underset{\displaystyle H}{C}}-\overset{\displaystyle H}{\underset{\displaystyle H}{C}}-O-H$$

Ethene   +   Water   ⟶   Ethanol

Indeed, ethene is one of the primary raw materials in the petrochemical industry.

$$+ \underset{H}{\overset{H}{C}}=\underset{H}{\overset{H}{C}} + \underset{H}{\overset{H}{C}}=\underset{H}{\overset{H}{C}} + \underset{H}{\overset{H}{C}}=\underset{H}{\overset{H}{C}} + \ldots \longrightarrow -\underset{H}{\overset{H}{C}}-\underset{H}{\overset{H}{C}}-\underset{H}{\overset{H}{C}}-\underset{H}{\overset{H}{C}}-\underset{H}{\overset{H}{C}}-\underset{H}{\overset{H}{C}}-+\cdots$$

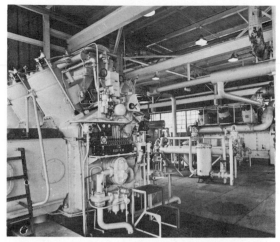

Courtesy Canadian Industries Limited

Fig. 37.6 *Gas compressors used in preparing ethene for polymerization to polythene*

The Electronic Structure of Unsaturated Compounds, sp² Hybridization

In the molecule of ethene, each carbon atom is joined to three other atoms; namely, one carbon atom and two hydrogen atoms. For such bond-ing, the carbon atom needs to provide three orbitals. These are obtained by hybridizing one *s* and two *p* of the four outer orbitals of the carbon atom, thereby forming three *sp²* orbitals as shown in Fig. 37.7.

In order for the three *sp²* orbitals to be oriented as symmetrically as possible, they must be at 120 degrees to each other, all lying in the same plane.

The one half-filled *p* orbital still present in the atom orients itself at right angles to the rest of the molecule.

An *sp²* orbital of one carbon atom overlaps end to end with an *sp²* orbital of another carbon atom to form the skeleton of the new molecule.

The *p* orbitals may overlap side-by-side only if they are parallel. For this reason, they take up such a side-by-side position. Finally, the four *sp²* orbitals left overlap with the *s* electron cloud orbitals of four hydrogen atoms to complete the molecule.

The geometrical pattern of ethene occurs whenever a C=C bond is present in a molecule. Many dyes, explosives, drugs, and plastics are

Fig. 37.7 *sp² orbitals in the bonding carbon atom*
The carbon atom has three sp² orbitals formed by hybridizing one s and two of its p orbitals. The sp² orbitals lie in the same plane and lie at 120° angles with each other. A half-filled p orbital remains, and is at right angles to the plane of the molecule. Examples of molecules formed by sp² orbitals are ethene and benzene.

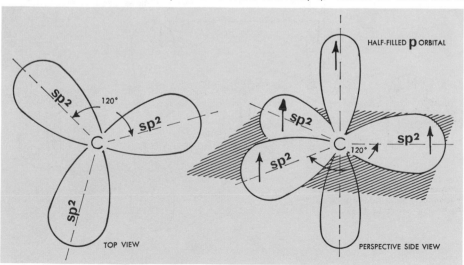

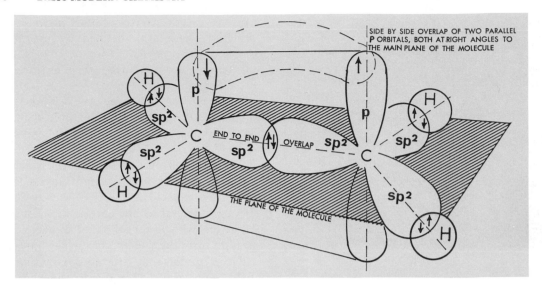

Fig. 37.8   *The planar ethene molecule*
All sp² orbitals lie in the same plane.

made from compounds whose molecules contain such bonds.

In acetylene, each carbon atom is joined to two other atoms, one of these a carbon atom and the other hydrogen. Therefore the carbon atom uses two orbitals for bonding. These are obtained by hybridizing one *s* and one *p* into two *sp* orbitals, as was the case with carbon in

Fig. 37.9   *The linear acetylene molecule*
The sp orbitals are in a straight line.

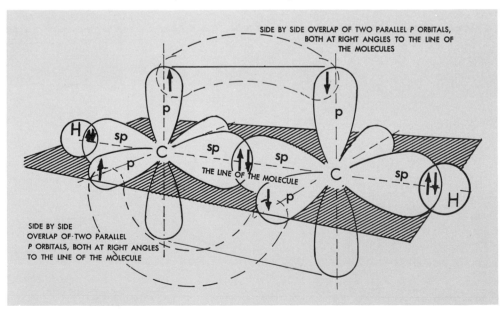

CO_2. As a result the acetylene molecule is linear. Two singly filled p orbitals remain in each carbon atom, and these orient themselves in a parallel position at right angles to the molecule, thus forming a triple bond as seen in Fig. 37.9.

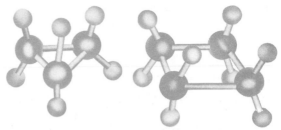

37:11   Cyclic Hydrocarbons

In another class of hydrocarbons, called the cyclic hydrocarbons, the carbon atoms form a ring. Two examples of this class are cyclopropane and cyclobutane:

cyclopropane   cyclobutane

In the molecule of cyclopropane, the three carbon atoms are at the corners of an equilateral triangle. This causes the angles between bonds to be 60 degrees, which is much smaller than the usual value of 109°28′ found in the open-chain saturated hydrocarbons. The higher reactivity of cyclopropane compared to other saturated hydrocarbons may be explained by the "straining" of the molecule as a result of the 60-degree angles between the bonds. In cyclobutane the angle between the bonds is 90 degrees, and thus this molecule is also strained,

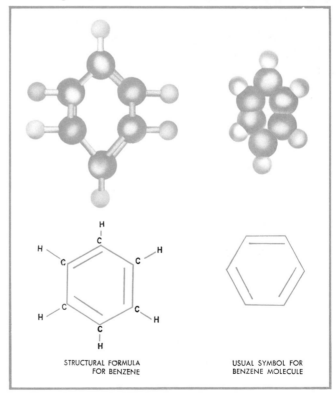

STRUCTURAL FORMULA FOR BENZENE

USUAL SYMBOL FOR BENZENE MOLECULE

Fig. 37.10   *The ring structure of benzene*

although not to the same extent as cyclopropane.

37:12 Aromatic Hydrocarbons

Another class of hydrocarbons of great industrial and theoretical interest is related to benzene, C_6H_6, a liquid obtained in the destructive distillation of coal. These are termed the aromatic hydrocarbons, and a large number of dyes, perfumes, medicines, and explosives have been obtained from them.

Benzene is the parent of the aromatic compounds just as methane is the parent of the open-chain substances. Benzene is the simplest of the aromatic compounds which, in turn, may be regarded as derived from the parent substance.

C_6H_6—A Puzzle

The formula of benzene, C_6H_6, baffled the early organic chemists, when they attempted to write its structure as they would write the structure of, say, hexane C_6H_{14}:

$$H-\underset{\underset{H}{|}}{\overset{\overset{H}{|}}{C}}-\underset{\underset{H}{|}}{\overset{\overset{H}{|}}{C}}-\underset{\underset{H}{|}}{\overset{\overset{H}{|}}{C}}-\underset{\underset{H}{|}}{\overset{\overset{H}{|}}{C}}-\underset{\underset{H}{|}}{\overset{\overset{H}{|}}{C}}-\underset{\underset{H}{|}}{\overset{\overset{H}{|}}{C}}-H$$

Obviously, there were "too few" hydrogen atoms in the C_6H_6 molecule for it to be written as a straight line.

THE RING STRUCTURE

The difficulty was finally overcome by Kekulé, a German chemist, who suggested that the six carbon atoms were arranged in a closed hexagonal ring, joined by alternate double and single bonds.

This would explain why benzene had only one isomer when one hydrogen was replaced by a chlorine atom to form chlorobenzene.

Apparently, there is no difference between the positions around the hexagon to which the chlorine atom could be attached. If, on the other hand, the six carbon atoms were in a straight line,

$$-\overset{1}{\underset{|}{C}}-\overset{2}{\underset{|}{C}}-\overset{3}{\underset{|}{C}}-\overset{4}{\underset{|}{C}}-\overset{5}{\underset{|}{C}}-\overset{6}{\underset{|}{C}}-$$

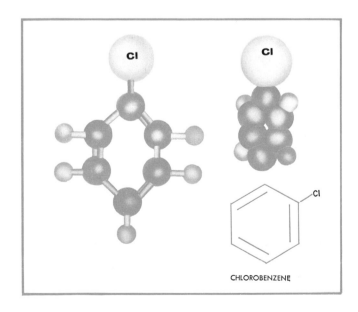

CHLOROBENZENE

positions 1, 2, and 3 would be different, and at least three isomers would result.

Nevertheless, the Kekulé structure was not entirely satisfactory because benzene was less reactive than would be expected from the presence of the three double bonds in its molecule. Modern orbital theory explains the reduced reactivity of benzene by *resonance.*

Orbitals in Benzene

In the benzene molecule, each carbon atom is joined to three other atoms, as in ethene. Therefore, the carbon atom employs sp^2 orbitals. Such orbitals lie in a common plane and are at 120 degrees to each other (Fig. 37.7). The benzene molecule, formed by means of side-by-side electron cloud overlap of sp^2 orbitals, is a flat or planar hexagon from whose corners radiate the sp^2 orbitals to which the hydrogen atoms attach themselves. Furthermore, each carbon atom still has half-filled p orbitals, again as was the case in ethene. The six half-filled p orbitals

are at right angles to the plane of the molecule, and they may overlap forming a common electron cloud. Whenever more than two p orbitals overlap, the molecule becomes more stable than expected and is said to show resonance. This occurs with benzene (Fig. 37.11).

Compounds Related to Benzene

Toluene is a liquid similar to benzene in properties, having a methyl, CH_3-, group in place of one of the hydrogen atoms of benzene.

Trinitro toluene, a high explosive, is made from this compound.

Phenol is a hygroscopic solid, having a hydroxyl, $OH-$, group in place of one of the hydrogens of benzene (Fig. 37.12).

Phenol is used as a disinfectant and as a raw material for making plastics. Aniline is a liquid having an amino, NH_2-, group in place of one of the hydrogen atoms of benzene. Many dyes and drugs are made from aniline and its derivatives.

Fig. 37.11   *Orbitals in the benzene molecule*

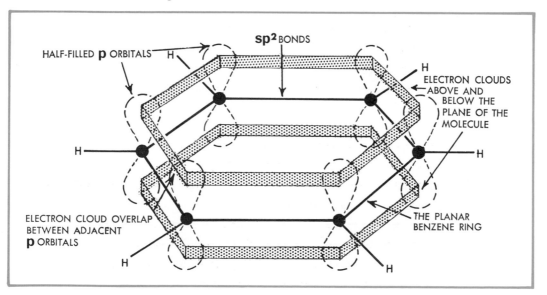

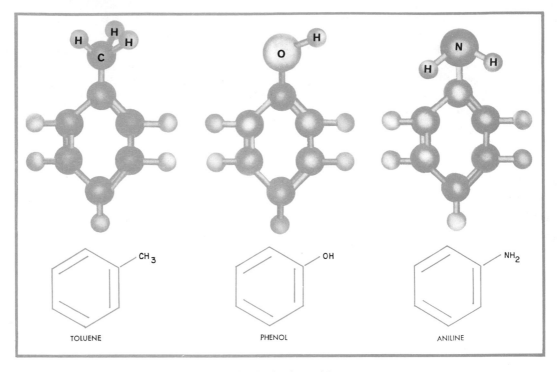

TOLUENE   PHENOL   ANILINE

Fig. 37.12 *Derivatives of benzene*

QUESTIONS

1. (a) What are hydrocarbons?
   (b) Mention some important hydrocarbons.

2. Distinguish between saturated and unsaturated hydrocarbons.

3. What are the alkanes?

4. Describe the structure of methane, using a diagram.

5. List the principal physical properties of methane. Why does methane have these properties?

6. How may methyl chloride and carbon tetrachloride be made from methane?

7. Summarize the chemical properties of methane.

8. Illustrate how methane, ethane, and propane are part of a homologous series.

9. Define and give an example of isomerism.

10. What are alkyl radicals? Illustrate your answer with an example.

11. Summarize the general rules of naming organic compounds.

12. What are the common properties of the saturated hydrocarbons?

13. Write a note on the importance of natural gas.

14. Account for the origin of natural gas.

15. Write a note on oil exploration.

16. Describe the operation and construction of a bubble tower.

17. List the main products separated from petroleum by distillation.

18. What are the most important components of gasoline?

19. List and describe briefly the methods of increasing the yield of gasoline from petroleum.

20. Explain clearly the cause and effects of engine knock.

21. Explain how the octane number of a motor fuel is determined.

22. What is the importance of petrochemistry?

23. What are some possible substitutes for petroleum products?

24. (a) What facts support the belief that unsaturated hydrocarbons contain a double or triple bond?
    (b) What is meant by *sp*^{2} orbitals?

25. (a) Write the structural formulas for ethene and acetylene.
    (b) What are some uses of these compounds?

26. Define *polymerization*. Illustrate your answer by reference to the formation of polythene.

27. Give two examples of cyclic hydrocarbons.

28. (a) What is an example of an aromatic hydrocarbon?
    (b) Draw its structural formula.

29. A gaseous compound contains 85.72 per cent carbon and 14.28 per cent hydrogen. A liter of the gas at STP weighs 2.50 g. Find its molecular formula.

30. $CaC_2 + 2H_2O \rightarrow Ca(OH)_2 + C_2H_2$
    Calculate the weight of calcium carbide required to yield two moles of acetylene.

31. Find the density of the gas butane, C_4H_{10}, at STP in g/l.

32. Find the weight in grams of 10^{18} molecules of methane.

CHAPTER

38 Oxygen-Containing Organic Compounds

38:1 Alcohols

When one or more of the hydrogen atoms in a hydrocarbon molecule is replaced by a hydroxyl OH— group, the molecule that results represents a new type of compound called an *alcohol*. These compounds form a homologous series.

Functional Group

The entry of the polar hydroxyl group into the molecule permits hydrogen bonding. For this reason, alcohols are very different from hydrocarbons. Alcohols are liquids while hydrocarbons with an equal number of atoms in their molecules are gases. The alcohols of lower molecular mass dissolve in water and react with sodium to liberate hydrogen. Hydrocarbons do neither.

It is the hydroxyl group that gives alcohol its distinctive properties. A group that is characteristic of an entire series is called a *functional group*. The hydroxyl OH is the functional group of the alcohols. If R stands for any alkyl group, the alcohols may be represented by ROH.

Naming Alcohols

The longest chain of carbon atoms that includes the hydroxyl group is the basis for the name of an alcohol. This name has the ending −*ol*. The position of the hydroxyl group is indicated by the number of the carbon atom to which it is attached.

While alcohols are derivatives of hydrocarbons, the substitution of a hydroxyl radical for a hydrogen is done by indirect means. This can be seen in the preparation and properties of the two most common alcohols, methanol and ethanol.

Methanol

Most of the methanol used today is produced synthetically by passing a mixture of carbon monoxide and hydrogen over a catalyst consisting of the oxides of zinc, copper, and chromium. A temperature of 400°C and a pressure of 150 atmospheres are used. The following reaction occurs:

$$CO + 2H_2 \rightarrow CH_3OH$$

This compound is also known as wood alcohol because a small amount is obtained when wood is destructively distilled.

Methanol is a colorless liquid, miscible with

Fig. 38.1   *A scientist is studying a motor driven by a fuel cell battery. This device converts chemical energy from a liquid fuel, methanol, directly into electricity.*

Courtesy Esso Research and Engineering Company

312

TABLE 38.1

Some Common Alcohols

Name and Formula	Molecular Structure

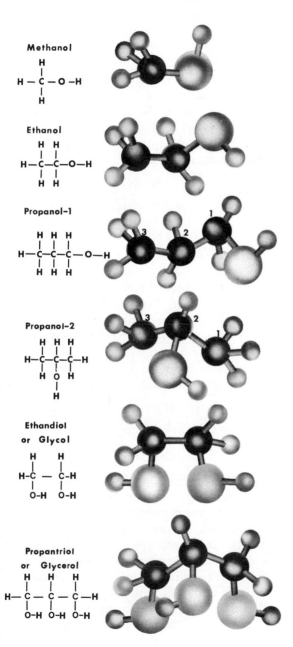

Methanol

$$H - \overset{\displaystyle H}{\underset{\displaystyle H}{C}} - O - H$$

Ethanol

$$H - \overset{\displaystyle H}{\underset{\displaystyle H}{C}} - \overset{\displaystyle H}{\underset{\displaystyle H}{C}} - O - H$$

Propanol-1

$$H - \overset{\displaystyle H}{\underset{\displaystyle H}{C}} - \overset{\displaystyle H}{\underset{\displaystyle H}{C}} - \overset{\displaystyle H}{\underset{\displaystyle H}{C}} - O - H$$

Propanol-2

$$H - \overset{\displaystyle H}{\underset{\displaystyle H}{C}} - \overset{\displaystyle H}{\underset{\displaystyle O}{C}} - \overset{\displaystyle H}{\underset{\displaystyle H}{C}} - H$$

Ethandiol or Glycol

$$H - \overset{\displaystyle H}{\underset{\displaystyle O-H}{C}} \quad \overset{\displaystyle H}{\underset{\displaystyle O-H}{C}} - H$$

Propantriol or Glycerol

$$H - \overset{\displaystyle H}{\underset{\displaystyle O-H}{C}} - \overset{\displaystyle H}{\underset{\displaystyle O-H}{C}} - \overset{\displaystyle H}{\underset{\displaystyle O-H}{C}} - H$$

water in all proportions. It boils at about 66°C and has a characteristic odor. Both the liquid and vapor are poisonous and are capable of causing blindness or death. Methanol burns with a pale blue flame:

$$2CH_3OH + 3O_2 \rightarrow 2CO_2\uparrow + 4H_2O$$

Methanol is used as a raw material in the manufacture of formaldehyde, HCHO, from which some plastics are made. It is used as a solvent for shellac and varnishes and as a fuel additive in aircraft when extra power is needed, such as at take-off. Much methanol is also used to denature grain alcohol. Denaturing renders grain alcohol unfit for drinking but does not interfere with most of its industrial uses.

Ethanol

More than 50 per cent of the ethanol produced is made from ethene. The simplified equation for its production is as follows:

$$\overset{\displaystyle H \quad H}{\underset{\displaystyle H \quad H}{C=C}} + H-O-H \xrightarrow{H_2SO_4} H-\overset{\displaystyle H}{\underset{\displaystyle H}{C}}-\overset{\displaystyle H}{\underset{\displaystyle H}{C}}-OH$$

This alcohol is commonly produced by fermentation, a chemical change brought about by the growth of bacteria, yeasts, or moulds. These living organisms produce enzymes.

Ethanol is obtained when glucose, $C_6H_{12}O_6$, a monosaccharide (Chapter 39), is fermented. Since glucose occurs in a large number of fruit juices, any of these may be used to prepare ethanol. The process is catalyzed by an enzyme called zymase found in yeast:

$$C_6H_{12}O_6 \xrightarrow{\text{zymase}} 2C_2H_5OH + 2CO_2\uparrow$$

Wines are prepared by such fermentation of fruit juice.

Starch, a polysaccharide (Chapter 39) obtained from corn, barley, rice, wheat, and potatoes, may also ferment to produce ethanol.

However, when starch is used, its large molecule must first be broken into molecules of glucose. This is done with the aid of diastase, an enzyme found in malt, which is obtained commercially from sprouting barley seeds.

In making beer, the starch is first fermented with the aid of diastase to glucose; then the glucose is fermented to alcohol with the aid of of zymase:

$$(C_6H_{10}O_5)_n + nH_2O \xrightarrow{\text{diastase}}$$
Starch

$$nC_6H_{12}O_6 \xrightarrow{\text{zymase}} n(C_2H_5OH + 2CO_2)$$
Glucose \qquad\qquad Ethanol

It is also possible to obtain ethanol from sucrose. In this case, the sucrose, a disaccharide, must first be broken down to glucose and fructose of which it is composed. This is done with the aid of invertase, another enzyme found in yeast. Thus the addition of yeast, which contains both invertase and zymase, to sugar, produces ethanol. Molasses, a by-product in refinement of sucrose from sugar cane, is fermented to ethanol in this way.

Fermentation stops when the concentration of ethanol reaches 12 per cent. The alcohol is distilled from the mixtures and may be thus concentrated to about 95 per cent. A 95 per cent ethanol–water mixture is constant boiling and cannot be further separated by distillation. Calcium oxide, CaO, may be added to remove the water if absolutely pure ethanol is required. The calcium oxide does not combine with the alcohol; nor is it soluble in the alcohol.

PROPERTIES OF ETHANOL

Ethanol is a colorless liquid with a characteristic odor and burning taste. It is miscible with water in all proportions, but it is lighter than water; it boils at about 78°C, and it burns with a pale blue flame, as follows:

$$C_2H_5OH + 3O_2 \rightarrow 2CO_2\uparrow + 3H_2O$$

Ethanol is next to water in importance as a solvent. It is also used in the preparation of rubber, ether, vinegar, chloroform, perfumes, medicines, varnishes, lacquers, and antifreeze. In some countries ethanol is mixed with the gasoline to serve as a motor fuel.

Ethylene Glycol and Glycerol

Ethanol and methanol have one hydroxyl group in their molecules and are, therefore, termed *monohydroxy* alcohols. Ethylene glycol, or ethanediol, $C_2H_4(OH)_2$, is an example of a *dihydroxy* alcohol. Its two hydroxyl groups are present on adjacent carbon atoms.

Ethylene glycol is used as permanent antifreeze because it has a low freezing point and it does not evaporate readily. The liquid is also a valuable solvent. The two hydroxyl groups increase the hydrogen bonding in the liquid, thereby causing ethylene glycol to have higher viscosity than ethanol.

Glycerol is the most important *trihydroxy* molecule. Its strucural formula is

This alcohol has long been produced as a by-product of the soap industry.

Due to hydrogen bonding, glycerol is a thick, syrupy liquid, heavier than water, and mixes with water in all proportions. It is colorless and has a sweet taste. Because it is *hygroscopic* (that is, it absorbs and retains moisture), it is used in ointments, medicines, cosmetics, and dentifrices, and also as a substance to retain moisture in tobacco, candy, adhesives, cellophane, and leather. Its chief use, however, is in making nitroglycerine, commonly used in dynamite. When used to make dynamite, glycerine is treated with a mixture of sulfuric and nitric acid:

$$C_3H_5(OH)_3 + 3HNO_3 \xrightarrow{H_2SO_4} C_3H_5(NO_3)_3 + 3H_2O$$

glycerol   nitroglycerine

The sulfuric acid absorbs the water formed. This reaction must be conducted with rigid temperature control to prevent premature explosion. The nitroglycerine must be highly purified after its formation, otherwise it is not safe to handle. Minute amounts of impurities have been found to render it unstable. When nitroglycerine explodes, it disintegrates into gaseous products.

For use in dynamite, the nitroglycerine is absorbed in some material like starch or wood pulp. Dynamite is quite safe to handle because the absorbed nitroglycerine is very resistant to detonation unless subjected to the explosive force of a percussion cap.

38:2   Oxidation of Organic Compounds

When methane is ignited, it burns to produce carbon dioxide (CO_2), and water. Carbon dioxide represents the most complete state of oxidation of carbon. If, however, the oxidation is carried out more gently, compounds other than carbon dioxide are formed.

Suppose it were possible to introduce one oxygen atom at a time into each of the carbon–hydrogen bonds of methane. In the first step methanol would be obtained from methane:

$$\begin{array}{c} H \\ | \\ H-C-H \\ | \\ H \end{array} \xrightarrow{O} \begin{array}{c} H \\ | \\ H-C-OH \\ | \\ H \end{array}$$

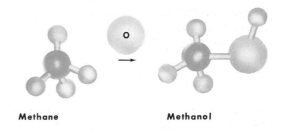

Methane   Methanol

where $\xrightarrow{O}$ is the symbol for introducing an oxygen atom.

In the second step, the following structure would result:

$$\begin{array}{c} H \\ | \\ H-C-OH \\ | \\ H \end{array} \xrightarrow{O} \begin{array}{c} OH \\ | \\ H-C-OH \\ | \\ H \end{array}$$

Methanol   Unstable Molecule

Now there are two OH groups on the same carbon atom. Owing to hydrogen bonding and their proximity to each other, these form a molecule of water which breaks away from the rest of the molecule leaving:

$$\begin{array}{c} H \\ | \\ H-C=O \end{array}$$

Methanal   +   Water
(Formaldehyde)

This compound is the first member of the

aldehyde (*al*cohol–*dehyd*rate) series. Its name is *methanal* or formaldehyde. The functional group of the aldehyde series is:

$$-\overset{\displaystyle }{\underset{\displaystyle H}{C}}=O$$

and it is written as $-CHO$, not as $-COH$, to avoid confusing this functional group with that of the alcohols.

The next stage of oxidation would produce the acid:

$$H-\overset{\displaystyle H}{\underset{\displaystyle }{C}}=O \xrightarrow{O} H-\overset{\displaystyle OH}{\underset{\displaystyle }{C}}=O$$

Methanoic or formic acid

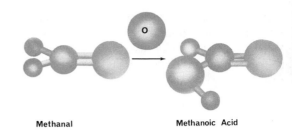

Methanal   Methanoic Acid

Aldehydes and Ketones

Formaldehyde, CH_2O, is made by the partial oxidation of methanol, achieved by passing vaporized methanol and air over a catalyst such as vanadium at a temperature of 250 - 300°C.

$$H-\overset{\displaystyle OH}{\underset{\displaystyle }{C}}=O \xrightarrow{O} HO-\overset{\displaystyle OH}{\underset{\displaystyle }{C}}=O \rightarrow O=C=O + H_2O$$

methanoic   carbonic   carbon
acid   acid   dioxide

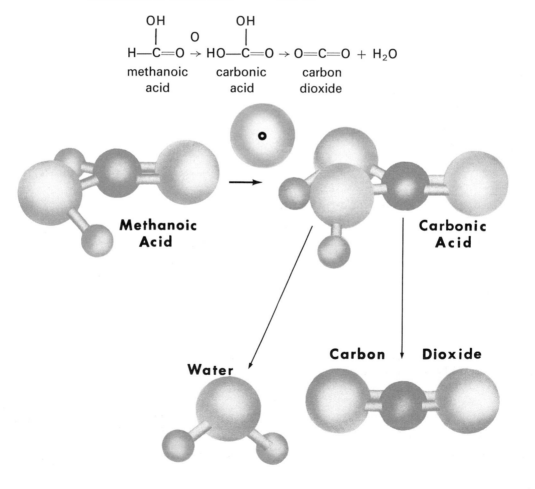

Methanoic Acid

Carbonic Acid

Water

Carbon   Dioxide

H
|
H—C=O

Other catalysts used are copper or silver gauze. Another method uses copper gauze at 300°C and vaporized methanol only.

Formaldehyde is a colorless gas. Without OH there is no hydrogen bonding in the molecule, so that the boiling point of formaldehyde is relatively low. Formaldehyde is very soluble in water and its solution is called *formalin*. It is used as a disinfectant, an embalming fluid, a preservative for specimens, and as an ingredient of Bakelite. Another of its products is phenolic resins. These substances have a variety of uses such as adhesives in the manufacture of weatherproof plywood.

Bakelite is made by heating formaldehyde and phenol together. Water is eliminated in the process, and polymerization of the residues produces the Bakelite. Because it is a nonconductor of electricity and a tough plastic, it is used extensively to make parts for many electrical instruments.

Phenol is related to benzene in the same way as methanol is related to methane. Its structural formula is:

—OH

Ketones are compounds having the general formula:

R
\
C=O
/
R

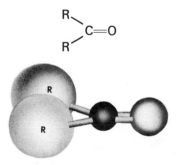

They resemble aldehydes except that the hydro-

gen of the aldehyde group is replaced by an alkyl group.

The simplest ketone is acetone:

CH₃
\
C=O
/
CH₃

Acetone

This compound is formed in small amounts when wood is destructively distilled. It is made by special fermenting bacteria from isopropyl alcohol, obtained from petroleum. It is a colorless, fragrant, inflammable liquid which is an excellent solvent for acetylene, oil, resins, explosives, lacquers, nail polish, and other organic compounds.

38:3 Organic Acids

The most common functional group of organic acids is the carboxyl group:

O
||
—C—O—H

This group has a double bond consisting of four electrons between a carbon and an oxygen atom. Such double bonds have the effect of withdrawing electrons from adjacent atoms. In this way, the bond between the hydrogen and the oxygen of the OH group is weakened, and ionization results. This causes the compound to be an acid. Nevertheless, the effect is rather limited; hence organic acids are weak electrolytes.

Note that the acid hydrogen is attached to an oxygen atom, not to a carbon atom. The C—H

TABLE 38.2	
Some Organic Acids	
Name	Formula
Methanoic acid (formic acid)	HCOOH
Ethanoic acid (acetic acid)	CH_3COOH
Palmitic acid	$CH_3(CH_2)_{14}COOH$
Stearic acid	$CH_3(CH_2)_{16}COOH$
Oleic acid	$CH_3(CH_2)_7CH = CH(CH_2)_7COOH$

bond is too non-polar for it to form hydronium ions in solution readily.

Three examples of organic acids are lactic acid of sour milk, tartaric acid in many fruits, and citric acid in lemons.

Acetic Acid

Dilute solutions of ethanol, if allowed to remain exposed to air, slowly turn sour. Examination of the material shows that the sour taste results from acetic acid. It is known that spores of *bacillus aceti* are present in the air. When they grow in a solution containing ethanol they produce an enzyme which causes the oxidation of the ethanol to acetic acid:

$$C_2H_5OH + O_2 \rightarrow CH_3COOH + H_2O$$
$$\text{ethanol} \qquad \text{acetic acid}$$

This reaction explains why wine and cider may turn sour. Our grandparents used to make their own vinegar by inoculating solutions of sugar with bacillus aceti which they called "mother

of vinegar". A bottle of the bacillus used to be a common pantry article.

About 50 per cent of the commercial acetic acid used to day is made from fermentation of sugar solutions. The rest is made synthetically as a by-product of the petroleum industry.

Pure acetic acid is a liquid that solidifies at 16.7°C to form ice-like crystals; hence its name, *glacial acetic acid*. The acid has an odor like vinegar, which is not surprising since vinegar is a five per cent acetic acid solution. Glacial acetic acid boils at 118°C. Its high boiling point is due to hydrogen bonding. It mixes with water, alcohol, and ether in all proportions and is a weak acid.

Acetic acid is used widely in foods, and it is used to make many synthetic products such as artificial silk, dyes, drugs, and white lead, a common ingredient of paints.

Esters

If the hydrogen of a carboxyl radical is replaced

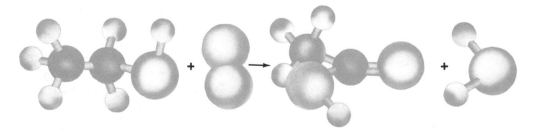

by an alkyl radical, the resultant material is called an *ester*. Esters are made most easily by allowing an organic acid to react with an alcohol. This reaction is analogous to neutralization. But an ester is not a salt; it is a covalent compound and does not form ions. To make the reaction go to completion, it is necessary to remove the water that forms by means of concentrated sulfuric acid. Otherwise the ester has a tendency to react with the water, and an equilibrium is established. The formation of esters is called *esterification*. A typical example of esterification would be:

Esterification
$$H_2SO_4$$
$$CH_3COOH + C_2H_5OH \rightleftharpoons CH_3COOC_2H_5 + H_2O$$
acetic acid   ethanol   ethyl acetate
Hydrolysis

The reaction of the ester with water is called *hydrolysis*.

Ethyl acetate has a very fragrant odor. This is characteristic of many esters. For example, isoamyl acetate, $CH_3COOC_5H_{11}$, smells like pears; methyl butyrate, $C_3H_7COOCH_3$, like pineapples; isoamyl isovalerate, $C_4H_9COOC_5H_{11}$, like apples; and octyl acetate, $CH_3COOC_8H_{17}$, like oranges. Thus, many fragrant odors found in nature are due to esters.

38:4   Fats and Oils

Animal and vegetable fats and oils are mixtures of esters. They are made of glyceryl radicals attached to complex acid radicals like palmitic, stearic, and oleic.

These fats hydrolyze slightly in hot water. The glycerol formed gives a sweet taste to cooked fats on roast meats.

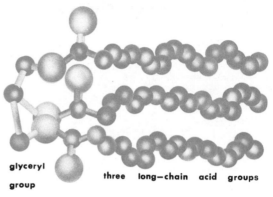

glyceryl group   three long-chain acid groups

A molecule of natural fat: an ester of glycerol, an alcohol, and 3 long-chain acids

Soap

Animal and vegetable fats react chemically with bases to form soap and glycerol. A *soap* is a metallic salt of a fatty acid. A good example of a reaction forming soap is the following:

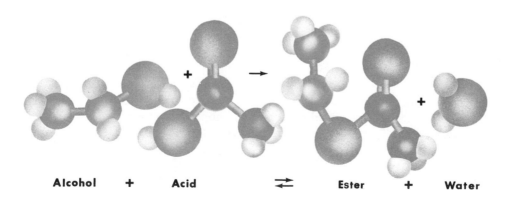

Alcohol   +   Acid $\rightleftharpoons$ Ester   +   Water

TABLE 38.3

Some Common Fats and Oils

Name	Formula	Occurrence	m.p.
Stearin (glyceryl stearate)	$C_3H_5(OOC(CH_2)_{16}CH_3)_3$	Lard and beef tallow	71°C
Palmitin (glyceryl palmitate)	$C_3H_5(OOC(CH_2)_{14}CH_3)_3$	Lard and beef tallow	60°C
Olein (glyceryl oleate)	$C_3H_5(OOC(CH_2)_7CH = CH(CH_2)_7CH_3)_3$	Olive Oil	17°C

$$C_3H_5(C_{17}H_{35}COO)_3 + 3NaOH \rightarrow$$

stearin, a fat

$$3C_{17}H_{35}COONa + C_3H_5(OH)_3$$

sodium stearate,   glycerol

a soap

This type of reaction is called *saponification*.

Crude soap has been known for centuries and was likely first discovered when fats were accidentally spilled on hot ashes. Potassium carbonate found in ashes would saponify the fat. Modern factories make soap by heating fats from animals, plants, and even fish, with sodium carbonate.

The essential steps in making soap are the following.

1. *Saponification:* A ten per cent solution of sodium carbonate is boiled with fat by passing steam into the mixture. The saponification reaction occurs according to the above equation.

2. *Salting Out:* Soap is not soluble in salt solution; therefore brine is added to the mixture, and curds of soap collect below in a water layer. The water layer is drawn off and the glycerine is recovered from it by steam distillation.

3. *Soap Treatment:* The curds of soap are then treated with steam and water to remove the impurities. The melted soap is run into containers where coloring matter, perfume, medicants, and sometimes a filler such as talc are added. Rosin is often added to soap because it increases its lathering power. Some soaps contain water softening agents so that they can be used in untreated hard water. Floating soap has air whipped into it before it solidifies. Most soaps contain about 30 per cent water. The soap is finally cooled and cut or pressed into bars.

SPECIAL KINDS OF SOAP

If sodium carbonate is used as the base in soap making, the resultant soap is hard. Potassium carbonate forms soft soap, which is used in liquid soap, shampoo, and shaving cream. Stearic acid or glycerol are usually present in shaving cream to make a stable lather.

If bases other than potassium, sodium, or ammonium are used in making soap, the product is insoluble. Many such "soaps" are very valuable for purposes other than cleaning. Zinc stearate is used to prevent chafing of the skin on babies and adults. Calcium, aluminum, and lithium soaps are useful in lubricating greases. Aluminum soaps are used to thicken oil, in making paint, and in waterproofing fabrics. Soap is also used as an emulsifying agent in the synthesis of certain plastics and rubber.

Naphtha laundry soap contains naphtha or other grease solvents. These solvents are volatile and, hence, ineffective in hot water. Soap powders usually contain soap, washing soda, borax, or trisodium phosphate. Detergents, which will be discussed in the next chapter, have largely supplanted soap powders.

HOW SOAP CLEANS

The most outstanding characteristic of soap is that its long molecule is non-polar at one end and polar at the other.

The non-polar
alkyl chain
$C_{17}H_{35}$

The polar
sodium
carboxylate end

$$\overset{O}{\underset{\|}{C}}-O^-Na^+$$

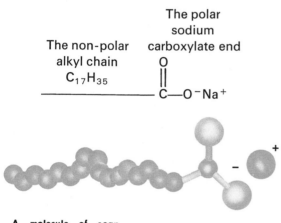

A molecule of soap
(Hydrogen atoms are omitted)

When soap is added to an insoluble mixture of oil or grease and water, the non-polar end goes to the oil portion while the polar end remains in the water. This means that the soap molecule must place itself at the boundary between the oil and the water. It weakens the boundary of separation and permits the oil droplets to disperse in the water. This is called *emulsification*. The resulting *emulsion* is water soluble and may be flushed away with a stream of water.

Soap solutions also have a very low surface tension, which allows such solutions to wet a surface more easily than water. The combination of low surface tension and emulsifying power accounts for the cleaning power that soap has.

Hard water usually contains Ca^{2+}, Mg^{2+}, or Fe^{3+} ions. These ions precipitate soap in the form of curds, thus destroying its cleaning power. A typical reaction would be:

$2C_{17}H_{35}COONa + Ca^{2+} \rightarrow$
sodium stearate
   (soluble)

$$(C_{17}H_{35}COO)_2Ca\downarrow + 2Na^+$$
calcium stearate
(insoluble)

When these ions are present, the soap cannot do its cleaning job. It is possible, however, to eliminate these ions from hard water by some water softening process such as is discussed in chapter 44.

38:5 Ethers

Ethers are compounds with this general formula, R—O—R.

In water, the oxygen atom is joined to two hydrogen atoms; in alcohol, it is joined to one hydrogen and one carbon atom; in ether, it is joined to two carbon atoms:

Water   H—O—H
Alcohol R—O—H
Ether   R—O—R

In this example R represents the alkyl group symbol.

With the elimination of OH, there is almost no possibility of hydrogen bonding, and therefore ether is far more volatile than either alcohol or water. It does not dissolve in water. On the other hand, molecules of organic compounds find it easy to separate the weakly attracted molecules of ether. Many organic substances dissolve in ether that cannot dissolve in water.

Diethyl ether's main use is to extract organic products from plants or other materials. Ether is still used to some extent as an anaesthetic. Its boiling point of 35°C makes ether easy to remove from its extracts.

Because ether is so very volatile and its heavy vapors are highly inflammable, great care must be exercised in its use.

Ethers are usually made by the dehydration of alcohols. For example, the most common ether, diethyl ether, is made by heating ethanol gently with sulfuric acid:

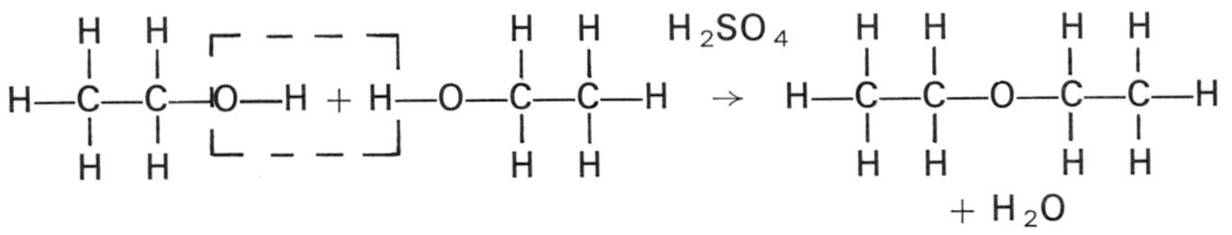

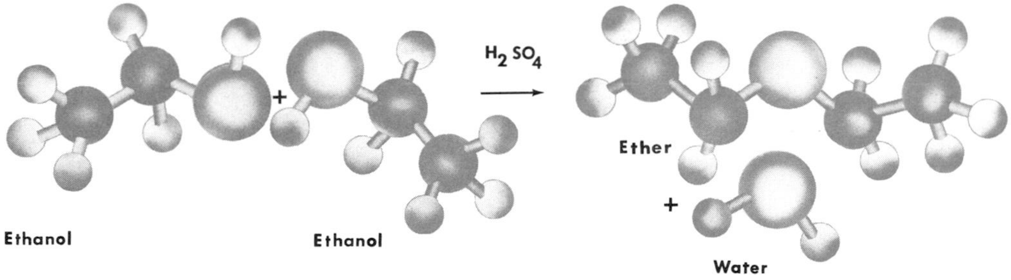

Ethanol   Ethanol

Ether

Water

QUESTIONS

1. What is an *alcohol?*

2. Why is the OH group called a functional group?

3. Write a note on the naming of alcohols.

4. (a) Write the structural formula of methanol.
   (b) How is methanol made?
   (c) List the properties of methanol.
   (d) What are the principal uses of this alcohol?
   (e) Write the equation for the burning of methanol.

5. What is *fermentation?*

6. Write the structural formula of ethanol.

7. Outline the production of ethanol from starch, giving the names of the principal enzymes involved.

8. How may "absolute alcohol" be produced?

9. Write the equation for the production of ethanol from ethene.

10. (a) List the properties of ethanol.
    (b) Write the equation for the burning of ethanol.
    (c) Give the main uses of ethanol.

11. (a) Write the structural formula for glycerol.
    (b) What is the source of this material?
    (c) List the main properties of this alcohol.

12. What are the uses of glycerol?

13. (a) What functional group is found in all organic acids?
    (b) Write its structural formula.

14. Why are organic acids weak electrolytes?

15. Give the names and formulas of three organic acids.

16. Butane's formula is C_4H_{10}. What should be the formula for butanoic acid?

17. Explain clearly why wine or cider may turn sour on standing.

18. Write the equation for the formation of acetic acid from ethanol.

19. What are the sources of acetic acid?

20. What is glacial acetic acid?

21. List the properties and uses of acetic acid.

22. What is an *ester?*

23. Why are esters not electrolytes?

24. (a) Write an equation to illustrate esterification.
    (b) Why is sulfuric acid necessary for this reaction?

25. Name three esters, write their formulas, and give one fact about each.

26. Explain fully why baked fats have a sweet taste.

27. What is a *soap?*

28. Write an equation to illustrate saponification.

29. How was soap likely discovered?

30. Describe the steps in commercial soap making.

31. Give some uses of soap other than for cleaning.

32. What are the characteristics of a good soap?

33. Explain clearly how soap cleans.

34. What ions are usually present in hard water?

35. Give an equation to show how these ions react with soap.

36. What different compounds could be formed by the stepwise oxidation of methane? Illustrate your answer with equations.

37. (a) Describe the commercial production of methanal (formaldehyde).
    (b) What are the properties of methanal?
    (c) List the uses of this material.

38. (a) What is Bakelite?
    (b) What are some of its uses?

39. What are *ketones?*

40. (a) Write the structural formula of acetone.
    (b) What are the sources of acetone?
    (c) List the properties and uses of this material.
    (d) Why is acetone a good solvent of organic materials?

41. Alcohol contains 52.12 per cent carbon, 13.13 per cent hydrogen and 34.74 per cent oxygen; the molecular mass is 46. Find its true formula.

42. Glucose ferments as follows:
    $$C_6H_{12}O_6 \rightarrow 2C_2H_5OH + 2CO_2$$
    How many liters of carbon dioxide could be obtained from 12 g of glucose, if the gas is measured at 19°C and 770 mm pressure?

43. If 500 ml of 0.4 M $MgSO_4$ solution are evaporated to dryness, how many grams of dry magnesium sulfate are obtained?

44. Methanol burns as follows:
    $$2CH_3OH + 3O_2 \rightarrow 2CO_2 + 4H_2O$$
    What weight of water is formed by burning 50 g of methanol?

39 Carbohydrates and Proteins

39:1 Carbohydrates

This class of compounds is made up of molecules containing carbon, hydrogen, and oxygen. The hydrogen and oxygen atoms are usually present in the ratio of two to one, as they are in water. Sugars, starches, and celluloses are the most common carbohydrates.

The different properties possessed by sugars and starches are due to the size of the molecules of these substances. Glucose, the unit that builds many carbohydrate and sugar molecules, is an example of a *monosaccharide*. Sucrose (table sugar) is a disaccharide consisting of a molecule of glucose linked to one of fructose. Starch, which is a long chain or polymer, each unit of which is a glucose molecule, is a *polysaccharide*.

Glucose, a Monosaccharide

Pure glucose, sometimes called dextrose, is a white, crystalline material with the molecular formula $C_6H_{12}O_6$. Each molecule contains five hydroxyl groups and one aldehyde group. For simplicity it is represented by G-OH.

The blood normally contains about 70 to 90 mg of glucose per 100 ml. Glucose is oxidized in the body to form carbon dioxide and water, as energy is released for keeping the body warm and allowing it to work.

Commercially, glucose is made by the decomposition of starch by a process called hydrolysis. The action is catalyzed by dilute hydrochloric acid:

$$(C_6H_{10}O_5)_n + nH_2O \rightarrow nC_6H_{12}O_6$$
$$\text{starch} \qquad\qquad\qquad \text{glucose}$$

Glucose is not as sweet as cane sugar, but it is nevertheless used in candy, jams, jellies, ice cream, soft drinks, and table syrups. The glucose used in foods is often made from corn. It is quite impure, and contains other carbohydrates, such as maltose and dextrin. The latter material is a gummy substance consisting of partially hydrolyzed starch molecules. Glucose has been made from wood by heating the wood with steam and sulfuric acid.

A mild reducing agent because of its aldehyde group, glucose reduces blue copper (II) sulfate, in either Fehling's or Benedict's solution, to brick-red, insoluble copper (I) oxide. It is therefore called a reducing sugar.

Fructose is another monosaccharide and is an isomer of glucose. Its formula is therefore $C_6H_{12}O_6$ as well, and may be represented by F—OH. Fructose is a non-reducing sugar because it does not contain an aldehyde group.

Sucrose, a Disaccharide

A disaccharide consists of two monosaccharide units joined together. This is done by the removal of a molecule of water between glucose and fructose:

$$G{-}O| H + HO |{-}F \rightarrow G{-}O{-}F + H_2O$$

When sugar is eaten and digested, its molecule is split by the re-introduction of the molecule of water. This is an example of hydrolysis. All digestive processes are hydrolyses and are catalyzed by enzymes.

Sucrose is obtained from sugar cane and sugar beet. It is also present in maple sugar.

In the process for making pure sucrose from

either sugar cane or sugar beets, the canes or beets are first shredded and then crushed between rollers to extract the juice. Calcium hydroxide is added to the juice to neutralize acids and to precipitate some of the impurities as insoluble calcium compounds. The resultant solution is then filtered through boneblack and diatomaceous earth*, and a clear, colorless syrup is produced. Then the syrup is evaporated until only sugar crystals and molasses remain. These materials are placed in a centrifuge and rotated at high speed. This *centrifugation* separates the molasses and the white sugar crystals. Finally, the crystals are washed with a small amount of water, dried, sifted, and packaged.

Most molasses produced is used in making ethanol, but it is also a valuable food for both humans and cattle. It consists of a mixture of both reducing and non-reducing sugars.

If sucrose is heated to about 210°C, it changes to a yellowish substance called caramel, which is used to color and flavor foods and to cure meat. Sucrose changes to glucose and fructose during digestion or if it is heated with a small amount of hydrochloric acid:

$$C_{12}H_{22}O_{11} + H_2O \rightarrow C_6H_{12}O_6 + C_6H_{12}O_6$$
sucrose   glucose   fructose

This reaction is called the "inversion" of sucrose, and the mixture of glucose and fructose is called invert sugar.

Maltose, $C_{12}H_{22}O_{11}$, is also a disaccharide because its molecule consists of two glucose units chemically united. This sugar is important because it is one of the intermediate materials formed in the digestion of starch, and in the production of ethanol from starch.

Starches, Polysaccharides

Starch is the stored carbohydrate in many plants, and it forms a high percentage of the composition of cereals, potatoes, corn, and rice.

The granules of starch from various sources differ in both size and appearance.

The chemical structure of all starches is similar but not identical. It has been determined that starch molecules consist of glucose units, chemically united. The molecular mass of starch molecules varies from 10,000 to 1,000,000. The glucose units may be arranged in chains as much as 30 glucose units long. Branched chains account for the presence of as many as 6,000 glucose units in a given starch molecule. The formula of starch is usually written as $(C_6H_{10}O_5)n$.

Starch is tasteless and odorless. In hot water the starch granules break up and thus some starch dissolves, but most starches do not dissolve in cold water. When mixed with iodine, starch turns bluish-black in color. This is frequently used to test for starch.

Heating to about 200°C causes the molecules of starch to break down into fragments with smaller molecular mass. The mixture of fragments is called *dextrin*. Dextrins are used in infant foods and malted milk because they are more easily digested than starch. Because it is sticky when wet, dextrin is used as mucilage on stamps and stationery. Dextrins give toast and bread-crust a slightly sweetish taste.

Because it gives a good finish to fabrics, starch is often used in laundering. It also holds down small surface fibres and helps prevent the fabric from holding dust and dirt. In ironing starched articles, dextrins are formed which give the articles a stiff and shiny appearance.

Starch is called a *polysaccharide* because it is built up in plants from many glucose molecules. Each glucose molecule is attached to the chain by removal of a molecule of water. The molecule of starch may therefore be represented by

—G—O—G—O—G—O—G—O—

where G—O— is the remainder of a glucose molecule and stands for $C_6H_{10}O_5$.

*Diatomaceous earth is a porous earth built up of the silicon skeletons of diatomes, microscopic animals that inhabit natural water wherever food is available.

During digestion, the bonds in starch are broken by hydrolysis. Parts of water molecules are re-introduced into the severed fragments of the starch molecules which eventually are completely broken down into glucose. It is then released from the digestive tract to enter the blood stream.

$$G-O-G-O-G-O-G \rightarrow_n (G-O-H)$$
$$H-O-H \quad H-O-H$$

Cellulose

This material is the main constituent of cotton, wood, linen, straw, and many other substances. It is the structural material of plant life and like starch, consists of chains of glucose units, though the units are combined differently and the cellulose chains are not branched. The molecular mass of cellulose is from 500,000 to 3,000,000, depending on chain lengths. As a result, there are many classes of cellulose. The formula of cellulose is often written as $(C_6H_{10}O_5)_n$.

Cotton is about 95 per cent cellulose with impurities of fats and wax. When these impurities are removed, the product is called *absorbent cotton*. Linen is also a cellulose material but it has a higher percentage of impurities than cotton. The cellulose of wood is essential to the paper-making industry.

Cellulose is insoluble in water and most organic solvents. The straight chains of cellulose allow close packing of the molecules so that fibres may result. As there are no enzymes in man's digestive system that can break the type of bonds found in cellulose, cellulose is indigestible. Many organisms do have the required enzymes, however, so that cellulose may be used by them as a food.

Cellulose reacts with nitric acid to form cellulose nitrates. Extensive nitration of the molecules produces an explosive called guncotton; less nitration forms pyroxylin. Cloth coated with pyroxylin becomes extremely hard, durable, and waterproof. The cover of this book has been treated with pyroxylin to make it strong and water-resistant.

Cellophane is made by treating cellulose with carbon disulfide and sodium hydroxide. This results in the formation of a soluble material known as *sodium xanthate*. If the sodium xanthate is run into water containing sulfuric acid, the reaction is reversed. The re-formed cellulose is called *cellophane*. Most rayon is made by this same process. However, some rayon fibres are made by dissolving cellulose acetate in acetone and forcing the solution through fine openings. A current of warm air evaporates the acetone, forming a thin fibre of cellulose acetate. These fibres are then twisted into thread. Motion picture film is also made of cellulose acetate.

Paper

The making of paper, one of Canada's chief industries, requires separating the cellulose of the wood from the other constitutents, called lignin. This is done by grinding the wood into small chips, and cooking these at high pressure and temperature with chemicals which attack and dissolve the lignin. The cellulose fibres are removed, washed, and bleached, and form a product called *pulp*. This is suspended in water, and other ingredients such as size, fillers, and a little glue are added. The suspension is agitated and deposited on a rapidly moving screen. As the water drains away, the remaining mat of paper is pressed and dried by passing it through hot rollers.

39:2 Proteins

The chief constituent of animal cells is *protein*. Proteins contain carbon, hydrogen, oxygen, nitrogen, and in some cases sulfur and phosphorus. Proteins are essential components of the jelly-like material that is found in the cells of all living matter. Some examples of protein are egg albumen, casein of milk, glutenin of wheat, gelatin in bones, insulin of the pancreas, and haemoglobin of the blood.

Muscle and skin are mostly protein, and even silk and wool are members of this class of compounds. Molecular mass of proteins range from about 5,000 to about 6,700,000. These compounds are very sensitive to heat. For example, the protein in raw egg is soluble, but heating makes it insoluble. Drying proteins also makes them insoluble.

When concentrated nitric acid comes in contact with a protein, a yellow compound called *xanthoproteic acid* is formed. This reaction is frequently used as a test for proteins. The skin and finger nails turn yellow on contact with nitric acid as a result of this reaction.

Plants are able to synthesize proteins from inorganic materials such as soluble nitrates, carbon dioxide, and water. Animals cannot do this; so they must depend upon plants or other animals for their protein supply.

In the digestive process, certain enzymes, such as *pepsin* in the stomach and *trypsin* in the small intestine, break proteins down into simpler substances called *amino acids*. The amino

acids combine to form proteins by the elimination of a molecule of water between every pair of combining amino acids. (Fig. 39.1.) These amino acids pass through the intestine walls into the blood stream, and after being transported to the cells, they are synthesized into the proteins of the body.

39:3   Amino Acids

The amino acids, out of which nature builds all the proteins of the plant and animal world, are remarkably consistent in their structure.

Imagine that in the methane molecule,

$$H-\overset{\displaystyle H}{\underset{\displaystyle H}{C}}-H$$

one hydrogen atom is replaced by the acidic carboxyl group $-\overset{\displaystyle O}{C}-O-H$, and another by the basic amino group $-NH_2$. The other two bonds may remain as they are, attached to hydrogen atoms, or they may be attached to alkyl groups. The resulting molecule would be:

$$H-\overset{}{\underset{\displaystyle H}{N}}-\overset{\displaystyle R}{\underset{\displaystyle H}{C}}-\overset{\displaystyle O}{C}-O-H$$

Fig. 39.1   *Bonds between the amino acids of a protein molecule*

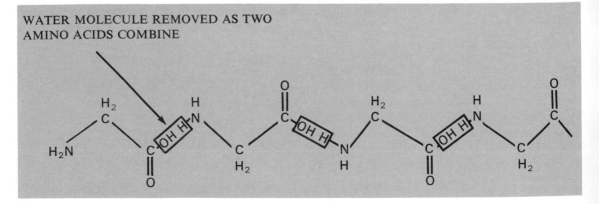

WATER MOLECULE REMOVED AS TWO
AMINO ACIDS COMBINE

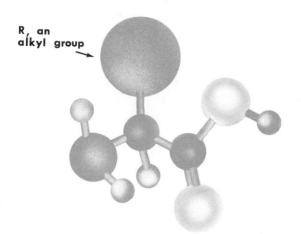

R, an
alkyl group ➚

General   Structure   of   an

Amino   Acid

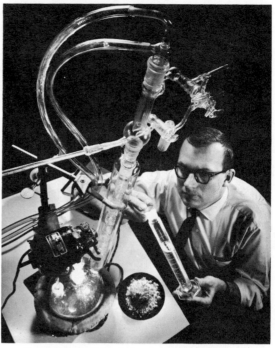

Courtesy General Electric Research and Development Center

Fig. 39.2 *A scientist separates synthetic amino acids for study of their individual properties*

By changing this R group, nature produces about 25 different amino acids, which become the building blocks of thousands of proteins for an unlimited number of species of living organisms.

Protein is digested by the reintroduction of the molecule of water.

QUESTIONS

1. What are *carbohydrates?*

2. (a) Why is glucose called a monosaccharide?
    (b) How is glucose involved in vital processes?
    (c) How is this sugar made commercially?
    (d) What are some uses of glucose?
    (e) Why is glucose known as a reducing sugar?

3. What is *fructose?*

4. What is a *disaccharide?*

5. What change occurs when sucrose is digested?

6. Outline the production of cane sugar.

7. What is meant by the inversion of sugar?

8. What is *maltose?*

9. How is the starch molecule related to sugar?

10. Write a note on the occurrence of starch.

11. What is the test for starch?

12. List the main properties of starch.

13. What is *dextrin* and how may it be formed?

14. Why does ironing starched materials give them a shiny appearance?

15. Describe the digestion of starch.

16. How is the cellulose molecule related to sugar?

17. Why are there many different classes of cellulose?

18. What is *absorbent cotton?*

19. Describe the structure of wood.

20. Why is man unable to digest cellulose while some organisms can do so?

21. What are some chemical materials produced from cellulose?

22. How is cellophane made?

23. (a) Write a note on the importance and occurrence of proteins.
    (b) What are some properties of proteins?
    (c) What is the test for protein?

24. From what raw materials do plants synthesize protein?

25. Explain the digestion of proteins.

26. Describe the structure of amino acids.

40 Synthetic Products

40:1 Synthetic Detergents

A large number of synthetic detergents are now on the market, and many of them are better cleaning agents than soap. Detergents consist of molecules designed along similar lines to soap molecules; that is, they have a long non-polar carbon chain of 12 to 18 atoms and a highly polar group at one end of the molecule. The advantage that these materials have over ordinary soap is that they do not form insoluble precipitates with calcium, magnesium, and iron (III) ions and, as a result, they work equally well in hard or soft water. At the present time in Canada the consumption of detergents far exceeds the consumption of soap.

One of the most commonly used synthetic detergents is sodium lauryl sulfate:

$$CH_3(CH_2)_{10}CH_2OSO_2O^-Na^+$$

The long non-polar hydrocarbon chain is grease soluble and the polar sodium sulfate end is water soluble. In the manufacture of this material, fats, treated with sodium hydroxide, are decomposed to long-chain acids and glycerol. The acids are then changed to alcohols by reacting them with hydrogen over a nickel catalyst. One of these alcohols is lauryl alcohol, $CH_3(CH_2)_{10}CH_2OH$, which is treated with sulfuric acid to form lauryl hydrogen sulfate:

$$CH_3(CH_2)_{10}CH_2OH + HOSO_2OH \rightarrow$$

lauryl alcohol   sulfuric acid

$$CH_3(CH_2)_{10}CH_2OSO_2OH + HOH$$

lauryl hydrogen sulfate

Next, the lauryl hydrogen sulfate is treated with sodium hydroxide to form the sodium lauryl sulfate:

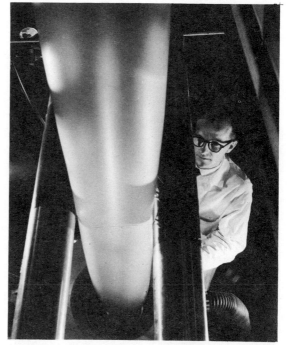

Courtesy Mobil Oil Corporation

Fig. 40.1 *A tube of polythene film being extruded*

$$CH_3(CH_2)_{10}CH_2OSO_2OH + Na^+OH^- \rightarrow$$
$$CH_3(CH_2)_{10}CH_2OSO_2O^-Na^+ + H_2O$$
sodium lauryl sulfate

Several detergents with this same general structure may be formed from other long-chain molecules.

Another important group of detergents is made by the alkylation of benzene with propene or another similar unsaturated compound. The product is then treated with sulfuric acid and sodium hydroxide to form the following material:

R—⟨ ⟩—SO$_2$O$^-$Na$^+$

sodium alkylaryl sulfonate*

Where R is an alkyl group.

40:2   Polythene

Ethene gas is capable of combining with itself by polymerization to form chains 2000 or more carbon atoms in length. The product of this combination is called polythene. Originally, this could be done only at high temperatures and pressures; but quite recently catalysts have been discovered which make this reaction possible at room temperature and atmospheric pressure.

Although like paraffin wax in appearance and touch, polythene is strong and melts at

Fig. 40.2   *The synthetic rubber plant of Polymer Corporation, Sarnia, Ontario*
The storage spheres hold the alkene hydrocarbons to be polymerized into rubber. The towers serve to concentrate butene by distillation.

Courtesy Polymer Corporation Limited

*The sulfonate group is the residue left when one OH is removed from H$_2$SO$_4$.

110-120 °C. This material can be moulded, extruded, and spun into filaments in the same manner as many other plastics. When in the form of sheets or pipes, it can be welded into complex articles by hot-air (150°C) torches. It makes an excellent packaging material, is very inert chemically, and does not dissolve in solvents at room temperature. These properties make it a good material for handling chemicals. It is even used in drains and pipes. Polythene is an excellent insulator and as a result, it is used to insulate underwater telephone cables.

40:3   Rubber

Columbus was the first European to become acquainted with rubber, finding that the natives of the West Indies had toys fashioned of it with which they liked to play. Eventually, some of this natural rubber, which was obtained from the sap of certain tropical trees, was taken to England. Priestley found it was of great value in rubbing away pencil marks from paper, and so he gave it its name.

Natural rubber is a polymeric material of a high molecular mass. The unit of this polymer is called *isoprene*, which has the formula

$$CH_2{=}\underset{\displaystyle CH_3}{C}{-}CH{=}CH_2$$

There may be as many as 2000 isoprene units in one rubber molecule combined as follows:

$$x \; \underset{H}{\overset{H}{C}} = \underset{H}{\overset{CH_3}{C}} - \underset{H}{\overset{H}{C}} = \underset{H}{\overset{H}{C}} \rightarrow \left[\underset{H}{\overset{H}{C}} - \underset{H}{\overset{CH_3}{C}} = \underset{H}{\overset{H}{C}} - \underset{H}{\overset{H}{C}} \right]_x$$

The elastic character of rubber is due to the shape of the molecule. It is in the form of a fairly compact coil. The application of a stretching force causes this coil to lengthen, and the removal of the force allows the coil to return to its original size.

Crude rubber is found suspended in the latex obtained from various trees and plants. For example, the sap of milkweed and dandelion contains crude rubber, but not in sufficient amount to be used commercially. Raw rubber may be precipitated from the latex by acidifying it or by passing an electric current through it.

Crude rubber precipitated from latex is sticky when warm and brittle when cold. It is very easily severed, and it deteriorates because of slow oxidation. About 120 years ago Charles

Fig. 40.3 *Production of neoprene rubber film*

Courtesy Du Pont of Canada Limited

Goodyear discovered *vulcanization*. In this process, rubber is heated with sulfur. It is known that the sulfur atoms form cross links between the isoprene chains, which make the rubber more stable, so that it is not soft in hot weather or brittle in cold weather.

Various fillers and pigments are added to rubber during vulcanization to increase the wearing qualities of rubber or to give it a desired color. Some of these materials are carbon black, zinc oxide, antimony sulfide, and white lead.

At the present time there are many rubbers which have many important uses; for example, in the making of automobile tires.

Butyl rubber is a copolymer of butadiene and isobutene, obtained from petroleum cracking processes.

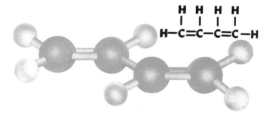

Butadiene

Isobutene

This rubber is resistant to chemical action and impervious to gases. It is widely used for inner tubes.

Neoprene was the first American synthetic rubber. It is a polymer of *chloroprene*, which

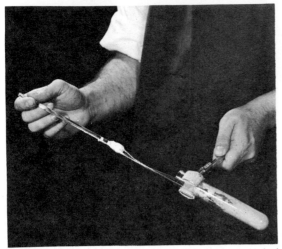

Courtesy Du Pont of Canada Limited

Fig. 40.4   *A man-made fiber is born*
It was an experiment such as this that suggested the fiber-forming possibilities of nylon. Here, in its most elementary form, is the birth of a man-made fiber in a research chemist's test tube.

is made from acetylene and hydrogen chloride. Chloroprene differs from isoprene only in that chlorine replaces the methyl radical. The unit is thus:

$$\left[\begin{array}{c} Cl \\ | \\ CH_2-C=CH-CH_2 \end{array} \right]$$

Because of its strength, its chemical inertness, and its insolubility in petroleum products, neo-prene is used in gaskets, boots and shoes, gasoline hose, and floor tiles.

Courtesy General Electric Research and Development Center

Fig. 40.5   *A scientist studies a new family of plastic materials. These are produced as films only a few millionths of an inch thick and have possible uses ranging from superior electrical insulation to corrosion-resistant protective coatings for metals.*

QUESTIONS

1. What advantages have detergents over soaps?

2. How are soaps and detergents similar?

3. (a) List the properties of polythene.
   (b) Discuss the uses of polythene.
   (c) Why is polythene an efficient insulator?

4. What is *isoprene?*

5. Account for the elasticity of rubber.

6. What different properties does rubber have after vulcanization?

7. Write a note on synthetic rubber.

CHAPTER
41 The Metals

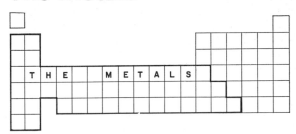

41:1 The Importance of Metals

About 80 of the elements are metals, some of which are among the most useful substances of our industrial civilization. In the ancient world, gold, silver, and copper were well-known and used as ornaments. Such metals were found free in nature because of their chemical inertness. Iron, lead, tin, and mercury were also known and used, but to a smaller degree. In the modern world, iron, copper, aluminum, nickel, chromium, zinc, and lead are among the most important metals in general use; but many others are also used for special purposes.

41:2 What is Metallurgy?

Metallurgy is the science that deals with the recovery of metals from their ores and the alloying of these metals for their many uses.

Metals are usually found in combined form. Often they are themselves part of mixtures, called ores, which have various percentages of metal content, sometimes as low as 2 per cent of the weight of the ore. Metal is recovered from ores by both physical and chemical means. The physical methods are used to separate the ore from the rock, where this is possible, while the chemical change is one of converting the metallic ion to the atom by donating electrons to it. Chemically, this is an example of reduction.

41:3 Properties of Metals

Metals generally may be recognized by their appearance. They have a lustre or shiny reflection which non-metals like sulfur or salts like sodium chloride do not possess.

Metals are good conductors of electricity and heat, whereas non-metals are poor conductors and, therefore, make good insulators. Copper and aluminum are two of the best conductors of electricity, which is why they are used extensively in electrical wiring. The ability of an element to conduct current is a good test of its metallic nature. The few intermediate elements that conduct electricity only to a small extent are called *metalloids*.

Metals show other properties as well. They can be hammered into different shapes or drawn into long thin wires; hence they are said to be *malleable* and *ductile*. Some are so hard that they can be made into tools such as hammers and chisels. Yet there are metals which are soft; for example, the alkali metals can be cut with a knife. Metals, as a rule, have a high melting point, with the result that furnaces, engines, and radiators are made of metals. However, there are metals that have a low melting point. Mercury, for instance, is a liquid at room temperature.

Many metals have a high density; gold has a density of 22 g/cm³. On the other hand, some metals have a low density. Garden furniture is made of aluminum because it is light, among other reasons. There are other metals that are lighter than aluminum, and most of the alkali metals are even lighter than water.

Chemically, all metallic atoms have one important property in common. They all become positive ions, or cations, in binary salts.

41:4   The Metal Bond

The electronic structure of the atoms of metals is a satisfactory explanation for the large variation in properties shown by metals and for their formation of cations in binary salts, such as Na^+Cl^-.

The atoms of metals have relatively few outer electrons and, what is most important, these electrons are not confined to any particular atom. Instead, they move freely from atom to atom, and their motion has been compared to that of the molecules of a gas.

Since the outer electrons are not attached to atoms, the atoms should be considered to be positively charged ions. *Electronically, therefore, a metal is defined as a substance consisting of positively charged ions, fixed in the crystal lattice, with negatively charged electrons moving freely through the crystal.* The free electrons act as a cohesive force, without which the positive ions alone would repel each other. For this reason the mobile electrons are said to be the *metallic bond*.

41:5   Explanation of Metallic Properties

Lustre

Metallic lustre is explained by the free electronic motion. The electrons readily absorb light falling upon them, whereupon they assume a higher energy level. They do not remain at this higher level but fall back to a lower one immediately. This is accompanied by the emission of the light absorbed. Thus, most of the light is readily re-emitted, causing the metallic lustre.

Conductivity

Metals are good conductors of electricity because of the freedom of the electrons to move through the crystal lattice.

When a negative electrode comes in contact with the metal at one end and a positive electrode contacts the other end, electrons move through the lattice almost without resistance. If electrons enter one end of a conducting metal, an equivalent number of electrons are drained off at the other end. Heat conductance results because thermal energy is transferred from one mobile electron to another when the metal is heated. Electrical resistance increases with a rise of temperature because the metallic ions vibrate more vigorously about their lattice points in the crystal, and the movement of the electrons is thus interfered with.

Malleability and Ductility

Since the metallic bond is cohesive but not rigid, when a metal is hammered into a different shape, it is merely necessary for the atoms to assume different positions. No fixed covalent bonds, such as those of carbon or sulfur, are present to prevent the atoms from assuming different positions. For this reason metals are malleable and ductile, whereas non-metals are brittle.

Melting Points of Metals

All metals except mercury are solids at room temperature. In general, the larger the atomic radius of a metal, the lower its melting point. This is so because as the atoms become more massive, the force of cohesion by the electrons becomes less effective, with the result that less heat is needed to break metal bonds.

Many metals have an unfilled d subshell of electrons. While this subshell is not filled, its electrons are free to move about from atom to atom, acting as a cohesive force or metal bond. When the d subshell is filled to its capacity of 10 electrons, the electrons tend to remain close to individual atoms. When this occurs the metal must depend on the limited number of outer *s* electrons, only two per atom, for bonding. The metal bond is thus weakened and the melting point of the metal is lowered. This explains why mercury is a liquid. In mercury atoms, the 5*d* subshell is full to its capacity of 10 electrons. Zinc and cadmium, whose atomic subshells of 3*d* and 4*d* are filled with 10 electrons, are also easily melted.

On the other hand, iron, cobalt, and nickel have incomplete *d* subshells. Their electrons are free to move about and thus act as part of the metal bond. Indeed, there are enough electrons even to form some covalent bonds. Consequently, these metals have very high melting points.

Hardness and Density

Hardness and high density may be explained in the same way. The alkali metals have only one outer electron per atom. The "electron pool" is low and the metal bond is weak: hence the metals are soft and of low density. Generally, the more outer electrons a metal has per atom, the harder the metal will be and the greater will be its density.

Activity, or Electromotive Series

Metals are the elements whose atoms most readily lose their electrons; therefore they have low electronegativity. This easy loss of electrons determines the chemical properties of the metals and causes them to become positive ions.

The ability of a substance to lose electrons is relative; there must be another substance able to receive the electrons being lost by contact with the first. The two systems can be connected together electrically to form a continuous flow of electrons from one electrode to another, during which movement the electrons possess energy and can do work. Such work is measured as *voltage*. The voltage of a battery represents the number of units of work done (in *joules*) for the passage of each unit of electric charge (in *coulombs*).

By measuring the voltage in cells that use different metals as one electrode and hydrogen as the other, an accurate measure of the chemical activities of the metals can be obtained.

Hydrogen gas has the property of adsorbing on platinum metal. A glass tube with a side arm is sealed to a strip of platinum and hydrogen gas is admitted under one atmosphere of pressure. This apparatus immersed in a 1 molar

Fig. 41.1 *Experimental determination of the electrochemical series*

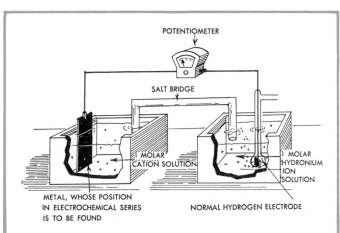

solution of strong acid is called the Standard Hydrogen Electrode, with which other electrodes are coupled.

The metals that give the highest voltage when used as electrodes are placed at the top of the series called the *Electromotive Activity Series* (see Chapter 13). This series is useful in remembering the chemical properties of the metals: the higher a metal is in the series, the more easily it becomes an ion; any metal will displace one below it from its solution; any metal above hydrogen will displace hydrogen from acids.

41:6   Alloys

A substance consisting of two or more metallic elements which are soluble in each other when

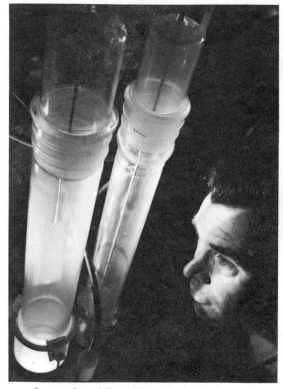

Courtesy General Electric Research and Development Center

Fig. 41.2 *A new method for creating space-age alloys on the surface of a wide variety of materials called "metalliding", uses a bath of molten fluoride salts as a "solvent" to diffuse metals and metalloids (such as silicon) into the surface of other metals and alloys. This photo shows a scientist removing an iron sample from a metalliding cell. Chromium has been diffused into the surface of the sample to produce a stainless steel "alloy surface".*

TABLE 41.1

Some Alloys

Alloys	Components
Simple brasses	Cu, Zn
Tin brasses	Cu, Zn, Sn
Nickel silver (German silver)	Cu, Ni, Zn
Ordinary bronze	Cu, Sn
Phosphor bronze	Cu, Sn, P
Zinc bronze	Cu, Sn, Zn, (P)
Aluminum bronze	Cu, Al
	Cu, Al, (Fe, Mg, Mn, Ni, Pb, Si)

Alloys of Gold, Silver, and Copper

Name	Percentage Composition
18-carat gold	Gold, 75%; copper, silver
14-carat gold	Gold, 58%; copper, silver
Gold coin	Gold, 90%; copper, 10%
Silver coin	Silver, 90%; copper, 10%
Nickel coin	Copper, 75%; nickel, 25%
Sterling silver	Silver, 92.5%; copper, 7.5%

molten, or which do not separate into distinct layers when solid, is called an *alloy*. One of the first man-made alloys was bronze, consisting of tin and copper. This alloy was so important to man's progress that a pre-historic period is known as the Bronze Age.

Some alloys may be considered as *solid solutions*. Brass, consisting of copper and zinc, has some zinc atoms in place of copper atoms in the cubic structure characteristic of pure copper.

Sterling silver, consisting of silver and copper is another example. Steel is also a solid solution in that the carbon atoms are located in some of the spaces between the iron atoms. Copper and gold may be mixed in all proportions.

Some alloys consist of crystals of the elements, heterogeneously mixed. Bismuth-cadmium alloys are examples of these. Other alloys are like compounds in that the composition is definite. Sodium-zinc or magnesium-copper mixtures are examples.

The properties of an alloy may be radically different from those of the elements that compose it. Alloys are usually harder and more resistant to breakage and wear than the pure elements. Pure iron is so soft that it is useless for many purposes; if, however, it is alloyed with silicon, carbon, manganese, chromium, and vanadium, the resultant chrome-vanadium steel is so hard that it may be used for making gears or tools which will withstand enormous pressures without breakage. Pure aluminium is very soft, but when mixed with copper, manganese, and magnesium it forms "duralumin", a light but tough product used for aircraft and other structural purposes. Our modern industrialized civilization would be impossible without alloys.

QUESTIONS

1. Write a paragraph on the importance of metals.

2. How do metals usually occur in nature?

3. Define these terms: *metallurgy, metalloids, malleable, ductile*.

4. What common properties do metals have?

5. Define the term *metal*, and describe the metallic bond.

6. Explain the following terms by means of the electronic theory in reference to metals: *lustre, conductivity, malleability, ductility*.

7. Why is electrical conductance of a metal less at a higher temperature?

8. Why do zinc, cadmium, and mercury have low melting points?

9. Why do some metals, such as iron, cobalt, and nickel, have a relatively high melting point?

10. Why are some metals, such as sodium, soft while others are hard?

11. (a) What is voltage?
    (b) Relate voltage released by metals used in an electrical cell to the activity of a metal.

12. Define the term *electromotive series* and give an example to show the meaning of this term.

13. Define *alloy*. Give two examples of alloys.

14. Write a paragraph on the structure of alloys.

15. Why are alloys so useful? Give specific examples of their usefulness.

16. If 0.8 g of a certain metal liberates 442 ml of hydrogen from hydrochloric acid, when the hydrogen is measured over water at 22°C and 762 mm pressure, find the weight of the metal that will liberate a mole of gas at STP.

17. What weight of silver chloride could be obtained from 100 ml of a 0.2 M solution of silver nitrate by precipitation with excess sodium chloride?

18. Find the molarity of sulfuric acid when 45 ml of 0.5 M potassium hydroxide neutralizes 25 ml of sulfuric acid.

19. Describe how to prepare 50 ml of (a) 0.2 M sodium chloride from the dry salt (b) 0.2 M magnesium sulfate from the hydrated crystals, $MgSO_4 \cdot 7H_2O$.

20. Give the weight of the metal ion in each of the following solutions: (a) 250 ml of 0.2 M $AgNO_3$ (b) 50 ml of 0.5 M $CdCl_2$ (c) 125 ml of 1.5 M $CuSO_4$.

21. Write the oxidation number of each atom in the following:
(a) $Zn(IO_3)_2$ (b) $(NH_4)_3PO_4$ (c) $NaAlO_2$

CHAPTER
42 Iron and Steel

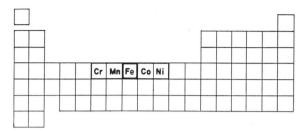

42:1 Importance

Steel, an alloy of iron, is the backbone of modern industry. It is of this metal that tools, machines, and engines are built. Steel is used to make cars, ships, and trains and to reinforce highways and buildings.

The annual world production of iron and steel is well over 300 million tons. A century ago, a year's production of iron would not meet our present requirements for a single day. Iron is the most important of all the metals; it is the cheapest, and it ranks next to aluminum in abundance.

42:2 Iron

Occurrence

The earth's crust is approximately 5 per cent iron, and there is a possibility that the center of the earth may be composed of iron. While the small amounts of free iron found in the earth are probably from meteorites, deposits of iron ore are widely distributed. The most important ore is hematite, impure Fe_2O_3, a dark red material found in the famous Mesabi Range in Minnesota, in Wisconsin and Michigan, and in the important deposits of Quebec and Labrador. The latter deposits, already known to be very rich, have not yet been fully explored.

Mines in the Mesabi Range yield a volume of iron every two weeks equal to the Great Pyramid of Egypt. Other leading producers are the U.S.S.R., France, Germany, and Sweden.

The brown color of many soils and rocks is caused by hydrated iron oxide, $2Fe_2O_3 \cdot 3H_2O$, which, in concentrated form, is called limonite. Magnetite, Fe_3O_4, the richest of the ores, is so-called because it is magnetic. Pyrite, FeS_2, is found in sufficiently large amounts to be an important source of sulfur. After roasting, the remaining oxide is used as a source of iron. Iron is also present in the haemoglobin of the blood.

Metallurgy of Iron

Iron is extracted from its ore in the blast furnace. The raw materials are iron ore, coke, limestone, and heated air. The product is an impure form of iron called crude, or pig, iron.

The blast furnace is a vertical steel tower about 150 feet high, 30 feet in diameter at its widest part, and lined with firebrick. The furnace tapers towards the top and bottom. At the top is a trap called the *bell*, through which carefully weighed portions of ore, scrap iron, limestone, and coke are fed. The proportions of these materials are determined by analysis of the ore being used. Valves in the bell permit the charge to be added with a minimum loss of heat. Immediately below the widest part of the furnace is a constriction called the *bosh* which supports the charge. The bottom is called

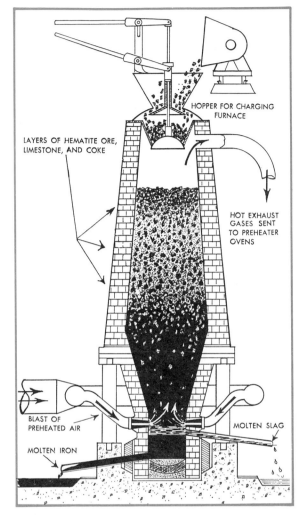

and the reducing agent to free the iron from its ore. As the coke burns, a temperature of about 1800°C is produced:

$$C + O_2 \rightarrow CO_2\uparrow + heat$$

The carbon dioxide is quickly reduced to carbon monoxide which also serves as reducing agent:

$$CO_2 + C \rightarrow 2CO\uparrow$$
$$Fe_2O_3 + 3CO \rightarrow 3CO_2\uparrow + 2Fe$$

The iron melts at about 1150°–1250°C and collects in the crucible at the bottom of the furnace as a liquid.

Impurities in the ore are called *gangue*. Usually the impurity is mostly silica, SiO_2, which has a very high melting point and cannot be removed easily as a solid. To melt it, the limestone combines with the silica to form a molten material called *slag*. First the limestone breaks down to calcium oxide:

$$CaCO_3 \rightarrow CaO + CO_2\uparrow$$

Then the calcium oxide combines with the silica to form calcium silicate:

$$CaO + SiO_2 \rightarrow CaSiO_3$$

This slag is a liquid at the temperature of the molten iron.

The material that removes impurities is called a *flux*. Limestone is used as a flux in the above reaction. Other ores contain limestone as an impurity or gangue. Where these ores are used, the flux is sand, SiO_2. The reactions are similar.

Liquid slag is less dense than liquid iron; therefore it collects on top of the molten iron in the crucible and is drawn off as necessary through a special opening. It is usually run into water where it solidifies and breaks up into small pieces. Slag may be discarded, but sometimes it is used in the manufacture of cement.

The molten iron is drawn off about once every four hours. It flows along a gutter lined with firebrick to special molds where it collects and solidifies into blocks called ingots. If ingots are not desired, the iron is run directly into huge ladles capable of holding 100 tons of metal.

HOPPER FOR CHARGING FURNACE

LAYERS OF HEMATITE ORE, LIMESTONE, AND COKE

HOT EXHAUST GASES SENT TO PREHEATER OVENS

BLAST OF PREHEATED AIR

MOLTEN SLAG

MOLTEN IRON

Fig. 42.1 *The blast furnace*
A blast furnace is operated continuously, by charging at the top and removing the molten iron at the bottom.

the *crucible*. Preheated air is blown into the furnace near the bottom to support the combustion of the fuel in the charge. The gas issuing from the top of the furnace contains considerable carbon monoxide. This gas is not wasted but instead is burned in special stoves to heat the air to 600°C. Then it is blown back into the furnace through pipes called *tuyeres*.

The coke is both the fuel to heat the furnace

These ladles, on trolley-cars, take the iron directly to the steel-making plant.

Blast furnaces vary in size. A typical furnace may produce from 600 to 1500 tons of pig iron daily. One ton of pig iron requires two tons of iron ore, one ton of coke, 1000 pounds of limestone and three and one-half tons of air. Several million gallons of water, used to cool the furnace walls, are fed into the furnace daily.

A blast furnace works twenty-four hours a day seven days a week. It would not be economical to shut it down and start it up casually, both because it is difficult to empty the furnace completely and also because of the time needed to bring the furnace to operating temperature.

Cast Iron

Pig iron contains from 2 to 5 per cent carbon and small amounts of sulfur, manganese, and phosphorus. These impurities render it too brittle for most structural use. About 5 per cent of the pig iron produced is used for articles that are subject to little strain, such as radiators, stoves, and furnaces.

Pig iron may be adapted for making other articles, however, by controlling its rate of cooling and by alloying it with scrap iron or with other metals. Pig iron so treated is called cast iron, of which there are several varieties.

If pig iron cools slowly, some of the carbon separates out as flakes of graphite, leaving a product known as *grey cast iron*. It has low tensile strength, is brittle, and cannot be welded or forged. If, on the other hand, pig iron cools rapidly, most of the carbon remains chemically combined with the iron in the form of iron carbide, Fe_3C, or *cementite*. Iron produced in this way is very hard but still brittle; it is called *white cast iron*. Pig iron is often melted with scrap iron for casting. If this type of cast iron is allowed to cool very slowly, more of the carbon separates and the product is called *malleable cast iron*. This is not as strong as steel, but it is cheap and can be machined

and welded. It is used for many machine parts not subjected to severe shock.

Wrought Iron

This form of iron is used for bolts, chains, pipes, and ornamental work exclusively. Wrought iron is useful because it is easily welded, and it is very malleable and ductile. The melting point is high, around 1500°C. These properties are due to the removal of most of the impurities found in pig iron. Only about 0.1 per cent carbon remains. Among the impurities that do remain is a small amount of slag, which gives wrought iron a granular appearance. In 1925, James Aston discovered that purified iron obtainable from the Bessemer converter (see Fig. 42.3) could be poured into slag to produce wrought iron. This process is used to make most wrought iron today. At one time, wrought iron had to be refined by hand-stirring, which gave it its name.

Wrought iron production forms about one per cent of the total output of iron.

42:3 Steel

Steel is an alloy of iron containing between 0.2 and 1.5 per cent carbon. With less than 0.2 per cent carbon, steel is too soft; with more than 1.5 per cent carbon, it is too brittle. The alloy is free of sulfur and phosphorus but usually contains alloying metals. It is produced by burning off the impurities found in pig iron and then adding back certain amounts of various ingredients to produce steel with desired characteristics. The products are called *alloy steels*. Several hundred alloy steels are available for special purposes. Most steel made contains equal parts of scrap iron and pig iron.

Alloy Steels

The most important metals used in alloy steels are manganese, nickel, chromium, tungsten, vanadium, molybdenum, copper, cobalt, and silicon. Silicon steel is hard and acid resistant.

TABLE 42.1

Some Alloy Steels

Percentage Composition	Properties	Uses
3.5 Ni	Hard, strong	Armor plate
3.5 Ni, 1.5 Cr	Hard, tough, strong	Armor plate, projectiles, objects enduring shock or strain
17-18 W, 3.5-4.5 Cr, Co, Mo	Hard and temper holding	High-speed lathe tools
12 Mn	Strong, tough	Burglarproof safes
13 Cr, 0.35 C	Rust-resisting	Stainless cutlery

Copper and chromium increase corrosion resistance. Molybdenum and vanadium produce tough steel for axles, springs, gears, rails, and tools. Tungsten, molybdenum, and chromium produce high-speed cutting tool steel. Nickel and chromium make tough armor plate. Cobalt steel is used in jet engines where high temperatures are encountered. Manganese steel is very tough and is used in heavy machines, for instance, in rock crushers, in brake shoes, and for safes. Stainless steel contains large amounts of chromium and nickel, with smaller amounts of manganese, silicon, and carbon. Most of the pig iron produced is used to make steel.

There are three methods for making steel.

The most important is the open hearth method, which furnishes 90 per cent of all the steel used. The other methods are the Bessemer Converter and the electric furnace, which supply about 5 per cent each.

Open Hearth Method

An open hearth furnace is as large as an eight-room house. The base of the furnace is about 50 feet long and 15 feet wide. Fuel gases and air enter at one side, are ignited, and the flame is directed downward by the low roof made of firebrick. This heats the charge in the manner that a gigantic blowtorch would. The exhaust gases heat the grill-work of brick at the outlet

Fig. 42.2 *Open hearth furnace for steelmaking*

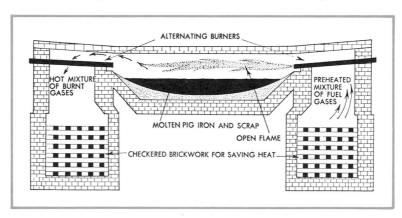

on the opposite side. Periodically the fuel-air mixture is reversed from side to side, which preheats the entering mixture. This is called a *regenerative process*. The furnace heating from the top in the manner of the open hearth is called *reverberatory*.

The floor of the furnace is lined with a flux. Silica is used to form slag when calcium and magnesium are the main impurities in the pig iron. Dolomite is used as the lining when the main impurities are phosphorus and sulfur. Silica is the oxide of a non-metal, silicon, and is thus an acid anhydride. Removal of impurities with silica is termed an *acid process*. Dolomite, calcium, and magnesium carbonate furnish metallic oxides CaO and MgO. These are basic anhydrides. Their use is called a *basic process*.

The carbon is oxidized by the air, and the other impurities form slag. Deoxidizers are added near the end of the process, and just before the charge is poured into molds, the required amounts of other metals are added for alloying.

The open hearth process takes about 12 hours to complete. This allows time to analyze samples of the steel while it is still in the molten state, and changes in its composition could be made if such were deemed necessary. Thus the open hearth makes possible complete control over the quality of the steel.

Bessemer Process

The Bessemer converter uses a blast of air to oxidize the iron impurities. As these burn off, they provide the heat for keeping the iron in the molten state until the alloying metals can be mixed with it. In this process, the molten iron is placed in an egg-shaped vessel known as a *converter*. It is about 10 feet in diameter and 20 feet deep. It is lined to a thickness of 1½ feet with heat-resistant brick made largely of sand or of dolomite, as in the open hearth.

A blast of air is forced through the molten

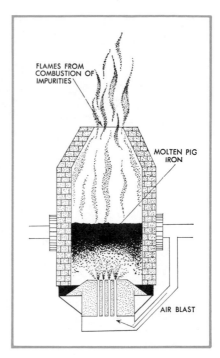

Fig. 42.3   *The Bessemer converter*

mass. The rapidly oxidized impurities impart characteristic colors to the flame shooting from the mouth of the converter, showering sparks and flame in a pyrotechnical display not to be matched by any other industrial process. The flame color changes from brown to blue and then to whitish blue in about 20 minutes. The experienced operator determines when the oxidation of impurities is complete by the flame color.

He then quickly turns the flame off lest the purified iron begin to oxidize. At this point, when the iron is molten, alloy metals are added to form the desired composition. After allowing time for the alloying metals to melt and diffuse, the converter is finally tilted, and the charge is poured into molds to cool. The resulting ingots are rolled or forged into various shapes as desired.

Bessemer steel cannot be made as uniformly as open hearth steel, and it must be quickly

Courtesy Bethlehem Steel Corporation

Fig. 42.4   *The "blowing" of a Bessemer converter*

poured into molds to avoid oxidation. This kind of steel is satisfactory for sheets, pipes, and bars. Most other steel objects are made of open hearth steel.

Recently, successful tests have been carried out using pure oxygen instead of air in the Bessemer Converter.

Electric Furnace Process

High-quality steel for special purposes is made in crucibles heated by an electric arc between carbon elements. This furnace is similar to the open hearth furnace except for the source of heat. Conditions may be controlled more carefully than in the open hearth. Even the atmosphere above the metal may be made to consist of some inert gas. Steel for tools, surgical instruments, springs, knives, and razor blades is usually made in this way.

Electric furnace steel is sometimes heated by

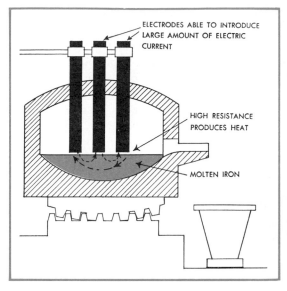

ELECTRODES ABLE TO INTRODUCE
LARGE AMOUNT OF ELECTRIC
CURRENT

HIGH RESISTANCE
PRODUCES HEAT

MOLTEN IRON

Fig. 42.5   *The electric furnace*

induction. In this method high frequency current is passed into a coil of wire surrounding the steel and the alternating magnetic field causes the atoms of iron to oscillate. The heating effect soon melts the steel. This type of heating is completely clean.

Fig. 42.6   *An electric furnace discharges its heat of steel into a transfer ladle*

Courtesy Bethlehem Steel Corporation

42:4   Tempering of Steel

The carbon content of steel is regulated according to the use to which the steel is to be put. If from 0.5 to 1.5 per cent carbon is present, the steel can be tempered.

Carbon in melted iron combines with the iron to form cementite. The molten iron can dissolve about 1.8 per cent of its weight of cementite in the molten state. As iron cools, its crystalline structure changes at about 700°C to a form that cannot dissolve cementite. Consequently, if steel is cooled slowly, the cementite precipitates at 700°C and the steel is relatively soft. On the other hand, if steel is cooled quickly, as would result if it were plunged into cold water, the cementite cannot precipitate, and the product is very hard but brittle. This effect is produced if red-hot steel is quickly cooled. The process is called *quenching*.

Quenched steel can be made much tougher, without losing much of its hardness, if it is reheated after quenching to temperatures up to 650°C. This allows some crystallization of the cementite. The process is known as *tempering*.

The peculiar behavior of cementite makes it possible to prepare slowly cooled steel which can be machined into tools of various kinds. These may then be quenched and tempered and made hard enough to cut untempered steel. Steel is a most versatile material!

42:5   Case Hardening

Wrought iron or soft steel objects may have a thin layer of high-carbon steel formed on the surface, if the objects are heated in contact with coke or charcoal. This process, called *case hardening*, gives a hard skin over a tough interior, an ideal condition for many gears and machine parts. This method was used by skilled artisans in making swords and armor centuries ago.

42:6   Properties of Iron

Physical Properties

Pure iron is prepared in small quantities as a laboratory reagent. It is silvery-white, ductile, malleable, and quite soft. It is easily magnetized and melts at 1535°C. It is a good conductor of heat and electricity. Its density is 7.87 g/cm^3.

Chemical Properties

Iron rusts if exposed to oxygen and water at the same time:

$$\overset{H_2O}{2Fe + 3O_2 \rightarrow Fe_2O_3}$$

Rust appears to be a hydrated iron (III) oxide with the formula $2Fe_2O_3 \cdot 3H_2O$. The chief cause of corrosion is the removal of electrons from the iron by the oxygen of the air. Iron may be protected from corrosion by coating it with zinc. The zinc loses electrons more easily than the iron, so that the iron remains uncorroded. A coat of paint also prevents the oxygen of the air from corroding iron by covering its surface.

Iron forms two series of compounds: iron (II), where the charge of iron is 2+ and iron (III), where the charge is 3+. Iron (II) salts can be easily converted to iron (III) salts by atmospheric oxygen. Iron (II) salts are usually white if anhydrous and greenish when hydrated; iron (III) salts are usually orange when hydrated.

Chemically, iron is quite active. It combines rapidly with oxygen at high temperature, giving off a shower of sparks of white-hot oxide:

$$3Fe + 2O_2 \rightarrow Fe_3O_4 \text{ (or } Fe_2O_3 \cdot FeO)$$

It combines with chlorine and sulfur:

$$2Fe + 3Cl_2 \rightarrow 2FeCl_3$$
$$Fe + S \rightarrow FeS$$

It displaces hydrogen from acids and, at high temperatures, from steam:

$$Fe + 2HCl \rightarrow FeCl_2 + H_2 \uparrow$$
$$3Fe + 4H_2O \rightarrow Fe_3O_4 + 4H_2 \uparrow$$

Blue-black writing ink consists of iron (II) sulfate and tannic acid, which unite to form iron (II) tannate. Iron (II) tannate is colorless, but oxidizes in air to form black iron (III) tannate.

Iron (III) hydroxide, $Fe(OH)_3$, is precipitated as a reddish gel from solutions of iron (III) salts by the addition of a soluble hydroxide. It also forms slowly in solutions of certain salts, such as iron (III) chloride, by hydrolysis. If iron (III) hydroxide is heated highly, it forms the red powder iron (III) oxide, Fe_2O_3. This is known as jewellers' rouge and Venetian red. It is often used as a pigment in paint.

A complex compound of iron called potassium hexacyanoferrate, $K_3Fe(CN)_6$, forms a blue compound, iron (II) hexacyanoferrate, $Fe_3(Fe(CN)_6)_2$, with iron (II) salts:

$$3FeCl_2 + 2K_3Fe(CN)_6 \rightarrow$$
$$Fe_3(Fe(CN)_6)_2 + 6KCl$$

This is used in making blueprints.

$[Fe(CN)_6]^{3-}$ is a complex ion. A complex ion consists of a metal ion attached to molecules or other ions by means of *co-ordinate covalent bonds*. Such a bond forms when one atom or ion accepts a pair of electrons from another. In complex ions, the metal ion accepts the pair of electrons while neutral molecules or ions donate the electron pair. When molecules or ions act as electron-pair donors, they are called *ligands*, this is illustrated by the cyanide ion CN^- above.

Fe^{3+} has the ability to bond to six ligands. This is possible with the six vacant orbitals which the Fe^{3+} ion presents because of its structure. To provide this the iron (III) ion hybridizes one s, three p, and two d orbitals into six d^2sp^3 orbitals. Such orbitals arrange themselves so that they point to the corners of an octahedron, that is an 8-sided figure formed when two pyramids are placed base-to-base.

Fig. 42.7   *The hexacyanoferrate complex ion has the shape of a regular octahedron*

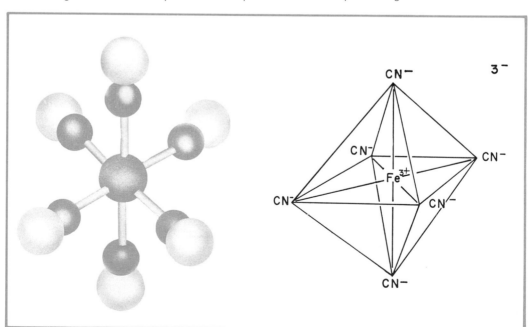

QUESTIONS

1. Write a paragraph on the importance of iron and steel.

2. How does iron occur in nature?

3. (a) Describe, with the aid of a labelled diagram, the operation of the blast furnace.
   (b) Write the equations for the main reactions in the blast furnace.

4. Define the terms: *gangue*, *flux*, *slag*.

5. (a) What is the usual daily production of a blast furnace?
   (b) List the amounts of raw materials necessary for this production.

6. List the main properties of pig iron.

7. Explain why ordinary cast iron is very brittle.

8. How is malleable cast iron made, and what are its properties?

9. (a) How is wrought iron made?
   (b) List its main properties.

10. (a) What are the most usual components in steel?
    (b) Give three examples of steel and tell for what they are used.

11. Describe the open hearth process.

12. Explain the difference between the basic and acidic open hearth processes.

13. Explain the Bessemer process.

14. Describe the electric furnace process.

15. Give some idea of the differences in the steels produced by the open hearth, Bessemer, and electric furnace processes.

16. (a) What are the chemical properties of pure iron?
    (b) What oxidation numbers does iron show when combined chemically?

17. (a) What is case-hardening?
    (b) What are some advantages of this type of tempering?

18. Find the volume of 2 molar sulfuric acid required to react completely with 30 g of iron to form iron (II) sulfate.

19. Find the weight of a sample of 80 per cent pure iron (II) sulfide required to yield 100 l of hydrogen sulfide measured at 19°C and 763 mm pressure.

20. Calculate the volume of hydrogen obtained by the action of 10.0 g of iron on hydrochloric acid, if the gas is measured over water at 33°C and 779 mm pressure.

21. Sand and hydrofluoric acid react as follows:
$$SiO_2 + 2H_2F_2 \rightarrow SiF_4 \uparrow + 2H_2O$$
If sand is 70 per cent SiO_2, how much sand would produce 10 l of silicon fluoride?

22. Calculate the weight of iron sulfide required to yield 3 moles of hydrogen sulfide.

43 Aluminum

43:1 Occurrence

Aluminum is the third most abundant element, being exceeded only by silicon and oxygen. This metal is too active to occur free, but its compounds are widely distributed. The most common of these are feldspar, $KAlSi_3O_8$, mica, $KH_2Al_3(SiO_4)_3$, and clay, $H_2Al_2(SiO_4)_2 \cdot H_2O$.

Aluminum oxide occurs as corundum, ruby, sapphire, emerald, topaz, and amethyst. The difference in the color of these gems comes from the presence of small amounts of the oxides of chromium, titanium, manganese, and iron. Artificial rubies are made by the fusion of pure aluminum oxide with a small amount of chromium (III) oxide. Blue sapphires are made similarly by adding cobalt oxide. Synthetic gems of this type differ from natural stones only in that they are more perfectly formed than the natural ones.

Garnet contains aluminum, silicon, oxygen, calcium, iron, and magnesium. Turquoise is a basic copper-aluminum phosphate. The topaz is a basic aluminum fluorosilicate. Emery consists of aluminum oxide and iron oxide. Both garnet and emery are used as abrasive materials.

The commercial ore of aluminum is bauxite, $Al_2O_3 \cdot (xH_2O)$, which usually contains the oxides of silicon and iron as impurities. Bauxite is found in France (its name is derived from Baux, a region in France), British Guiana, Jamaica, Italy, Hungary, Yugoslavia, the U.S.S.R., Greece, and the United States.

43:2 History and Discovery of its Successful Metallurgy

While clay, which contains aluminum, is abundant and alum, a compound containing aluminum, has been known for centuries, the extraction of this metal itself is quite recent because of the difficulties that had to be overcome.

The problem in producing aluminum is to release an extremely active metal from its compounds. The naturally occurring compounds of this metal are very stable. Water solutions of its salts do not yield aluminum by electrolysis, because the element is more active than hydrogen. The molten salts are also found to be extremely difficult to electrolyze owing to their high melting point and chemical stability. Furthermore, to be useful, the aluminum produced must be relatively free of impurities, such as the iron and silicon usually found in its ores.

The earliest method used to obtain aluminum was to displace it from its salts by means of potassium and sodium:

$$AlCl_3 + 3K \rightarrow 3KCl + Al$$
$$AlCl_3 + 3Na \rightarrow 3NaCl + Al$$

This tied the cost of aluminum to the cost of sodium, which made it expensive, about $550 a pound (potassium is even more costly than sodium). Napoleon III had a set of tableware made of aluminum, which at that time was classed as precious metal. Improvement in the method of producing sodium brought the price of aluminum down to $8 a pound by 1886.

Woehler, a famous German chemist, pioneered the use of potassium to extract aluminum. One of Woehler's students in Germany later became a professor of chemistry at Oberlin College, Ohio, where in his lectures he referred to the fame awaiting anyone who could discover an inexpensive way of making aluminum. This captured the interest of 22-year-old Charles Martin Hall, a student at Oberlin.

Attracted by the idea, Hall performed experiments in a woodshed at the rear of his house, using very primitive equipment. He felt that the logical source of aluminum would be the oxide. This could be produced in quantity in a very pure state, but because of the very high temperature needed, melting this material was impractical. He reasoned that electrolysis of the oxide might work if it were dissolved in a suitable solvent. After trying many materials as possible solvents, eventually he prepared some molten cryolite, $3NaF \cdot AlF_3$, which can be liquefied without too much difficulty. He found that aluminum oxide dissolved in this liquid easily. To Hall's great joy, a direct current passed into this solution caused aluminum to be liberated at the cathode. This famous discovery was made on February 23, 1886.

Only three months later, the French chemist, Paul Héroult, made the identical discovery. He had no knowledge of Hall's work at the time. Essentially the same process is used today for producing aluminum, and it is commonly known as the Hall–Héroult process. Refinements of the process have brought the price of the metal down to less than 20 cents a pound.

Hall achieved world fame and lived to see his discovery become the basis of a great industry. He died in 1914.

43:3   The Hall-Héroult Process

A modern electrolytic cell for the production of aluminum uses a large carbon anode made of petroleum coke and pitch. The cell, about 10 feet by 16 feet in area, is made of steel and is lined with powdered coke mixed with tar, which is baked until hard. This serves as the cathode.

Before entering the electrolytic cell, the bauxite must be purified. It is pulverized and then heated with sodium hydroxide to separate pure aluminum oxide from the impurities of bauxite ore. The purified aluminum oxide from the ore reacts with the sodium hydroxide to form sodium aluminate ($NaAlO_2$):

$$2NaOH + Al_2O_3 \rightarrow 2NaAlO_2 + H_2O$$

The impurities, mostly the oxides of iron and silicon, do not dissolve and can be separated by filtering. As the sodium aluminate cools, aluminum hydroxide is precipitated:

$$NaAlO_2 + 2H_2O \rightarrow NaOH + Al(OH)_3\downarrow$$

When the aluminum hydroxide is heated, crystals of aluminum oxide remain:

$$2Al(OH)_3 \rightarrow Al_2O_3 + 3H_2O$$

Now the pure aluminum oxide is placed in the electrolytic cell, along with cryolite* and calcium fluoride (called fluorspar). Application of an electric current melts the fluorides, and aluminum oxide is then added to the molten mass and is dissolved. The applied electric current decomposes the oxide and liberates the aluminum metal.

Since the temperature of this cell is about 900°C, the aluminum collects at the bottom as a liquid, where it is drawn off and cast into ingots. These ingots may be as much as 99.9 per cent pure.

Since the electronegativities of aluminum and oxygen are 1.5 and 3.5 respectively, the difference of 2.0 causes the compound to be ionic. It is supposed that the oxide ions form oxygen atoms at the carbon anode. This explains the reaction of the oxygen with the carbon of the anode.

For simplicity the reaction involved may be regarded as follows:

$$Al_2O_3 \rightarrow 2Al^{3+} + 3O^{2-}$$

Cathode: $2Al^{3+} + 6e \rightarrow 2Al$

Anode: $3O^{2-} - 6e \rightarrow 3O$

$$3O + 2C \text{ (of anode)} \rightarrow CO + CO_2$$

The anode is thus constantly being used up.

*Cryolite occurs naturally in Greenland, but so great is the demand for this substance in the extraction of aluminum that it is now manufactured synthetically.

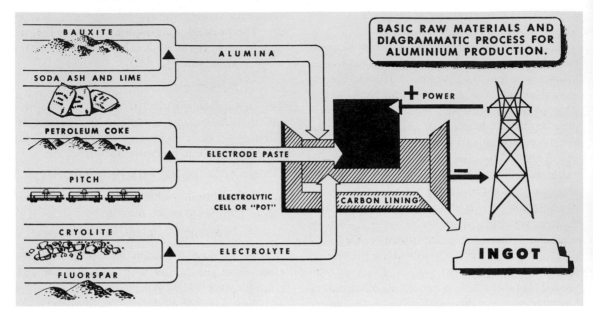

Fig. 43.1   *Flow sheet for the production of aluminum*

The voltage is adjusted so that aluminum is released, but not the sodium of the cryolite or the calcium of the fluorspar.

An electrolytic cell may use 4000 pounds of aluminum oxide and 1000 pounds of carbon anode, and it can produce 2000 pounds of high

Fig. 43.2   *Electrolysis of aluminum oxide to aluminum*

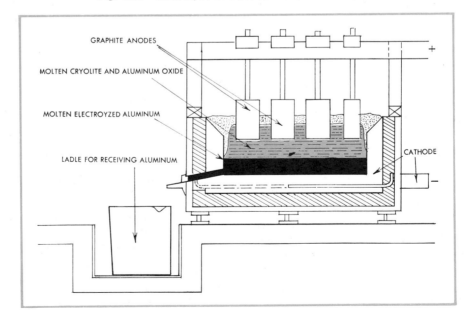

grade aluminum daily. About 10 kilowatt hours of electricity are required for each pound of metal produced.

Because of the great amount of electricity needed, the aluminum industry must be located near sources of cheap electrical energy. Since electricity made by burning coal is too expensive, hydro-electric power is the energy used. It is also essential that aluminum plants have easy access to supplies of cryolite, bauxite, and coke. Arvida, Quebec, and Kitimat, British Columbia, where there is abundant hydro-electric power, are great producers of aluminum. Bauxite from British Guiana and cryolite from Greenland can be shipped easily by water. The coke is obtained mainly from Texas. The world's production of aluminum at present is well over three million tons a year of which Quebec alone produces nearly 700,000 tons.

43:4 Electronic Structure and Properties

With three valence electrons, the metal bond in aluminum is stronger than in the metals of groups I and II of the periodic table but not as strong as in the case of the transition metals (Chapter 45). This explains the properties of aluminum.

It is silver-white metal with a density of 2.7 g/cm^3. This is greater than that of either sodium or magnesium, but only about one-third that of iron. It is quite soft, but like steel it becomes very hard when alloyed with certain metals. It is ductile and very malleable. Aluminum is an excellent conductor of heat and electricity. It melts at 660 °C and can be welded or brazed.

Aluminum unites with oxygen to liberate a large amount of heat. It does not corrode in air because a thin film of oxide, about 4×10^{-6} inches thick, forms on its surface. The great strength of the aluminum-oxide bond prevents the easy removal of this coating so that further oxidation does not take place. The strong bond of aluminum oxide is due to the small atomic radii and large electronegativity difference. At high temperatures aluminum burns with a brilliant white light:

$$4Al + 3O_2 \rightarrow 2Al_2O_3 + 800,000 \text{ cal}$$

Aluminum does not react with water or nitric acid, even though it is high in the electromotive series. This is due to the oxide coating. It reacts with both hydrochloric acid and sodium hydroxide:

$$2Al + 6HCl \rightarrow 2AlCl_3 + 3H_2\uparrow$$
$$2Al + 2NaOH + 2H_2O \rightarrow 2NaAlO_2 + 3H_2\uparrow$$
$$\text{Sodium}$$
$$\text{Aluminate}$$

Aluminum hydroxide also reacts with both acids and bases:

$$Al(OH)_3 + 3HCl \rightarrow AlCl_3 + 3H_2O$$
$$Al(OH)_3 + NaOH \rightarrow NaAlO_2 + 2H_2O$$

Elements and hydroxides that react with both acids and bases are called *amphoteric*.

Aluminum is a powerful reducing agent. It reacts with iron oxide to produce enough heat to melt the liberated iron.

$$2Al + Fe_2O_3 \rightarrow Al_2O_3 + 2Fe + 202,000 \text{ cal}$$

43:5 Uses

Aluminum may be rolled into girders, rods, or sheets to be used in cars, trucks, airplanes, bicycles, buildings, furniture, and appliances. It makes an excellent roofing and decorative metal because of its resistance to corrosion. This property also makes aluminum suitable for door and window frames in homes and buildings. In vehicles, particularly aircraft, it is a great weight saver. Sheets almost as thin as cigarette paper are used in packaging and preserving foods. Thicker sheets are used in tubes for toothpaste, cosmetics, and pharmaceutical preparations.

The metal is often used for electrical power transmission lines. Comparison of copper and aluminum cables of equal weight shows that aluminum is a much better conductor since the aluminum cable is larger in cross-section. However, if the cables are the same diameter, copper is better. The use of aluminum cable with a steel core to supply strength allows the use of fewer supporting towers, because of the lighter weight.

For cooking utensils, aluminum has many desirable features, including good heat conductivity and non-toxic properties. In view of its action with alkalis, such substances should not be stored in aluminum; nor should they be used for cleaning the metal.

Powdered aluminum is used as a pigment in some paints. It is also used as a reducing agent in the iron and steel industry to remove oxygen and thus prevent flaws in the metal.

Mixed with iron oxide, aluminum powder forms *thermit*, which is used for welding steel in locations where ordinary methods cannot be used. The thermit is placed in a fire-clay lined hopper above a mold surrounding the object to be welded. The mixture is ignited by means of a magnesium-potassium chlorate mixture. The molten iron formed at about 3000 °C runs into the mold and welds the steel. Thermit has also been used in fire bombs.

43:6   Alloys of Aluminum

Aluminum by itself is quite soft and not very strong—a one-inch test bar will support only 15,000 pounds. Modern metallurgy has produced several hundred alloys of aluminum, all with different characteristics. A one-inch test bar of some alloys will support more than 80,000 pounds. Some alloys are very resistant to corrosion, and some may be made more durable or harder by heat treatment.

The most common elements alloyed with aluminum are magnesium, manganese, silicon, copper, zinc, and nickel.

43:7   Compounds of Aluminum

Aluminum oxide or *alumina* in the form of sapphires is used as jewels in watches and scientific instruments. Fused alumina is made in an electric furnace. It is almost as hard as diamond and makes an excellent abrasive. Fused alumina is often used in objects subjected to high temperatures, such as firebricks, spark plugs, crucibles, and some types of cement. Materials used in this way are called *refractories*. Alumina, because of its inertness, is often used as a catalyst support.

Porous alumina, used for adsorption purposes, is called activated alumina. An interesting process covers aluminum objects with a resistant oxide coating. The object is made an anode in a bath of chromic acid to which is added, in some cases, certain dyes. The object becomes coated with oxide and is colored at the same time. Anodized aluminum is the name of this product.

Aluminum hydroxide is a white, jelly-like precipitate formed when a soluble aluminum salt reacts with a hydroxide. It is also produced by hydrolysis of aluminum salts. This compound is used as a *mordant*; that is, it will adhere to many fabrics that certain dyes will not affect. The dye may then attach itself to the mordant.

Aluminum chloride is sometimes used in deodorants and anti-perspirants.

If potassium sulfate is dissolved in aluminum sulfate solution, crystals of potassium aluminum sulfate are obtained upon evaporating:

$$K_2SO_4 + Al_2(SO_4)_3 + 24H_2O \rightarrow$$
$$2KAl(SO_4)_2 \cdot 12H_2O$$

This material is common alum. The *alums* are a group of double sulfate salts which form eight-sided crystals, are soluble, and have the general formula $XY(SO_4)_2 \cdot 12H_2O$. X may be K^+, Na^+, or NH_4^+, while Y may be Al^{3+}, Fe^{3+}, or Cr^{3+}.

Common alum is used in water purification, in baking powder, and in the sizing* of paper.

*The sizing of paper causes the sheet to be less porous, and, therefore, impressions made by writing and printing are sharp and clear. Without sizing, the paper would be porous like filter paper.

Municipal water filtration plants use alum to help purify the drinking water supply since it precipitates even finely suspended impurities.

Chrome alum is used in tanning leather and in certain photographic processes to harden emulsions on film.

QUESTIONS

1. What are the principal materials in which aluminum is found in nature?
2. Give the names and formulas of the ores used as the commercial source of aluminum.
3. Why is aluminum difficult to remove from its ores?
4. Why is it difficult to reduce aluminum oxide?
5. How was aluminum first produced in quantity?
6. (a) Describe, with the aid of a labelled diagram, the Hall-Héroult process for making aluminum. Write the ionic equation for the process.
   (b) Describe how bauxite is purified for use in the process.
7. Explain why Quebec and British Columbia are important producers of aluminum when neither of these provinces has deposits of bauxite or cryolite.
8. How does the electronic structure of aluminum account for its properties?
9. (a) List the physical properties of aluminum.
   (b) List the chemical properties of aluminum.
10. Define the term *amphoteric* and show how this property is applied to aluminum.
11. List the principal uses of aluminum and give a property that determines each of these uses.
12. What is thermit and for what is it used?
13. What metals are mostly alloyed with aluminum?
14. Give the uses of fused alumina.
15. How is anodized aluminum made?
16. (a) What is a *mordant*?
    (b) What properties of aluminum hydroxide make it a good mordant?
    (c) How is aluminum hydroxide used to purify water?
17. What is an *alum*?
18. Mention some uses of alums.
19. Aluminum and sodium hydroxide react as follows:
    $$2Al + 2NaOH + 2H_2O \rightarrow 2NaAlO_2 + 3H_2$$
    sodium aluminate

    How many grams of aluminum would be needed to produce 150 l of hydrogen measured at 720 mm and 40°C?
20. How many moles of sulfuric acid are needed to react with 10 g of aluminum?
21. How many grams of aluminum are required to release 12 l of hydrogen from hydrochloric acid?
22. How much aluminum could be obtained from 30 lbs of bauxite, $Al_2O_3 \cdot 2H_2O$?

44

The Light Metals and Their Compounds

Li	Be												B				
Na	Mg													Si			
K	Ca																
Rb	Sr																
Cs	Ba																
Fr	Ra																

44:1 The Alkali Metals

The elements of group I in the periodic table called the alkali metals, are lithium, sodium, potassium, rubidium, cesium, and francium. The term alkali comes from the Arabic, *al-quili*, meaning plant ashes, which are rich in both sodium and potassium carbonate. Any substance with distinctly basic properties may be called an alkali.

Occurrence

The alkali metals appear in nature only in the combined state. Lithium is quite rare, but it is found in some rocks. Sodium occurs principally as sodium chloride in the sea and salt lakes, and as a solid deposit where lakes or seas have dried up. Potassium chloride mixed with other salts is found in large deposits at Strassfurt, Germany, and Carlsbad, New Mexico. Recently, huge amounts have been discovered in Saskatchewan; so Canada may become a leading producer. Rubidium and cesium are trace elements in a number of minerals. Francium has an unstable nucleus and is radioactive. Traces of it have been prepared in nuclear reactors.

Both sodium and potassium ions are found in living tissue. They take part in many enzyme actions. In plants, the potassium ion is an important cation. Plants selectively absorb this ion from the soil. Fertilizers should, therefore, contain a large amount of soluble potassium compounds.

Properties

The properties of alkali metals agree with the electronic theory of the metal bond. The atoms have only one outer electron. This results in a weak metallic bond which becomes less effective as the atoms become larger is size and in mass. As a result, the following physical properties of the alkali metals are found:

a. They have the lowest density of all the metals. With only one mobile electron bonding two atoms, they are attracted weakly. Since there are relatively few atoms per unit volume, their density is low.

b. They are soft and may be cut with a knife. Because of their weak bonding, they cannot resist the intrusion of a cutting edge or other shearing force.

c. They have low melting and boiling points. These properties are explained by the weak bonding provided by the single electron. Little kinetic energy is needed to separate the atoms in the solid or the liquid.

Chemically, they are highly reactive. Their

Courtesy International Minerals & Chemical Corporation

Fig. 44.1   *A modern potash refinery*
In the flotation cells (foreground) potash particles rise to the surface of the brine solution. All operations are monitored from the control panel in background.

single outer electron is relatively easy to remove as shown by the low electronegativity. Another indication of the same property is the high position of the alkali metals in the Electromotive Series.

The distribution of electrons in the atomic orbitals of the alkali metals shows that the atoms of the respective elements have one outer electron in the top *s* orbital.

44:2   Lithium

The most important ore of lithium is a lithium aluminum silicate found mainly in parts of the United States, Canada, and Africa. The ore, first made porous by heating, is then treated with sulfuric acid to make soluble lithium sulfate. This is converted to the chloride by adding hydrochloric acid in excess. The chloride is fused for electroylsis in an apparatus similar to that used for producing sodium (Section 44:3). Pure lithium is released at the cathode.

Because the density of lithium is only 0.53 g/cm^3, it is the lightest of all solid elements; so it is often added to other metals such as magnesium and aluminum to make very light alloys. It is used in the refining of metals and in electroplating, welding, and brazing. Its importance is increasing rapidly. Lithium compounds are used in greases, glass catalysts, and rocket fuels.

		\multicolumn{17}{c}{TABLE 44.1}

\multicolumn{19}{c}{TABLE 44.1}

TABLE 44.1

Electron Configuration of the Elements of Group V

		\multicolumn{17}{c}{Energy Levels}

Element	Atomic Number	n = 1	2		3			4				5			6		7
		\multicolumn{17}{c}{Sublevels and Orbitals}
		1s	2s	2p	3s	3p	3d	4s	4p	4d	4f	5s	5p	5d	6s	6p	7s
Lithium	3	2	1														
Sodium	11	2	2	6	1												
Potassium	19	2	2	6	2	6		1									
Rubidium	37	2	2	6	2	6	10	2	6			1					
Cesium	55	2	2	6	2	6	10	2	6	10		2	6		1		
Francium	87	2	2	6	2	6	10	2	6	10	14	2	6	10	2	6	1

44:3 Sodium

Sodium metal may be produced by electrolysis of molten sodium salts in a Downs Cell (Fig. 44.2).

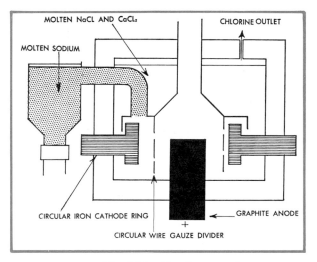

Fig. 44.2 *The Downs cell*

Sodium chloride containing impurities of calcium chloride or sodium sulfate is added to the cell. The impurities lower the melting point of the sodium chloride so that, when the current is applied, the heat, due to electrical resistance, melts the salt:

Cathode Reaction $Na^+ + 1e \rightarrow Na°$
Anode Reaction $Cl\ - 1e \rightarrow Cl°$
                    $2Cl°\ \ \ \ \rightarrow Cl_2$

The perforated partition keeps the chlorine from coming in contact with sodium. The molten sodium metal is drawn off and cast into sticks.

Properties and Uses

Freshly cut sodium is silvery, but oxidation in air quickly tarnishes it. It burns vigorously in air or oxygen:

$$2Na + O_2 \rightarrow Na_2O_2$$
$$\text{sodium peroxide}$$

In sodium peroxide the oxygen atoms are joined by a single bond, thus

$$Na—O—O—Na$$

The oxidation number of oxygen is taken as $1-$ in all peroxides instead of the usual $2-$. Sodium reacts violently with water to release hydrogen:

$$2Na + 2HOH \rightarrow 2NaOH + H_2\uparrow$$

To prevent oxidation or reaction with water, sodium must be stored in oil or in airtight, moisture-proof containers. Despite its peculiar properties, sodium has many uses. Because of its reaction with water, sodium is sometimes employed as a drying agent for organic compounds. It is such a good conductor of electricity that it is sometimes encased in pipes for this purpose; and, because of its high heat conductivity, it is used to keep valves cool in internal combustion engines. The hollow valve is filled with sodium, which conducts heat rapidly away from the valve surface, preventing damage to the valve. Highways are often lighted with sodium vapor lamps which give an intense yellow light without glare. Sodium is used to conduct heat away from thermo-nuclear reactors.

Metallic sodium is a strong electron donor or reducing agent. It combines readily with chlorine to form salt:

$$2Na + Cl_2 \rightarrow 2NaCl$$

It reacts with chlorine and sulfur in organic compounds thereby permitting the remainder of these compounds to combine. In this way special hydrocarbons, dyes, and plastics are synthesized. Sodium and lead form an alloy from which tetraethyl lead is made, a substance that improves the performance of gasoline in engines. Sodium dissolves in mercury to form an amalgam, in which form the metal is easier to handle.

44:4 Potassium

Potassium metal is produced on a much smaller scale than sodium. It is prepared by electrolysis of its fused salts. Owing to the relative scarcity of these salts, the metal is more expensive than sodium.

Potassium and sodium are so similar that for most purposes the metals and their compounds are interchangeable, except where cost is a factor.

44:5 Cesium and Rubidium

Both of these metals are released from their compounds by electrolysis.

Cesium loses electrons on exposure to light so that it is used in photoelectric cells. Color television is possible partly because cesium is most sensitive to red light, while cesium oxide is more sensitive to blue light.

44:6 Flame Spectra

When compounds of the alkali metals are placed in the non-luminous bunsen flame, they give off characteristic colors. Lithium makes the flame red; sodium, yellow; potassium, violet; rubidium and cesium, reddish-violet. These are called *flame spectra*. The yellow of sodium flame is so intense that it may mask other colors that might be present. The sodium content in glass imparts a yellow hue to a flame when glass is heated.

Flame spectra may be explained by the easy promotion of the outer electron of the atom to a higher energy level. Even the heat of a bunsen flame will accomplish this. As the electron moves back to its original position, the energy it had absorbed is now sent out as light. This gives the characteristic color in each case.

44:7 Compounds of the Alkali Metals

While the metals themselves are of limited usefulness, their compounds, on the other hand, are among the most useful substances known to chemistry. Among these are sodium chloride, sodium hydroxide, and sodium carbonate. Sodium chloride was discussed in Chapter 29.

Hydroxides

The most important hydroxides, those of sodium and potassium, are produced in the Nelson Cell (Chapter 28) and other similar cells. They are colorless, slightly waxy-looking solids that dissolve in water and alcohol, liberating much heat in the process. In dilute solution, they are completely ionized and are very strong bases.

The electronegativities of the alkali metals are so low that the bond with oxygen is ionic.

When the hydroxides are added to water, the polar water molecules easily hydrate both the metal ions and the hydroxide ions. Much heat is liberated in the process. Such interaction causes these compounds to be soluble. Indeed, so great is the affinity for water that the alkali hydroxides are hygroscopic and show little tendency to decompose on heating. This is unusual, because most hydroxides lose water to form oxides when heated.

Sodium and potassium hydroxides are called caustics because they dissolve most plant and vegetable material. They feel slippery in solution because they dissolve thin layers of skin. They even slowly dissolve glass, etching the bottles in which they are kept. Therefore, polythene bottles are being used more and more to store them. Sodium hydroxide is commonly called lye.

As bases, they neutralize acids:

$$NaOH + HCl \rightarrow NaCl + H_2O$$

They react with acid anhydrides:

$$2NaOH + CO_2 \rightarrow Na_2CO_3 + H_2O$$

USES

The hydroxides are of great industrial importance. Mercerized cotton is made shiny by passing it through a solution of sodium hydroxide. This process swells the cotton fibres. Sodium hydroxide is also used in making rayon, reclaiming rubber, making paper, and refining petroleum. Potassium hydroxide is used much less, but two specific uses are for making soft soap and for removing carbon dioxide from the atmosphere of submarines.

Sodium Carbonate and Hydrogen Carbonate

Sodium carbonate, Na_2CO_3, is an important industrial compound. It is used to make glass and soap, to soften water, to cleanse textiles during manufacture, and in many other ways.

Commercially, it is prepared by the *Solvay Process*, which uses expensive ammonia and cheap carbon dioxide, salt, and water. Solvay, the inventor of this process, discovered how to recover almost all of the ammonia. In this way, it is used over and over again, and, as a result, the cost of the sodium carbonate is kept low.

The ammonia, carbon dioxide, and water react to form ammonium bicarbonate:

$$NH_3 + H_2O + CO_2 \rightarrow NH_4HCO_3$$

Salt is added in large amounts to form the less soluble sodium hydrogen carbonate. Its solubility is even less at low temperatures. This makes possible its removal by filtration:

$$NaCl + NH_4HCO_3 \rightarrow NaHCO_3 + NH_4Cl$$

The sodium hydrogen carbonate is removed and heated to form sodium carbonate:

$$2NaHCO_3 \rightarrow Na_2CO_3 + CO_2 + H_2O$$

The ammonia is recovered from the ammonium chloride by reacting it with calcium oxide. This is obtained from limestone, $CaCO_3$, which provides CO_2, another ingredient of the process:

$$CaCO_3 \rightarrow CaO + CO_2\uparrow$$
$$2NH_4Cl + CaO \rightarrow 2NH_3\uparrow + CaCl_2 + H_2O$$

Other Compounds

Sodium and potassium form a great number of very useful compounds such as the nitrates, sulfates, sulfites, and phosphates.

All the alkali metals combine with hydrogen to form hydrides:

$$2Li + H_2 \rightarrow 2LiH$$

TABLE 44.2		
Some Compounds of Sodium and Potassium		
Compound	Formula	Uses
Sodium cyanide	NaCN	To recover gold. In its metallurgy, gold is soluble in sodium cyanide
Sodium fluoride	NaF	To supply fluoride ion to water
Sodium nitrate	$NaNO_3$	Fertilizer ingredient
Sodium sulfate	Na_2SO_4	Glass and paper making
Sodium sulfite	Na_2SO_3	Anti-Chlor (a substance that stops bleaching action of chlorine on cotton when desired)
Sodium chlorate	$NaClO_3$	Weed killer
Sodium tetraborate (borax)	$Na_2B_4O_7 \cdot 10H_2O$	Cleaner, water softening, glass making
Cryolite	Na_3AlF_6	Making aluminum
Potassium nitrate	KNO_3	Fertilizer ingredient
Potassium chlorate	$KClO_3$	Oxidizing agent

In these compounds, the hydrogen is more electronegative than the alkali metal. The hydrogen atom, therefore, is the negative part of the molecule, while the alkali atom is the positive. This is unusual behavior for hydrogen, but it is readily explained by the electronegativity difference between hydrogen (2.5) and the alkali metals (1 or less).

In LiH, the oxidation number of hydrogen is taken as 1– because it is more electronegative than lithium.

44:8   The Alkaline Earth Metals

Group II of the periodic table contains the elements beryllium, magnesium, calcium, strontium, barium, and radium. They are called the alkaline earth metals because their oxides have definite alkaline properties. The alchemists referred to any substance that was unchanged by fire as an earth. Calcium and magnesium oxide can indeed withstand enormous heat.

These metals are active, although less so than the alkalies. Because they have two outer electrons, the metallic bond is stronger than in the case of the alkalies. Therefore, their density, hardness, and melting points are higher, and their chemical reactivity is lower. As expected, the electronegativity of the metals decreases with atomic size.

The similarity of the alkaline earth metals is due to the two electrons in the outermost s orbital of their atoms*. These electrons are easily transferred to elements like chlorine, oxygen, and sulfur which are of greater electronegativity. The electronegativity difference is great enough for the bonds to be ionic in the compounds thus formed.

The most important alkaline earths are magnesium and calcium. These elements will now be studied in some detail.

44:9   Magnesium

Magnesium is one of the most abundant of the useful metals. One cubic mile of sea water contains about twelve billion pounds of magnesium as magnesium chloride. This salt is also found in some salt wells. An important mineral of magnesium is dolomite, $MgCO_3 \cdot CaCO_3$.

Metallurgy

World War II created an enormous demand for lightweight metals. This led to the extraction of magnesium from sea water. Lime (CaO) added to sea water forms calcium hydroxide, which reacts with the magnesium salts present to form insoluble magnesium hydroxide:

$$Mg^{2+} + Ca(OH)_2 \rightarrow Ca^{2+} + Mg(OH)_2\downarrow$$

This is filtered out and treated with hydrochloric acid to form magnesium chloride:

$$Mg(OH)_2 + 2HCl \rightarrow MgCl_2 + 2H_2O$$

This is mixed with other salts to lower its melting point and the mixture is poured into an electrolytic cell:

Cathode reaction	$Mg^{2+} + 2e \rightarrow Mg^\circ$
Anode reaction	$Cl^- - 1e \rightarrow Cl^\circ$
	$2Cl^\circ \rightarrow Cl_2\uparrow$

The magnesium obtained is about 99.9 cer cent pure.

Another method for obtaining magnesium takes advantage of its relatively low boiling point of less than 1150°C. Magnesium oxide is reduced with ferrosilicon. At high temperature and in a vacuum, this alloy of iron and silicon is a powerful electron donor which reduces the magnesium oxide to magnesium. The magnesium forms a vapor, is condensed to liquid, then is cast into molds. This process was worked out by Dr. L. M. Pidgeon, a Canadian chemist.

*The electron distribution of the elements of group II is similar to that of group I (Table 44.1) except that the outer s orbital now contains two electrons instead of the one present for the alkali metals.

Physical Properties

Magnesium is a soft, silvery-white metal weighing about 40 per cent less than aluminum (density 1.75 g/cm³). It has little structural strength in the pure form and is quite brittle.

Chemical Properties

Magnesium is an active metal. It releases hydrogen from boiling water or steam and reacts vigorously with acids:

$$Mg + H_2O \rightarrow MgO + H_2\uparrow$$
$$Mg + 2HCl \rightarrow MgCl_2 + H_2\uparrow$$

It burns with a brilliant light when ignited in air, combining with both oxygen and nitrogen:

$$2Mg + O_2 \rightarrow 2MgO$$
$$3Mg + N_2 \rightarrow Mg_3N_2$$

At ordinary temperatures, magnesium is protected by a thin coating of magnesium oxide. This metal combines readily with the halogens and with sulfur.

Uses

Many important alloys of magnesium are structural materials for aircraft parts where weight must be kept to a minimum. Such alloys are made with aluminum, manganese, zinc, and other metals, and some are used in place of aluminum alloys, being lighter. Structural shapes can be made as strong as steel, with only a fraction of the weight. Magnesium is used in flash bulbs, together with oxygen gas; and flares made of magnesium serve for military operations, fireworks, or as distress signals.

Magnesium is a reducing agent for extracting certain metals from their ores; zirconium, uranium, and titanium are examples.

44:10   Calcium

This metal is prepared by the electrolysis of fused calcium chloride. The physical and chemical properties of calcium are very similar to those of magnesium. Calcium, being too active to occur free in nature, is found usually as calcium carbonate. Deposits of calcium carbonate are built up on the ocean floor from the remains of the shells of sea animals which are slowly compressed into porous chalk or compact limestone. The limestone may be elevated to dry land by movement of the ocean floor.

Limestone, CaCO₃

Volcanic heat sometimes melts limestone, and while molten it may become mixed with certain metallic impurities, thereby forming marble. Molten limestone, if cooled very slowly, forms a transparent crystalline solid known as calcite. Large crystals of calcite separate light rays so

TABLE 44.3		
Compounds of Magnesium		
Name	Formula	Use
Magnesium oxide	MgO	Furnace lining
Magnesium hydroxide (Milk of Magnesia)	Mg(OH)₂	Medical anti-acid
Magnesium carbonate	MgCO₃	Heated to form MgO
Magnesium sulfate (Epsom salts)	MgSO₄·7H₂O	Tanning of leather cathartic
Magnesium chloride	MgCl₂	Source of magnesium
Asbestos and talc are two naturally occurring magnesium silicates.		

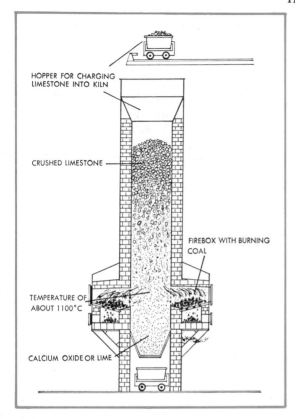

Fig. 44.3 *Vertical lime kiln*

that an object viewed through such a crystal appears double.

Lime

If calcium carbonate is heated to a high temperature, calcium oxide remains:

$$CaCO_3 \rightarrow CaO + CO_2\uparrow$$

Calcium oxide is called *quicklime*. Commercially it is made in large kilns.

Calcium oxide is a white solid that gives off a brilliant white light when it is highly heated. For example, carbon rods used for arc lamps usually contain a core of CaO to give a very intense light. Stage lighting used to be done chiefly by heating a piece of lime, and the light was known as a limelight. We still refer to someone in the public eye as being "in the limelight".

Calcium oxide forms a base with water:

$$CaO + H_2O \rightarrow Ca(OH)_2 + heat$$

Calcium hydroxide, known as slaked lime, is used to remove the hair from hides in the tanning industry. It is also used to neutralize acids in soil, a process called *liming*. In solution, although it is not really very soluble, it is known as *limewater*.

Mortar

Sand and calcium hydroxide mixed together make *mortar*, a substance used to hold building stone and brick together. When mortar hardens, both calcium silicate and calcium carbonate are formed:

$$Ca(OH)_2 + SiO_2 \rightarrow CaSiO_3\downarrow + H_2O$$
$$\text{sand}$$
$$Ca(OH)_2 + CO_2 \rightarrow CaCO_3\downarrow + H_2O$$

Cement

The term *cement* is used for any material that can bond substances together. A more specific meaning applies to *Portland Cement* used in construction. This material is a mixture of powdered limestone and clay that has been strongly heated in a kiln. The mixture is brought almost to its melting point and a solid mass called a *clinker* forms. The clinker is then pulverized to a fine powder. A small amount of calcium sulfate, $CaSO_4$, is added to improve setting quality. When the cement is to be used, water is added, together with sand and crushed rock. This mixture, called *concrete*, may be used in the construction of dams, highways, and buildings.

Concrete in which steel bars are embedded is known as *reinforced concrete*, a much stronger material than ordinary concrete. An even stronger variety is made by stretching steel cables and pouring concrete around them. When the tension is removed, the steel cables contract in length, thereby pressing the concrete more compactly than otherwise. Such concrete is called *pre-stressed*. It is replacing steel girders in some cases as a strong structural material.

The hardening of cement is probably a union of the ingredients with water to form insoluble hydrates. The process takes several days for completion, but it takes place even under water. The process is a remarkable one and is not fully understood.

Plaster of Paris

Gypsum, $CaSO_4 \cdot 2H_2O$, has been used since ancient times to make plaster. When heated it forms a white powder called *plaster of Paris*:

$$2CaSO_4 \cdot 2H_2O \rightarrow 3H_2O + (CaSO_4)_2 \cdot H_2O$$

When water is added, the reaction is simply reversed. Since a slight increase in volume occurs when it hardens, plaster of Paris makes an excellent material for statuary, for plastering walls and ceilings, and for protecting broken bones.

Superphosphate

Calcium dihydrogen phosphate is soluble; therefore it can be used by plants as a source of calcium and phosphorus. Its preparation was discussed under sulfuric acid (Chapter 31).

44:11   Hard Water

Water containing calcium or magnesium ions is known as hard water because these ions react with soap to form an insoluble curdlike precipitate:

$$2C_{17}H_{35}COONa + Ca^{2+} \rightarrow 2Na^+ +$$

    a soap $(C_{17}H_{35}COO)_2Ca\downarrow$
(sodium stearate)

Soft water contains little or none of these ions. To soften water, calcium and magnesium ions must be precipitated or combined into a complex ion.

There are two kinds of hard water, temporary and permanent. Temporary hard water contains the calcium or magnesium ions in the form of hydrogen carbonates. Merely boiling such

water precipitates these ions as insoluble carbonate salts:

$$Ca(HCO_3)_2 \rightarrow CaCO_3\downarrow + H_2O + CO_2\uparrow$$

Permanent hard water contains calcium or magnesium sulfates. Boiling has no effect on these compounds. Calcium and magnesium ions may be removed from water by adding sodium carbonate (washing soda):

$$Ca^{2+} + Na_2CO_3 \rightarrow CaCO_3\downarrow + 2Na^+$$

Trisodium phosphate, Na_3PO_4, may also be used. It forms insoluble calcium or magnesium phosphate. Sodium metaphosphate, $NaPO_3$, is used in dishwashing powders. It prevents the reaction of calcium and magnesium ions with soap by complexing them.

Ion-Exchange

"Permutit" water softeners have become very popular within recent years, both in the home and in industry. Certain natural complex sodium silicate minerals called *zeolites* hold sodium ions rather loosely. As a solution containing calcium or magnesium ion (for example, hard water) comes in contact with the zeolite, these ions displace the sodium ions and are thus removed from the solution. The reaction may be represented by the equation:

$$Na_2(zeolite) + Ca^{2+} \rightarrow Ca(zeolite) + 2Na^+$$

This is called *ion-exchange*. Since sodium ions are not objectionable in water for most purposes, ion-exchange using zeolite is a good way to soften water. Synthetic materials called *ion-exchange resins* are now available for the same purpose.

When all of the sodium ions in the zeolite have been replaced, the ion-exchanger may be recharged by passing concentrated sodium chloride solution through it. The calcium or magnesium zeolite becomes sodium zeolite again. Many softeners are automatic and recharge themselves from a vat of rock salt which supplies the sodium chloride solution.

Synthetic resins have been prepared which can replace the cation of a solution with the hydronium ion. Other resins can replace the anion of a solution with the hydroxide ion. These are known as *cation* and *anion exchange resins* respectively:

$$Na^+Cl^- + H_3O^+ \rightarrow H_3O^+Cl^- + Na^+\downarrow$$

| from | from | absorbed |
| solution | resin | in resin |

$$H_3O^+Cl^- + OH^- \rightarrow 2H_2O + Cl^-\downarrow$$

| from | from | absorbed |
| solution | resin | in resin |

By using these resins, one after the other, it is possible to de-mineralize water almost completely. Many laboratories use this method instead of distillation to obtain pure water.

Ion exchange methods are used in separating and purifying vitamins, antibiotics, and other pharmaceutical products.

44:12 Boron

The elements of group III are all classed as metals except boron, which is a non-metal. The small atomic radius accounts for its high electronegativity of 2.0, and such values of electronegativity occur among the non-metals. Its compounds are exclusively covalent.

Boron exists in both amorphous and crystalline forms. The amorphous form is made by reducing compounds of boron with active metals, such as sodium. If molten boron is cooled slowly, crystalline boron is obtained, which is nearly as hard as diamond.

Because the oxidation of boron releases more energy per unit weight than most other elements, boron is becoming ever more important as a fuel for rockets and missiles. It combines with hydrogen to form borane, BH_3, diborane, B_2H_6, and tetraborane, B_4H_{10}. These important compounds resemble the hydrocarbons in their behavior as energy-producing fuels. Indeed, methyl and ethyl groups may replace the hydrogen atoms. The resulting compounds release even greater amounts of energy. Boron is also used in solar batteries and transistors.

Borax, $Na_2B_4O_7\cdot 10H_2O$, is the most common compound of boron. It is found in dried-up lakes, mainly in California. Borax hydrolyzes in water to form a basic solution, and as such it can decompose grease; it is therefore used for cleaning. Furthermore, it precipitates calcium and magnesium salts as hydroxides and borates so that it may be used to soften water. Metallic oxides react with melted borax to form colored borates, which may identify certain metals in chemical analysis. Borax is also used as a flux in welding and a raw material in the manufacture of some types of glass.

A very weak acid and a mild antiseptic, boric or boracic acid, H_3BO_3, is found mixed with borax. Its main use is in eyewash preparations and ointments.

Titanium boride and boron carbides are among the hardest substances known; hence they are used as abrasives.

44:13 Silicon

Silicon has the same importance in the mineral world that carbon has in the organic world. It is the second most abundant element in the earth's crust. As SiO_2 it forms sand, flint, quartz, and opal. Combined with various metals, it is found in practically all rocks, clays, and soils. Compounds of silicon are used in cement, mortar, glass, and brick.

The silicon atom, like the carbon atom, has a combining capacity of 4. If all four bonds are filled with OH, we obtain:

$$H-O-\underset{\underset{\overset{\textstyle |}{\textstyle H}}{\overset{\textstyle |}{\textstyle O}}}{\overset{\overset{\textstyle H}{\overset{\textstyle |}{\textstyle O}}}{\textstyle Si}}-O-H$$

or H_4SiO_4, silicic acid.

H₄SiO₄

Silicic   Acid

The salts of this acid are the silicates, and they are much more abundant and important than the acid.

The silicate ion SiO_4^{4-} is a tetrahedral like methane, CH_4. Silicate ions may share oxygen atoms to form long chains, as is the case of asbestos fibres. In some substances, such as mica for example, the ions may form a two-dimensional sheet; or as another alternative, the ions may form a three-dimensional network, resulting in quartz and sand.

Silicon Dioxide, Silica, Quartz

Quartz is a crystalline form of silicon dioxide. It has a structure similar to diamond, except that two types of atoms, Si and O, are present in the crystal lattice. Like diamond, it has a high melting point and is extremely hard.

When melted, it softens to a liquid resembling melted glass. In this condition, it can be made into laboratory apparatus of extraordinary properties. Since quartz has a very small coefficient of expansion with temperature, a quartz dish may be heated red hot and plunged into water without breaking.

Ceramics

When silicates are heated to a temperature just below that of fusion, changes take place which cause the mass partially to resemble glass. This is called *vitrification*, and it is the basis of the ceramic industries. Products of these industries are brick, tiles, dishes, porcelain, enamel, and glass.

Glass

It is difficult to realize what living would be like without glass. Envisage, if you can, what homes, offices, stores, and cars would be like without windows. Imagine how primitive science would be without the microscope and telescope, whose lenses are made of glass.

ORIGIN AND NATURE OF GLASS

Glass has been known from ancient times. Perhaps the beginning of the glass-making art occurred when some prehistoric tribesmen noticed a glassy substance left as an ash after an intense fire on sand. The art was well developed in ancient Egypt, Greece, and Rome.

Fig. 44.4 *A need for a special type of glass Windows of the Apollo space-craft are made of glass which withstands tremendous heat and the thermal shock of re-entry. The window assembly has three panels of glass. The outer pane is made of fused silica glass; the two inner panes are of an aluminosilicate glass.*

Courtesy National Aeronautics and Space Administration

Chemically, glass forms when the oxides of silicon, sodium, and calcium, are melted. The ions in the molten mass do not assume a crystalline formation upon cooling, therefore, although glass is both as rigid as a solid and as transparent as a colorless liquid, it does not have a sharp melting point. It is termed a *supercooled liquid* in the *vitreous state*.

To make glass industrially, SiO_2 from sand, Na_2O from sodium carbonate, and CaO from calcium carbonate are melted together in large vats. Certain other oxides are added for special purposes. For example, Pyrex glass contains boron oxide, B_2O_3, in addition to a high proportion of silicon dioxide.

The Solar Battery

In a solar battery, two plates are separated by an insulator. One plate contains silicon and a metalloid, such as arsenic while the other contains silicon and boron. Arsenic has five outer electrons, four of which form covalent bonds with the silicon:

Si ⟍ one electron too many
Si : As : Si
Si

There is one extra unshared electron, as shown in the structural formula. Boron, on the other hand, has only three outer electrons, and in forming bonds with silicon there is a deficiency of electrons:

Si — one electron too few
Si : B : Si
Si

When light falls on the silicon-arsenic combination, the extra electrons are easily moved towards the silicon-boron plate, which can receive these electrons. Thus the current flows. Transistors work on a similar principle.

Silicones

Silicones are a very important group of compounds which are used as lubricants. They are also used in polishes, because they are very resistant to heat, and as linings for cooking utensils. Their chemical composition is shown in the formula:

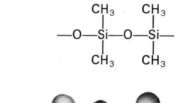

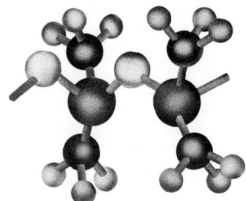

QUESTIONS

1. (a) List the elements of group I from the periodic table.
   (b) Why are these elements called the alkali metals?

2. Where are the alkali metal compounds found in nature?

3. Of what importance are sodium and potassium ions in living things?

4. Why are the alkali metals not found free in nature?

5. List the main common properties of the alkali metals, and explain why the metals have these properties.

6. How is lithium removed from its ore?

7. Of what importance is lithium?

8. (a) Draw a labelled diagram of the Downs cell.
   (b) Write the equations for the reactions involved.

9. List the properties of sodium, and give a use to which these properties lead.

10. (a) What is an *amalgam?*
    (b) For what is sodium amalgam used?

11. Mention some uses of potassium, cesium, and rubidium.

12. What is the cause of flame spectra?

13. What are the flame spectra of the alkali metals?

14. What are the most important alkali metal compounds?

15. List the common properties of the alkali metal hydroxides.

16. Why are these hydroxides so soluble in water?

17. Why are sodium and potassium hydroxides called caustics?

18. Complete, and balance, these equations:
    $NaOH + HCl \rightarrow$
    $KOH + CO_2 \rightarrow$
    $NaOH + SO_2 \rightarrow$

19. Mention some important uses of the caustics.

20. Outline the Solvay process and write the chemical equations involved.

21. (a) Why is hydrogen negative in the alkali metal hydrides?
    (b) What are two unusual oxidation numbers of hydrogen and oxygen encountered in alkali compounds?

22. What are the alkaline earths and why are they so-called?

23. Contrast the properties of the alkaline earth elements with those of the alkali metals. Account for the differences.

24. How does the theory of the metal bond explain the properties of the alkaline earths?

25. How does magnesium occur in nature?

26. Describe how magnesium is obtained from sea water.

27. (a) List the physical properties of magnesium.
    (b) List the chemical properties of magnesium.
    (c) What is its orbital notation?

28. Give the uses of magnesium and a property that accounts for each use.

29. Account for the formation of limestone deposits in nature.

30. How was marble formed from limestone?

31. Describe with the aid of a diagram how calcium oxide is made. Write the equation.

32. List the important properties and uses of calcium oxide.

33. What is *mortar?*

34. Explain how cement is made.

35. (a) What is the composition of plaster of Paris?
    (b) Write the equation for the production of this material and also for the reaction when it hardens.

36. (a) What is hard water, and why is it so-called?
    (b) Distinguish between temporary and permanent hardness in water.

37. (a) How is washing soda used to soften water?
    (b) Give an equation to illustrate your answer.

38. Explain the operation of a zeolite water softener.

39. Explain the operation and use of cation and anion exchange resins.

40. Why is boron classed as a non-metal?

41. Why are boron compounds used as fuels for rockets?

42. What are some uses of borax?

43. Give a use for boric acid, titanium boride, and boron carbide.

44. What is the importance of silicon compounds?

45. (a) What are silicones?
    (b) Mention some uses of these materials.

46. Describe with the aid of structural formulas how a solar battery operates.

47. Calculate the molarity of sulfuric acid if 18 ml of it are neutralized by 36 ml of 0.1 M sodium hydroxide.

48. Find the number of milligrams of sodium hydrogen carbonate that will react with 60 ml of 0.5 M sulfuric acid.

49. Give the oxidation number of each atom in the following:
    (a) $Fe_2(SO_4)_3$　　　(b) $Ca_2P_2O_7$　　　(c) $PtCl_6^{2-}$　　　(d) UO_2^{2+}

50. $Mg + H_2SO_4 \rightarrow MgSO_4 + H_2$
    What weight of sulfuric acid is needed to combine with 8 g of magnesium?

51. How many moles of magnesium could be produced from 150 g of magnesium chloride?

CHAPTER

45　Some Heavy Metals

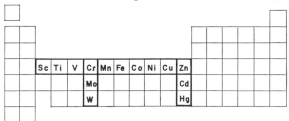

45:1　The Transition Metals

Elements in which the number of electrons is increasing from one to 10 in the *d* subshell next to the outer *s* outer shell are called *transistion elements*. To the left of these in the periodic table are the most metallic elements, and to the right the most nonmetallic.

Transition elements are metallic in the free state, and their properties are very similar. The atoms have one or two outer electrons from the *s* subshell but, in addition, the electrons of

the incomplete *d* subshell also take part in compound formation to varying extents. For this reason the transition elements are highly variable in their oxidation numbers.

The first 10 transition metals are shown in Table 45.1. It is interesting that the third row of transition elements, starting with lanthanum, includes elements wherein both the 5*d* and 4*f* subshells fill up. The atoms in which the 4*f* subshells fill up are called the rare earth elements of atomic number from 57 to 71.

Similarly, the atoms whose 5*f* subshell is

TABLE 45.1														
The first 10 Transition Metals														
Element	Symbol	\multicolumn{6}{c}{Electron configuration}						Melting point (°C)	Density (g/cm³)	\multicolumn{3}{c}{Oxidation numbers (all positive)}		
Scandium	Sc	2	2	6	2	6	1	2	1400	2.5			3
Titanium	Ti	2	2	6	2	6	2	2	1725	4.5		2 3 4
Vanadium	V	2	2	6	2	6	3	2	1900	5.9		3 4 5
Chromium	Cr	2	2	6	2	6	5	1	1550	7.1		2 3 6
Manganese	Mn	2	2	6	2	6	5	2	1250	7.2	2 3 4 6 7
Iron	Fe	2	2	6	2	6	6	2	1540	7.9		2 3 6
Cobalt	Co	2	2	6	2	6	7	2	1500	8.9		2 3
Nickel	Ni	2	2	6	2	6	8	2	1450	8.9		2 4
Copper	Cu	2	2	6	2	6	10	1	1085	8.9		1 2
Zinc	Zn	2	2	6	2	6	10	2	420		

being filled are those that have been produced by nuclear reactions. These are elements of atomic number 93 to 103.

In this chapter, chromium, tungsten, zinc, cadmium, and mercury are briefly discussed. Tin and lead are also included even though they actually belong to group IV.

45:2   Chromium

The chromium family is one of the most important of the transition families. All the elements in this family, chromium, molybdenum and tungsten, are well known both in the free state and in the form of their compounds, and they have important industrial applications. They are tough, heavy metals with very high melting points.

Occurrence

These elements occur naturally only in the combined form, and chromium is the most abundant. An important source of this metal is chromite ore, impure $Fe(CrO_2)_2$.

Metallurgy, Properties, and Uses

Pure chromium metal can be prepared by the reduction of chromic oxide with aluminum.

$$Cr_2O_3 + 2Al \rightarrow 2Cr + Al_2O_3$$

It melts at 1550°C, has a density of 7.14 g per cm³, and is a hard, silvery-white metal that takes a high polish. Though it reacts with oxygen and with water at high temperatures, chromium metal resists atmospheric corrosion and retains its brilliant lustre almost indefinitely under ordinary conditions. These properties have greatly stimulated the use of chromium as a plating metal over iron and steel. High-chromium steels, usually called *stainless* steels, contain more than 10 per cent chromium.

45:3   Tungsten

Tungsten has a melting point of 3300°C. Although some is used in its pure form as the filament in light bulbs, most tungsten is alloyed with steel to make high-speed cutting tools. Tungsten steel keeps a sharp cutting edge even when it becomes red hot. One of the best abrasives known is *Carboloy*, another name for tungsten carbide.

45:4   Zinc

Occurrence

The most important ore of zinc is the sulfide, ZnS, called sphalerite or zinc blende. Other ores are the carbonate, $ZnCO_3$ smithsonite; ZnO, zincite; mixed oxides of zinc, iron, and manganese, called franklinite; and a silicate, $ZnSiO_4$, willemite.

Metallurgy

Two types of operations are used in the metallurgy of zinc.

A. CHEMICAL REDUCTION

Zinc sulfide ores, after first being concentrated by flotation or otherwise, are roasted in air:

$$2ZnS + 3O_2 \rightarrow 2ZnO + 2SO_2\uparrow$$

The sulfur dioxide is often used in the production of sulfuric acid. The zinc oxide, mixed with powdered coal, is heated in vertical retorts:

$$ZnO + C \rightarrow Zn + CO$$

At the temperature of the reaction (over 900°C), the reduced metal is volatile and distills away, to be condensed at the ends of the retorts.

B. THE ELECTROLYTIC PROCESS

Increasing quantities of zinc are obtained by electrolysis. By this method the sulfide ore is roasted at a low temperature so that much of it is converted into zinc sulfate, the remainder being present as the oxide. This material is treated with sulfuric acid, and the resulting zinc sulfate solution is electrolyzed between lead anodes and aluminum cathodes. Sheets of zinc are deposited on the cathode.

Uses

Galvanized iron is iron coated with zinc to resist corrosion. The coating may be applied in three ways: by immersing acid-cleaned sheet iron into molten zinc; by depositing zinc on the iron by electrolysis; or by placing powdered zinc on the iron and heating it to 300°C. In the latter method, called *sherardizing*, the zinc fuses to the iron. The iron is protected from corrosion, because zinc has a lower electronegativity than iron. When coated with zinc, iron does not rust even if the protective coating is scratched through. This is because the remaining zinc continues to lose electrons in place of the iron.

Zinc is also used as the cathode in dry cells, because it so readily loses electrons, and in many alloys of which bronze, brass, and German silver are the chief examples. The latter is an alloy of nickel, zinc, and silver. Zinc dust combines readily with the halogens, oxygen, and sulfur.

Compounds of zinc are used in many products. Zinc oxide is a pigment in white paint, an antiseptic in some ointments, and an ingredient in rubber goods, making the latter more resistant to wear. Zinc chloride hydrolyzes to form an acid solution. This acid removes oxides from metal and acts as a flux in soldering. Paper soaked in it forms parchment. Zinc sulfide gives off visible light when subjected to cathode rays or X rays. Some television tubes are coated with zinc sulfide to help form the image. Substances with this property are called *phosphors*.

45:5   Cadmium

Although somewhat harder than zinc, cadmium resembles zinc and is usually found mixed with zinc in ores. It is used to plate other metals and in alloys for bearing metal. It is also used in low-melting-temperature alloys like Wood's metal, which is composed of bismuth, lead, tin, and cadmium and which melts at about 65°C depending on composition. Cadmium sulfide is used as a yellow pigment in paints.

45:6   Mercury

Because it occurs in small amounts in the free state, mercury has been known since early times. Its chief ore, cinnabar, HgS, is easily decomposed by heating to yield mercury and sulfur dioxide.

Physical Properties

The Latin name for mercury, *hydrargyrum*, meaning liquid silver, indicates its color and state. It is the only metal that is a liquid at room temperature (on hot days the metals cesium, melting point 28.5°C, and gallium, melting point 29.8°C, are also liquids). Mercury freezes at -39°C and boils at 357°C. Its density is 13.6 g/ml.

Chemical Properties

Mercury forms compounds in which its oxidation state is $1+$ or $2+$, called mercury (I) and mercury (II), respectively. In mercury (I) compounds, two mercury (I) ions form a covalent bond so that they exist in pairs Hg_2^{2+}. For this reason the formula of mercury (I) chloride is written Hg_2Cl_2.

Mercury vapor is very poisonous. Even long exposure to the metal itself should be avoided.

In general, mercury reacts with oxidizing acids as copper does. No hydrogen is formed.

$$\overset{0}{3Hg} + \overset{5+}{8HNO_3} \text{ (dilute)} \rightarrow$$
$$\downarrow$$
$$3 \times 2e$$

$$\overset{2+}{3Hg(NO_3)_2} + \overset{2+}{2NO}\uparrow + 4H_2O$$
$$\uparrow$$
$$2 \times 3e$$

$$\overset{0}{Hg} + 4H\overset{5+}{N}O_3 \text{ (conc.)} \rightarrow$$

$$\downarrow$$
$$2e$$

$$H\overset{2+}{g}(NO_3)_2 + 2H_2O + 2\overset{4+}{N}O_2\uparrow$$

$$\uparrow$$
$$2 \times 1e$$

Heated in air or oxygen, mercury forms mercury (II) oxide.

$$2Hg + O_2 \rightarrow 2HgO$$

Liquid mercury forms alloys by dissolving many metals, especially the softer ones, such as copper, silver, gold, and the alkalies. These alloys are called amalgams, some of which are liquids and some of which are solids. For example, the substance used by dentists to fill teeth is silver amalgam. The chemical activity of the dissolved metal is decreased in the amalgam.

Compounds of Mercury

If mercury (II) oxide is highly heated, it decomposes to yield mercury and oxygen:

$$2HgO \rightarrow 2Hg + O_2\uparrow$$

It was the formation of mercury (II) oxide and its decomposition that led Lavoisier to the true nature of burning.

Mercury (I) chloride, Hg_2Cl_2 is not very soluble. It is known as calomel and is used in medicine as a powerful cathartic. It is not as poisonous as mercury (II) chloride, $HgCl_2$, a corrosive sublimate that destroys all known bacteria.

Mercury fulminate, $Hg(CNO)_2$, is a violent explosive. It is used as a *detonator*. A detonator is exploded by heat or shock, and the violence of its explosion causes other less reactive materials to explode.

Uses

Mercury is used in thermometers because it expands at a constant rate upon heating. Its fluidity makes it an excellent material for use in barometers and other scientific instruments. Silent switches are often made with two electrodes in a glass tube containing a drop of mercury. When the tube is tilted, the mercury flows to connect the electrodes.

A drop of mercury in an evacuated glass tube equipped with electrodes vaporizes when electricity is passed into the electrodes. The vapor conducts the current and gives off light rich in ultraviolet radiation. Sun lamps work on this principle. Since glass is not a good conductor of ultraviolet rays, a quartz bulb is frequently used in such lamps.

Fluorescent lights use the same principle as the sun lamp but the amount of visible light produced is greatly increased by using phosphors on the inside of the tube. Fluorescent lamps are much more efficient than the hot filament type. They convert about 30 per cent of the electrical energy supplied to them to visible light. Hot filament lamps convert only about 10 per cent; the remaining 90 per cent of the energy is converted to invisible radiations or heat.

45:7   Tin

Tin is found in nature mostly in the oxide, SnO_2. This is reduced by the use of coke. Most of the tin ore comes from Malaya, Indonesia, and Bolivia.

Tin is a silvery-white, soft, malleable metal which melts at 232°C. At low temperature, it crumbles into an allotropic powder called grey tin. Chemically, it is not very active. It is highly resistant to oxidation, and it is scarcely affected by fruit acids or even by dilute hydrochloric acid.

The familiar "tin cans" in which many foods are packed are in fact iron cans coated with a shield of tin which may be as little as 30 millionths of an inch thick! Cleaned sheets of metal may be dipped into molten tin in the coating process, but better control is obtained by electrolytic depositions. The electrolytic process is continuous and is performed as the steel leaves the fabricating machine. Unlike iron coated with zinc, the iron of the tin can rusts quickly if a break in the tin coating appears, because tin is more electronegative than iron. The iron loses electrons more readily than tin and thus corrodes.

Tin is also used in alloys such as bronze (copper and tin), solder (lead and tin), type-metal (lead, tin, and antimony), and Babbitt metal (tin, antimony, and copper). Pewter is about 75 per cent tin and 25 per cent lead.

Tin forms two classes of compounds: tin (IV), where tin has an oxidation number of $4+$; and tin (II) where it has a value of $2+$.

45:8   Lead

Lead occurs in nature principally in the ore galena, PbS. The method generally used to obtain the lead is to roast the ore and then reduce the resultant oxide with coke.

Properties

Pure lead is a soft metal of low melting point. It has a silvery lustre when freshly cut, but it quickly tarnishes owing to the formation of oxide and carbonate on its surface. Lead reacts very slowly with most strong acids.

Lead compounds are cumulatively poisonous; that is, the body does not eliminate the metal, and small amounts acquired over a long period of time may eventually affect the entire body.

Uses

Lead and its compounds are used in a great many manufactured articles and products, such as storage batteries, covering for cables, tetraethyl lead fluid, pigment in paint, pipes, X ray protective shields, and in alloys such as solder, type-metal, and babbitt.

White lead is mostly $Pb(OH)_2 \cdot 2PbCO_3$. It is made by converting lead to lead acetate, using acetic acid. The lead acetate is then exposed to carbon dioxide. The lead carbonate formed, on being boiled in water, yields the white lead.

White lead has been used as a pigment in paint. Actually, *paint* is pigment plus a liquid vehicle that hardens to a plastic-like, surface-film material. Linseed oil from flaxseed slowly oxidizes to form such a tough film. This is frequently the liquid vehicle for oil paints. Other ingredients of paint are a *thinner*, usually turpentine; a *drier* to catalyse the oxidation process; and an *extender* or *filler* to decrease the cost. Common fillers are calcium sulfate, barium sulfate, fine sand, and calcium carbonate. Cheap paints usually contain a lot of filler and do not wear well. Manganese dioxide and lead oxide are often used as driers.

QUESTIONS

1. (a) What are the transition elements, and why are they so-called?
   (b) Why do these elements have such variable oxidation numbers?
   (c) What is the maximum number of electrons in the *d* subshell?

2. (a) List the properies of chromium.
   (b) Why is chromium so resistant to corrosion?

3. Give some uses of tungsten.

4. What is *sherardizing*?

5. Why is a zinc coating on iron so effective in helping the iron to resist corrosion?

6. List some uses of zinc compounds.

7. (a) What is Wood's metal?
   (b) Give some uses of cadmium.

8. (a) List the physical properties of mercury.
   (b) What are the chemical properties of this element?
   (c) In terms of its d orbital, offer an explanation of why mercury is a liquid.

9. Complete these equations: (a) $Hg + HNO_3$ (dilute) (b) $Hg + HNO_3$ (concentrated) (c) $Hg + O_2$.

10. What are some uses of the chlorides of mercury?

11. Explain what a *detonator* is, giving an example to illustrate your answer.

12. List various uses of mercury.

13. (a) List the properties of tin.
    (b) What are some uses of this metal?
    (c) Why does tin-coated iron corrode quickly if there is a break in the tin coating?

14. List the properties of lead metal and the uses to which these properties lead.

15. Explain the term *cumulative poison*.

16. What are the principal ingredients of paint?

17. How is lead used in paint?

18. How much lead metal could be obtained from 20 lbs of lead sulfide?

19. Calculate the weight of mercury needed to produce 10 g of mercury (II) nitrate.

CHAPTER
46   More Transition Metals

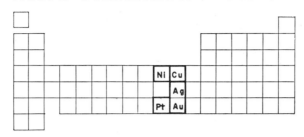

46:1   Nickel

Nickel-bearing ores are widely distributed, because this metal is often associated in nature with copper and iron; but ores that can be mined profitably are relatively rare. Canada is fortunate in having rich nickel ores and produces about 65 per cent of the world's total nickel supply. Most of Canada's nickel ore comes from the Sudbury district of Ontario. Nickel is also a constituent of meteorites.

In extracting nickel ores, both physical and chemical separations are used. Some nickel ores are pulverized and concentrated by *flotation*. In the flotation process, the ore is crushed to a fine powder, then a frothing agent, such as pine oil, is added, together with some agent which adheres to the particles of ore but not to the particles of rock. When the mixture is placed in water and air is blown through, the froth carries the ore particles upward, but the rock

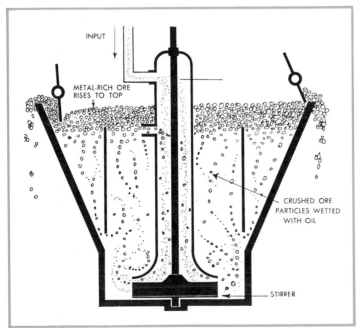

Fig. 46.1   *Froth flotation method of concentrating ores*

Courtesy International Nickel Company of Canada, Limited

Fig. 46.2 *The industrial electrolysis of nickel Nickel is deposited on a pure nickel cathode during an electrolysis period which lasts 10 days. Here, the man is inspecting the quality of a cathode.*

particles are unaffected. This separates the ore from the rock.

The concentrate is then roasted to remove sulfur and to convert the nickel to its oxide. Reduction of this oxide with carbon produces impure nickel. Pure nickel is made by electrolysis or by passing carbon monoxide over the nickel. The volatile nickel carbonyl, $Ni(CO)_4$, that is formed, is removed from the impurities by distillation. After removal it is heated to 200 °C, at which temperature it decomposes to pure nickel and carbon monoxide:

$$Ni(CO)_4 \rightarrow Ni + 4CO\uparrow$$

Nickel is a silvery-white, magnetic metal which may be polished to a high lustre. Although the metal is quite hard, it is both malleable and ductile. It has a density of 8.85 g/cm^3.

The chemical reactions of nickel are like those of iron, but nickel is less reactive. Nickel does not corrode easily and its reaction with hydrochloric or sulfuric acid is very slow.

About 65 per cent of the world's nickel production goes into iron alloys to improve their strength and corrosion resistance. Some nickel is used for plating steel and as a catalyst in hydrogenation processes. The rest of the nickel production goes into nickel-copper alloys and coinage.

46:2 Platinum

This metal is so inactive chemically that it usually occurs either free or alloyed with other metals in nature. Its alloys have been used since antiquity. During the eighteenth century, the

TABLE 46.1		
Some Important Nickel Alloys		
Alloy	Major Constituents	Important Use
Alnico	Fe, Co, Ni, Al	Permanent magnets
Refractory	Ni, Co, Cr, Fe, Mo, Ti	Jet engines
Monel metal	Ni, Cu, Fe	Kitchen equipment
Nichrome	Ni, Cr	Resistance heating wire (household appliances)
Nickel steel	Fe, Ni	Machine parts
Stainless steel	Fe, Cr, Ni	Cutlery, decorative metal, cookery equipment

Spaniards discovered that the natives of Peru and Mexico were using a very heavy silver-colored metal for jewellery. Some of this metal was taken to Europe, and there it was found to be a new element. It was called platinum from the Spanish word *platina* meaning "little silver"

At first, importing platinum into Europe was restricted because unscrupulous persons began using it to adulterate gold. The properties of platinum soon made people realize that it was much more valuable than gold. Its resistance to corrosion makes it a good jewellery metal. Its high melting point (1,750°C), its low conductivity of electricity, its inert nature toward other materials, and its resistance to acids make platinum a good metal for crucibles, resistance thermometers, electrodes, and other laboratory apparatus. Platinum combines with the alkali metals and their hydroxides, with nitrates, and with peroxides. These materials should not be heated in platinum apparatus.

Platinum is used as a catalyst in the Contact and Ostwald Process (Chapters 31 and 33), in the form of wire gauze or in the finely divided state. For laboratory use, finely divided platinum may be obtained by dissolving platinum in *aqua regia*. The evaporated solution yields chloroplatinic acid, $(H_2PtCl_6)6H_2O$. Asbestos fibres soaked in the solution of the acid become coated with finely divided platinum, when heated to a high temperature in a test tube or other container. This combination may be used as catalyst in the Contact Process. However, it has been replaced for this purpose by vanadium pentoxide, a less expensive material.

46:3   Copper

Copper was the first metal used in large amounts by man. It was found free in nature, and, because it is soft and therefore easy to forge and has a high tensile strength, it was a logical material for both implements and decorations. The Bronze Age, one of the earliest eras in history, owes its name to the use of mixtures of tin and copper, called bronze. This alloy is harder than copper.

The discovery by Michael Faraday, in 1831, that a magnet moving through a coil of wire created an electric current opened the way for the modern electric age. Copper forms the nervous system of modern industry. Copper cables transmit the electric power needed in factories and homes, and copper is used in the construction of communication cables for underwater or land transmission of television and sound. Great amounts of copper are used in the construction of electric motors, radios, and appliances, and in all electronic devices.

Chemical Properties

Copper occurs below hydrogen in the Electromotive Series. It loses electrons less readily than iron, zinc, tin, and hydrogen. It is, however,

TABLE 46.2

Distribution of Electrons in Atomic Orbitals

| Element | Atomic Number | n = 1 | 2 | | 3 | | | 4 | | | | 5 | | | 6 | |
		s	s,	p	s,	p,	d	s,	p,	d,	f	s,	p,	d	s,	p
Cu	29	2	2	6	2	6	10	1								
Ag	47	2	2	6	2	6	10	2	6	10		1				
Au	79	2	2	6	2	6	10	2	6	10	14	2	6	10	1	

more active than silver, mercury, or gold. This is why a strip of iron placed in a copper sulfate solution becomes coated with copper, while a strip of silver remains unchanged:

$$Cu^{2+} + Fe^\circ \rightarrow Fe^{2+} + Cu^\circ$$

Copper forms a protective coating of copper (I) oxide when it is exposed to air. If the air is moist and carbon dioxide is present, a greenish layer of copper hydroxide carbonate is formed by the reaction of water and carbon dioxide with the oxide:

$$2Cu_2O + 2H_2O + CO_2 \rightarrow 2CuCO_3 \cdot Cu(OH)_2$$

Because of its ability to form a protective coating that prevents corrosion, copper is useful for roofing, pipes, and statues.

Copper unites with nearly all of the non-metals, especially at high temperatures. Heated copper burns in chlorine to form dark brown fumes of copper (II) chloride:

$$Cu + Cl_2 \rightarrow CuCl_2$$

Copper cannot release hydrogen from acids, but it can react with strong oxidizing acids, like nitric and sulfuric acids:

$$\underset{\underset{\downarrow}{0}}{3Cu} + \underset{5+}{8HNO_3} \rightarrow$$
$$3 \times 2e$$

$$\underset{\underset{\uparrow}{2+}}{3Cu(NO_3)_2} + 4H_2O + \underset{\underset{\uparrow}{2+}}{2NO\uparrow}$$
$$2 \times 3e$$

$$\underset{\underset{\downarrow}{0}}{Cu} + \underset{6+}{2H_2SO_4} \text{ (hot conc.)} \rightarrow$$
$$2e$$

$$\underset{\underset{\uparrow}{2+}}{CuSO_4} + 2H_2O + \underset{\underset{\uparrow}{4+}}{SO_2\uparrow}$$
$$2e$$

Alloys

The most widely used alloys of copper are bronze and brass, both of which are more easily machined and more durable than pure copper. They are used for bearings, hardware, and machine parts. Another of copper's alloys is German silver. This metal finds a wide use in cutlery, tableware, and various implements that must resist corrosion. Many alloys of steel, aluminum, and magnesium also contain copper. Copper and its alloys rank next to steel in their world-wide importance as engineering materials (Chapter 41).

Compounds of Copper

Copper (I) compounds, in which copper has an oxidation number of $1+$, are not as important as those of copper (II). The copper (I) ion is unstable in solution and forms copper metal and copper (II) ion.

$$2Cu^+ \rightarrow Cu^{2+} + Cu^\circ$$

Dilute aqueous solutions of copper (II) compounds are all greenish-blue, owing to the formation of the hydrated copper (II) ion, $Cu(H_2O)_4^{2+}$. Many crystals of copper (II) salts are blue for this same reason. For example, hydrated copper sulfate, $CuSO_4 \cdot 5H_2O$, is blue. If this is heated, the water of hydration may be driven off, and a white anhydrous powder is formed:

$$\overset{\text{heat}}{CuSO_4 \cdot 5H_2O \rightleftharpoons CuSO_4 + 5H_2O}$$

Since this reaction is reversible, anhydrous copper (II) sulfate may be used as a test for water. It turns blue in the presence of water because of the formation of hydrated copper (II) ion.

Copper (II) bromide forms a deep red-brown color in concentrated solution, owing to the formation of $CuBr_4^{2-}$. Dilution yields the greenish-blue color:

$$2CuBr_2 + 4H_2O \rightarrow Cu(H_2O)_4^{2+} \rightarrow CuBr_4^{2-}$$
$$\text{blue} \qquad \text{red-brown}$$

$$Cu(H_2O)_4^{2+} + CuBr_4^{2-} + 4H_2O \rightarrow$$
$$2Cu(H_2O)_4^{2+} + 4Br^-$$
$$\text{blue}$$

Most living cells contain small amounts of copper, which the cells need to help assimilate iron. Plant cells are unable to synthesize chlorophyll without copper. While copper is beneficial to most living cells, small amounts of copper sulfate in water kill algae and other lower forms of life. This salt is sometimes used in reservoirs to help keep the growth of algae from giving a bad taste to the water.

Copper (II) salts in water frequently hydrolyze to yield a pale blue flaky precipitate of copper (II) hydroxide:

$$Cu^{2+} + 4HOH \rightarrow Cu(OH)_2\downarrow + 2H_3O^+$$

Alkalies added to solutions containing the copper (II) ion also form this precipitate. When heated, the precipitate changes to black copper (II) oxide. Copper forms many complex ions. When concentrated ammonium hydroxide is added to copper sulfate, the solution turns an intense and opaque blue, due to the formation of a complex ion whose composition is [Cu (NH₃)₄]²⁺, called tetraammine copper (II) complex ion (Fig. 46.3). The overall equation is:

$$CuSO_4 + 4NH_4OH \rightarrow [Cu(NH_3)_4]SO_4 + 4H_2O$$
$$\text{tetraammine copper (II)}$$
$$\text{sulfate}$$

In the complex ion, $[Cu(NH_3)_4]^{2+}$ the NH_3 molecules act as the electron-pair donors or ligand, while Cu^{2+} acts as electron-pair acceptor.

An interesting feature of the complex ions of copper is their square shape. Up to this point, many molecules and ions having a tetrahedral shape were studied. Such a structure originates generally from sp^3 hybridization.

Because of its structure, the copper atom hybridizes one s, one p, and two d orbitals into four spd^2 orbitals which point to the corners of a square with the copper and nitrogen atoms lying in the same plane.

Fig. 46.3   *The tetraammine copper (II) complex ion has a flat, square shape*

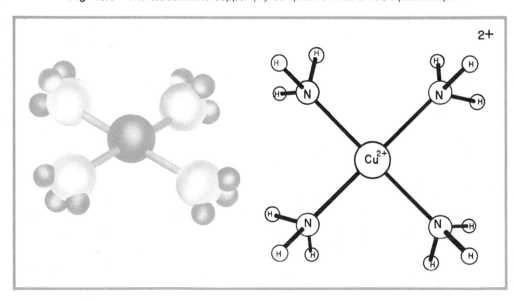

Metallurgy of Copper

The most important compound of copper in nature is the sulfide. This is concentrated by flotation. The concentrated copper sulfide is roasted to convert it to copper oxide. Then the oxide is reduced to metallic copper in the reverberatory furnace (Chapter 42) using coke. To remove the bulk of its impurities, the metallic copper is then heated in a Bessemer converter. The copper obtained is called *blister copper* because it contains many gas bubbles and defects. Most blister copper contains small amounts of metals, such as silver, gold, zinc, and arsenic.

Conductivity of electricity by copper may be greatly decreased by a small amount of impurities. As little as 0.03 per cent of impurities lowers conductivity by 14 per cent. Therefore, the copper must be made very pure for practical use.

Blister copper is most easily purified by electrolysis. The impure copper is cast into anodes about one yard square and one inch thick.

Fig. 46.4 *The froth flotation process*

Courtesy Cominco Ltd.

These are suspended in tanks containing warm copper sulfate and sulfuric acid. The anodes are all connected to a source of direct current. At each end of the tank and between each anode is placed a thin sheet of pure copper. These sheets are all connected to the cathode.

The following ions are present in the solution: Cu^{2+}, SO_4^{2-}, H_3O^+, OH^-.

$$\begin{cases} CuSO_4 \rightarrow Cu^{2+} + SO_4^{2-} \\ H_2SO_4 + 2H_2O \rightarrow 2H_3O^+ + SO_4^{2-} \\ 2HOH \rightarrow H_3O^+ + OH^- \end{cases}$$

At the cathode, copper ions are discharged instead of hydronium ions, because they have greater attraction for electrons than the hydronium ions:

$$Cu^{2+} + 2e \rightarrow Cu^\circ$$

In this way pure copper is deposited on the cathode. Copper atoms of the anode lose electrons to go into solution replacing the ions removed at the cathode:

$$Cu^\circ \rightarrow Cu^{2+} + 2e$$

In about 28 days, the anodes dissolve completely. The negative ions present in the solution are not electrolyzed at the anodes because the copper atoms lose their electrons more readily than these ions.

The voltage is adjusted so that no metals less active than copper are electrolyzed into ions at the anodes. Thus, if any silver and gold are present in the impure copper, these elements remain in the metallic condition while the copper is being electrolyzed. This happens because a greater amount of energy is required to remove electrons from silver and gold than from copper.

The silver and gold in impure copper form a sludge in the electrolytic tank. These and other metals are later separated from the residue in the tank.

Use of Copper in Printing

The same process used for refining copper is

also employed for electroplating type in the printing industry. Type-metal from a linotype machine is so soft that it sometimes prints fewer than 50,000 copies before wearing out. When many copies are necessary, a wax impression is made of the type. The wax is made into a conductor of electricity by carefully dusting it with graphite powder. Then the wax is plated with copper by making it the cathode in a copper sulfate-sulfuric acid bath. A bar of pure copper is used as the anode. Next, the copper-plated wax mold is removed from the bath and the wax is melted away. Finally the thin copper shell is backed with molten lead alloy. The finished plate can be bent for use on a rotary press and will make more than 100,000 printings before wearing out. For extremely long service, the copper may be plated with nickel.

46:4   Silver

Silver is found in nature in the free state, usually mixed with copper, gold, or mercury. Much silver comes from sulfide ores, of which argentite (Ag_2S) is the most important. Most of the world's silver is obtained as a by-product in the metallurgy of copper, lead, and zinc. Together, Mexico, Canada, and the United States produce over half the world's silver supply.

Because silver occurs uncombined and its ores are quite easily reduced, the metal has been known for many centuries. As long ago as 2000 B.C. silver mining was an important industry. In later years the alchemists associated this white metal with the moon. Apothecaries still refer to silver nitrate as "lunar caustic".

To obtain silver from ores containing metallic silver, the ores usually are treated with mercury. The resulting amalgam is separated from the unwanted residue and is then heated to boil off the mercury. The mercury is condensed and used over again. Ores containing free silver or silver chloride may be treated with sodium cyanide. In this process, complex sodium silver cyanide, $Na[Ag(CN)_2]$, is formed. Silver is displaced from this compound by adding powdered aluminum or zinc.

Sulfide ores are roasted to form the oxide and the latter is reduced to metallic silver by means of carbon in the form of charcoal or coke. A silver-lead alloy is formed by this reduction. This alloy is melted and zinc is added. The silver dissolves in the zinc, and the silver-zinc alloy floats on top of the molten lead. The silver-zinc alloy is removed and distilled; zinc boils away leaving the silver.

Gold-silver mixtures may be treated with nitric acid to obtain both gold and silver. The acid dissolves the silver, but not the gold. Copper metal displaces the silver from the resultant silver nitrate:

$$Cu + 2AgNO_3 \rightarrow Cu(NO_3)_2 + 2Ag$$

Another method used to separate a gold-silver alloy is electrolysis. The alloy serves as anode, pure silver as cathode, and silver nitrate solution is the electrolyte. The freed gold is caught in a porous bag surrounding the anode. The following reactions occur:

Cathode: $Ag^+ + e \rightarrow Ag^\circ$
Anode: $Ag^\circ \quad\quad \rightarrow Ag^+ + e$

Properties

Silver metal is intermediate in hardness between copper and gold. At normal temperatures it is the best conductor of electricity of all the common metals, but its high cost prevents its common use in electric wiring. It is very malleable and ductile.

Silver is almost white, unless it is finely divided, in which case it appears black. This is because the small particles of the metal scatter the reflected light in all directions. Silver forms alloys with many metals, and most of these are harder than pure silver.

Silver is one of the least active metals. It unites neither with oxygen nor with dilute acids at ordinary temperatures. Strong oxidizing acids, like nitric or sulfuric acid, react with it to form silver salts. The reactions are similar to those of copper. Reactions of silver with hydrogen sulfide were discussed in Chapter 31.

An interesting method of removing the tarnish from silverware is to place the articles in a hot solution of salt and washing soda in an aluminum dish:

$$Na_2CO_3 + 3H_2O + 2Al \rightarrow$$
$$2NaAlO_2 + CO_2 + 3H_2\uparrow$$
$$H_2 + Ag_2S \qquad \rightarrow 2Ag + H_2S$$

The aluminum dish is slowly dissolved and the silver sulfide is reduced.

Compounds of Silver

One of the most important compounds is silver nitrate, $AgNO_3$. This is obtained by dissolving silver in nitric acid. The addition of halogen salts to solutions of silver nitrate forms the very insoluble silver halides:

$$AgNO_3 + NaCl \rightarrow AgCl \downarrow + NaNO_3$$
$$\text{white}$$
$$AgNO_3 + NaBr \rightarrow AgBr \downarrow + NaNO_3$$
$$\text{pale yellow}$$
$$AgNO_3 + NaI \rightarrow AgI \downarrow + NaNO_3$$
$$\text{yellow}$$

Silver chloride dissolves in ammonium hydroxide to form the silver ammonia complex ion, $Ag(NH_3)_2^+$:

$$AgCl + 2NH_3 \rightarrow Ag(NH_3)_2^+ + Cl^-$$

Silver chloride dissolves upon addition of concentrated ammonium hydroxide due to the formation of the soluble silver ammonia complex ion $[Ag(NH_3)_2]^+$. The overall equation is:

$$AgCl + 2NH_4OH \rightarrow Ag(NH_3)_2Cl + 2H_2O$$
silver   concentrated   silver
chloride   ammonium   diammine
hydroxide   chloride

Because of its structure, the silver ion is able to hybridize one s and one p orbital into two sp orbitals for receiving the electron pairs from the ammonia molecule. With sp orbitals, the structure that results, $[Ag(NH_3)_2]^+$, is a straight line, as was the case with CO_2 and C_2H_2 (Fig. 46.5).

Uses of Silver and Its Compounds
COINS AND JEWELLERY

Silver metal, alloyed with about 10 per cent copper to harden it, is used extensively in coinage, jewellery, and silverware. More than 33 1/3 per cent of the world's production of silver goes into coinage. Small amounts of silver are used for dental and soldering alloys.

PLATING

A large amount of silver is used for electroplating. In this process, the electrolyte could be silver nitrate, but in practice silver potassium cyanide is used. The latter material is very poisonous and some prussic acid, HCN, is formed during the electrolysis so that good ventilation is necessary. Silver nitrate is difficult

Fig. 46.5   *The diammine silver complex ion has the shape of a straight line*

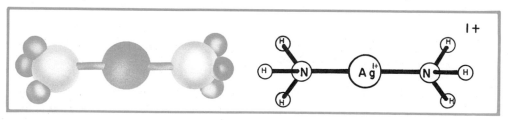

to use because the silver is discharged so easily that it usually forms a black powder on the object rather than actually plating it. Since the plating works best in a slightly basic solution, a typical plating bath contains potassium carbonate, potassium cyanide, and silver cyanide. The anode is a bar of pure silver; the cathode is the object to be plated. The following reactions occur:

$$\text{Cathode:} \quad Ag^+ + e \rightarrow Ag°$$
$$\text{Anode:} \quad Ag° \qquad \rightarrow Ag^+ + e$$

Depth of plate is controlled by the time of operation and the amount of current used. The solution must be stirred to ensure even plating (Fig. 14.4).

MIRRORS

To make a mirror, glass is polished, cleaned, and rinsed with distilled water. A mixture of silver nitrate and ammonia, together with some reducing agent like tin (II) chloride or formaldehyde, is sprayed on the glass. The reducing agent is mixed with the silver nitrate as the spraying is done. The finely divided silver precipitated on the glass forms the mirror. It is protected with a layer of lacquer.

INFECTIONS

A one per cent solution of silver nitrate is added to the eyes of new-born babies to prevent an infection that used to be a frequent cause of blindness.

PHOTOGRAPHY

One of the outstanding characteristics of the silver halides is that they are reduced to metallic silver on exposure to light. This is the basis of the photographic film. The basic steps in a film's construction, exposure, and development arc as follows:

1. *Preparation of film*: A thin sheet of cellulose acetate is coated, in the dark, with a suspension of silver bromide and silver iodide particles in a gelatin emulsion. The gelatin acts as a protective colloid to prevent the coagulation of the particles.

2. *Exposure of film*: Since a picture consists of light and shadows of different intensities, various parts of the film receive different amounts of light when the picture is *exposed*. The light entering the camera produces a latent image on the film. The silver ions affected by light absorb energy and are more readily reduced than ions unaffected by light.

3. *Developing*: The exposed film is placed in a mild reducing agent, which is known as a *developer* because it brings out or develops the latent image. The ions struck by light are reduced by this solution:

$$Ag^+ + 1e \rightarrow Ag°$$

The extent of this reduction depends upon the amount of light energy absorbed. A negative image appears on the film.

4. *Fixing*: After developing, there is still much unchanged silver bromide in the emulsion. This is sensitive to light and therefore must be dissolved out, which is accomplished by using sodium thiosulfate (hypo) solution.

5. *Printing*: Light is projected through the negative to paper coated with an emulsion similar to that on the original film. Development of the latent image on the paper produces a positive print.

46:5   Gold

Down through the ages, gold has been one of man's most prized possessions. Proof of this is the elaborately designed ornaments which have been found as relics from older civilizations.

Occurrence

Gold is mainly found uncombined in nature. It occurs as nuggets or small flakes in veins of quartz or in alluvial sand. Silver and platinum are sometimes mixed with native gold. Today, most gold mining is done in South Africa, the United States, the U.S.S.R., and Canada.

Metallurgy

In order to obtain gold from sand, a pan containing the sand is held in running water and shaken gently in a rotary motion. The density of the gold is so high that it soon sinks to the bottom of the pan. Placer mining uses the same principle but employs sluices through which the sand-gold mixture runs. The gold settles out during the process.

Gold-bearing quartz is first crushed. The gold may then be amalgamated with mercury by rolling the mercury and ore in a barrel. The mercury is then distilled off, leaving the gold. Another method is to treat the crushed ore with sodium cyanide. Sodium gold cyanide is formed, from which the gold may be displaced by zinc. Sometimes the ore is treated with chlorine to form gold chloride. From this, the gold is obtained by electrolysis, in which case the electrolyte is gold chloride containing some hydrochloric acid.

Properties

Pure gold is bright yellow, very lustrous, soft, dense, ductile, and malleable. In fact it is the most malleable of all metals and can be beaten into sheets a mere one hundred thousandth of an inch thick! One ounce of gold can be drawn into a wire 50 miles long.

Gold is very inert. It is not affected by exposure to the air. It does not combine with oxygen, sulfur, or hydrogen sulfide. It combines

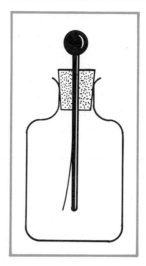

Fig. 46.6   *The gold leaf electroscope*
In this electroscope, an extremely thin sheet of gold is attached to a metal rod. Gold is used because it is a good conductor and, when it is well beaten out it is very flexible. Hence it responds quickly and vigorously to small electrostatic forces.

with chlorine slowly. No single acid attacks it, but it dissolves in *aqua regia*.

Uses

Pure gold is too soft for most purposes, and so it is often alloyed with copper. The purity of gold is measured in carats; 24-carat gold is pure, while 18 carats is an alloy containing 75 per cent gold. Gold is used mostly for jewellery, gold reserves of governments, dental work, electrical equipment, color photography, and gold plating.

Gold plating uses an anode of gold and an electrolyte of gold potassium cyanide.

To decorate books, windows, buildings, dishes, and monuments, gold leaf is often used. Dishes are sometimes decorated with an organic salt of gold which leaves a gold film when fired.

White gold, which is used in some rings and other kinds of jewellery, is an alloy of gold and palladium or nickel.

QUESTIONS

1. (a) Describe the metallurgy of nickel.
   (b) Write a note on flotation.

2. List the physical and chemical properties of nickel.

3. Why is nickel less active than iron?

4. List the important uses of nickel.

5. What properties make platinum a valuable metal?

6. What precautions should be observed when using platinum apparatus in the laboratory?

7. Explain how finely divided platinum is prepared for use as a catalyst.

8. (a) What is the common oxidation number of copper, silver, and gold.
   (b) Why do these elements have more than one oxidation number each?
   (c) Why are these elements less active than the alkali metals?

9. Write a paragraph on the importance of copper.

10. Why does iron displace copper from a solution of its salts?

11. What chemical changes occur to cause copper to turn green when exposed to air?

12. Describe the reaction of copper with chlorine. Write the equation.

13. Explain and illustrate the reaction of copper with acids.

14. Write a note on the alloys of copper.

15. Why are most crystals of copper (II) salts blue in color?

16. Explain why a concentrated solution of copper (II) bromide is brown while the dilute solution is blue.

17. Of what importance is copper in vital processes?

18. In what ways may copper (II) hydroxide be formed?

19. Describe the metallurgy of copper.

20. Explain clearly the purification of blister copper by electrolysis. Write the equations.

21. How is copper used in printing?

22. What are the most important sources of silver?

23. How is native silver removed from its ores?

24. How is silver obtained from (a) sulfide ores (b) gold-silver alloys.

25. List the principal physical and chemical properties of silver.

26. Describe a method of removing tarnish from silver by reduction.

27. Complete these equations:
    (a) $AgNO_3 + Cl^- \rightarrow$
    (b) $AgNO_3 + Br^- \rightarrow$
    (c) $AgNO_3 + I^- \rightarrow$
    (d) $AgCl + NH_3 \rightarrow$

28. List the uses of silver.

29. Explain the silver plating process.

30. Describe a method of silvering mirrors.

31. Outline the fundamental steps of the photographic process.

32. How does gold occur in nature?

33. Describe the metallurgy of gold.

34. What are the principal properties and uses of gold?

35. What volume of hydrogen measured at $-30°C$ and 700 mm is required to reduce 400 g of copper (II) oxide?

36. Find the volume of hydrogen sulfide at STP required to precipitate all the copper from 50 ml of a 2 M solution of copper sulfate.

37. Calculate the simplest formula of a compound containing 74.9 per cent copper and 20.1 per cent sulfur.

38. How much silver would be required to prepare 12 lbs of silver nitrate by means of the following reaction?

$$Ag + 2HNO_3 \rightarrow AgNO_3 + H_2O + 2NO$$

39. If 15 ml of a sodium chloride solution are added to excess silver nitrate solution, and the dried precipitate of silver chloride is found to weigh 2.14 g, find the molarity of the sodium chloride solution used.

CHAPTER
47 The Nucleus and Radioactivity

47:1 Nuclear Change

In physical changes, the size, shape, or state of a substance is altered but not its composition. In chemical reactions, the composition of a substance changes. There is yet another type of change which is neither physical nor chemical. Because it involves the nucleus of the atom, it is termed *nuclear*.

Categories of nuclear changes may be classified as:

a. *Transmutation*, in which an isotope of an element is changed into another isotope of about the same atomic number;

b. *Fission*, in which an isotope of an element is split into smaller fragments;

c. *Fusion*, in which the nuclei of smaller atoms combine (or fuse together) to form a larger nucleus. In such reactions, tremendous amounts of energy are released, far in excess of the greatest energies of a physical or chemical change. Such energy is termed atomic or nuclear energy.

47:2 Discovery of Radioactivity

In 1896, the French physicist Becquerel (Chapter 14) found that a salt of uranium placed on a photographic plate left its picture on the film as if it had been photographed. After careful experiments had shown that the same effect could be had even if the photographic plates were wrapped in thin metal sheets, Becquerel concluded that the uranium compound emitted rays that were able to penetrate metal foil.

Becquerel also found that an electrically charged electroscope was discharged by the mere presence of the uranium compound. He concluded that the rays emitted by the uranium salt had the ability of changing the molecules of air into ions. These ions were then attracted to the charged electroscope, thus discharging it.

This property of a substance, to emit rays without stimulus from any external source, was termed *radioactivity*. From the modest beginnings described above, the phenomenon of radioactivity has grown into the powerful source of energy known the world over as *nuclear energy*.

47:3 The Discovery of Radium

Pierre Curie and his wife, Marie, who were colleagues of Becquerel, extended the study of radioactivity (Chapter 14). Using the ore from which the uranium compound was obtained, Marie Curie discovered two other elements, *radium* and *polonium*, which were even more radioactive than uranium. In order to accomplish this, Marie Curie had to purify about one ton of ore to recover 0.1 gram of radium and an even smaller amount of polonium. The story of Marie Curie is truly inspiring for its perseverance and courage.

47:4 Radiations from the Radioactive Elements

What are the radiations coming from such radioactive elements as uranium, polonium, and radium? What is their nature and their origin?

The eminent British scientist Ernest Rutherford began his study of radioactivity to find answers to such questions. In the course of his research, he made many fundamental discoveries about atomic structure (Chapter 15). Rutherford placed a few grains of radioactive

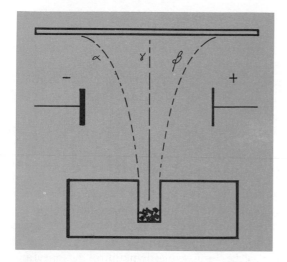

Fig. 47.1 *Separation of alpha, beta, and gamma rays*

matter in a thick-walled lead container open only at the top, as illustrated in Fig. 47.1. Above the opening was a screen with a coating of zinc sulfide. He discovered that when rays from radioactive elements struck this screen, tiny flashes of light, called scintillations, could be observed. In studying the rays, Rutherford found that when a strong magnetic or electrostatic field was placed around the beam of radiation, three spots appeared on the zinc sulfide screen. Rutherford concluded that the beam of radiation contained three rays. One of these was positively charged, another negatively charged, and a third was neutral. He named them *alpha* (α), *beta* (β), and *gamma* (γ) rays and undertook further study to identify them.

The alpha rays were found to be a stream of helium nuclei, He^{2+}. Their positive charge was shown by their attraction to the negative electrode in the above experiment. They travel at high speeds and strongly ionize air or any gas through which they pass.

Alpha particles may be observed indirectly in a cloud chamber (Fig. 47.2). This apparatus contains air saturated with water vapor and is fitted with a cooling device which may be a

movable piston, a rubber bulb, or a cube of dry ice. A small source of alpha particles is present in the air chamber. To make the paths of the alpha particles visible, the air is cooled directly by the dry ice, or by suddenly increasing its volume by the motion of the piston, or by the action of the rubber bulb. As the temperature drops, water condenses on the ions of air formed along the paths of the particles, thus making the paths visible.

The beta rays were found to be electrons travelling even faster than alpha particles. Their negative charge was shown by their attraction to the positive electrode. Beta rays consist of electrons travelling at high velocities, in some cases approaching the speed of light. Beta rays have higher penetrating power than do alpha rays, but their ionizing power is much less, and they produce only faint tracks in a cloud chamber.

Gamma rays are similar to X rays except that they have a shorter wave length and greater energy and penetrating power. They are not affected by either magnetic or electric fields.

A single element does not emit both alpha and beta particles as a rule. Gamma rays are emitted with either alpha and beta radiation.

Fig. 47.2 *The cloud chamber*

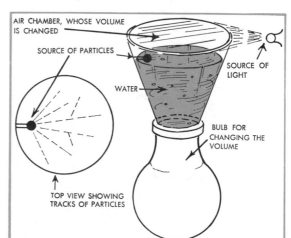

47:5 Geiger Counter

A valuable instrument for measuring radio-activity is the Geiger counter. It consists of a metal cylinder, the cathode, and a fine tungsten wire along the axis of the cylinder, the anode. Both cathode and anode are enclosed in a thin-walled, glass tube filled with gas (usually argon) at low pressure.

The anode is charged to a high voltage of about 1000 volts. This is not enough to ionize the argon; so no current flows. If, however, an alpha or a beta particle enters the tube, electrons are knocked out of the atoms of argon by collision with the high energy particles. Such electrons rush toward the positively charged anode and a pulse of electric current flows through the tube. Thus even a single alpha or beta particle could be detected since it may cause the pulse of current. The pulses may be amplified, recorded, or flashed.

47:6 The Unusual Features of Radioactivity

In the studies on radioactivity by Becquerel, Curie, and Rutherford, much evidence had been collected that indicated that radioactivity was not just another chemical reaction:

1. Radioactive materials emit rays of unusual nature.
2. Temperature and pressure have no effect on the intensity of radioactivity, whereas these factors, particularly temperature, influence chemical reactions.
3. All the compounds of a radioactive element are radioactive.
4. The energy of radioactivity is about 100,000 times as great as that of chemical reactions.

47:7 Rutherford's Theory of Radioactivity

Radioactivity is the process whereby the atoms of one element change into the atoms of another.

Radioactivity causes the nucleus of the atom to be altered. To illustrate, radium belongs to the same family of elements as magnesium; namely, group II of the periodic table. In radio-active change, radium is changed to radon, a Rare Gas. In the process the atom of radium has changed to the atom of radon. In the same process, an alpha particle has been emitted. This is an instance of a radioactive change called the *transmutation* of atoms. It is caused by changes in the nucleus of the atoms and is accompanied by the emission of alpha, beta, or other particles along with gamma rays.

Since alpha and beta particles are charged, their emission from an atom results in a change in the nuclear charge and, therefore, of the atomic number. Hence an isotope of an element has been produced that is different from the

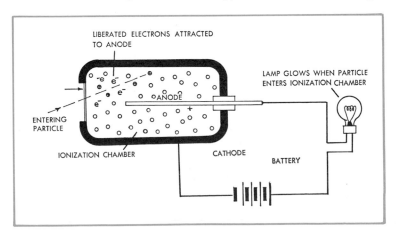

LIBERATED ELECTRONS ATTRACTED TO ANODE

LAMP GLOWS WHEN PARTICLE ENTERS IONIZATION CHAMBER

ANODE

ENTERING PARTICLE

IONIZATION CHAMBER

CATHODE

BATTERY

Fig. 47.3 Geiger counter

original. When an atom emits an alpha particle from its nucleus, the resulting nucleus has two less positive charges, and the new atom has an atomic number two less and a mass number four less than the original.

The transmutation of radium to radon could therefore be represented by the equation:

$$\underset{88}{\overset{226}{}} Ra \rightarrow \underset{86}{\overset{222}{}} Rn + \underset{2}{\overset{4}{}} He$$

Nuclear reactions may be written like chemical reactions, with equations to show what change has taken place. One obvious difference is that all the terms of the equation are symbols since these changes involve only atoms, not molecules. It is of course necessary to identify the particular isotope of the element that enters the reaction. This is done by a number in the upper left hand corner of the symbol. Finally, it is also necessary to show the atomic numbers of the atoms involved, since protons are given out in some nuclear reactions. Atomic numbers are usually shown in the lower left hand corner.

In the preceding equation, the superscript refers to the mass number and the subscript to the atomic number. The mass number is the nearest integral value of the mass of an isotope in atomic mass units. Inspection shows that the atomic numbers and the atomic masses balance:

$$\boxed{\begin{array}{c} 88p \\ 138n \\ \hline 226 \end{array}} \rightarrow \boxed{\begin{array}{c} 86p \\ 136n \\ \hline 222 \end{array}} + \boxed{\begin{array}{c} 2p \\ 2n \\ \hline 4 \end{array}}$$

47:8 The Rate of Nuclear Change; The Half-life of a Radioactive Element

Rutherford studied the nuclear changes in three series of elements found to be naturally radioactive. He identified about 40 elements in the step-by-step alteration of the nucleus of larger atoms to smaller ones. He also determined the rate at which each radioactive isotope changed to its successor, and reported such rates of change in terms of the *half-life* of the isotope.

The rates at which nuclear changes occur vary widely. ^{238}U disintegrates very slowly while polonium, on the other hand, disintegrates very rapidly. In all cases, however, the number of atoms of any radioactive element that changes in unit time is a constant fraction of the total number of atoms of the isotope present. As more and more atoms change, the number changing per unit time decreases. For this reason, the rates of nuclear change are expressed by means of the *half-life*, defined as the time required for half of the isotope in any given sample to disintegrate.

If a radioactive element has a half-life of one year, then the record of its disintegration would be as shown in Table 47.1, if one started with 1 gram on January 1, 1970.

TABLE 47.1	
Date	Mass of Radioactive Element
Jan. 1, 1970	1 gram
Jan. 1, 1971	0.5 gram
Jan. 1, 1972	0.25 gram
Jan. 1, 1973	0.125 gram

47:9 Nuclear Structure and Binding Energy

What is the nucleus of the atom, and what is its source of energy? Although all the particles composing the nucleus have not yet been identified (even the discovery of such important particles as the neutron is fairly recent), a tentative picture of nuclear structure might be suggested.

As stated earlier atomic nuclei are made up of protons and neutrons, held together by powerful forces which are not entirely understood, but which are known to be different from the familiar gravitational and electrostatic forces. The small size of the nucleus would indicate that nuclear forces operate over very short distances only. Newly discovered particles, such as *mesons*, are also present and they may help explain how the nucleus holds together.

It is significant that the mass of an atomic nucleus is generally less than the sum of the mass of protons and neutrons which are present. For example, the helium nucleus contains two protons and two neutrons. The sum of the masses of these particles is 2(1.0073) + 2(1.0087) or 4.032 atomic mass units. The helium nucleus has a mass of only 4.0017 atomic mass units. Apparently 0.0303 amu of mass were lost in the formation of the nucleus of a helium atom.

The explanation of this loss is provided by the principle that mass and energy are interconvertible according to the equation:

$$E = mc^2$$

where E is energy in ergs, m is mass in grams, and c is the speed of light in centimeters per second. Since the speed of light is very great, 3×10^{10} cm/sec, or 186,000 miles per second, a small mass could produce a large amount of energy. According to this equation, the conversion of one kilogram of mass to energy should yield 25 billion (2.5×10^{10}) kilowatt-hours of electrical energy. This is equal to the total output of electric power in Canada for a two-year period. The formation of one mole of helium from protons and neutrons would liberate 650 billion (6.5×10^{11}) calories of heat. The conversion of hydrogen nuclei to helium nuclei is the source of the sun's energy and is an instance of *atomic fusion*.

Research is being done to learn how to harness this type of energy for electric power.

The *binding energy* is the energy equivalent to the difference between the actual mass of the nucleus of an isotope and the sum of the masses of the protons and neutrons that compose it, expressed as energy. The binding energy is greatest for the elements of atomic mass from 40 to 100, and gradually decreases for both the very large and the very small atoms.

QUESTIONS

1. How is nuclear change different from a physical or chemical change?

2. Describe how nuclear changes are classified.

3. Describe briefly how radioactivity was discovered.

4. What are the main characteristics of the three types of rays given off by radioactive materials?

5. Describe the operation of a cloud chamber.

6. How does a Geiger counter work and for what is it used?

7. List four characteristics of radioactivity.

8. Outline Rutherford's Theory of Radioactivity.

9. Write an equation to demonstrate transmutations. Give the meaning of each number and symbol used.

10. Define *half-life*. What is the purpose of this term?

11. Explain clearly why the mass of an atomic nucleus is generally less than the sum of the masses of the particles that comprise it.

12. Define the term *binding energy*.

CHAPTER

48 Radioisotopes

48:1 Nuclear Reactions

Radioactivity and nuclear change were first discovered with the elements of high atomic number. Nuclear physicists were always curious to find out whether the atoms of any element could be made to undergo nuclear change or become radioactive as well.

In 1919, when Rutherford bombarded nitrogen with alpha particles ($^4_2$He) from a radioactive substance, he found that a minute amount of oxygen of atomic mass 17 was formed — an isotope of ordinary oxygen. A proton was also liberated in this nuclear reaction, the first successful artificial transmutation:

$$^{14}_{7}N + ^{4}_{2}He \rightarrow ^{17}_{8}O + ^{1}_{1}H$$

The alpha particles used by Rutherford were not effective in producing much change. Since they were liberated by the naturally occurring radioactive elements, they were the only projectiles available for nuclear experiments until 1932.

48:2 The Cyclotron

With the invention of the cyclotron in 1932 by Professor E. O. Lawrence, it became possible to accelerate charged particles, such as protons H^+ and deuterons D^+, the heavy isotope of hydrogen, to such velocities that they could be used in similar nuclear experiments. The cyclotron consists of a pair of semicircular metal chambers, called *dees* because of their shape, mounted between the poles of an extremely powerful electromagnet (Fig. 48.1). A high-frequency alternating current is passed through them, causing their polarity to change rapidly.

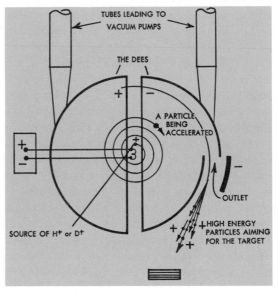

Fig. 48.1 *The cyclotron*

A charged particle, such as a proton, is liberated near the centre of one of the dees, and the alternating current causes it to go in a circular path from one dee to the other and back. Each time the particle passes from one dee to the other it is given an additional electrical boost to make it go faster. Finally, it emerges with a velocity nearly equal to that of light and strikes the target with enough energy to penetrate the nucleus and to cause nuclear change.

The following are typical transmutations accomplished by the cyclotron:

$$^{7}_{3}Li + ^{1}_{1}H(proton) \rightarrow ^{4}_{2}He + ^{4}_{2}He$$

$$^{24}_{12}Mg + ^{2}_{1}D \rightarrow ^{24}_{11}Na + ^{1}_{1}H + ^{1}_{1}H$$

Through these studies, important discoveries

were made. A particle similar to the electron was discovered, differing only in charge. The particle was named the *positron* because its charge is positive. The cyclotron has also revealed particles called *mesons*, and they may prove to be involved in nuclear cohesive forces. Another major discovery was that the atoms were changed into new isotopes of other atoms. The isotopes thus produced were radioactive in many cases. Thus the cyclotron succeeded in changing elements into other elements, and in causing elements to be radioactive artificially. On a small scale, the cyclotron produced transmutation and radioactivity. How could these be carried out on a large scale?

Methods for causing nuclear reactions discussed thus far, namely, bombardment by naturally emitted alpha particles, or bombardment in the cyclotron, involved the expenditure of great amounts of energy, and the products formed were insignificantly small. This could be explained by the fact that the positive particles used as projectiles were repelled as they approached the positively charged nuclei of atoms.

48:3   Discovery of the Neutron

Scientists realized that the ideal particle for use as an atomic projectile would be the neutron. Its lack of a positive charge would permit it to enter the nuclei of atoms freely; but without an electric charge, this particle was difficult to detect and to manage. Finally, in 1932, it was discovered by physicists that when a light element like magnesium was bombarded with alpha particles, transmutation occurred of magnesium to silicon, and at the same time, a stream of neutrons issued from the reaction. The reaction could be represented by this equation:

$$_{12}^{24}\text{Mg} + _{2}^{4}\text{He} \rightarrow _{14}^{27}\text{Si} + _{0}^{1}\text{n}$$

The silicon nucleus thus produced is unstable, and it undergoes radioactive disintegration according to the equation:

$$_{14}^{27}\text{Si} \rightarrow _{13}^{27}\text{Al} + _{1}^{0}\text{e}$$

This nuclear change was important for the following reasons:

1. A method was provided for obtaining neutrons.

2. Both transmutation and radioactivity had been achieved artificially.

3. An element was prepared whose atom was larger than the original.

Scientists did not believe at first that neutrons were produced in this manner, but careful experimentation showed that this was indeed the case. It was this reaction that proved to be the birth of the present atomic and nuclear age.

As a result of the new instruments and the newly discovered particles for studying the nucleus of the atom, much progress has been made in nuclear science in recent years.

48:4   Neutron Bombardment of Uranium, New Elements, and Atomic Fission

In the reaction of magnesium with the alpha particle, a silicon atom is produced. The silicon has a higher atomic number than the magnesium. It is thus possible to produce larger atoms as well as smaller atoms by nuclear change. What would occur if the largest atom in the periodic table were treated in a similar way? Would we obtain an atom whose kind never existed in nature? These questions were thought about by the Italian scientist Enrico Fermi almost as soon as the neutron's existence was verified. He attempted to obtain the answer experimentally; by bombarding atom number 92 (uranium), he hoped to obtain atom number 93.

Fermi's attempt was successful. He found the isotope of ^{238}U captures a neutron to become ^{239}U, an unstable isotope which in turn changes to neptunium (At.No.93) and plutonium (At.No.94). Both of these are new elements that have never been found in nature but have been synthesized by man.

In 1938, other scientists, repeating this experiment, discovered that another isotope of uranium, ^{235}U, breaks up into two or more fragments, such as the nuclei of krypton and barium, when struck by a neutron. Such a nuclear change is an example of *atomic fission*. Furthermore, during the break-up of the nucleus of ^{235}U, more neutrons are released as well as great amounts of energy. The approximate equation is:

$$^{235}_{92}U + ^{1}_{0}n \rightarrow ^{137}_{56}Ba + ^{84}_{36}Kr + 3^{1}_{0}n$$

Here, neutrons produced a fission which liberated neutrons that could, in turn, produce more fissions, and so on. Thus a "chain reaction" (Fig. 48.2) could be started which would be self-sustaining and which would make possible the release of atomic energy. This became the basis of the atomic bomb. An atomic explosion results when just the right amount of fissionable material is brought together to be split by neutrons in chain reaction. This amount is called the *critical mass* of the atomic bomb.

TABLE 48.1
Mass of Reactants and Products in Nuclear Reactions

Reactants	
1 uranium isotope	235 amu
1 neutron	1 amu
	236 amu

Products	
1 barium isotope	137 amu
1 krypton isotope	84 amu
3 neutrons	3 amu
	224 amu

It will be observed in the preceding equation that the atomic mass of the products is less than that of the reactants. This is so because twelve

Fig. 48.2 *Atomic fission of ^{235}U*

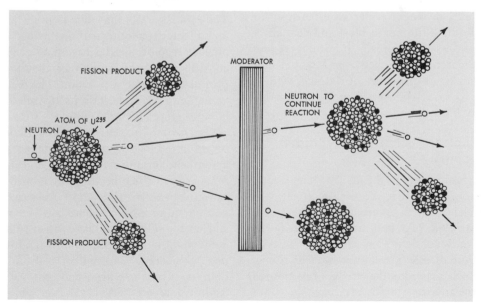

amu of mass have been transformed into energy (Table 48.1).

48:5   The Atom Bomb

The instantaneous release of vast energy produces temperatures of many millions of degrees. The heat accounts for the flash burns which could be fatal to victims who are as far as a mile away from the explosion. The heat also produces a violent expansion of air, with a resulting blast that flattens most buildings within an area of several square miles from the centre of the explosion. Along with the heat and blast comes the gamma radiation that is liberated. This travels with the speed of light from the centre of the blast and can be fatal at distances up to a mile or more. At shorter distances it is always fatal unless one is shielded by several feet of concrete or earth.

An atomic explosion also contributes danger of another sort. The fission products may themselves be radioactive, and they may cause particles in the atmosphere to become radioactive as well. Such matter is termed *fall-out*. If the explosion occurs high in the air, there is a certain amount of fall-out; but an explosion at ground level or under water would cause far more fall-out. Although its blast and heat effect would be less widespread, it would render adjacent materials radioactive and would hurl into the air great quantities of radioactive dust or water. Thus a widespread and long-lasting secondary hazard would exist.

48:6   Nuclear Fusion: the Hydrogen Bomb

The source of energy in the nuclear reactor and in the atomic bomb is the fission of ^{235}U or ^{239}Pu nuclei. Even larger amounts of energy per unit mass of nuclear fuel are liberated by the union of nuclei of light elements to form heavier ones, a type of reaction termed *nuclear fusion*. It is by such reactions that the energy emitted by the sun and the stars is produced.

Substances that might be used as fuels for fusion reactions include some of the isotopes of hydrogen, lithium, and boron. A reaction that is particularly efficient, in terms of energy released per gram of fuel, is that in which tritium and deuterium react to give helium, as shown by the equation:

$$^{3}_{1}H + {}^{2}_{1}D \rightarrow {}^{4}_{2}He + {}^{1}_{0}n$$

The chief problem to be overcome in the application of nuclear fusion, especially for industrial purposes, lies in the fact that such reactions take place only at temperatures higher than 1,000,000°C, such as prevail on the sun, but which are very difficult to attain on earth. In the construction of the hydrogen bomb, an atomic bomb of the fission type is used as a detonator.

Since the explosion of a hydrogen bomb depends upon the attainment of a very high temperature rather than a critical mass there is no apparent upper limit to the possible size of such a weapon, or to its destructive power.

48:7   The Nuclear Reactor (Atomic Pile)

The explosion of an atomic bomb is an instantaneous and uncontrolled chain reaction. In a nuclear reactor, similar fissioning occurs but is controlled in such a manner that *one* fission produces only one *new* fission. The reaction can be made barely to sustain itself while giving off large amounts of heat.

One form of nuclear reactor consists of a pile of graphite blocks through which are dispersed a number of uranium rods encased in aluminum. Slots are provided through which boron steel or cadmium control rods can be inserted. Boron and cadmium absorb neutrons. The reactor is started by pulling out the control rods so that neutrons produce more fissions, and it is stopped by pushing the control rods in until so many neutrons are absorbed that the reaction cannot maintain itself. The graphite blocks

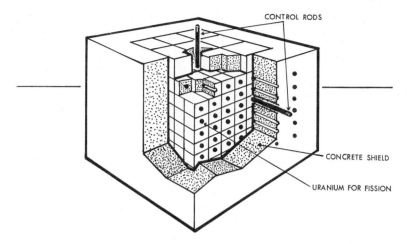

CONTROL RODS

CONCRETE SHIELD

URANIUM FOR FISSION

Fig. 48.3 *The nuclear reactor or atomic pile*

moderate or slow down the neutrons so that they are readily captured by other ^{235}U nuclei. Trays are provided by means of which substances to be irradiated can be introduced

Fig. 48.4 *The atomic reactor at Chalk River, Ontario*

Courtesy Atomic Energy of Canada Limited

to the high neutron flux. The entire mass is enclosed in a wall of concrete several feet thick to prevent escape of dangerous gamma rays and neutron radiation. Provision is also made for circulating cooling water or some other heat transfer medium through the reactor. A diagrammatic representation of the series of events which may take place in a nuclear reactor is given in Fig. 48.2.

Many elements or materials may be inserted into the reactor for irradiation with neutrons, thus converting them to radioactive forms. This is the source of the wide range of radioactive materials now being used by medicine for research and treatment and by industry for many purposes.

48:8 Uses of Radioisotopes

a. Tracer Research

Radioactive isotopes have the same chemical properties as do normal atoms. They and their compounds undergo the same chemical reactions as their normal counterparts, as a rule. If, for example, a plant uses carbon dioxide for its nourishment, it does not differentiate between the normal carbon dioxide and the radioactive type whose molecules contain a radioactive atom of carbon. By allowing such radioactive carbon dioxide to be inhaled by the plant, an experimenter may then follow the path of carbon dioxide through the plant. Thus he learns what chemical reactions take place involving carbon dioxide. Such information would be extremely difficult to obtain in any other way.

Since, in this method, a compound is followed through the intricate chemical reactions which go on in living organisms, the method is called *tracer research*. One scientist has said that tracer research is as effective in studying the chemistry of living organisms as the microscope and the X ray combined.

b. Industrial Applications

In industry, radioactivity is used in several ways. In the oil industry it is sometimes necessary to transport different types of oil in succession through a pipe line. In order to identify a new type of oil that has been introduced into the pipe, some radioactive matter is added to the new batch. Its radiations may be detected by an instrument at the receiving station. Thus, it is easy to tell when the new batch has arrived.

In the paper industry, it is necessary to produce a sheet of uniform thickness. To ensure this, a thickness gauge based on the penetrating power of the rays from isotopes is used. The sheet of paper is passed between the source of radiation and the radiation detector. Such a gauge might be connected to the main power drive to regulate the speed at which the paper is formed, thus regulating the thickness. Similar gauges are used to control the thickness of aluminum, copper, rubber, and glass sheets.

These are but two examples of the many practical applications of isotopes in industry.

c. Medical Applications

Radioactive cobalt, ^{60}Co, has taken over much of the medical work formerly done by radium. In one installation, ^{60}Co, in wafers the size of

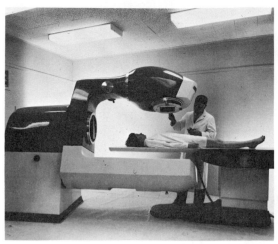

Courtesy Atomic Energy of Canada Limited

Fig. 48.5 *Here, radiations from cobalt-60 are being used to treat cancer*

25-cent pieces, is enclosed in a lead-lined case. Cancerous tissue is exposed by briefly opening a window in the case. The radiation is said to be 25 times as powerful as the strongest radium units, and the cost is less than one thousandth that of an equivalent amount of radium. Thus many small hospitals can now afford an effective radiation source for purposes of treatment.

Radioactivity is being used increasingly in medical diagnosis. A dye tagged with ^{131}I has been proposed for the diagnosis and location of brain tumors. The dye is said to concentrate in the tumor, permitting its location and study by a Geiger counter.

d. Carbon Dating

One radioisotope of carbon ^{14}C has a half-life of about 5,600 years. This isotope has been helpful to anthropologists in establishing the dates of articles and events of the distant past.

Radioactive carbon (^{14}C) forms when cosmic rays, upon reaching the earth, release neutrons in the upper atmosphere which in turn cause nitrogen atoms to change to this radioactive isotope of carbon.

$$_0^1n + {}_7^{14}N \rightarrow {}_6^{14}C + {}_1^1H$$

Such carbon atoms mix with normal ^{12}C atoms in the carbon dioxide of the air. This results in a certain ratio of ^{14}C to ^{12}C in atmospheric carbon dioxide at all times. This ratio carries over to the carbon content of organic substances in plants and animals, notably wood, formed by the carbon dioxide. When an article made of such wood becomes buried, the ^{14}C continues to disintegrate according to its half-life and, as a result, the ratio of ^{14}C to ^{12}C will be different in this article from the normal value.

Scientists can determine this difference and from it calculate the age of the article. This technique is called *carbon dating*.

48:9 Nuclear Energy for Power

The practical application of nuclear energy lies in the heat developed within the nuclear reactor. A heat transfer liquid is circulated through the reactor, where it becomes heated. The liquid is then pumped to a heat interchanger where it converts ordinary water to steam. From this point the power is conventional. For example, the steam can be used to power a ship's propellers or an electrical generator. In order to control the reaction for such purposes, a moderator is used to absorb the excess neutrons which would cause the reaction to proceed at an ever faster rate. Even greater power would be released if science could learn how to control a fusion reaction of hydrogen to helium. In view of the many dramatic discoveries that have been made even in our own lifetime, and particularly in recent years, it would not be surprising to hear that this challenging problem may soon be solved.

This book ends as it began, on the theme of problems and their solution by the scientific method. It seems that the process will go on forever because man is always faced by new and often bewildering difficulties.

Fig. 48.6 *Power from a nuclear reactor*
Uranium fission in the reactor produces heat. The heavy water surrounding the uranium rods serves both as a moderator to absorb extra neutrons emitted by the uranium and as a conductor to absorb heat. In the heat exchanger, the heat from the heavy water converts ordinary water to steam, which drives the turbine which in turn drives the generator.

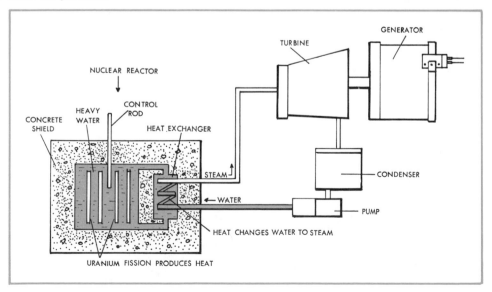

QUESTIONS

1. Describe with the aid of an equation the first successful artificial transmutation.

2. (a) Explain the operation of the cyclotron.
   (b) What rays may be produced directly by a cyclotron?
   (c) How are these rays of greater use than natural radiations?

3. (a) How was a stream of neutrons first produced artificially?
   (b) Why are neutrons so valuable for producing transmutations?

4. Describe how neptunium and plutonium were first synthesized.

5. (a) Explain how ^{235}U may produce a "chain-reaction".
   (b) How does such a reaction produce energy?

6. (a) What is meant by "fall-out"?
   (b) Write a paragraph to explain the dangers encountered in an atomic fission explosion.

7. (a) What is *nuclear fusion*?
   (b) Write an equation to demonstrate how deuterium may be used for nuclear fusion.
   (c) How is nuclear fusion in the H-bomb triggered?
   (d) Why is controlled nuclear fusion difficult?

8. (a) What are "moderators" as used in a nuclear reactor?
   (b) Describe how moderators function.

9. What are *radioisotopes*?

10. Write a paragraph to demonstrate some of the uses of tracer research.

11. Explain how ^{14}C is used in carbon dating.

12. How is the energy of nuclear fission changed into useable power at the present time?

Appendix 1

Measurements in science

Measurements in scientific work report three important kinds of information:

1. The *magnitude* of the quantity being measured, reported as a number.
2. The *units* in which the quantity is scaled, indicated by such terms as grams and centimeters.
3. The *limit of accuracy* in the method of measurement, indicated by the *significant figures*.

Thus, for example, a sample is reported as weighing $1.052 \pm .001$ grams. Such notation tells us how large the mass is, that the unit of the reported numbers is the gram, and that there is doubt in the last thousandth of a gram.

The numerical part of a quantity is best reported in the exponential notation (appendix 2). The units of a quantity are indicated, calculated, or checked by reference to the measurement, or to the mathematical formula in which the quantity is calculated. Significant figures must be judged by an appreciation of the apparatus used.

Units

The units of a numerical measurement indicate its nature and the scale upon which it was measured. Only quantities with the same units may be added to or subtracted from each other. If they do not have the same units, they may be interconverted, provided the quantities are of the same dimension. Thus, to add 50 centimeters to one meter, we must reduce both to centimeters or meters. When quantities of similar units are added, the answer has the same units as the component parts. When lengths of 50 cm and 100 cm are added, a *length* of 150 cm results.

When quantities are multiplied (or divided), the product is in the same units as the original units. For example, if the length of a rectangle is 100 cm and the width is 50 cm, the area is 5000 cm².

A body with a mass of 10 g and a volume of 5 cm³ has a density of $\dfrac{10 \text{ g}}{5 \text{ cm}^3}$ or 2 g/cm³.

Conversion Factors

Conversion factors are used to change from one set of units to another of the same nature; for example, to change milligrams to pounds. To work out conversion factors it is helpful to use these rules:

1. Write the required units on the left hand side of the equation.
2. Write the given units on the right hand side.
3. Multiply or divide by the suitable *unit factor* to cancel out unwanted terms and replace them by required ones.
4. Write the numerical value for each unit factor.

Example:

How many milligrams are there in one ton?

Required units   = given unit ×   suitable unit factor

Steps 1, 2, and 3:
milligrams   =   ton $\times \dfrac{\text{pounds}}{\text{ton}} \times \dfrac{\text{grams}}{\text{pound}} \times \dfrac{\text{milligrams}}{\text{gram}}$

Step 4:
No. of milligrams   =   1 $\times \dfrac{2000}{1} \times \dfrac{454}{1} \times \dfrac{1000}{1}$

                    =   1 $\times 2 \times 10^3 \times 4.54 \times 10^2 \times 10^3$

              $= 9.08 \times 10^8$

Significant Figures

Numbers which express the result of a measurement such that only the last digit is in doubt are called significant figures. Thus there is a difference in meaning between the statements a length of 24 cm and a length of 24.0 cm. The first statement indicates that the measurement is reliable to the nearest centimeter only. The second statement indicates that the measurement is reliable to the nearest tenth of a centimeter.

When two or more quantities are combined, the accuracy of the result cannot be better than that of the *least* accurate of all the numbers involved. Thus if a length reported to be 1.125 cm is added to another length of 5.4 cm, the final result must be reported only as 6.5 cm, not 6.525 cm. The latter would imply that we know the precision of this length to *four* significant figures. This would be a misrepresentation since the precision of one part of the sum is limited to only two significant figures.

Similarly, when numbers are multiplied or divided, the answer must be consistent with the least precisely known quantity. In rounding off such answers, we increase the last significant digit, if the discarded digit is five or greater. For example, if an answer of 0.7684 is valid to only two significant figures, it should be reported as 0.77.

When numbers are expressed in the exponential notation, the number of significant figures is shown by the "digital multiplier"; for example, in 2.4×10^1 there are 2 significant figures and in 2.40×10^{-5} there are 3 significant figures.

Appendix 2

The Exponential Notation

(a) Large and Small Numbers

Many measurements in science involve very large or very small numbers, which often need to be multiplied or divided. So that this can be done conveniently, such numbers should be expressed as the product of two factors. The first factor, known as the digital factor, is a number between 1 and 10. The other, called the exponential factor, is the correct power of 10. Here are a few examples:

$$\text{Number} = \text{Digital factor} \times \text{exponential factor}$$

Number		Digital factor	exponential factor
185	=	1.85	$\times 10^2$
1,850	=	1.85	$\times 10^3$
18,500	=	1.85	$\times 10^4$
0.185	=	1.85	$\times 10^{-1}$

In these examples, the numbers are of different size, although they have the same digits in the same order. In changing them to the exponential form, we divide or multiply the original number, then multiply or divide to an equal and opposite extent by means of the suitable power of 10.

The reason for converting numbers to exponential form is that the numbers between 1 and 10 are by far the easiest to visualize and to work with.
The difficulty due to the largeness or the smallness of the number is removed by the use of exponents.

Example

Multiply $20,000 \times 0.04$. While this could be done by means of long multiplication, it must be admitted that there is the chance of misplacing the decimal point, and no one can deny that 20,000 is less familiar than 2, and 0.04 is less familiar than 4.

$$\text{Using exponents, } 20,000 = 2 \times 10^4$$
$$\text{and } 0.04 = 4 \times 10^{-2}$$
$$20,000 \times 0.04 = 2 \times 10^4 \times 4 \times 10^{-2}$$
$$= 2 \times 4 \times 10^{4-2}$$
$$= 8 \times 10^2 \text{ or } 800.$$

(b) Rules for Handling Exponential Numbers

RULE 1 When powers of ten are moved from denominator to numerator or vice versa, the signs of the exponents are changed. Example:

$$\frac{6}{3 \times 10^{-4}} = \frac{6 \times 10^4}{3}$$

RULE 2 When we wish to multiply powers of ten, we add the exponents. Examples:

(a) $2 \times 10^4 \times 2 \times 10^3 = 2 \times 2 \times 10^{4+3} = 4 \times 10^7$

(b) $3 \times 10^7 \times 2 \times 10^{-4} = 3 \times 2 \times 10^{7-4} = 6 \times 10^3$

RULE 3 When we wish to divide powers of ten, we subtract the exponents. Examples:

(a) $\dfrac{8 \times 10^5}{2 \times 10^2} = \dfrac{8 \times 10^{5-2}}{2} = 4 \times 10^3$

(b) $\dfrac{6 \times 10^{-5}}{2 \times 10^{-2}} = \dfrac{6 \times 10^{-5+2}}{2} = 3 \times 10^{-3}$

RULE 4 Before adding or subtracting exponential numbers, we must change them to the same powers of ten. Example:

$(2 \times 10^4) + (2 \times 10^5) = (2 \times 10^4) + (20 \times 10^4) = 22 \times 10^4$

(c) Approximations

In many cases, calculations involve several numbers, each consisting of several digits, e.g. $1850 \times 760 \times 0.022$. In calculations involving such numbers, the numbers are expressed with the aid of the exponential factors. In addition, the digital factor is expressed as an approximation of the nearest whole number so that an idea of the size of the answer can be quickly obtained. This adds confidence to the search for an exact answer by calculation. The exact answer is then found by multiplication and division or by using a slide rule. However the answer is subject to the rules concerning significant figures.

Example

Multiply $1850 \times 760 \times 0.022$

$1850 = 1.850 \times 10^3 \doteq 2 \times 10^{3}*$

$760 = 7.60 \times 10^2 \doteq 8 \times 10^2$

$0.022 = 2.2 \times 10^{-2} \doteq 2 \times 10^{-2}$

Approximate answer is $2 \times 8 \times 2 \times 10^{3+2-2}$

or 32×10^3

or $32,000$

Obtained by multiplication of $1.85 \times 7.6 \times 2.2 \times 10^{3+2-2}$, the exact answer is 30,932.

*The symbol $\doteq$ means "approximately equals".

Appendix 3

The Metric System

Length

1 meter (1 m) = 10 decimeters = 100 centimeters (100 cm) = 1000 millimeters (1000 mm)

1 kilometer = 1000 meters (1000 m) = 0.6214 mile

1 meter = 1.094 yd = 3.281 ft = 39.37 in

Volume

1 liter = 1000 milliliters (1000 ml) = 1000 centimeters³ (cc)

1 liter (1 *l*) = 0.03432 cu ft = 61.03 cu in = 0.8799 quarts (Canadian) = 35.2 fl oz = 1.057 quarts (US)

1 fluid ounce (US) = 29.57 ml; 1 fluid ounce (Can.) = 28.4 ml

1 cu ft = 28.32 *l*

Mass

1 gram (1 g) = wt of 1 ml of water at 4°C

1 kilogram = 1000 g

1 gram = 10 decigrams = 100 centigrams (100 cg) = 1000 milligrams (1000 mg)

1 kilogram (1 kg) = 2.205 lb avoirdupois

1000 kilograms = 2205 lbs = 1 metric ton

1 lb avoir = 453.6 g

1 oz avoir = 28.35 g

Prefixes of the Metric System			
micro	$= \dfrac{1}{1,000,000}$	deca	$= 10$
milli	$= \dfrac{1}{1,000}$	hecto	$= 100$
centi	$= \dfrac{1}{100}$	kilo	$= 1,000$
deci	$= \dfrac{1}{10}$	mega	$= 1,000,000$

Appendix 4

VAPOR PRESSURE OF WATER AT VARIOUS TEMPERATURES

Temperature °C	Pressure mm	Temperature °C	Pressure mm
0	4.6	23	21.1
1	4.9	24	22.4
2	5.3	25	23.8
3	5.7	26	25.2
4	6.1	27	26.7
5	6.5	28	28.3
6	7.0	29	30.0
7	7.5	30	31.8
8	8.0	35	42.2
9	8.6	40	55.3
10	9.2	45	71.9
11	9.8	50	92.5
12	10.5	55	118.0
13	11.2	60	149.4
14	12.0	65	187.5
15	12.8	70	233.7
16	13.6	75	289.1
17	14.5	80	355.1
18	15.5	85	433.6
19	16.5	90	525.8
20	17.5	95	633.9
21	18.7	100	760.0
22	19.8	105	906.1

Appendix 5

Heats of Formation of Common Compounds (In Calories)			
CaO	131,000	$Hg(ONC)_2$	−64,500
CO	29,000	HNO_3	41,600
CO_2	97,000	H_2S	4,800
C_2H_2	−54,000	KCl	105,000
$C_{12}H_{22}O_{11}$	536,000	$KClO_3$	90,000
CS_2	−19,000	MgO	146,000
FeS	24,000	NH_3	12,000
HgO	21,500	NaCl	97,800
HCl	22,000	NaOH	103,000
HBr	8,400	P_4O_{10}	740,000
HF	37,400	NO	−21,600
HI	−6,100	SO_2	69,000
H_2O	68,400	ZnS	46,000

Answers to Problems

Chapter 2

7. (a) 1,200 ml
   (b) 1,200,000 mg; 1.2 kg
   (c) (i) 108.0 cm,
       (ii) 10.80 dm,
       (iii) 1.080 m

9. (a) 2.50 g/ml
   (b) 11.4 ml

14. (a) 21.1°C; (b) 37.0°C;
    (c) −28.8°C; (d) −40°C;
    (e) 87.7°C

15. (a) 212°F; (b) 392°F;
    (c) −302.8°F;
    (d) 6332°F; (e) −40°F

16. (a) 0°K; (b) 233°K;
    (c) 273°K; (d) 323°K;
    (e) 546°K

17. (a) 227°C; (b) −173°C;
    (c) −1°C; (d) −223°C;
    (e) 27°C

Chapter 3

19. Oxygen, 5 ml

20. (a) Oxygen, 7½ ml
    (b) Hydrogen, 2 ml

21. 88.79% oxygen
    11.21% hydrogen

Chapter 4

4. 730 lb

6. (a) A. 0.269 g; B. 0.134 g

15. (a) 2 amu; (b) 40 amu
    (c) 18 amu;
    (d) 342 amu;
    (e) 36.5 amu
    (f) 16 amu; (g) 44 amu;
    (h) 98 amu; (i) 28 amu;
    (j) 17 amu

Chapter 7

7. 1.58 l

8. 160 ml

9. 368 ml

10. 3.89 l

11. 4 atmospheres

12. 500 mm

17. 718 ml

18. 240 ml

19. −24°C

20. 313°C

21. 21.4 l

22. 780 ml

23. 138 ml

24. 147 l

25. 837°C

28. (a) 749 mm
    (b) 1.95 l

29. 0.84 l

32. 2:1

33. 4 cm from end oxygen
    introduced

34. 4 hr

Chapter 8

6. 600 mm

Chapter 9

9. 1.88×10^{22} molecules

Chapter 10

2. (b) 1.5 moles
   (c) 2.08 g

8. 2.016 g

9. 46.1 g

10. 2.28 g

11. 0.57 g

12. 112 l

13. 2.04 l

14. 32.8 g

15. 0.39 g

16. 0.72 g/l

20. 10 g

21. (a) 2.51×10^{23} atoms
    (b) 1.88×10^{23} atoms

22. 0.23 moles of carbon atoms,
    0.46 moles of oxygen atoms

23. (a) 11.5 g
    (b) 161.8 g

24. 21 g

Chapter 11

3. (a) 72:6 or 12:1
   (b) 92.3% carbon;
       7.7% hydrogen

6. AgF

7. $NaHCO_3$

8. Na_2SO_4

9. (a) $CaSO_4$
   (b) $K_2Cr_2O_7$

11. $C_6H_{12}O_6$

12. (a) SCl
    (b) S_2Cl_2

13. CO_2

14. C_6H_6

15. H_2SO_4

16. (a) 98 amu; (b) 98 amu;
    (c) 40 amu; (d) 74 amu;
    (e) 78 amu; (f) 310 amu;
    (g) 180 amu;
    (h) 342 amu;

(i) 48 amu;
(j) 246 amu

17. (a) 7; (b) 8; (c) 3;
    (d) 5; (e) 7; (f) 13;
    (g) 24; (h) 45; (i) 3;
    (j) 27

18. 40% calcium; 12% carbon;
    48% oxygen

19. 32.4% sodium;
    22.5% sulfur;
    45.1% oxygen

20. 10.4%

21. 20.9%

22. 8.6 kg

23. 67.2 l

24. 3 l

25. 44.8 g

26. 64 g

27. 0.54 g

28. 19.6 g

29. 42.3 lb

30. 35.5 g

31. 42 g

32. Molecular mass = 30.0 amu
    Formula is NO

33. 2.85 g/l

Chapter 12

11. (b) 2 moles
    (c) 2 molecules

12. (b) 1 mole (c) 58.5 g

13. (a) 10 moles of water
    (b) 112 l (c) 320 g

14. 10.4 g

15. 322 g

16. 42 g

17. 24 moles

18. (a) 11.2 l (b) 24.6 l

19. 55 moles

20. 13.4 l

21. 237 g

22. 67.2 l; 54 g

23. (a) 250 l (b) 222 l

Chapter 13

5. 163 g

6. 104 g

11. 10 l hydrogen,
    20 l hydrogen chloride

12. (a) 33.6 l; (b) 22.4 l

13. (a) 6 l; (b) 6 l

15. 44.8 l

21. (a) 7.4%; (b) 39.1%

22. 255 g

Chapter 14

11. 3.12×10^{19} electrons

14. 27 g

15. 12.1 g

16. (a) 2 electrons
    (b) 1.2×10^{24} electrons
    (c) 1.9×10^{5} coulombs

Chapter 19

6. (a) 43.8 kcal evolved
    (b) 110.9 kcal absorbed

Chapter 21

19. 5400 cal

Chapter 22

17. 56%

18. 64 lb

Chapter 23

17. 7.5 g

26. 6.3 g

27. (a) 101 g; (b) 196 g;
    (c) 61.25 g; (d) 34.2 g;
    (e) 189 g

28. (a) 29.3 g; (b) 22.4 g;
    (c) 1.1 g; (d) 30.6 g;
    (e) 161 g

29. (a) 0.1 M; (b) 0.27 M;
    (c) 0.13 M; (d) 0.25 M;
    (e) 0.09 M

Chapter 24

14. 1.89×10^{23} electrons

15. (a) 1.1 g hydrogen;
        8.9 oxygen;
    (b) 12.1 l

16. 15.3 g

17. 1.12×10^{23} electrons

Chapter 25

15. (a) 0.27 M; (b) 2.7 M

16. 0.2 M

17. (a) 3.65 g HCl;
    (b) 8.1 g HBr;
    (c) 9.8 g H_2SO_4;
    (d) 9.8 g H_3PO_4;
    (e) 4.0 g NaOH;
    (f) 7.4 g $Ca(OH)_2$

18. (a) 0.28 M; (b) 2.0 M;
    (c) 1.0 M; (d) 0.04 M

19. 2.5 M

20. 2.1 g

21. 0.4 M HCl; 0.15 M H_2SO_4;
    Conc H_3O^+ is 0.7 moles/l

30. 5.7 g

Chapter 27

5. 100,000,000 Å, 100,000 Å,
    10,000,000 Å, 100 Å

Chapter 28

23. 37.2 g

27. 3.80 l

28. 30 g
29. $AlCl_3$
30. 5 ml of chlorine, 6 ml of hydrogen chloride
31. 15.5 g bromine, 16.9 g iodine

Chapter 29

33. 16.8 g
34. 2.2 g, 1.4 g

Chapter 30

19. 20.5 g
20. $MgSO_3$
21. 74.7 tons

Chapter 31

27. 0.69 moles
28. 8 g
29. 0.14 M
30. 2.58 l
31. 164 lbs
32. 16.2 lbs
33. 1.37:1
34. 81.6 lbs

Chapter 32

27. (a) H_2NO (b) $H_4N_2O_2$ or NH_4NO_2
28. (a) P_2O_5 (b) P_4O_{10}
29. 96.8 g
30. 2.53×10^{22} molecules

Chapter 33

46. (a) 0.17 g (b) 1.7 g

47. 300 ml of nitrogen, 900 ml of hydrogen
49. 1.76 g
50. 17 g

Chapter 34

31. C_2H_2
32. 9.3 l
33. 233 g
34. (a) 2.14 l (b) 0.004 M

Chapter 35

31. (a) 3.52 tons
    (b) 2.84 tons
32. 0.78 moles
33. (a) 44.8 g (b) 17.9 l
34. 34.9 l
35. $CaCO_3$ yields 1.12 l; Na_2CO_3 yields 1.06 l; difference 0.06 l

Chapter 37

29. C_4H_8
30. 128 g
31. 2.59 g/l
32. 2.66×10^{-5} g l

Chapter 38

41. C_2H_5OH
42. 3.12 l
43. 24.0 g
44. 56.3 g

Chapter 41

16. 43.8 g
17. 2.87 g

18. 0.9 M
19. (a) 0.59 g dissolved in water and diluted to 50 ml
    (b) 2.46 g dissolved in water and diluted to 50 ml
20. (a) 5.4 g (b) 2.8 g
    (c) 12 g

Chapter 42

18. 0.27 l
19. 461 g
20. 4.4 l
21. 38.3 g
22. 264 g

Chapter 43

19. 99.6 g
20. 0.56 mole
21. 9.6 g
22. 11.7 lbs

Chapter 44

47. 0.2 M
48. 5040 mg
50. 32.7 g
51. 1.58 moles

Chapter 45

18. 17.3 lbs
19. 6.2 g

Chapter 46

35. 109 l
36. 2.24 l
37. Cu_2S
38. 7.62 lbs
39. 1 M

Index

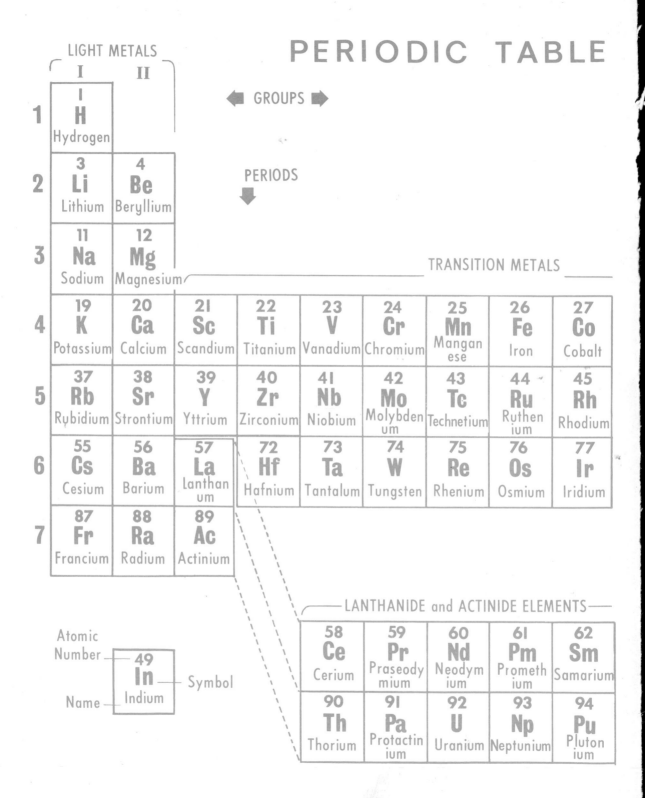

PERIODIC TABLE

LIGHT METALS

GROUPS

PERIODS

TRANSITION METALS

	I	II
1	1 **H** Hydrogen	
2	3 **Li** Lithium	4 **Be** Beryllium
3	11 **Na** Sodium	12 **Mg** Magnesium

4	19 **K** Potassium	20 **Ca** Calcium	21 **Sc** Scandium	22 **Ti** Titanium	23 **V** Vanadium	24 **Cr** Chromium	25 **Mn** Manganese	26 **Fe** Iron	27 **Co** Cobalt
5	37 **Rb** Rubidium	38 **Sr** Strontium	39 **Y** Yttrium	40 **Zr** Zirconium	41 **Nb** Niobium	42 **Mo** Molybdenum	43 **Tc** Technetium	44 **Ru** Ruthenium	45 **Rh** Rhodium
6	55 **Cs** Cesium	56 **Ba** Barium	57 **La** Lanthanum	72 **Hf** Hafnium	73 **Ta** Tantalum	74 **W** Tungsten	75 **Re** Rhenium	76 **Os** Osmium	77 **Ir** Iridium
7	87 **Fr** Francium	88 **Ra** Radium	89 **Ac** Actinium						

Atomic Number — 49 **In** Indium — Symbol

Name

LANTHANIDE and ACTINIDE ELEMENTS

58 **Ce** Cerium	59 **Pr** Praseodymium	60 **Nd** Neodymium	61 **Pm** Promethium	62 **Sm** Samarium
90 **Th** Thorium	91 **Pa** Protactinium	92 **U** Uranium	93 **Np** Neptunium	94 **Pu** Plutonium